LECTURES ON FUNCTIONS OF A COMPLEX VARIABLE

Lectures on Functions of a

COMPLEX VARIABLE

Edited by

WILFRED KAPLAN

with the assistance of

MAXWELL O. READE *and* GAIL S. YOUNG

THE UNIVERSITY OF MICHIGAN PRESS

Ann Arbor

Library of Congress Catalog Card Number: 55–7150

Second Printing, 1958

PRINTED IN THE UNITED STATES OF AMERICA BY
WAVERLY PRESS, INC., BALTIMORE, MARYLAND

FOREWORD

THIS volume constitutes the "proceedings" of the Conference on Functions of a Complex Variable which was held at the University of Michigan, June 17—July 1, 1953. The conference was in many respects parallel to the Topology Conference of 1940, and the present work may be considered a companion to *Lectures in Topology* (Ann Arbor: The University of Michigan Press, 1941), which reported on the 1940 conference. The world situation in 1953 did not, as it had in 1940, prevent the conference from being international in character, and the fact that many countries could be represented contributed greatly to its success.

The field of complex variables has become so vast, and its ramifications are so varied, that one cannot hope to survey all its aspects in a single volume. Yet the thirty-one articles here presented do range widely over the subject and should provide a valuable perspective.

Several of the lectures delivered at the conference are being published elsewhere, namely, those of L. Ahlfors, "Some general properties of quasi-conformal mappings"; of A. Beurling, "An extension of the Riemann mapping theorem"; of L. Bers, "Function-theoretic methods in gas dynamics"; of H. Bremermann, "Tube and semi-tube domains"; of B. Lepson, "Transfinite diameter and the convergence of hyperdirichlet series" and "Exceptional sets of convergence of hyperdirichlet series"; and of W. Kaplan, "Close-to-convex schlicht functions."

The editors wish to voice, on behalf of those who attended the conference, their appreciation to all the officers of the University of Michigan whose aid made the meetings possible and the living quarters comfortable. The conference owed its financial support to research funds of the Mathematics Department and to the Alexander Ziwet Fund of the University of Michigan; for this support we express our gratitude. The editors also thank their colleagues J. W. Addison, T. R. Jenkins, G. Livesay, A. J. Lohwater, G. Piranian, R. K. Ritt, H. Samelson, D. A. Storvick, C. J. Titus, and J. L. Ullman for assistance in reading proof.

W.K., M.O.R., and G.S.Y.

TABLE OF CONTENTS

AUTHORS

INTRODUCTORY TOPOLOGICAL ANALYSIS

G. T. WHYBURN

1. Introduction. The program of what I have called *topological analysis* consists of those basic theorems of analysis, especially of the functions of a complex variable, which are essentially topological in character, developed and proved entirely by topological and pseudotopological methods. In this program a minimum use is made of all such machinery and tools of analysis as derivatives, integrals, and power series; indeed, these remain largely undefined and undeveloped.

Lest this appear to be a rather sterile program, in which only known, old theorems are proved by new methods that may be more pleasing to a certain group of mathematicians, let me hasten to add that the real objective here is the promotion, encouragement, and stimulation of the interaction between topology and analysis to the benefit of both. Certainly many new and important developments in topology, some of recent discovery, owe their origin directly to facts emerging from studies of the topological character of analytic results. Also, I would venture the opinion that basic recent developments in analysis are due in considerable measure to the better understanding of the fundamental nature of the classical situations provided by topological concepts, results, and methods. Mention may be made in particular of the outstanding work of the Nevanlinnas, Ahlfors, and others on exceptional values. Here it is my own firm conviction that the topological connection is capable of much greater and more fruitful exploitation, particularly with regard to the relation between exceptional values and semicontinuity of collections of sets.

Now this is a very large program, and in no major sense is its conception original with me. Of course, the topological character of many of the classical results of analysis has been recognized since Riemann and Poincaré, and even before them. Indeed, the very fact of this character and its recognition is in large part responsible for the origins and development of the field of topology itself. However, the full depth of the penetration of topological nature into analytical results was surely not realized until the fairly recent past.

My own modest connection with this program is concerned with some of its modern phases, phases related primarily to the properties of open or interior transformations. I have organized some of this material into what appears to be a logical and comprehensive treatment; in what follows I shall outline the content of this treatment. Among the numerous mathematicians whose ideas enter into this approach to the subject mention should be made of Stoïlow [6], the originator of the interior transformation, Morse and Heins [5], whose methods lean somewhat more to the analytical, Kuratowski [4] and Eilenberg [2], who introduced and used so effectively the exponential representation which I have adopted, and Eggleston and Ursell [1], as well as Titus and Young [8], who have given elementary proofs of openness and lightness of analytic mappings in response to a need to which I directed attention in an earlier paper [9].

2. Topological background. The portion of topology which is used is surprisingly small and is entirely set-theoretic in character. It consists, in brief, of (1) introductory material on compact sets, continua, and locally connected continua in separable metric spaces; (2) a discussion of continuity of transformations and of the extensibility of a uniformly continuous mapping to the closure of its domain, and a proof of the basic theorem characterizing the locally connected continuum as the image of the interval under a mapping; (3) the most basic theorems of plane topology, that is, the Jordan curve theorem, the Phragmén-Brouwer theorem, and the plane-separation theorem, which permits the separation of disconnected parts of compact sets in the plane by simple closed curves. The last group, as well as much of the first two, could be largely avoided by leaning on polygonal approximations to general curves. However, it is felt that while this would effectively reduce the topological base on which the discussion rests at present, the use of arbitrary simple arcs and simple closed curves is more natural in the theory of functions of a complex variable.

3. Analytical background. On the analytical side, use is made of the simple properties of the complex number system and the complex plane, limits and continuity of functions, and the definition of the derivative together with its representation in terms of the partial derivatives of the real and imaginary parts of the function, but nothing beyond this for the complex derivative other than differentiability of rational combinations of differentiable functions. The mean-value theorem for real functions is presupposed. Also, the definition and the simpler properties of the exponential and logarithmic function of the complex variable are introduced and used; for example, I use the fact that the logarithms of a complex number are distributed vertically in the plane 2π units apart and the fact that the logarithm has continuous branches, but use nothing at all about the form of the logarithm or its derivative in terms of power series. Integration is never defined.

4. The circulation index. One of the basic and not wholly elementary notions which we use is that of the circulation index of a mapping about a point. In order to clarify the status of this notion I have found it desirable to follow the lead of Kuratowski and others in giving it a nonintuitive treatment based on simple properties of the logarithm.

We take an arbitrary mapping $\phi(x)$ of an interval or simple arc ab into the complex plane Z and let p be any point of $Z - E$, where $E = \phi(ab)$ is the image of ab. Any continuous function $u(x)$, $x \in ab$, satisfying

$$(1) \qquad e^{u(x)} = \phi(x) - p, \qquad x \in ab$$

is called a continuous branch of the logarithm of $\phi(x) - p$ and (1) is referred to as an exponential representation of $\phi(x) - p$. It is readily shown that every ϕ has such representations and, further, that the $u(x)$ is uniquely determined up to an additive constant. Thus when we define the circulation index

$$(2) \qquad \mu_{ab}(\phi, p) = u(b) - u(a),$$

it follows that μ is independent of the particular $u(x)$ entering into the representation (1). Also, of course,

$$(3) \qquad \mu(\phi, p) = \mu(\phi - p, 0)$$

and for any factorization $\phi(x) - p = \phi_1(x) \cdot \phi_2(x)$, we have

$$(4) \qquad \mu(\phi, p) = \mu(\phi_1, 0) + \mu(\phi_2, 0).$$

We note here that when no confusion is likely to result some or all of the symbols ab, ϕ, and p in the expression $\mu_{ab}(\phi, p)$ may and will be omitted.

Now in case $\phi(b) = \phi(a)$ so that our "curve" or image is closed, $\mu(\phi, p)$ has the form $2k\pi i$, k an integer, so that $\mu(\phi, p)/2\pi i = k(\phi, p)$ is integer valued; for $u(x)$ is a logarithm of $\phi(x) - p$ and thus of the form $\log |\phi(x) - p| + i \operatorname{amp} [\phi(x) - p]$. Further, as a function of p, $\mu(\phi, p)$ is continuous in p and thus is constant in each component of $Z - E$. From this it follows that $\mu(\phi, p) = 0$ for all points p in the unbounded component of $Z - E$. Indeed, for some such p sufficiently remote from E, the angle subtended by E at p is $< 2\pi$; hence the variation of $u(x)$ on E is $< 2\pi$ in modulus, so that $k = 0$ and $\mu = 0$.

Let J be a simple closed curve and let f be a continuous function from J to the complex plane. We understand by a *traversal* of J a mapping ζ of an interval or simple arc ab onto J with $\zeta(a) = \zeta(b)$ but with $\zeta^{-1}(y)$ unique for $y \in J - \zeta(a)$. It is readily shown that $\mu_{ab}(f\zeta, p)$ depends only on the sense in which ζ traverses J; that is, if α, β, and γ are distinct points on J, then μ depends on whether, as x moves from a to b on ab, $\zeta(x)$ takes on in turn an even or an odd permutation of the order α, β, γ of these values. Thus for two traversals ζ and ζ_1 of J we have $\mu(f\zeta, p) = \pm \mu(f\zeta_1, p)$, the sign being $+$ or $-$ according as ζ and ζ_1 agree or disagree in sense. By comparing with the case when J is a circle centered at p, it is easily shown that for any traversal ζ of an arbitrary J in the complex plane and any point p within J, we have

$$\frac{1}{2\pi i}\,\mu_{ab}(\zeta, p) = \pm 1. \tag{5}$$

Hence we define a *positive traversal* of J as a ζ for which we get $+1$ in (5).

It is clear that for any continuous complex-valued function $w = f(z)$ defined on a simple closed curve J in Z, all positive traversals of J give the same value of $\mu_{ab}(f\zeta, p)$ for $p \in W - f(J)$. Since we thus can compute μ directly from f on J we write $\mu_J(f, p)$ instead of $\mu_{ab}(f\zeta, p)$, when the traversal is positive, and $\mu_{-J}(f, p)$, when it is negative.

In terms of traversals of simple closed curves it is now an easy matter to discuss and clarify in logical and conventional manner traversals of the boundaries and of subdivisions of elementary regions in the plane and to exhibit the behavior of the circulation index under such traversals. (By an *elementary region* is meant a limited region bounded by a finite number of disjoint simple closed curves.)

5. Differentiable functions. We proceed now to a consideration of the basic topological properties of differentiable functions. Let $w = f(z)$ be nonconstant and have a finite derivative at every point of a region S in the z-plane Z; the w-plane is denoted by W. It is stressed that we assume only the existence of the derivative of $f(z)$ and proceed without ever assuming or proving even as much as its continuity. Our primary lemma asserts simply that if C is any simple closed curve in S with interior R in S, then the image E of $A = C + R$ consists of $f(C)$ together with certain bounded components of $W - f(C)$, i.e.,

(6) $f(C + R) = f(C) +$ *bounded components of* $W - f(C)$.

The proof of this fundamental fact is an easy deduction from the following four statements, the first of which has already been noted above and the first two of which hold without the differentiability condition on f:

(i) $\mu_C(f, p)$ *as a function of* p *is constant on each component* Q *of* $W - f(C)$ *and vanishes in the unbounded component;*
(ii) $p \notin f(A)$ *implies* $\mu_C(f, p) = 0$;
(iii) $f'(z_0) \neq 0$ *implies that for any sufficiently small circle* J *about* z_0, $\mu_J(f, w_0)/2\pi i = 1$, *where* $w_0 = f(z_0)$;
(iv) $p \in f(A) - f(C)$ *implies* $\mu_C(f, p)/2\pi i > 0$.

Any point of $f(A)$ not in $f(C)$ would have to be in a bounded component of $W - f(C)$ by (i) and (iv); any bounded component Q of $W - f(C)$ containing any point of $f(A)$ would lie wholly in $f(A)$ by (ii) because by (iv) and (i) $\mu_C(f, p) \neq 0$ at all $p \in Q$. Thus we get (6).

Now (i) has already been established and we prove (ii) for arbitrary continuous f and for any closed elementary region A by taking a subdivision of the region A fine enough that for each closed region Δ of the subdivision, p lies in the unbounded component of $W - f(\Delta)$. This makes the circulation index vanish when taken over the boundary of Δ; thus by its additivity it vanishes when taken over the boundary C of A.

To prove (iii) we write

$$(7) \qquad f(z) - w_0 = (z - z_0)[f'(z_0) + \epsilon(z)],$$

where $\lim_{z \to z_0} \epsilon(z) = 0$. If C is taken sufficiently small it will lie inside R and neither side of (7) will vanish on C. Thus for a positive traversal of C by (4) above we have

$$\begin{aligned} \mu_C(f, w_0) &= \mu_C(z - z_0, 0) + \mu_C[f'(z_0) + \epsilon(z), 0] \\ &= \mu_C(z, z_0) + \mu_C[\epsilon(z), -f'(z_0)]. \end{aligned}$$

The first term on the right is $2\pi i$ by (5) above; the second term is zero for C sufficiently small by (i), because $\epsilon(C)$ lies in an arbitrarily small neighborhood of 0.

Finally, to prove (iv) we show that we can take, in the component Q of $f(A) - f(C)$ containing p, a point q so that $f'(z_0) \neq 0$ for all points z_0 in $f^{-1}(q)$. To do this we first note that $f^{-1}(Q)$ is open, hence it has a component on which f is nonconstant and thus it has a point z_0 where $f'(z_0) \neq 0$. By (iii), $\mu_J(f, z_0) \neq 0$ for a small circle J lying with its interior in $f^{-1}(Q)$, so that all points of a component of $W - f(J)$ lie in $f(J +$ its interior) and thus in Q. Thus Q contains the interior of a square and hence contains a point q of the desired type, because the image set of the set of all zeros of $f'(z)$ cannot contain the interior of any square. Now to finish the proof let the (necessarily finite in number) points of $f^{-1}(q)$ in R be $q_1, q_2, \cdots, q_m$. Let $J_1, J_2, \cdots, J_m$ be disjoint circles in R centered at $q_1, \cdots, q_m$ respectively, with disjoint interiors and small enough so that $\mu_{J_n}(f, q) = 2\pi i$ for each $n = 1, 2, \cdots, m$. This gives

$$\frac{1}{2\pi i} \mu_C(f, p) = \frac{1}{2\pi i} \mu_C(f, q) = \frac{1}{2\pi i} \sum_1^m \mu_{J_n}(f, q) = m > 0$$

by (ii) and its proof, since f does not take the value q in the closure of the elementary region between C and the J_n, $n = 1, 2, \cdots, m$.

6. The fundamental topological properties. We are now in position to establish the two fundamental topological properties of differentiable functions, that is, lightness and openness of the mapping of the z-plane into the w-plane generated by such a function. To say that a mapping $f: X \to Y$ is light means that for each $y \in Y$, $f^{-1}(y)$ contains no continuum consisting of more than one point, or, in other words, that f is not constant on any continuum. Openness as we are using it here, in its strongest sense, means that each open set U in X has an open set $f(U)$ as its image in Y. Now these two topological properties are of fundamental significance for analytic functions in the sense that all other purely topological properties of such functions are necessarily consequences of these two. This is the primary conclusion as originally formulated by Stoïlow; it is this result which has led to such a rich development of the open or interior transformation in much more general situations than that of a mapping between two-dimensional manifolds.

Of the two properties lightness and openness, the former seems the more difficult to establish. Once it is proved, openness follows readily from lightness in the presence of other conclusions already obtained.

THEOREM 1. *If $w = f(z)$ is nonconstant and differentiable in a region R of Z, then f is not constant on any nondegenerate continuum in R.*

We suppose, on the contrary, that $f(z) = a$ for all z on a continuum M in R and proceed to a contradiction on the basis of this supposition. The method in brief is this: Our primary lemma gives us the maximum-modulus theorem to the effect that if a differentiable function is in modulus $\leqq m$ on a simple closed curve, the same holds inside the curve. However, supposing f constant on a continuum, we are able to construct a differentiable function $g(z)$ for which this fails to hold.

To do so we let R_0 be the (open) subset of R for which $f(z) \neq a$ and then take a subcontinuum N of M which is in the boundary of R_0, is well within the region R, and is irreducible between two of its points. It is then a simple matter to construct a circle C centered at a point z' of R_0, intersecting N in a pair of points s and t such that the angle $sz't$ is a rational multiple of 2π, say $\measuredangle sz't = 2\pi p/q$. Then the function

$$g(z) = \prod_{r=0}^{q-1} \{f[(z - z')e^{2\pi ipr/q} + z'] - a\}$$

will meet our requirements.

In the first place, for N and C suitably chosen $g(z)$ will be differentiable inside a circle C' with center z' and radius twice that of C plus the diameter of N. Also since $g(z) \equiv 0$ on N, whereas $g(z') \neq 0$, we can join s to t by a polygonal arc st inside C' such that

$$(8) \qquad |g(z)| < \delta = \tfrac{1}{2}|g(z')|$$

for all z on st. Let $h(x)$ be a homeomorphism of (0, 1) onto st with $h(0) = s$; we define, for any x in the interval $(1, q)$,

$$h(x) = [h(x - r) - z']e^{2\pi irp/q} + z', \quad \text{for} \quad r < x \leqq r + 1,$$
$$(r = 1, 2, \cdots, q - 1).$$

Then h maps the interval $I = (0, q)$ onto a set E inside C' and $|g(z)| < \delta$ for $z \in E$ by (8), because $g(E) = g(st)$.

However, we note that if

$$e^{u(x)} = h(x) - z', \qquad 0 \leqq x \leqq 1$$

is an exponential representation of $h(x) - z'$ on (0, 1), then

$$e^{u(x-r)+2\pi ipr/q} = h(x) - z', \quad \text{for} \quad r \leqq x \leqq r + 1,$$
$$r = 0, 1, \cdots, q - 1.$$

Thus by direct computation we get

$$\mu_{(0,q)}(h, z') = \sum_0^{q-1} \mu_{(r,r+1)}(h, z') = q[u(1) - u(0)] \neq 0.$$

Since $h(q) = s = h(0)$, z' is in a bounded component of $W - E$ and thus is within a simple closed curve (polygon!) J in E. But since $|g(z)| < \delta$ on J, this must also hold within J contrary to (8).

Thus lightness of f is established and it is now easy to prove openness:

THEOREM 2. *Under the hypotheses of Theorem* 1, *f is also open in R.*

Let U be any open set in R, let $w_0 \in f(U)$ and $z_0 \in U \cdot f^{-1}(w_0)$. Using lightness we see that there exists a simple closed curve (polygon!) C lying with its interior I in R and such that $f(z) \neq w_0$ on C. By our main lemma (6), $f(C + I)$, and therefore also $f(U)$, contains the component of $W - f(C)$ to which w_0 belongs. Accordingly, $f(U)$ is open in W, as was to be proved.

7. Applications. Maximum-modulus results. We observed earlier that our principal lemma yields a form of the maximum-modulus theorem. Using openness, it is now a simple matter to obtain this theorem in its strongest form to the effect that a nonconstant function $f(z)$ differentiable in a bounded open set G, continuous on $\bar{G}$, and satisfying $|f(z)| \leqq m$ on the boundary of G, satisfies $|f(z)| < m$ in G. For a discussion of this and numerous other related applications of openness to give classical properties of analytic functions, including the fundamental theorem of algebra, see [9].

8. The scattered inverse property. As indicated above, lightness and openness are the basic topological properties of differentiable functions, and all other such properties are derivable from these two. Indeed, they are most frequently obtainable as consequences of general theorems on light open mappings in a much broader setting than that afforded by the mapping from one complex plane into another. However, we shall continue to keep this latter situation as our focus, though in some cases we shall indicate the broader connection.

Now lightness asserts that our function (nonconstant) can take on a given value only on a totally disconnected set in its region R. However, we know from classical analysis that the set $f^{-1}(w)$ is a completely scattered set in the sense that no point whatever of $f^{-1}(w)$ is a limit point of $f^{-1}(w)$. We refer to this much stronger property as the *scattered inverse property.* It is now easily deduced in either of two ways. We can obtain it readily by using properties of the circulation index already developed. But it is obtainable in a more interesting way for an arbitrary light open mapping f on a two-dimensional manifold X with the aid of general properties of such mappings and of a modest amount of plane topology.

If we suppose some $x \in f^{-1}(w)$ $[w \in f(X)]$ is a limit point of $f^{-1}(w)$, then, using the fact that w is necessarily the vertex of a triod in $f(x)$, we can exhibit the existence, in a two-cell neighborhood U of x, of three disjoint regions Q_1, Q_2, and Q_3 in $X - f^{-1}(w)$ such that some three points a, b, and c of $f^{-1}(w)$ in U are each accessible from each of the regions Q_n. But then we can construct in $Q_1 + Q_2 + a + b + c$ a θ-curve consisting of three arcs x_1ax_2, x_1bx_2, x_1cx_2, disjoint except for their end points. This is impossible because Q_3 must lie in some one of the three regions complementary to θ in U and thus one of the points a, b, and c could not be accessible from Q_3.

9. Local topological analysis. A complete analysis of the local topological action of the mapping generated by a differentiable function is now within our reach. Indeed, this is possible for an arbitrary light open mapping operating on any two-dimensional manifold whatever. It can be shown under such conditions that the image set is itself necessarily a two-dimensional manifold and the topological nature of the action of the mapping in the small can be completely determined. However, to simplify the description, we discuss a more limited situation which includes the differentiable function mapping.

Let A and B be two-manifolds without edges and let $f(A) = B$ be a light open mapping of A onto B. It can then be shown that for any $y \in B$ and any $x \in f^{-1}(y)$ there exist two-cell neighborhoods V of y and U of x such that $f(U) = V$ and the mapping of U on V is topologically equivalent to a power mapping $w = z^k$ on $|z| \leqq 1$ for some integer k. The proof of this basic result of Stoïlow's is not entirely easy, though it is of elementary character from the topological viewpoint. No attempt will be made to indicate the detailed argument. The conclusion is derivable from two lemmas together with reasoning permitting the general situation to be localized so that they apply. The first lemma asserts that a light open map of one closed two-cell E onto another one F which maps the edge of E topologically onto the edge of F is necessarily a homeomorphism of E onto F—this in itself is a well-known classical result for analytic functions. In the second we assume only that the edge and only the edge of E maps into the edge of F and that some interior point of F has a unique inverse, and conclude from this that the mapping of E onto F is topologically equivalent to a power mapping.

10. Degree. Zeros. Rouché theorem. It is now a short step to the introduction of the notion of degree in a near-classical fashion. In general, of course, our mapping $f(A) = B$ (light, open; A and B two-manifolds as before) may have infinite point inverses or may have some infinite and some finite point inverses or, indeed, all may be finite sets and yet there may be no relation between or control on the number of points in a given point inverse. However, if the mapping is *compact*, none of these situations is possible and a finite and natural degree for the mapping always exists. Compactness for f means that the inverse image of every compact set in B is compact, or, equivalently, that each point inverse is compact and the mapping is closed, in the sense that the image of every closed set is closed.

Thus it is true that if f is compact, there always exists a positive integer k such that for any point y in B the sum of the multiplicities of all the points in $f^{-1}(y)$ is exactly k. Here the multiplicity of any point $x \in f^{-1}(y)$ is the integer k_x such that a suitably chosen two-cell neighborhood of x maps onto a neighborhood of y by a mapping topologically equivalent to the power mapping $w = z^{k_x}$ on $|z| \leqq 1$. Of course, it is clear now that the set of all points in A of multiplicity different from 1 can have no limit point whatever in A, so that, in particular, this set is countable.

Compactness of f would appear to be a strong restriction, and this is indeed the case from a general viewpoint. However, it is not so restrictive as to exclude many interesting situations. For it can be shown that for any light open mapping $f(A) = B$ and any region R in B each conditionally compact component Q of $f^{-1}(R)$ maps onto R and the mapping $f: Q \to R$ is compact. Thus if A and B are two-manifolds this latter mapping of Q onto R has a finite degree, as stated earlier.

Now in case of a differentiable function $w = f(z)$, it will be no surprise that degree and circulation index are closely related. The relation is simply this: Let $w = f(z)$ be nonconstant and differentiable in a region S on Z including the interior I of a simple closed curve $C \subset S$, let p be any point in $f(I)$ not in $f(C)$, and let R be the component of $W - f(C)$ containing p. Then for any positive traversal of C,

$$(9) \quad \frac{1}{2\pi i}\,\mu_C(f, p) = \text{degree of } f \text{ on } I\cdot f^{-1}(R)$$

$$= \text{sum of multiplicities of the points in } I\cdot f^{-1}(R).$$

When p is the origin, this relation gives the number of zeros of f inside C, since it gives in general the number of p-places; and this number is constant on the component of $W - f(C)$ containing p. For a function $f(z)$ which is meromorphic inside C and analytic and $\neq 0$ on C we easily derive the classical relation

$$(10) \qquad \frac{1}{2\pi i}\,\mu_C(f, p) = N - P$$

connecting the number N of zeros and P of poles of f inside C with the circulation index.

Rouché's theorem is also a ready consequence of relation (9), or of relation (10). For it is readily shown in a quite elementary way that if $f(z)$ and $f_1(z)$ are mappings of a simple closed curve C into Z satisfying $| f_1(z) - f(z) | < | f(z) - p |$ on C, then $\mu_C(f, p) = \mu_C(f_1, p)$. Thus we need only take p as the origin and let $f_1(z) = f(z) + g(z)$ to conclude from (9) and (10) that $f(z)$ and $f(z) + g(z)$ have the same number of zeros inside C when $| g(z) | < | f(z) |$ on C.

11. Global analysis. We make only brief mention of the global analysis of the topological action of the mapping generated by analytic functions and related light interior ones. Here the situation is far from clarified in the general case of noncompact manifolds or for noncompact mappings, although a few special types of functions have yielded to topological analysis in the large even on noncompact manifolds. This is notably true of the entire functions of order $< \frac{1}{2}$, which are included in a class of developable functions treated by Stoïlow [7] and in a similar class of expansive functions discussed in [9].

For light interior mappings $f(A) = B$ of one compact two-manifold A onto another, B, the analysis is very nearly in complete and satisfactory form, though detailed studies are still lacking. However, it can be shown, for example, that if for simplicity we make A and B closed in the sense of having no edges, then simplicial subdivisions K_a and K_b of A and B exist so that f maps each simplex of K_a topologically onto a simplex in K_b and, further, we have the relation

$$k\chi(B) - \chi(A) = kr - n \tag{11}$$

connecting the degree k of f, the Euler characteristics χ of A and B, the number r of singular points of f in B (i.e., images of points where f is not locally topological), and the number n of distinct inverse points of those r singular points. This, together with invariance of nonorientability and the local topological analysis discussed earlier, constitutes a reasonably definitive clarification of the topological action in this case.

As applied to analytic functions, this case includes that of the rational functions and nothing more; relation (11) becomes a classical formula of Hurwitz. However, a similar analysis and formula are valid for compact manifolds with edges, and can be made to yield results for more general classes of functions, as indicated earlier, particularly as applied to compact submanifolds of noncompact manifolds.

12. Sequences of functions. In conclusion, we discuss briefly two aspects of the situation concerned with uniformly convergent sequences of differentiable functions. At first glance one would hardly suspect a result such as the Weierstrass double-series theorem of having essential topological character or of being accessible in any sense by topological methods. Of course, by the theorem itself, when the limit function of such a sequence is nonconstant it is analytic and therefore it generates a light open mapping. Thus the topological character of the functions does go over to the limit from the members of the sequence.

At this point one is tempted to jump to the conclusion that this would be the case for uniformly convergent sequences of arbitrary light open mappings. However, this is readily seen not to be so even when the range space is the complex sphere. For the sequence of homeomorphisms defined by

$$w_n = z \quad \text{for} \quad r \geqq 2 \qquad\qquad (r = |z|),$$

$$w_n = z/n \quad \text{for} \quad r \leqq 1,$$

$$w_n = (r - 1)z + (2 - r)z/n \quad \text{for} \quad 1 < r < 2,$$

converges uniformly to the function $f(z)$ which is the identity for $r \geqq 2$, vanishes identically for $r \leqq 1$, and is $(r - 1)z$ for $1 < r < 2$. Thus $f(z)$ is neither light nor open.

Despite this seemingly discouraging observation, the remarkable thing is that for sequences of *differentiable functions*, the lightness and openness of the limit function is none the less deducible by topological methods. We have a general topological theorem which identifies a larger class of mappings than light open ones, namely quasi-monotone mappings, as being closed under the operation of taking limits of uniformly convergent sequences. A mapping $f(A) = B$ on a locally connected continuum A is called quasi-monotone (A. D. Wallace) provided that for each region R in B each component Q of $f^{-1}(R)$ maps onto R under f. Any open mapping on A is quasi-monotone and any quasi-monotone mapping on A admits of factorization in the form $f = f_2 f_1$, where $f_1(A) = M$ is monotone in the sense that each point inverse is a continuum and $f_2(M) = B$ is light and open. Thus a light mapping is open when and only when it is quasi-monotone. It will be noted in the example above that the limit function is quasi-monotone, as indeed it must be by the general theorem quoted, but not light.

For a sequence of differentiable functions $w = f_n(z)$ converging uniformly to a nonconstant function $f(z)$ in a region R, however, a very slight modification of the proof of Theorem 1 suffices to show that $f(z)$ is necessarily light. Since it is also quasi-monotone, it is therefore both light and open.

As a second and final example of results on sequences, we mention the theorem of Hurwitz: for an m-fold zero ζ of a not identically zero function $f(z)$ which is the limit of a uniformly convergent sequence of analytic functions in a region R, every sufficiently small neighborhood D of ζ contains exactly m zeros of $f_n(z)$ for $n > N(D)$. This theorem is an easy consequence of results we have discussed earlier. For, as just indicated, f would have to be light so that the circulation index could be used, and the index-invariance theorem quoted in connection with Rouché's theorem gives the Hurwitz theorem. Thus this theorem in its full strength is obtained with the aid of almost none of the usual tools of analysis.

BIBLIOGRAPHY

1. Eggleston, H. G., and Ursell, H. D. *On the lightness and strong interiority of analytic functions*, J. London Math. Soc. 27 (1952), 260–271.
2. Eilenberg, S. *Transformations continues en circonférence et la topologie du plan*, Fund. Math. 26 (1936), 61–112.
3. Kuratowski, C. *Sur les espaces des transformations continues en certains groupes abéliens*, Fund. Math. 31 (1938), 231–246.
4. —— *Homotopie et fonctions analytiques*, Fund. Math. 33 (1945), 316–367.
5. Morse, M., and Heins, M. *Deformation classes of meromorphic functions and their extensions to interior transformations*, Acta Math. 79 (1947), 51–103.
6. Stoïlow, S. *Principes topologiques de la théorie des fonctions analytiques*. Paris, 1938.
7. —— *Sur les surfaces de Riemann normalement exhaustibles et sur la théorie des disques pour ces surfaces*, Compositio Math. 7 (1939–1940), 428–435.
8. Titus, C. J., and Young, G. S. *A Jacobian condition for interiority*, Michigan Math. J. 1 (1952), 89–94.
9. Whyburn, G. T. *Open mappings on locally compact spaces*, Amer. Math. Soc. Mem., No. 1. New York, 1950.

University of Virginia

POTENTIAL THEORY AND ALMOST-COMPLEX MANIFOLDS

D. C. SPENCER

On a complex-analytic variety the exterior differential operator d for forms is the direct sum of operators ∂, $\bar{\partial}$, where, in terms of local analytic coordinates $z^1, \cdots, z^n$, ∂ is the differential with respect to the z^k and $\bar{\partial}$ is the differential with respect to the complex conjugate coordinates $\bar{z}^k$. The operators ∂, $\bar{\partial}$ are differentials of degree 1. Here we define antiderivatives ∂, $\bar{\partial}$ of degree 1 on almost-complex manifolds which coincide with the operators described above in case the structure is complex-analytic, and, in terms of an arbitrary almost-Hermitian metric, introduce the adjoint operators $\bar{\mathfrak{d}}$, $\mathfrak{d}$. Although the squares of these operators do not necessarily vanish, most of the potential theory usually associated with complex structure is carried through for the Laplacian $\Delta = 2(\mathfrak{d}\bar{\partial} + \bar{\partial}\mathfrak{d})$. If the variety is complex-analytic, then $\bar{\partial}^2 = \mathfrak{d}^2 = 0$.

1. Almost-complex structure

1.1. Definition of an almost-complex manifold. Let $\mathfrak{V}$ be a real, differentiable manifold of dimension $2n$ and of class C^∞, and let L_{2n} be the real linear group of nonsingular $2n \times 2n$ matrices, CL_n the complex linear group. If the tangent bundle of $\mathfrak{V}$ is equivalent in its group L_{2n} to a bundle with group CL_n, $\mathfrak{V}$ is said to be almost-complex. We assume throughout that $\mathfrak{V}$ is a Hausdorff space and is paracompact, hence normal.

If $\gamma \in CL_n$, then $\gamma = \alpha + i\beta$, where α, β are real $n \times n$ matrices and, as an element of L_{2n}, γ is represented by the $2n \times 2n$ real matrix

$$\gamma = \begin{Vmatrix} \alpha & -\beta \\ \beta & \alpha \end{Vmatrix}.$$

Conversely, any matrix of L_{2n} which has this form belongs to CL_n. It is known (see Steenrod's book [11]) that $\mathfrak{V}$ is almost-complex if and only if its tangent sphere bundle is equivalent in the group O_{2n} of real orthogonal $2n \times 2n$ matrices to a bundle with unitary group U_n. Denote by W_n the subgroup of O_{2n} composed of real, skew-symmetric matrices; then W_n can be identified with O_{2n}/U_n such that, under the identification, a left translation of the coset space by an element of O_{2n} corresponds to conjugation of W_n. Then (see [11]) $\mathfrak{V}$ is almost-complex if and only if the bundle with fibre W_n which is weakly associated with the tangent sphere bundle of $\mathfrak{V}$ has a cross-section. If such a cross-section exists, $\mathfrak{V}$ is orientable and there exists a field of real, skew-symmetric, orthogonal $2n \times 2n$ matrices h ($h^2 = -I$, I the identity matrix).

1.2. The direct-sum decomposition of the tangent space. Suppose that $\mathfrak{V}$ is almost-complex, and let p be a point of $\mathfrak{V}$. The space T_p of tangent vectors of $\mathfrak{V}$ at p is a $2n$-dimensional vector space over the reals R, and the matrix h at p defines an isomorphism h_p of T_p onto itself, $h_p^2 = -$ identity. If v is an element of T_p, v and $h_p v$ are independent in the real sense, and we can assign a complex structure to T_p by taking $w = u + iv = u + h_p v$ ($i = h_p$). Then T_p becomes a complex vector space of dimension n.

Let C denote the field of complex numbers, and write $CT_p = T_p \otimes C$, where the tensor product is over the reals R. We denote by F_p the space of functions of class C^∞ at the point p and, given $u \otimes c' \in CT_p$, $f \otimes c'' \in F_p \otimes C$, we define $(u \otimes c')(f \otimes c'') = u(f) \otimes c'c''$. Let $\prod_{1,0}: CT_p \to CT_p$ be defined by $\prod_{1,0}(u \otimes c) = \frac{1}{2}(u \otimes c + iu \otimes ic)$, $u \in T_p$, $c \in C$, and similarly let $\prod_{0,1}: CT_p \to CT_p$, where $\prod_{0,1}(u \otimes c) = \frac{1}{2}(u \otimes c - iu \otimes ic)$. Then

$$\textstyle\prod_{1,0} \cdot \prod_{1,0} = \prod_{1,0}, \qquad \prod_{1,0} \cdot \prod_{0,1} = 0,$$
$$\textstyle\prod_{1,0} + \prod_{0,1} = \text{identity map of } CT_p,$$

and we have the decomposition

$$CT_p = \textstyle\prod_{1,0} CT_p \oplus \prod_{0,1} CT_p. \tag{1.2.1}$$

Now write

$$CT_p^* = L_R(CT_p, R),$$

where $L_R(CT_p, R)$ denotes the set of R-linear homomorphisms of CT_p into R; that is, CT_p^* is the vector space dual to CT_p. Let

$$\phi: L_R(CT_p, R) \to L_R(T_p, L_R(C, R))$$

be the natural isomorphism such that, for $f \in L_R(CT_p, R)$, $u \in T_p$, $c \in C$, we have $[\varphi(f)(u)](c) = f(u \otimes c)$, and let

$$\alpha: L_R(C, R) \to C$$

be defined by $\alpha(f) = f(1) - if(i)$, $f \in L_R(C, R)$. If, for $f \in L_R(C, R)$, we define $if(c) = f(ic)$, then $L_R(C, R)$ becomes a complex vector space and, since $\alpha(if) = if(1) + f(i) = f(i) + if(1) = i\alpha(f)$, we see that α is complex-linear. Finally, let

$$\psi: L_R(T_p, L_R(C, R)) \to L_R(T_p, C)$$

be the isomorphism defined by

$$\psi(g)(u) = \alpha(g(u)), \qquad g \in L_R(T_p, L_R(C, R)).$$

Then we have the isomorphism

$$\lambda: L_C(T_p, C) \oplus L_{\bar{C}}(T_p, C) \to L_R(T_p, C)$$

defined by $\lambda(f + g) = f + g$, $f \in L_C(T_p, C)$, $g \in L_{\bar{C}}(T_p, C)$, and hence

$$CT_p^* = L_R(CT_p, R) \approx L_C(T_p, C) \oplus L_{\bar{C}}(T_p, C). \tag{1.2.2}$$

Here $L_C(T_p, C)$ denotes the set of complex-linear homomorphisms $T_p \to C$, while $L_{\bar{C}}(T_p, C)$ denotes the set of conjugate complex-linear homomorphisms. We have $\prod_{1,0}^*: CT_p^* \to L_C(T_p, C)$, where $\prod_{1,0}^*$ is the annihilator of $L_{\bar{C}}(T_p, C)$; similarly $\prod_{0,1}^*$ is the annihilator of $L_C(T_p, C)$ and

$$CT_p^* = \textstyle\prod_{1,0}^* CT_p^* \oplus \prod_{0,1}^* CT_p^*. \tag{1.2.3}$$

A covariant tensor at p of rank r and type (ρ, σ) is an element of

$$(\textstyle\prod_{1,0}^* CT_p^*)^\rho \otimes (\prod_{0,1}^* CT_p^*)^\sigma,$$

where $(\prod_{1,0}^* CT_p^*)^\rho$ denotes the tensor product of $\prod_{1,0}^* CT_p^*$ with itself ρ times. Denote the Grassmann algebra associated with CT_p by CA_p:

$$CA_p = \oplus_r CA_p^r,$$

where $CA_p^0 = F_p \otimes C$ and where CA_p^r is the subset of CA_p composed of elements of degree r. We say that an element of CA_p^r, $r > 0$, is of type (ρ, σ), $\rho + \sigma = r$, if it belongs to

$$CA_p^{\rho,\sigma} = \textstyle\prod_{\rho,\sigma}^* \wedge_r CT_p^* = (\wedge_\rho \prod_{1,0}^* CT_p^*) \wedge (\wedge_\sigma \prod_{0,1}^* CT_p^*),$$

while an arbitrary element of CA_p^0 will be said to be of type (0, 0): $CA_p^0 = CA_p^{0,0}$.

We denote by $CT = \bigcup_p CT_p$ the complex tangent bundle over $\mathfrak{B}$, and by $CA = \bigcup_p CA_p$ the complex Grassman bundle. Given an open set $U \subset \mathfrak{B}$, let $\Gamma(CA, U)$ be the set of cross-sections of CA over U of class C^∞. An element $\phi \in \Gamma(CA^r, U)$ is a differential form on U of degree r and class C^∞. If $\phi \in \Gamma(CA^{\rho,\sigma}, U)$, $r = \rho + \sigma$, we say that ϕ is a differential form on U of type (ρ, σ), and we write $\phi = \prod_{\rho,\sigma} \phi$ (where, for simplicity of notation, we have dropped the *-superscript). Since

$$\Gamma(CA^r, U) = \oplus_{\rho+\sigma=r} \Gamma(CA^{\rho,\sigma}, U),$$

an arbitrary differential form ϕ on U of degree r has the decomposition

$$\phi = \sum_{\rho+\sigma=r} \prod_{\rho,\sigma} \phi.$$

We define a homomorphism $\partial: CA^r \to CA^{r+1}$ by the following conditions: (i) linearity; (ii) if $f \in CA_p^0$, ∂f is the element of CA_p^1 satisfying $\partial f(w) = \prod_{1,0} w(f)$ for every $w \in CT_p$; (iii) ∂ is an anti-derivation, that is, if ϕ is of degree r, then $\partial(\phi \wedge \psi) = \partial\phi \wedge \psi + (-1)^r \phi \wedge \partial\psi$; (iv) if $f \in CA_p^0$, then $\partial df = -d\partial f$.

It is easily verified from these axioms that, in general, $\partial d = -d\partial$.

The conjugate operator $\bar{\partial}$ is defined in a similar way, but with $\prod_{1,0}$ replaced by $\prod_{0,1}$. If d is the (real) operator of exterior differentiation (which is characterized by the four axioms above with $\prod_{1,0}$ in (ii) replaced by the identity operator), we plainly have

$$d = \partial + \bar{\partial}. \tag{1.2.4}$$

We remark that ∂, $\bar{\partial}$ are not generally differentials; that is, ∂^2, $\bar{\partial}^2$ are not necessarily the zero homomorphisms. Furthermore, the image of $CA^{\rho,\sigma}$, $\rho + \sigma = r$, in the map $\partial: CA^{\rho,\sigma} \to CA^{r+1}$ will not necessarily be contained in $CA^{\rho+1,\sigma}$ for $r > 0$.

1.3. Almost-Hermitian structure. We say that $\mathfrak{B}$ has an almost-Hermitian structure if it has a Riemannian metric which maps $\prod_{1,0} CT$ isomorphically onto $\prod_{0,1} CT^*$, $\prod_{0,1} CT$ isomorphically onto $\prod_{1,0} CT^*$. If $\mathfrak{B}$ is almost Hermitian, then

$$*\prod_{\rho,\sigma} = \prod^*_{n-\sigma,n-\rho}, \tag{1.3.1}$$

where $*: CA^r \to CA^{2n-r}$ is the duality operator for differential forms.

The existence of almost-Hermitian structure is equivalent to the existence of a cross-section in the bundle of real, symmetric, positive-definite $2n \times 2n$ matrices g satisfying

$$g = hgh'. \tag{1.3.2}$$

Since the subspace of the real, symmetric, $2n \times 2n$ matrices composed of positive-definite matrices is a convex, open, $n(n+1)/2$-dimensional cell, such a cross-section always exists. Hence we may assume that $\mathfrak{V}$ is almost-Hermitian.

If ϕ, ψ are differential forms on $\mathfrak{V}$ of degree r, and if sup (ϕ) (the support of ϕ) is contained in a domain of local coordinates $x^1, \cdots, x^{2n}$, we choose $dx^1, \cdots, dx^{2n}$ as a base for the complex $2n$-dimensional vector space $CT_p{}^*$ at each point p of this domain and define

$$(\phi, \psi) = \int_{\mathfrak{V}} \phi \wedge *\bar{\psi}. \tag{1.3.3}$$

For arbitrary differential forms ϕ, ψ of degree r, we define (ϕ, ψ) by means of a partition of unity. Let $\{U_j\}$ be a locally finite covering of $\mathfrak{V}$, $\sum \rho_j = 1$ a partition of unity subordinate to this covering (i.e., sup $(\rho_j) \subset \bar{U}_j$), and define

$$\|\phi\|^2 = (\phi, \phi) = \sum_j \int_{\mathfrak{V}} \rho_j \phi \wedge * \bar{\phi} \tag{1.3.4}$$

provided the sum on the right converges. If $\|\phi\| < \infty$, $\|\psi\| < \infty$, we write

$$(\phi, \psi) = \sum_j \int_{\mathfrak{V}} \rho_j \phi \wedge * \bar{\psi}.$$

By (1.3.1)

$$\textstyle\prod_{p,\sigma} \phi \wedge *\bar{\psi} = \prod_{p,\sigma} \phi \wedge \prod_{n-p,n-\sigma} *\bar{\psi} = \phi \wedge *(\overline{\prod_{p,\sigma} \psi});$$

that is,

$$(\textstyle\prod_{p,\sigma} \phi, \psi) = (\phi, \prod_{p,\sigma} \psi). \tag{1.3.5}$$

We define $\mathfrak{d}$ to be the formal adjoint of $\bar{\partial}$ in the sense that $(\bar{\partial}\phi, \psi) = (\phi, \mathfrak{d}\psi)$ for every $\phi, \psi \in C^\infty$, sup (ϕ) compact, and we let

$$\Delta = 2(\mathfrak{d}\bar{\partial} + \bar{\partial}\mathfrak{d}), \qquad \Delta_s = \Delta + s \qquad (s \geqq 0). \tag{1.3.6}$$

Let T be a current in the sense of de Rham (see [10]), and define $(\Delta_s T, \phi) = (T, \Delta_s \phi)$, $\phi \in C^\infty$, sup (ϕ) compact. We have:

LEMMA 1.3.1. (*Regularity theorem.*) *If* $\beta \in C^\infty$ *and* T *is a current such that* $(\Delta_s T, \phi) = (\beta, \phi)$, $\phi \in C^\infty$, sup (ϕ) *compact, then* T *is equal to a form of class* C^∞.

It is easily verified that $\Delta_s \phi = 0$ is a strongly elliptic system of partial differential equations of the second order, and the proof of Lemma 1.3.1 does not differ from the usual one for the real Laplace-Beltrami operator $\delta d + d\delta$ where $\delta = -*d*$ (if dim $\mathfrak{V}$ is even).

We define an almost-analytic function to be a current T of degree 0 which is closed under $\bar{\partial}$: $\bar{\partial} T = 0$. Since $\mathfrak{d} T = 0$, we have $\Delta T = 0$, and it follows from the regularity theorem that T is equal to a function f of class C^∞ which satisfies $\bar{\partial} f = 0$ in the ordinary sense. A function f will be called almost-analytic at a point $p \in \mathfrak{V}$ if f is almost-analytic in some neighborhood of p. The functions which are almost-analytic at p form a ring $\mathfrak{O}_p$ under ordinary multiplication.

A form ϕ of type $(r, 0)$ which satisfies $\bar{\partial}\phi = 0$ will be called almost-analytic.

1.4. Local properties of almost-complex structure. By a basis at a point $p \in \mathfrak{V}$ we mean any basis $e_1, \cdots, e_{2n}$ of T_p. The set of all bases at all points p of $\mathfrak{V}$ forms a bundle E called the basis bundle of $\mathfrak{V}$. A cross-section of E over an open set $U \subset \mathfrak{V}$ is called a moving basis over U.

Let p be a point of $\mathfrak{V}$, U a neighborhood of p contained in a domain of local coordinates $x^1, \cdots, x^{2n}$. Then $e_1, \cdots, e_{2n}$, where $e_j = \partial/\partial x_j$, is a moving basis over U. If $y^1, \cdots, y^{2n}$ is another system of local coordinates at p, and if

$$e(y) = \left\| \begin{matrix} \partial/\partial y^1 \\ \cdot \\ \cdot \\ \cdot \\ \partial/\partial y^{2n} \end{matrix} \right\|$$

is the corresponding moving basis, then $e(y) = a \cdot e(x)$ where $a = \| a_j^k \|$, $a_j^k = \partial x^k / \partial y^j$. The transformation of the matrix field h (acting in E) under the coordinate change is given by $h(y) =$

$a \cdot h(x) \cdot a^{-1}$, and at any point $p \in \mathfrak{V}$ we can find coordinates such that

$$
h_p = \left\| \begin{array}{cc|cc|ccc}
0 & 1 & 0 & 0 & \cdots & & 0 \\
-1 & 0 & 0 & 0 & \cdots & & 0 \\
\hline
0 & 0 & 0 & 1 & & & \\
0 & 0 & -1 & 0 & & & \\
\hline
0 & 0 & & \cdots & & 0 & 1 \\
0 & 0 & & \cdots & & -1 & 0
\end{array} \right\| \tag{1.4.1}
$$

at the point p. However, it will not be possible in general to find coordinates such that h has the form (1.4.1) in a neighborhood of p.

Now CT_p is isomorphic to the space of complex tangent vectors at p, a complex tangent vector being a map $w \colon CF_p \to C$ where CF_p is the space of complex functions of class C^∞ at p. Let $x^1, \cdots, x^{2n}$ be local coordinates at p such that h has the form (1.4.1) at this point, and let $z^k = x^{2k-1} + ix^{2k}$ $(k = 1, 2, \cdots, n)$,

$$
\begin{aligned}
\partial/\partial z^k &= \tfrac{1}{2}(\partial/\partial x^{2k-1} - i\partial/\partial x^{2k}), \\
\partial/\partial \bar{z}^k &= \tfrac{1}{2}(\partial/\partial x^{2k-1} + i\partial/\partial x^{2k}),
\end{aligned}
\qquad k = 1, 2, \cdots, n. \tag{1.4.2}
$$

Then $\partial/\partial z^1, \cdots, \partial/\partial z^n, \partial/\partial \bar{z}^1, \cdots, \partial/\partial \bar{z}^n$ is a complex moving basis over a neighborhood U of p: that is, a cross-section of the bundle CE over U, which forms at each point of U a complex basis for the complex tangent vectors. In the coordinates $z^1, \cdots, z^n, \bar{z}^1, \cdots, \bar{z}^n$, the matrix h at the point p has the form

$$
h_p = i \left\| \begin{array}{cc} I_n & 0 \\ 0 & -I_n \end{array} \right\|, \tag{1.4.3}
$$

and $\partial/\partial z^1, \cdots, \partial/\partial z^n$ form a basis for $\prod_{1,0} CT_p$, $\partial/\partial \bar{z}^1, \cdots, \partial/\partial \bar{z}^n$ a basis for $\prod_{0,1} CT_p$.

Complex coordinates in a neighborhood of p which have the form $z^1, \cdots, z^n, \bar{z}^1, \cdots, \bar{z}^n$ will be called self-conjugate. If self-conjugate coordinates have the further property that (1.4.3) is valid at p, we say that the coordinates are adapted (to the structure) at the point p. In the case of self-conjugate coordinates, it is convenient to introduce the notation $z^{n+j} = \bar{z}^j$ $(j = 1, 2, \cdots, n)$.

Suppose that there exist m almost-analytic functions $f^1, \cdots, f^m$

which are functionally independent in a neighborhood U of a point $p \in \mathfrak{B}$; that is, the $2m \times 2n$ matrix $\| \partial f^j / \partial x^k \|$, where $f^{n+j} = \bar{f}^j$, $j = 1, 2, \cdots, m$, has rank $2m$. We can then complete $f^1, \cdots, f^m$, $\bar{f}^1, \cdots, \bar{f}^m$ to a self-conjugate coordinate system $z^1, \cdots, z^n, \bar{z}^1, \cdots, \bar{z}^n$, where $z^k = f^k$ for $k = 1, 2, \cdots, m$. We have

$$0 = \bar{\partial} z^k = \frac{1}{2} \sum_{r=1}^{2n} \left(\frac{\partial z^k}{\partial x^r} + i \sum_{s=1}^{2n} h_r^{\ s} \frac{\partial z^k}{\partial x^s} \right) dx^r$$

for $k = 1, 2, \cdots, m$, where $h = \| h_j^{\ k} \|$ — i.e.,

$$\sum_{s=1}^{2n} h_r^{\ s} \frac{\partial z^k}{\partial x^s} = i \frac{\partial z^k}{\partial x^r}$$

$$(k = 1, 2, \cdots, m; \quad r = 1, 2, \cdots, 2n).$$

Multiplying both sides of this equation by $\partial x^r / \partial z^j$ and summing on r from 1 to $2n$, we obtain

$$\sum_{r,s=1}^{2n} h_r^{\ s} \frac{\partial z^k}{\partial x^s} \frac{\partial x^r}{\partial z^j} = i \sum_{r=1}^{2n} \frac{\partial z^k}{\partial x^r} \frac{\partial x^r}{\partial z^j} = i \delta_j^{\ k} \tag{1.4.4}$$

$$(k = 1, 2, \cdots, m; \quad j = 1, 2, \cdots, 2n),$$

where the left side is the value of $h_j^{\ k}$ in the coordinates z^j. Since $\bar{\partial} z^k = 0$ for $k = 1, 2, \cdots, m$, the matrix h in the coordinates z^j has the property that

$$h_j^{\ k} = \begin{cases} i\delta_j^{\ k} & \text{for } 2 \leqq k \leqq m, \quad 1 \leqq j \leqq 2n, \\ -i\delta_j^{\ k} & \text{for } n+1 \leqq k \leqq n+m, \quad 1 < j \leqq 2n, \end{cases} \tag{1.4.5}$$

throughout a neighborhood of p; that is, in a neighborhood of p the matrix h has the form

$$h = \left\| \begin{array}{c|c|c|c} i_m & & 0 & \\ \hline 0 & \cdots & -i_m & \cdots \\ \hline & & 0 & \end{array} \right\|, \quad i_m = iI_m.$$

Conversely, suppose that there exists a self-conjugate coordinate system $z^1, \cdots, z^n, \bar{z}^1, \cdots, \bar{z}^n$ for which (1.4.5) holds throughout a neighborhood of p. Then (1.4.4) is valid for $h_r^{\ s}(x)$. Multiplying both sides of (1.4.4) by $\partial z^j/\partial x^i$ and summing on j from 1 to $2n$, we obtain $\bar{\partial} z^k = 0$ for $k = 1, 2, \cdots, m$. Thus we conclude:

LEMMA 1.4.1. *The existence of a self-conjugate coordinate system such that* (1.4.5) *holds throughout a neighborhood U of a point $p \in \mathfrak{V}$ is equivalent to the existence of m almost-analytic functions having complex linearly independent gradients in U.*

Suppose that there exist n functionally independent almost-analytic functions in a neighborhood U of the point p. Then there exist self-conjugate coordinates $z^1, \cdots, z^n, \bar{z}^1, \cdots, \bar{z}^n, z^j = x^j + iy^j$ for $j = 1, 2, \cdots, n$ such that $\partial/\partial z^1, \cdots, \partial/\partial z^n$ is a cross-section of $\prod_{1,0} CE$ over U, $\partial/\partial \bar{z}^1, \cdots, \partial/\partial \bar{z}^n$ a cross-section of $\prod_{0,1} CE$, where

$$\frac{\partial}{\partial z^j} = \frac{1}{2}\left(\frac{\partial}{\partial x^j} - i\frac{\partial}{\partial y^j}\right), \qquad \frac{\partial}{\partial \bar{z}^j} = \frac{1}{2}\left(\frac{\partial}{\partial x^j} + i\frac{\partial}{\partial y^j}\right), \qquad j = 1, 2, \cdots, n. \tag{1.4.6}$$

Let $w^1, \cdots, w^n, \bar{w}^1, \cdots, \bar{w}^n$ be another self-conjugate coordinate system with the property that $\partial/\partial w^1, \cdots, \partial/\partial w^n$ and $\partial/\partial \bar{w}^1, \cdots, \partial/\partial \bar{w}^n$ are cross-sections of $\prod_{1,0} CE$ and $\prod_{0,1} CE$ respectively. Since $\partial/\partial z^1, \cdots, \partial/\partial z^n, \partial/\partial \bar{z}^1, \cdots, \partial/\partial \bar{z}^n$ is a moving basis over U, we have

$$\frac{\partial}{\partial w^j} = \sum_{k=1}^{n} \frac{\partial z^k}{\partial w^j}\frac{\partial}{\partial z^k} + \sum_{k=1}^{n} \frac{\partial \bar{z}^k}{\partial w^j}\frac{\partial}{\partial \bar{z}^k}, \qquad j = 1, 2, \cdots, n. \tag{1.4.7}$$

Since $\partial/\partial w^1, \cdots, \partial/\partial w^n$ is a cross-section of $\prod_{1,0} CE$, we must have $\partial \bar{z}^k/\partial w^j = 0$ for $j, k = 1, 2, \cdots, n$; that is, each z^k is a holomorphic function of $w^1, \cdots, w^n$ and vice versa. Therefore $\| \partial z^j/\partial w^k \|$ $(j, k = 1, 2, \cdots, 2n)$ has the form

$$\| \partial z^j/\partial w^k \| = \left\| \begin{matrix} J_n & 0 \\ 0 & J_n \end{matrix} \right\|,$$

where $J_n = \partial(z^1, \cdots, z^n)/\partial(w^1, \cdots, w^n)$ is the Jacobian of $z^1, \cdots, z^n$ with respect to $w^1, \cdots, w^n$, and we have the well-known result:

LEMMA 1.4.2. *An almost-complex manifold $\mathfrak{V}$ of real dimension $2n$ is complex-analytic if and only if each point of $\mathfrak{V}$ has a neighborhood in which there exist n almost-analytic functions with complex-linearly independent gradients.*

Suppose that there exist $m < n$ functionally independent almost-analytic functions in a neighborhood U of p. Then there exist self-conjugate coordinates $z^1, \cdots, z^n, \bar{z}^1, \cdots, \bar{z}^n, z^j = x^j + iy^j$ for $j = 1, 2, \cdots, n$ such that $\partial/\partial z^1, \cdots, \partial/\partial z^m$ and $\partial/\partial \bar{z}^1 \cdots, \partial/\partial \bar{z}^m$ are independent vectors of $\prod_{1,0} CT$ and $\prod_{0,1} CT$ respectively for each point of U. If $w^1, \cdots, w^n, \bar{w}^1, \cdots, \bar{w}^n$ is another set of self-conjugate coordinates with this property, we have (1.4.7) where $\partial\bar{z}^k/\partial w^j = 0$ for $j, k = 1, 2, \cdots, m$; that is, each z^k $(k = 1, 2, \cdots, m)$ is holomorphic in $w^1, \cdots, w^m$ and vice versa. The Jacobian matrix $\| \partial z^j/\partial w^k \|$ $(j, k = 1, 2, \cdots, 2n)$ has the form

$$\| \partial z^j/\partial w^k \| = \left\| \begin{array}{c|c} J_m & 0 \\ \hline 0 & \bar{J}_m \end{array} \right\|,$$

where $J_m = \partial(z^1, \cdots, z^n)/\partial(w^1, \cdots, w^m)$.

Given an almost-complex manifold $\mathfrak{V}$, let m $(m \leqq n)$ be the nonnegative integer such that: (i) every point of $\mathfrak{V}$ has a neighborhood in which there exist m functionally independent almost-analytic functions; (ii) at least one point of $\mathfrak{V}$ has the property that in any neighborhood of it any $m + 1$ almost-analytic functions are functionally dependent. We say that $\mathfrak{V}$ is almost-complex of type m. If $\mathfrak{V}$ is almost-complex of type m, there exists a locally finite covering $\{U_j\}$ of $\mathfrak{V}$ by neighborhoods U_j, where U_j is covered by self-conjugate coordinates $z_j^1, \cdots, z_j^n, \bar{z}_j^1, \cdots, \bar{z}_j^n$ and, in $U_j \cap U_k$, each z_j^r, $1 \leqq r \leqq m$, is holomorphic in $z_k^1, \cdots, z_k^m$. We say that these coordinate systems are almost-analytic (of type m). An almost-analytic function f expressed in almost-analytic coordinates $z^1, \cdots, z^n$, $\bar{z}^1, \cdots, \bar{z}^n$ which are of type m is a complex-analytic function of $z^1, \cdots, z^m$. The natural almost-complex structure of S^6 is of type 0.

It is helpful to compare almost-complex structure with almost-product structure. Given a real differentiable manifold $\mathfrak{V}$ (of class C^∞), we say that $\mathfrak{V}$ has almost-product structure if there exists a direct-sum decomposition of the tangent bundle T of $\mathfrak{V}$, $T = PT \oplus QT$, where PT, QT are differentiable fibre bundles of class C^∞ over $\mathfrak{V}$ whose fibers are vector spaces of dimensions $m', m'', m' + m'' = \dim \mathfrak{V} = n$. In analogy with § 1.2 we say that an element of A_p^r, $r > 0$, is of type (ρ, σ), $\rho + \sigma = r$, if it belongs to

$$A_p^{\rho,\sigma} = \prod\nolimits_{\rho,\sigma} \wedge_r T_p^* = (\wedge_\rho P^*T^*) \wedge (\wedge_\sigma Q^*T^*),$$

and we can define operators d', d'' satisfying

(1.4.8) $$d = d' + d''.$$

If each point $p \in V$ has a neighborhood U covered by local coordinates $x = (x', x'')$ such that $\partial/\partial(x')^k$ $(k = 1, 2, \cdots, m')$ and $\partial/\partial(x'')^k$ $(k = 1, 2, \cdots, m'')$ are moving bases over U for PT, QT respectively, then $\mathfrak{V}$ has locally a product structure. Under these circumstances it is clear that $(d')^2 = (d'')^2 = 0$. In fact, the condition $(d')^2 = 0$ is necessary and sufficient for the existence of a local product structure.

1.5. Green's and Neumann's operators. Assume that $\mathfrak{V}$ is almost-complex with Hermitian metric. Let

$$\mathbf{A}^r = \{\phi \text{ of degree r}, \| \phi \| < \infty\},$$

and define

$$\mathbf{A} = \oplus_r \mathbf{A}^r.$$

If $\phi \in \mathbf{A}$, then $\phi = \sum_r \psi^r$, where $\psi^r \in \mathbf{A}^r$, and we have in $\mathbf{A}$ the norm $\| \phi \| = (\sum \| \psi^r \|^2)^{\frac{1}{2}}$. Let $\mathbf{C}$ be the subspace of $\mathbf{A}$ composed of forms of class C^∞ with compact support.

We say that a form $\phi \in \mathbf{A}$ is in (the closure of) the domain of the operator $\bar{\partial}$ if there exists a sequence $\{\phi_\mu\}$, $\phi_\mu \in C^\infty$, $\| \phi_\mu \| < \infty$, $\| \bar{\partial}\phi_\mu \| < \infty$, such that $\| \phi - \phi_\mu \|$ and $\| \bar{\partial}\phi_\mu - \bar{\partial}\phi_\nu \|$ tend to zero $(\mu, \nu \to \infty)$. If there exists such a sequence with $\phi_\mu \in \mathbf{C}$, we say that ϕ is in the domain of the operator $\bar{\partial}_c$. Similar definitions are given relative to $\mathfrak{d}$, $\mathfrak{d}_c$. If a form ϕ is in the domain of an operator such as $\bar{\partial}$, we write $\phi \in \bar{\partial}$ and, if ϕ is of degree r, we attach a superscript r: $\phi \in \bar{\partial}^r$.

Let $D = \bar{\partial} \oplus \mathfrak{d}$, that is, $D\phi = \bar{\partial}\phi \oplus \mathfrak{d}\phi$, and write $D(\phi) = \| D\phi \|^2 = \| \bar{\partial}\phi \|^2 + \| \mathfrak{d}\phi \|^2$, where $D(\phi)$ is the Dirichlet integral for the operators $\bar{\partial}$, $\mathfrak{d}$. Given a positive number s, define further $D_s = \bar{\partial} \oplus \mathfrak{d} \oplus s/2$, where $s/2$ is the trivial operator of multiplication by $s/2$, and write $D_s(\phi) = \| D_s\phi \|^2 = \| \bar{\partial}\phi \|^2 + \| \mathfrak{d}\phi \|^2 + s/2 \cdot \| \phi \|^2$. The operators D, D_s have the same domain; a form $\phi \in D$ if there exists a sequence $\{\phi_\mu\}$, $\phi_\mu \in C^\infty$, $\| \phi_\mu \| < \infty$, $\| D\phi_\mu \| < \infty$, such that $\| \phi - \phi_\mu \|$ and $\| D(\phi_\mu - \phi_\nu) \|$ tend to zero $(\mu, \nu \to \infty)$. We define D_c by imposing the added restriction: $\phi_\mu \in \mathbf{C}$.

Next, introduce an operator $\mathfrak{D}$, $\mathfrak{D}(\alpha \oplus \beta) = \mathfrak{d}\alpha + \bar{\partial}\beta$, where the $+$ sign denotes ordinary addition of forms. We observe that

$\| \mathfrak{D}(\alpha \oplus \beta) \| = \| \mathfrak{d}\alpha + \bar{\partial}\beta \|$, and we say that $\alpha \oplus \beta$ is in the domain of $\mathfrak{D}$ if there exists a sequence $\{\alpha_\mu \oplus \beta_\mu\}$, $\alpha_\mu, \beta_\mu \in C^\infty$, $\| \alpha_\mu \oplus \beta_\mu \| < \infty$, $\| \mathfrak{D}(\alpha_\mu \oplus \beta_\mu) \| < \infty$, such that $\| (\alpha \oplus \beta) - (\alpha_\mu \oplus \beta_\mu) \| = (\| \alpha - \alpha_\mu \|^2 + \| \beta - \beta_\mu \|^2)^{\frac{1}{2}} \to 0$, $\| \mathfrak{D}(\alpha_\mu \oplus \beta_\mu) - \mathfrak{D}(\alpha_\nu \oplus \beta_\nu) \| \to 0$ $(\mu, \nu \to \infty)$. We proceed similarly for $\mathfrak{D}_c$, but with $\alpha_\mu, \beta_\mu \in C$.

Let $\Delta = 2\mathfrak{D}D$, $\Delta_c = 2\mathfrak{D}D_c$, ${}_c\Delta = 2\mathfrak{D}_c D$, and write $\Delta_s = \Delta + s$. If ϕ is in the domain of Δ, then ϕ is the domain of D and $D\phi$ is in the domain of $\mathfrak{D}$; similarly for Δ_c and ${}_c\Delta$. If $\phi \in \Delta_c$, we verify readily that

$$D(\phi, \psi) = \tfrac{1}{2}(\phi, \Delta\psi) \tag{1.5.1}$$

for all $\psi \in \Delta$ and, if $\phi \in {}_c\Delta$, that

$$D(\phi, \psi) = \tfrac{1}{2}(\Delta\phi, \psi) \tag{1.5.2}$$

for all $\psi \in D$. Let $\mathbf{G}$ be the space of all $\phi \in \Delta$ satisfying (1.5.1) for $\psi \in \Delta$, $\mathbf{N}$ the space of all $\phi \in \Delta$ satisfying (1.4.2) for $\psi \in D$. The domain of Δ_c is contained in $\mathbf{G}$, the domain of ${}_c\Delta$ in $\mathbf{N}$, and we shall see below that $\mathbf{G}$ is the domain of Δ_c, $\mathbf{N}$ the domain of ${}_c\Delta$.

If $\phi \in \mathbf{G}$, we have $(s/2) \cdot \| \phi \|^2 \leqq D_s(\phi) = (\Delta_s\phi, \phi) \leqq \| \Delta_s\phi \| \cdot \| \phi \|$; that is,

$$\| \phi \| \leqq (2/s) \cdot \| \Delta_s\phi \|. \tag{1.5.3}$$

Similarly, if $\phi \in \mathbf{N}$, then ϕ satisfies (1.5.3). If $\phi \in \mathbf{G}$ or $\mathbf{N}$, $\Delta\phi = 0$ implies $D(\phi) = 0$, and $\Delta_s\phi = 0$ implies $\phi = 0$. Let $H = \{\phi \mid \phi \in A, \Delta\phi = 0\}$, and define

$$\mathbf{F}_c = \mathbf{G} \cap \mathbf{H} = \{\phi \mid \phi \in D_c, \bar{\partial}\phi = \mathfrak{d}\phi = 0\},$$

$$\mathbf{F} = \mathbf{N} \cap \mathbf{H} = \{\phi \mid \phi \in D, \bar{\partial}\phi = \mathfrak{d}\phi = 0\}.$$

THEOREM 1.5.1. *For each $s > 0$ there exist one-to-one linear maps $G_s: \mathbf{A} \to \mathbf{G}$, $N_s: \mathbf{A} \to \mathbf{N}$, $G_s^{-1} = \Delta_s \mid \mathbf{G}$, $N_s^{-1} = \Delta_s \mid \mathbf{N}$. For $\phi \in \mathbf{A}$, $G_s\phi$ and $N_s\phi$ are symmetric operators satisfying*

$$D_s(G_s\phi) \leqq \| \phi \|^2/2s, \qquad D_s(N_s\phi) \leqq \| \phi \|^2/2s.$$

Proof. Given $\beta \in \mathbf{A}$, write $\gamma = \beta/s$ and define

$$E_s(\phi, \psi) = D(\phi, \psi) + \frac{s}{2}(\phi - \gamma, \psi - \gamma);$$

$$E_s(\phi) = D(\phi) + \frac{s}{2}(\phi - \gamma, \phi - \gamma).$$

Since

$$D_s(\phi - \psi) = D(\phi - \psi) + \frac{s}{2}(\phi - \psi, \phi - \psi)$$

$$= D(\phi, \psi) + \frac{s}{2}\Big((\phi - \gamma) - (\psi - \gamma), (\phi - \gamma) - (\psi - \gamma)\Big),$$

we have the formula

$$D_s(\phi - \psi) = E_s(\phi) - 2\mathrm{Re}\, E_s(\phi, \psi) + E_s(\psi). \tag{1.5.4}$$

Let $e = \inf E_s(\phi)$ for all r-forms ϕ. Then

$$\sqrt{D_s(\phi - \psi)} \leqq \sqrt{E_s(\phi) - e} + \sqrt{E_s(\psi) - e}. \tag{1.5.5}$$

For let σ, τ be arbitrary complex numbers with sum unity: $\sigma + \tau = 1$. Since $\sigma\phi + \tau\psi - \gamma = \sigma(\phi - \gamma) + \tau(\psi - \gamma)$, we have

$$E_s(\sigma\phi + \tau\psi) = |\sigma|^2 E_s(\phi) + 2\mathrm{Re}\,[\sigma\bar{\tau} E_s(\phi, \psi)] + |\tau|^2 E_s(\psi) \geqq e;$$

that is,

$$|\sigma|^2[E_s(\phi) - e] + 2\mathrm{Re}\,[\sigma\bar{\tau}(E_s(\phi, \psi) - e)] + |\tau|^2[E_s(\psi) - e] \geqq 0.$$

In this equation the requirement that $\sigma + \tau = 1$ can be dropped, so we may take for σ, τ arbitrary complex numbers, and we conclude that

$$|E_s(\phi, \psi) - e| \leqq \sqrt{E_s(\phi) - e}\cdot\sqrt{E_s(\psi) - e}.$$

Hence, using (1.5.4), we obtain

$$\begin{aligned} D_s(\phi - \psi) &= [E_s(\phi) - e] - 2\mathrm{Re}\,[E_s(\phi, \psi) - e] + [E_s(\psi) - e] \\ &\leqq [E_s(\phi) - e] + 2\,|E_s(\phi, \psi) - e| + [E_s(\psi) - e] \\ &\leqq [E_s(\phi) - e] + 2\sqrt{E_s(\phi) - e}\cdot\sqrt{E_s(\psi) - e} + [E_s(\psi) - e]. \end{aligned}$$

Let $\{\phi_\mu\}$ be a sequence such that $E_s(\phi_\mu) \to e$ $(\mu \to \infty)$. By (1.5.5), the ϕ_μ converge in D_s-norm to a limit α, $e = E_s(\alpha)$. Let $\phi \in D$; then $E_s(\alpha + \epsilon\phi) \geqq e$ for every complex number ϵ and we obtain by the usual reasoning that

$$D_s(\alpha, \phi) = \tfrac{1}{2}(\beta, \phi), \qquad \phi \in D. \tag{1.5.6}$$

If $\phi \in \mathbf{C}$, then $D_s(\alpha, \phi) = \frac{1}{2}(\alpha, \Delta_s\phi)$. Therefore, regarding α as a current, we have the equation

$$(\Delta_s\alpha, \phi) = (\beta, \phi), \qquad \phi \in \mathbf{C}, \tag{1.5.7}$$

where, by definition, $(\Delta_s\alpha, \phi) = (\alpha, \Delta_s\phi)$. Suppose that $\beta \in C^\infty$; then, by Lemma 1.3.1, α is equal to a form of class C^∞ and, in this case, the equation $\Delta_s\alpha = \beta$ is valid in the ordinary sense and (1.5.6) becomes

$$(1.5.8) \qquad D_s(\alpha, \phi) = \tfrac{1}{2}(\Delta_s\alpha, \phi), \qquad \phi \in D.$$

We write $\alpha = N_s\beta$, $\beta \in \mathbf{A}$. Given $\beta_1, \beta_2 \in \mathbf{A}$, let $\alpha_1 = N_s\beta_1$, $\alpha_2 = N_s\beta_2$, $\alpha = N_s(\beta_1 + \beta_2)$. By (1.5.8) we have $D_s(\alpha - \alpha_1 - \alpha_2) = 0$ and, choosing $\phi = \alpha - \alpha_1 - \alpha_2$, we conclude that $\alpha = \alpha_1 + \alpha_2$. Thus $N_s(\beta_1 + \beta_2) = N_s\beta_1 + N_s\beta_2$, that is, $N_s\beta$ is linear in β, $\beta \in \mathbf{A}$.

Next, taking $\phi = \alpha = N_s\beta$ in (1.5.6), we obtain $\tfrac{1}{2}s \,\|\, \alpha \,\|^2 \leqq D_s(\alpha) = \tfrac{1}{2}(\beta, \alpha) \leqq \tfrac{1}{2} \,\|\, \alpha \,\| \cdot \|\, \beta \,\|$ and therefore $\|\, \alpha \,\| \leqq \|\, \beta \,\|/s$, $D_s(\alpha) \leqq \|\, \alpha \,\|^2/(2s)$.

Let $\{\beta_\mu\}$, $\beta_\mu \in C^\infty$, $\beta_\mu \in \mathbf{A}$, be a sequence such that $\|\, \beta - \beta_\mu \,\| \to 0$ $(\mu \to \infty)$, and write $\alpha_\mu = N_s\beta_\mu$. By (1.5.8),

$$D_s(\alpha_\mu - \alpha_\nu, \phi) = \tfrac{1}{2}(\beta_\mu - \beta_\nu, \phi), \qquad \phi \in D,$$

where $\beta_\mu = \Delta_s\alpha_\mu$, $\beta_\nu = \Delta_s\alpha_\nu$. Taking $\phi = \alpha_\mu - \alpha_\nu$, we have

$$\begin{aligned} D_s(\alpha_\mu - \alpha_\nu) & \\ &= \tfrac{1}{2}(\beta_\mu - \beta_\nu, \alpha_\mu - \alpha_\nu) \leqq \tfrac{1}{2} \,\|\, \beta_\mu - \beta_\nu \,\| \cdot \|\, \alpha_\mu - \alpha_\nu \,\| \\ &\qquad \leqq \|\, \beta_\mu - \beta_\nu \,\|/(2s). \end{aligned}$$

Hence $\|\, \alpha_\mu - \alpha_\nu \,\|$, $D(\alpha_\mu - \alpha_\nu)$, $\|\, \Delta\alpha_\mu - \Delta\alpha_\nu \,\|$ tend to zero $(\mu, \nu \to \infty)$, and it follows that $\alpha = N_s\beta$ is in the domain of Δ, $\Delta_s N_s \beta = \beta$.

If $\phi, \psi \in \mathbf{A}$, then $(N_s\phi, \psi) = (N_s\phi, \Delta_s N_s\psi) = 2D_s(N_s\phi, N_s\psi) = (\phi, N_s\psi)$, so N_s is a symmetric operator.

A similar proof applies to G_s, but in this case we restrict the forms ϕ in the minimum problem for $E_s(\phi)$ to those which lie in $\mathbf{C}$, and we write $e_c = \inf E_s(\phi)$, $\phi \in \mathbf{C}$. If $\{\phi_\mu\}$, $\phi_\mu \in \mathbf{C}$, is a sequence such that $E_s(\phi_\mu) \to e_c$, we conclude as above that $\{\phi_\mu\}$ converges in D_s-norm to a limit α satisfying $D_s(\alpha, \phi) = \tfrac{1}{2}(\beta, \phi)$ for $\phi \in D_c$. Moreover, if ψ is in the domain of Δ,

$$D_s(\alpha, \psi) = \lim_{\mu\to\infty} D_s(\phi_\mu, \psi) = \lim_{\mu\to\infty} \tfrac{1}{2}(\phi_\mu, \Delta_s\psi) = \tfrac{1}{2}(\alpha, \Delta_s\psi).$$

Hence, writing $\alpha = G_s\beta$, we have $G_s\beta \in G$, $\Delta_s G_s \beta = \beta$, $D_s(G_s\beta) \leqq \|\, \beta \,\|^2/2s$.

Let $\phi \in \mathbf{N}$; then $\psi = \phi - N_s(\Delta_s\phi) \in \mathbf{N}$ and, since $\Delta_s\psi = 0$, we conclude that $\psi = 0$. That is, if $\phi \in \mathbf{N}$, then $\phi = N_s(\Delta_s\phi)$. Similarly, if $\phi \in G$, then $\phi = G_s(\Delta_s\phi)$.

For $\phi, \psi \in \mathbf{G}$, we have $(\Delta\phi, \psi) = 2D(\phi, \psi) = (\phi, \Delta\psi)$, and the same is true for Δ_c. Hence $\Delta \mid \mathbf{G}$ is a symmetric extension of Δ_c. But it can be proved[1] that Δ_c is self-adjoint, and it follows that $\Delta \mid \mathbf{G} = \Delta_c$. Similarly $\Delta \mid \mathbf{N} = {}_c\Delta$, so $\mathbf{G}$ is the domain of Δ_c, $\mathbf{N}$ the domain of ${}_c\Delta$.

Next,

$$\mathbf{F}_c = \{\phi \mid \phi \in \mathbf{A},\ \Delta G_s\phi = \phi - sG_s\phi = 0\}, \tag{1.5.9}$$

$$\mathbf{F} = \{\phi \mid \phi \in \mathbf{A},\ \Delta N_s\phi = \phi - sN_s\phi = 0\}. \tag{1.5.10}$$

In fact, if $\phi \in \mathbf{A}$, $\phi - sG_s\phi = 0$, then $\phi \in \mathbf{G}$, $\Delta\phi = 0$. Conversely, if $\phi \in \mathbf{G}$, $\Delta\phi = 0$, we have $\phi = G_s(\Delta_s\phi) = sG_s\phi$. A similar reasoning applies to (1.5.10).

We have the orthogonal decompositions:

$$\mathbf{A} = [\Delta\mathbf{G}] \oplus \mathbf{F}_c, \tag{1.5.11}$$

$$\mathbf{A} = [\Delta\mathbf{N}] \oplus \mathbf{F}, \tag{1.5.12}$$

where $[\Delta\mathbf{G}]$ denotes the closure under the norm $\|\phi\|$ of the space of forms $\phi = \Delta\psi$, $\psi \in \mathbf{G}$, and where $[\Delta\mathbf{N}]$ has a similar meaning with respect to the space $\mathbf{N}$. In fact, let $\phi \in \mathbf{A}$, $(\phi, \gamma) = 0$ for $\gamma \in [\Delta\mathbf{G}]$. Then $0 = (\phi, \Delta G_s\psi) = (\phi, \psi - sG_s\psi) = (\phi - sG_s\phi, \psi)$ for all $\psi \in \mathbf{A}$, so $\phi - sG_s\phi = 0$ and $\phi \in \mathbf{F}_c$. A similar reasoning applies to (1.5.12).

1.6. Bounded almost-complex domains. We say that a domain $\mathfrak{B}$ is a bounded almost-complex domain if $\mathfrak{B}$ is an open subset of an almost-complex manifold $\mathfrak{V}$ whose closure forms a compact subset of $\mathfrak{V}$. It is not necessary for $\mathfrak{B}$ to be connected. We suppose that $\mathfrak{V}$ has a Hermitian metric of class C^∞.

THEOREM 1.6.1. *For a bounded almost-complex domain $\mathfrak{B}$ the operator G_s $(s > 0)$ is completely continuous, and $\mathbf{F}_c$ is the space of harmonic forms on $\mathfrak{V}$ which vanish identically outside $\mathfrak{B}$.*

Proof. We recall that a completely continuous transformation is one which sends bounded sets into compact ones.

The proof is based on the construction of a parametrix γ in the neighborhood of an arbitrary point $p \in \mathfrak{V}$. In fact, given $p \in \mathfrak{V}$, there exists a neighborhood U of p (U depending on p) such that,

[1] M. P. Gaffney has communicated to me a proof for the corresponding Laplacian Δ_c in the case of the real operators d, δ $(\delta = -{*d*})$, and his proof carries over without essential change to the complex operators $\bar{\partial}$, $\mathfrak{d}$.

given a positive integer ν, a positive number η, and a nonnegative number s, there exists a double form $\gamma(x, y)$ in x and in y (x, y here stand for points of V expressed in terms of local coordinates $x^1, \cdots, x^{2n}$ and $y^1, \cdots, y^{2n}$ respectively) with the properties:

(i) The form $\gamma(x, y)$ is defined for $x \in \mathfrak{B}$, $y \in U$, and it is of class C^∞ in both the arguments x, y provided that $x \neq y$. If $r(x, y)$ is the geodesic distance of the points x, y, then $r(x, y)^{2n-2}\gamma(x, y)$ is of class C^∞ at $x = y$.

(ii) For fixed $y \in U$, sup (γ) has a diameter less than η.

(iii) $\Delta_s(x)\gamma(x, y) = \lambda(x, y)$, where $\lambda(x, y)$ is a double form of class C^∞ in both arguments x, y, $x \in \mathfrak{B}$, $y \in U$.

(iv) $(\phi(x), \bar{\partial}(x)\gamma(x, y))$ is a completely continuous transformation mapping the space $\mathbf{A}(\mathfrak{B})$ into $\mathbf{A}(U)$. Similarly, $(\phi(x), \mathfrak{d}(x)\gamma(x, y))$ is a completely continuous transformation of $\mathbf{A}(\mathfrak{B})$ into $\mathbf{A}(U)$.

The existence of a parametrix γ with these properties can be established by the method of Kodaira [6].

The domain $\mathfrak{B}$ can be covered by finitely many neighborhoods U with the property described above. Given $\phi \in \mathbf{A}$, let $\{\phi_\mu\}$, $\phi_\mu \in C$, be a sequence converging to $G_s\phi$ in the D_s-norm. For $y \in U \cap \mathfrak{B}$ we have

$$(1.6.1) \quad \phi_\mu(y) = 2D_s(\phi_\mu(x), \gamma(x, y)) - (\phi_\mu(x), \lambda(x, y)).$$

Letting $\mu \to \infty$, we obtain the formula

$$(1.6.2) \quad (G_s\phi)(y) = 2D_s(G_s\phi(x), \gamma(x, y)) - (G_s\phi(x), \lambda(x, y)), \qquad y \in U \cap \mathfrak{B},$$

which shows that $(G_s\phi)(y)$ is a completely continuous mapping from $\mathbf{A}$ into $\mathbf{A}(U \cap \mathfrak{B})$. Since $\mathfrak{B}$ is covered by finitely many neighborhoods U, the first statement of Theorem 1.6.1 follows.

The second statement is proved similarly. In fact, given $\phi \in F_c = F_c(\mathfrak{B})$, define ϕ to be identically zero outside $\mathfrak{B}$. Let p be a point on the boundary of $\mathfrak{B}$, U a neighborhood of p in $\mathfrak{B}$ for which there exists a parametrix $\gamma(x, y)$ satisfying (i) – (iv) with $s = 0$. Let $\{\phi_\mu\}$, $\phi_\mu \in \mathbf{C}$, be a sequence converging to ϕ in the D_s-norm for $\mathfrak{B}$, hence in the D_s-norm for $\mathfrak{B}$ since ϕ and ϕ_μ vanish outside $\mathfrak{B}$. For $y \in U$ we have (1.6.1) and hence, letting $\mu \to \infty$,

$$(1.6.3) \quad \phi(y) = 2D_s(\phi(x), \gamma(x, y)) - (\phi(x), \lambda(x, y)) = -(\phi(x), \lambda(x, y)), \qquad y \in U.$$

It follows from (1.6.3) that $\phi(y)$ (defined to be zero outside $\mathfrak{B}$) is of class C^∞ throughout the full neighborhood U of the boundary point p of $\mathfrak{B}$, and the second statement of Theorem 1.6.1 follows.

THEOREM 1.6.2. *On a bounded almost-complex domain there exists a one-to-one, linear, completely continuous map* $G_0: \mathbf{A} \ominus \mathbf{F}_c \to \mathbf{G} \ominus \mathbf{F}_c$, $G_0^{-1} = \Delta \mid \mathbf{G} \ominus \mathbf{F}_c$.

If we define G_0 to be the zero map on $\mathbf{F}_c$, we obtain a completely continuous transformation $G_0: \mathbf{A} \to \mathbf{G} \ominus \mathbf{F}_c$, and the kernel of the map G_0 is $\mathbf{F}_c$.

Proof of theorem. Given $\beta \in \mathbf{A}$, let s be a fixed positive number, and consider the equation $\Delta G_s\phi = \beta - F_c\beta$ where $F_c\beta$ is the component of β obtained by orthogonal projection onto $\mathbf{F}_c$ (see (1.5.11)). We therefore have the following equation for ϕ,

$$\phi - sG_s\phi = \beta - F_c\beta, \tag{1.6.4}$$

where we may assume that $F_c\phi = 0$. The solution space of the homogeneous transposed equation

$$\psi - sG_s\psi = 0 \tag{1.6.5}$$

is $\mathbf{F}_c$ and, since $\beta - F_c\beta$ is orthogonal to all the solutions of (1.6.5), there exists a unique solution ϕ of (1.6.4) satisfying $F_c\phi = 0$. We define $G_0\beta = G_s\phi$, $F_cG_0 = G_0F_c = 0$, $\Delta G_0\beta = \beta - F_c\beta$. The fact that G_0 is completely continuous may be easily verified.

We call G_0 the Green's operator of the bounded almost-complex domain.

Theorem 1.6.2 enables us to remove the brackets in equation (1.5.11); that is,

$$\mathbf{A} = \Delta\mathbf{G} \oplus \mathbf{F}_c. \tag{1.6.6}$$

In other words, given $\phi \in \mathbf{A}$, we have the orthogonal decomposition

$$\phi = \Delta G_0\phi + F_c\phi, \qquad F_cG_0\phi = 0. \tag{1.6.7}$$

Taking in particular $\phi = \Delta\theta \in \mathbf{A}$, $F_c\theta = 0$ and writing $\psi = \theta - G_0\Delta\theta$, we have

$$\Delta\psi = 0 \text{ in } B, \qquad F_c\psi = 0, \qquad \theta - \psi \in \mathbf{G}. \tag{1.6.8}$$

Therefore Theorem 1.6.2 yields the solution of the first boundary-value problem of potential theory for bounded almost-complex domains.

Let H denote orthogonal projection onto the space $\mathbf{H}$, and define

$$B_0\phi = (1 - H)G_0\phi. \tag{1.6.9}$$

Writing $\psi = (1 - H)\phi - B_0\Delta\phi$, we have $\Delta\psi = 0$, $H\psi = 0$, so $\psi = 0$; that is,

$$B_0\Delta\phi = (1 - H)\phi. \tag{1.6.10}$$

There exists a positive number c such that $\| G_0\phi \| < c\cdot\| \phi \|$, $\phi \in \mathbf{A}$, and we have $\| B_0\phi \| = \| (1 - H)G_0\phi \| \leqq \| G_0\phi \| < c\cdot\| \phi \|$. Hence, by (1.6.10),

$$\|(1 - H)\phi \| < c\cdot\| \Delta\phi \|. \tag{1.6.11}$$

1.7. The Neumann's operator. We say that a domain $\mathfrak{B}$ has a Neumann's operator if there exists a one-to-one linear map $N_0 \colon \mathbf{A} \ominus \mathbf{F} \rightarrow \mathbf{N} \ominus \mathbf{F}$ whose inverse is Δ. If N_0 exists, we extend its domain to the whole of $\mathbf{A}$ by defining it to be the zero map on $\mathbf{F}$.

Suppose that $\mathfrak{B}$ has a Neumann's operator N_0 of degree r. Then (1.5.12) may be replaced by the formula

$$\mathbf{A} = \Delta\mathbf{N} \oplus \mathbf{F}. \tag{1.7.1}$$

That is, an arbitrary $\phi \in \mathbf{A}$ has the orthogonal decomposition

$$\phi = \Delta N_0\phi + F\phi. \tag{1.7.2}$$

In particular, taking $\phi = \Delta\theta$, θ in the domain of Δ, $F\theta = 0$, and writing $\psi = \theta - N_0\Delta\theta$, we have

$$\bar{\partial}\Delta\psi = \mathfrak{d}\Delta\psi = 0 \text{ in } \mathfrak{B}, \qquad F\psi = 0, \qquad \theta - \psi \in \mathbf{N}. \tag{1.7.3}$$

Therefore the existence of a Neumann's operator N_0 implies the solvability of the second boundary-value problem for the complex operators, $\bar{\partial}$, $\mathfrak{d}$ (in a generalized sense).

Given θ in the domain of Δ, $F\theta = 0$, then among all forms ϕ, $F\phi = 0$, $\theta - \phi \in \mathbf{N}$, the form $\psi = \theta - N_0\Delta\theta$ imparts the smallest value to $\| \Delta\phi \|$. In fact, let $\phi = \psi + \epsilon\tau$ where $\tau \in \mathbf{N}$, $F\tau = 0$. Since $F\Delta\tau = 0$, we have

$$\begin{aligned} \| \Delta\phi \|^2 &= \| \Delta\psi \|^2 + 2\mathrm{Re}\,[\bar{\epsilon}(\Delta\psi, \Delta\tau)] + | \epsilon |^2\cdot\| \Delta\tau \|^2 \\ &= \| \Delta\psi \|^2 + | \epsilon |^2\cdot\| \Delta\tau \|^2 > \| \Delta\psi \|^2 \end{aligned}$$

unless $\Delta\tau = 0$, which implies that $\tau = 0$.

Let s be a fixed positive number. We have

$$\| (1 - H)N_s(1 - H)\psi \| < c \cdot \| \Delta N_s(1 - H)\psi \|$$

by (1.6.11) ($\mathfrak{B}$ a bounded domain);

$$\| HN_s(1 - H) \psi \| = \| HN_s(1 - H) \psi - \frac{1}{s}H(1 - H) \psi \|$$

$$= \frac{1}{s} \| H \Delta N_s(1 - H) \psi \| \leqq \frac{1}{s} \| \Delta N_s(1 - H) \psi \| .$$

Hence:

$$\| N_s(1 - H) \psi \| < \left(c + \frac{1}{s}\right) \| \Delta N_s(1 - H) \| . \tag{1.7.4}$$

Given $\phi \in \mathbf{A}$, let $m = \inf \| \phi - \Delta N_s \psi \|$ for $\psi \in \mathbf{A}$, $H\psi = 0$. From (1.7.4) and the usual reasoning we conclude that there exists a $\psi \in \mathbf{A}$, $H\psi = 0$, such that $\|\phi - \Delta N_s \psi \| = m$. Writing $\beta = \phi - \Delta N_s \psi$, we have

$$0 = (\beta, \Delta N_s \lambda) = (\beta, \lambda - sN_s \lambda) = (\beta - sN_s \beta, \lambda)$$

for every $\lambda \in \mathbf{A}$, $H\lambda = 0$, and this implies that $\Delta N_s \beta = \beta - sN_s \beta \in \mathbf{H}$. Thus (for a bounded domain):

$$\phi = \Delta N_s \psi + \beta, \qquad H\psi = 0, \qquad \Delta N_s \beta \in \mathbf{H}. \tag{1.7.5}$$

Let $\mathfrak{B}$ be a bounded domain, and G_0 the Green's operator of a bounded domain $\mathfrak{M}$ containing the closure of $\mathfrak{B}$ in its interior. Given θ in the domain of Δ on $\mathfrak{B}$, we have by (1.7.5) that $\Delta\theta = \Delta N_s \psi + \beta$. We define β on $\mathfrak{M}$ by setting $\beta = 0$ in $\mathfrak{M} - \mathfrak{B}$; then $\Delta G_0 \beta = \beta - F_c \beta$, where $F_c = F_c(\mathfrak{M})$ is the projection operator for $\mathfrak{M}$, and we have $\Delta\theta = \Delta N_s \psi + \Delta G_0 \beta + F_c \beta$. That is, $\Delta(\theta - N_s \psi - G_0(1 - F)\beta) = \Delta G_0 F \beta + F_c \beta = F\beta - F_c F \beta + F_c \beta = F\beta$, where F denotes orthogonal projection onto the space $F(\mathfrak{B})$, $F\beta = 0$ in $\mathfrak{M} - \mathfrak{B}$. Therefore we have in $\mathfrak{B}$

$$\theta = \sigma + G_0(1 - F)\beta + N_s \psi, \qquad \Delta\sigma = F\beta, \qquad F = F(\mathfrak{B}),$$

and it follows that the second boundary-value problem for the form θ in $\mathfrak{B}$ is equivalent to the second boundary-value problem for $G_0(1 - F)\beta$, $\Delta G_0(1 - F)\beta = (1 - F)\beta$.

If $\mathfrak{B}$ has a Neumann's operator N_0, then

$$G_0(1 - F)\beta = N_0(1 - F)\beta - H_0 \beta, \qquad H_0 \beta \in \mathbf{H}(\mathfrak{B}) \ominus \mathbf{F}_c(\mathfrak{B}).$$

But it is not possible to prove the solvability (at least in the strong sense) of the second boundary-value problem for every bounded subdomain unless the manifold $\mathfrak{B}$ is actually complex-analytic. In fact, given a point $p \in \mathfrak{B}$, and a self-conjugate coordinate system $z^1, \cdots, z^n, \bar{z}^1, \cdots, \bar{z}^n$ adapted at p with $z^j = 0$ at p, let $S_\epsilon = \{z \,\|\, z^1 |^2 + \cdots + | z^n |^2 < \epsilon^2\}$ be the coordinate sphere at p of radius ϵ with respect to these coordinates. We say that the second boundary-value problem for S_ϵ is strongly solvable if, given a function θ of class C^∞ in the closure of S_ϵ, there exists a function ψ of class C^∞ in the closure of S_ϵ such that $\bar{\partial}\Delta\psi = \mathfrak{b}\Delta\psi = 0$ in S_ϵ, $\psi - \theta \in \mathbf{N}$. It is easily shown that $\mathfrak{B}$ is complex-analytic if and only if every point $p \in \mathfrak{B}$ has a neighborhood with Hermitian metric and self-conjugate coordinate system in terms of which the second boundary-value problem is strongly solvable for every sufficiently small sphere S_ϵ. In fact, it is not difficult to show that the solvability of the second boundary-value problem enables one to construct n almost-analytic functions which are functionally independent in a neighborhood of the point p. Since it is quite probable that the existence of the Neumann's operator N_0 for a sphere S_ϵ implies the strong solvability of the second boundary-value problem, it is reasonable to expect that the existence of the Neumann's operator N_0 for a bounded domain $\mathfrak{B}$ must be based on the further supposition that $\bar{\partial}^2 = 0$, this being the condition that the almost-complex structure is integrable.

1.8. Cauchy's formula for almost-analytic functions. If G_0 is the Green's operator of degree r for a bounded subdomain of an almost-complex manifold, it is easily verified (see [10]) that G_0 is an integral operator; that is, $(G_0\phi)(y) = (\phi(x), g(x, y))$ where $g(x, y)$ is a symmetric double form of degree r in each argument, which, at y, has the same singularity as a local fundamental solution for the equation $\Delta\psi = 0$. Moreover, $\Delta(x)\cdot g(x, y) = -f_c(x, y)$ where $f_c(x, y)$ is the symmetric double form occurring in the formula $(F_c\phi)(y) = (\phi(x), f_c(x, y))$.

Let $\mathfrak{B}$ be a bounded submanifold of an almost-complex manifold $\mathfrak{B}$ whose boundary $b\mathfrak{B}$ is a $(2n - 1)$-dimensional submanifold of $\mathfrak{B}$ of class C^∞, and let $\mathfrak{M}$ be some bounded manifold containing the closure of $\mathfrak{B}$ in its interior. If ϕ is a function of class C^∞ in the closure of $\mathfrak{B}$, we have

$$\phi(y) = 2D(\phi(x), g(x, y)) + (\phi(x), f_c(x, y)) - 2 \int_{b\mathfrak{B}} \phi(x) \wedge * (\bar{\partial} g(x, y))^{-},$$

where the integration in the scalar products on the right is over $\mathfrak{B}$. If ϕ is almost-analytic, that is $\bar{\partial}\phi = 0$, this formula becomes

$$\text{(1.8.1)} \qquad \phi(y) = (\phi(x), f_c(x, y)) - 2 \int_{b\mathfrak{B}} \phi(x) \wedge * (\bar{\partial} g(x, y))^{-},$$

where the first term on the right is an almost-analytic function on $\mathfrak{M}$ belonging to the space F_c. If $\mathfrak{B}$ is a real-analytic manifold, the harmonic functions and forms are also real-analytic and it follows from an analytic continuation argument that the space $\mathbf{F}_c$ contains only the 0-form. In this case we have the Cauchy formula

$$\text{(1.8.2)} \qquad \phi(y) = -2 \int_{b\mathfrak{B}} \phi(x) \wedge * (\bar{\partial} g(x, y))^{-}.$$

2. Complex structure

2.1. Hermitian product-structure and complex structure. If $\mathfrak{B}$ is an almost-complex manifold, we define its conjugate manifold $\bar{\mathfrak{B}}$ to be the homeomorphic image of $\mathfrak{B}$ in which the point p of $\mathfrak{B}$ corresponds to the point $\bar{p}$ of $\bar{\mathfrak{B}}$ and whose almost-complex structure is defined at $\bar{p}$ by the matrix $h_{\bar{p}} = -h_p$. The product manifold $\mathfrak{B} \times \bar{\mathfrak{B}}$ whose points are the ordered pairs $(p, \bar{q})$ has the almost-complex structure defined at $(p, \bar{q})$ by the matrix

$$\begin{Vmatrix} h_p & 0 \\ 0 & -h_q \end{Vmatrix},$$

and its tangent space at $(p, \bar{q})$ is isomorphic to

$$(\textstyle\prod_{1,0} CT + \prod_{0,1} CT)_p + (\prod_{0,1} CT + \prod_{1,0} CT)_q .$$

At a point of the diagonal manifold $\mathfrak{D}$ of $\mathfrak{B} \times \mathfrak{B}$ where $p = q$, the tangent space of $\mathfrak{B} \times \bar{\mathfrak{B}}$ is therefore isomorphic to $CT_p + \overline{CT}_p$. It is convenient to identify $\mathfrak{B}$ with the diagonal manifold $\mathfrak{D}$.

Let indices j, k be identified modulo $2n$, write $\bar{j} = j + n$, and introduce the coordinates

$$z^k(p, \bar{q}) = \begin{cases} z^k(p), & k = 1, 2, \cdots, n \\ z^k(q), & k = n + 1, \cdots, 2n, \end{cases}$$

where $z^k(p)$, $z^k(q)$ are self-conjugate coordinates valid in neighborhoods of the points p, q of $\mathfrak{B}$ respectively. Then $z^k(p, \bar{q}) = z^{\bar{k}}(q, \bar{p})^-$ for $k = 1, 2, \cdots, 2n$, and on the diagonal $\mathfrak{D}$ we have $z^k = z^k(p, \bar{p}) = z^{\bar{k}}(p, \bar{p})^-$. If $\mathfrak{B}$ is complex-analytic, we choose for each $p \in \mathfrak{B}$ self-conjugate analytic coordinates $z^k(p)$ in terms of which $\partial/\partial z^1, \cdots, \partial/\partial z^n$ is a moving basis for $\prod_{1,0} CT$ over a neighborhood of p. The coordinates $z^1(p, \bar{q}), \cdots, z^{2n}(p, \bar{q}), \bar{z}^1(p, \bar{q}), \cdots, \bar{z}^{2n}(p, \bar{q})$ are the self-conjugate analytic coordinates in a neighborhood of $(p, \bar{q}) \in \mathfrak{B} \times \overline{\mathfrak{B}}$.

If $\mathfrak{B}$ is complex-analytic, then

$$(2.1.1)\qquad \begin{aligned} \bar{\partial}^2 &= 0, & \textstyle\prod_{\rho,\sigma+1} \bar{\partial} &= \bar{\partial} \textstyle\prod_{\rho,\sigma}, \\ \mathfrak{d}^2 &= 0, & \textstyle\prod_{\rho,\sigma-1} \mathfrak{d} &= \mathfrak{d} \textstyle\prod_{\rho,\sigma}, \end{aligned}$$

and hence $\Delta \prod_{\rho,\sigma} = \prod_{\rho,\sigma} \Delta$.

2.2. Real homotopy operators. Let $\mathfrak{B}$ be a real differentiable manifold of class C^∞ and dimension n. Given a point $p \in \mathfrak{B}$, let $x^1, \cdots, x^n$ be local coordinates with center at p which cover a neighborhood U of p, and denote by W the star of U with respect to the point p. That is, $W = W_x$ is the subdomain of U each point of which can be joined to p by a straight-line segment contained entirely in U. Given a function $f \in C^\infty$ in U, we define, for each integer $\lambda \geq 0$,

$$Q^\lambda(f) = \int_0^1 u^\lambda f(ux^1, \cdots, ux^n)\, du.$$

Then $Q^\lambda(f)$ is a function of class C^∞ throughout W, and we have

$$(2.2.1)\qquad \frac{\partial}{\partial x^k} Q^\lambda(f) = Q^{\lambda+1}\left(\frac{\partial f}{\partial x^k}\right) \quad (k = 1, 2, \cdots, n),$$

$$(2.2.2)\qquad f = \lambda Q^{\lambda-1}(f) + Q^{\lambda-1}\left(\sum_{\mu=1}^n x^\mu \frac{\partial f}{\partial x^\mu}\right), \qquad \lambda > 0.$$

Given a differential form ϕ of degree r, $1 \leq r \leq n$, and of class C^∞ in U which, in terms of the coordinates $x^1, \cdots, x^n$, has the form

$$\phi = \textstyle\sum_{j_1 < \cdots < j_r} \phi_{j_1 \cdots j_r}(x^1, \cdots, x^n)\, dx^{j_1} \cdots dx^{j_r},$$

we define

$$k\phi = \textstyle\sum_{j_1 < \cdots < j_{r-1}} (k\phi)_{j_1 \cdots j_{r-1}} dx^{j_1} \cdots dx^{j_{r-1}}$$

where

$$(2.2.3)\qquad \begin{aligned}(k\phi)_{j_1\cdots j_{r-1}} &= \sum_{j=1}^{n} Q^{r-2}(x^j\phi_{jj_1\cdots j_{r-1}})\\ &= \sum_{j=1}^{n}\int_0^1 u^{r-1}x^j\phi_{jj_1\cdots j_{r-1}}(ux^1, \cdots, ux^n)\,du.\end{aligned}$$

If ϕ is of degree 0, we define $k\phi = 0$. It is easily verified that $k^2 = 0$.

We have

$$\begin{aligned}(dk\phi)_{j_1\cdots j_r} &= \sum_{\mu=1}^{r}(-1)^{\mu+1}\frac{\partial}{\partial x^{j_\mu}}(k\phi)_{j_1\cdots j_{\mu-1}j_{\mu+1}\cdots j_r}\\ &= \sum_{j=1}^{n} Q^{r-1}\left(\sum_{\mu=1}^{r}(-1)^{\mu+1}\frac{\partial}{\partial x^{j_\mu}}(x^j\phi_{jj_1\cdots j_{\mu-1}j_{\mu+1}\cdots j_r})\right)\\ &= -(kd\phi)_{j_1\cdots j_r} + rQ^{r-1}(\phi_{j_1\cdots j_r})\\ &\quad + Q^{r-1}\left(\sum_{j=1}^{n} x^j\frac{\partial}{\partial x^j}\phi_{j_1\cdots j_r}\right)\\ &= -(kd\phi)_{j_1\cdots j_r} + \phi_{j_1\cdots j_r}\end{aligned}$$

by (2.2.2). Hence

$$(2.2.4)\qquad \phi = (dk + kd)\phi$$

throughout W, provided that the degree of $\phi \geq 1$. If the degree of $\phi = 0$, the corresponding formula is

$$(2.2.5)\qquad \phi = (kd + Q^0)\phi.$$

2.3. Complex homotopy operators. Suppose first that $\mathfrak{V}$ is a product variety, $\mathfrak{V} = \mathfrak{V}' \times \mathfrak{V}''$, where $\mathfrak{V}'$, $\mathfrak{V}''$ are real differentiable manifolds of class C^∞ and dimensions m', m'' respectively. Let $p = (p', p'')$ be a point of $\mathfrak{V}$, $p' \in \mathfrak{V}'$, $p'' \in \mathfrak{V}''$, let U', U'' be neighborhoods of p', p'' in $\mathfrak{V}'$, $\mathfrak{V}''$ which are covered by local coordinates x', x'' with centers at p', p'', and let W', W'' be the stars of U', U'' with respect to the points p', p'' respectively. If ϕ is a differential form in $U = U' \times U''$, then

$$\phi = \textstyle\sum_{\rho,\sigma}\prod_{\rho,\sigma}\phi$$

where $\prod_{\rho,\sigma}\phi \in (\wedge_\rho P^*T^*) \wedge (\wedge_\sigma Q^*T^*)$. For fixed $x' \in U'$, we may regard $\prod_{\rho,\sigma}\phi$ as a differential form of degree σ in U'' and, if

$\sigma \geq 1$, formula (2.2.4) may be applied. Therefore, if $\sum_\rho \prod_{\rho,\sigma} \phi = 0$,

$$\phi = (d''k'' + k''d'')\phi \tag{2.3.1}$$

throughout $U' \times W''$, where d'' denotes exterior differentiation with respect to the coordinates x'' and where k'' is defined in terms of these same coordinates.

Suppose now that $\mathfrak{V}$ is complex-analytic, and let $U = U' \times \bar{U}''$ be a neighborhood of a point $(p, \bar{q})$ of $\mathfrak{V} \times \overline{\mathfrak{V}}$ where U' is covered by analytic coordinates $z^1, \cdots, z^n$ with center at p, $\bar{U}''$ by conjugate analytic coordinates $\zeta^1, \cdots, \zeta^n$ with center at $\bar{q}$. Let W' be the star of U', $\bar{W}''$ the star of $\bar{U}''$. If ϕ is a differential form in U, then for fixed $z \in U'$ we may regard $\prod_{\rho,\sigma} \phi$ as a differential form of degree σ in $\bar{U}''$, and we denote by κ the operator k defined in $\bar{W}''$ in terms of the coordinates $\zeta^1, \cdots, \zeta^n$. If $\sum_\rho \prod_{\rho,\sigma} \phi = 0$, then

$$\phi = (\bar{\partial}\kappa + \kappa\bar{\partial})\phi \tag{2.3.2}$$

throughout $U' \times \bar{W}''$.

Let ϕ be a differential form of degree r which is real-analytic in the neighborhood of a point $p \in \mathfrak{V}$. Then ϕ, by analytic continuation, is a differential form in some neighborhood $U = U' \times \bar{U}'$ of the point $(p, \bar{p})$ on $\mathfrak{V} \times \overline{\mathfrak{V}}$ and hence ϕ satisfies (2.3.2) throughout $U' \times \bar{W}'$. Therefore, on $\mathfrak{D} = \mathfrak{V}$, ϕ satisfies (2.3.2) in the neighborhood $\mathfrak{D} \cap (W' \times \bar{W}')$ of the point $(p, \bar{p}) = p$.

Finally, let ϕ be a differential form which is closed under $\bar{\partial}$ (i.e., $\bar{\partial}\phi = 0$) throughout a domain U of $\mathfrak{V}$ covered by self-conjugate analytic coordinates z^k. The domain U may be regarded as a bounded domain of the complex Euclidean n-space defined by these coordinates and with the Euclidean metric. The operator $\bar{\partial}$ for the Euclidean space coincides in U with the operator $\bar{\partial}$ of $\mathfrak{V}$, and we define $\mathfrak{b}$ to be the adjoint operator with respect to the Euclidean metric. By Theorem 1.6.2 there exists an operator G_0 satisfying $\Delta G_0\phi = \phi - F_c\phi$ in U; that is,

$$\phi = 2(\bar{\partial}\mathfrak{b}G_0\phi + \mathfrak{b}\bar{\partial}G_0\phi) + F_c\phi$$

in U. The difference $\psi = \phi - 2\bar{\partial}\mathfrak{b}G_0\phi$ plainly satisfies $\bar{\partial}\phi = \mathfrak{b}\phi = 0$ in U, and is therefore harmonic, hence real-analytic, in U. Therefore, if ϕ is $\bar{\partial}$-closed in the neighborhood of a point $p \in \mathfrak{V}$, $\sum_\rho \prod_{\rho,\sigma} \phi = 0$, there exists a subneighborhood in which

$$\phi = \bar{\partial}\kappa'\phi \tag{2.3.3}$$

where

$$\kappa'\phi = \kappa(\phi - 2\bar{\partial}\mathfrak{d}G_0\phi) + 2\bar{\partial}\mathfrak{d}G_0\phi.$$

This method of reducing the proof of (2.3.3) to that for real-analytic forms is due to A. Grothendieck.

We see that the full strength of complex-analytic structure is required to prove (2.3.3). The only other place where complex-analytic structure enters is in the proof of the relations (2.1.1) (which follow immediately from the possibility of choosing coordinates in terms of which the matrix h has constant components).

2.4. Orthogonal decomposition. Let $[\bar{\partial}\mathbf{C}]$ denote the closure, in the sense of the norm $\| \psi \|$, of the space of forms $\psi = \bar{\partial}\phi$, $\phi \in \mathbf{C}$, and let $[\mathfrak{d}\mathbf{C}]$ denote the closure of the space of forms $\mathfrak{d}\phi$, $\phi \in \mathbf{C}$. Since $\bar{\partial}^2 = \mathfrak{d}^2 = 0$, we have the orthogonal decomposition

$$\mathbf{A} = [\bar{\partial}\mathbf{C}] \oplus [\mathfrak{d}\mathbf{C}] \oplus \mathbf{F}. \tag{2.4.1}$$

That is, given $\phi \in \mathbf{A}$, then $\phi = \alpha + \beta + \gamma$, $\alpha \in [\bar{\partial}\mathbf{C}]$, $\beta \in [\mathfrak{d}\mathbf{C}]$, $\gamma \in \mathbf{F}$. If $\phi \in C^\infty$, then α, $\beta \in C^\infty$. For, regarding α, β as currents and applying the operator $2\bar{\partial}\mathfrak{d}$ to both sides of the equation $\phi = \alpha + \beta + \gamma$, we obtain $2\bar{\partial}\mathfrak{d}\alpha = \Delta\alpha = 2\bar{\partial}\mathfrak{d}\phi \in C^\infty$.

By using (2.4.1) we can show that

$$\{\phi \mid \phi \in D\} = \{\phi \mid \phi \text{ in the domains of the operators } \bar{\partial}, \mathfrak{d}\}. \tag{2.4.2}$$

In fact, suppose that $\phi \in D$. Then there exists a sequence $\{\phi_\mu\}$ such that $D_s(\phi - \phi_\mu) \to 0$ $(\mu \to \infty)$; that is, $\| \bar{\partial}\phi_\mu - \bar{\partial}\phi_\nu \|$, $\| \mathfrak{d}\phi_\mu - \mathfrak{d}\phi_\nu \|$, $\| \phi - \phi_\mu \|$ tend to zero $(\mu, \nu \to \infty)$. Conversely, suppose that ϕ is contained in the domains of $\bar{\partial}$ and $\mathfrak{d}$. Then there exist two sequences $\{\phi_\mu'\}$, $\{\phi_\mu''\}$ such that $\| \bar{\partial}\phi_\mu' - \bar{\partial}\phi_\nu' \|$, $\| \phi - \phi_\mu' \| \to 0$ and $\| \mathfrak{d}\phi_\mu'' - \mathfrak{d}\phi_\nu'' \|$, $\| \phi - \phi_\mu'' \| \to 0$. By (2.4.1)

$$\phi = \alpha + \beta + \gamma, \qquad \phi_\mu' = \alpha_\mu' + \beta_\mu' + \gamma_\mu', \qquad \phi_\mu'' = \alpha_\mu'' + \beta_\mu'' + \gamma_\mu'',$$

where $\alpha, \alpha_\mu', \alpha_\mu'' \in [\bar{\partial}\mathbf{C}]$, $\beta, \beta_\mu', \beta_\mu'' \in [\mathfrak{d}\mathbf{C}]$, and $\gamma, \gamma_\mu', \gamma_\mu'' \in \mathbf{F}$. Define $\psi_\mu = \alpha_\mu'' + \beta_\mu' + \gamma$. Then $\| \bar{\partial}\psi_\mu - \bar{\partial}\psi_\nu \| = \| \bar{\partial}\phi_\mu' - \bar{\partial}\phi_\nu' \| \to 0$; $\| \mathfrak{d}\psi_\mu - \mathfrak{d}\psi_\nu \| = \| \mathfrak{d}\phi_\mu'' - \mathfrak{d}\phi_\nu'' \| \to 0$; and $\| \phi_\mu - \psi_\mu \| = \| (\alpha - \alpha_\mu'') + (\beta - \beta_\mu') \| \to 0$ by the orthogonality of the decomposition. Hence $\phi \in D$.

Under these circumstances it can be shown that[2]

$$(2.4.3) \qquad {}_c\Delta = 2\mathfrak{D}_c D = 2(\bar{\partial}_c\mathfrak{b} + \mathfrak{b}_c\bar{\partial}).$$

Therefore, if the manifold has a Neumann's operator N_0, formula (2.4.1) becomes (see (1.6.1))

$$(2.4.4) \qquad \mathbf{A} = \bar{\partial}_c\mathfrak{b}\mathbf{N} \oplus \mathfrak{b}_c\bar{\partial}\mathbf{N} \oplus \mathbf{F}.$$

However, we do not know that N_0 exists in general, and we have instead only the formula (valid for bounded complex manifolds)

$$(2.4.5) \qquad \mathbf{A} = \bar{\partial}_c\mathfrak{b}\mathbf{N} \oplus \mathfrak{b}_c\bar{\partial}\mathbf{N} \oplus \mathbf{F}_2$$

where

$$\mathbf{F}_2 = \{\phi \mid \phi \in \mathbf{N}, \Delta^2\phi = 0\}.$$

In fact, given $\phi \in \mathbf{A}$, we have, by (1.7.5),

$$\phi = \Delta N_s\psi + \beta = \Delta N_s(\psi + \beta) + sN_s\beta, \quad \text{where} \quad \Delta^2 N_s\beta = 0,$$

and this is the meaning of (2.4.5).

If the manifold is compact (closed), then $\mathbf{G} = \mathbf{N}$; $\mathbf{F}_2 = \mathbf{F} = \mathbf{F}_c$, and the formulas (2.4.4), (2.4.5) coincide with the formula (1.5.6). In this case the space $\mathbf{F}$ is finite-dimensional.

2.5. The $\bar{\partial}$-cohomology of a complex-analytic variety. The triple (S, π, X), where S, X are topological spaces and π is a mapping from S onto X, is called a sheaf (faisceau) if and only if: (i) $S_x = \pi^{-1}(x)$ is a K-module for each $x \in X$, where K is a fixed principal ideal domain; (ii) π is a local homeomorphism; (iii) local operations as a K-module are continuous. Condition (ii) means that, for each $s \in S$, there is an open set A_s containing s such that $\pi \mid A_s$ is a homeomorphism of A_s onto $\pi(A_s)$, where $\pi(A_s)$ is an open subset of X. In particular, the mapping π is continuous and open, π^{-1} is open, and the mapping $(\pi|A_s)^{-1}$ is a section over $\pi(A_s)$.

Given an open set $U \subset X$, then $\Gamma(S, U)$, the set of all sections of S over U, is a K-module.

Given a space X and a basis $\mathfrak{U} = \{U\}$ for the open sets U of X, a sheaf is usually obtained from a set $\{S_U\}$, where S_U is a K-module for each $U \in \mathfrak{U}$ such that, if $U, V \in \mathfrak{U}$, $U \supset V$, there is a K-ho-

[2] I am indebted to M. P. Gaffney for pointing out this identity. Gaffney's proof is based on a method to be found in his paper [3].

momorphism, $r_{UV}: S_U \to S_V$, $r_{UW} = r_{VW} \cdot r_{UV}$ for $U \supset V \supset W$. Let $\mathfrak{U}_x = \{U \mid U \in \mathfrak{U}, x \in U\}$; the system $\mathfrak{U}_x$ is nonempty, is partially ordered by inclusion, and the direct limit $S_x = \lim S_U$ exists and is a K-module (since module operations commute with the direct limit). Let $S = \bigcup_x S_x$ and define $\pi(s) = x$ for $x \in S_x$. The direct limit defines a K-homomorphism $S_U \to S_x$ for each $x \in U$. Given U and $q \in S_U$, let q_x be the image of q under this homomorphism, $x \in U$. The set $A_{q,U} = \{q_x \mid x \in U\}$ is defined to be an open set in S, and the topology in S is defined by the system $\mathfrak{A} = \{A_{1,U} \mid U \in \mathfrak{U}, q \in S_U\}$ as a basis. With this topology, π is a local homeomorphism and (S, π, X) is a sheaf.

In particular, let $X = \mathfrak{B}$ be a differentiable manifold and take for S_U the C-module of differential forms of class C^∞ over U. The resulting sheaf is the de Rham sheaf of germs of differential forms on $\mathfrak{B}$, and it will be denoted by D. We denote by D^r the subsheaf of D composed of forms of degree r: $D = \oplus D^r$. Suppose now that $\mathfrak{B}$ is complex-analytic; then $D = \oplus D^{\rho,\sigma}$, where $D^{\rho,\sigma}$ is the subsheaf of D of forms of type (ρ, σ), and we let Ξ be the sheaf of germs of differential forms closed under $\bar\partial$. We have the exact sequence of sheaves

$$0 \to \Xi^{\rho,\sigma} \xrightarrow{i} D^{\rho,\sigma} \xrightarrow{\bar\partial} \Xi^{\rho,\sigma+1} \to 0, \tag{2.5.1}$$

where i is the inclusion map, and where $\bar\partial$ maps a germ $\tau \in D^{\rho,\sigma}$ into $\bar\partial\tau \in \Xi^{\rho,\sigma+1}$. The mapping $\bar\partial$ is onto since, by (2.3.3), if $\tau \in \Xi^{\rho,\sigma+1}$, there exists a germ $\eta \in D^{\rho,\sigma}$ such that $\tau = \bar\partial\eta$.

The exact cohomology sequence corresponding to (2.5.1) is

$$\cdots \to H^{q-1}(\mathfrak{B}, D^{\rho,\sigma}) \to H^{q-1}(\mathfrak{B}, \Xi^{\rho,\sigma+1}) \to H^q(\mathfrak{B}, \Xi^{\rho,\sigma}) \to H^q(\mathfrak{B}, D^{\rho,\sigma}) \to \cdots.$$

Since $D^{\rho,\sigma}$ is a fine sheaf, $H^{q-1}(\mathfrak{B}, D^{\rho,\sigma}) = H^q(\mathfrak{B}, D^{\rho,\sigma}) = 0$ for $q > 1$, and it follows that

$$H^q(\mathfrak{B}, \Xi^{\rho,\sigma}) \approx H^{q-1}(\mathfrak{B}, \Xi^{\rho,\sigma+1}), \qquad q > 1.$$

Hence

$$H^q(\mathfrak{B}, \Xi^{\rho,\sigma}) \approx H^0(\mathfrak{B}, \Xi^{\rho,\sigma+1})/\bar\partial H^0(\mathfrak{B}, D^{\rho,\sigma+q-1}), \qquad q \geq 1. \tag{2.5.2}$$

Formula (2.5.2), due to Dolbeault [2], is the complex analogue of de Rham's theorem.

Assume that $\mathfrak{V}$ is compact; then

$$H^0(\mathfrak{V}, \Xi^{\rho,\sigma+q})/\bar{\partial}H^0(\mathfrak{V}, D^{\rho,\sigma+q-1}) \approx F^{\rho,\sigma+q} \tag{2.5.3}$$

where $F^{\rho,\sigma+q}$ is the subspace of $\mathbf{F}$ composed of forms of type $(\rho, \sigma + q)$. In fact, if $\phi \in H^0(\mathfrak{V}, \Xi^{\rho,\sigma+q})$, we have, by (2.4.4), $\phi = \bar{\partial}\alpha + \gamma$, $\gamma \in F^{\rho,\sigma+q}$. Since $\mathbf{F}$ is a finite-dimensional complex vector space, we conclude from (2.5.3) that $H^q(\mathfrak{V}, \Xi^{\rho,\sigma})$ is a finite-dimensional complex vector space (see [7]).

Now $\Xi^{\rho,0} = \Omega^\rho$, where Ω^ρ is the sheaf of germs of holomorphic ρ-forms on $\mathfrak{V}$, and we define

$$\chi^\rho = \sum_{q=0}^{n} (-1)^q \dim H^q(\mathfrak{V}, \Omega^\rho). \tag{2.5.4}$$

The quantity χ^0 is the arithmetic genus $\Pi(\mathfrak{V})$ of $\mathfrak{V}$, and is one of the two main analytic invariants of $\mathfrak{V}$.

The other, called the Todd genus $T(\mathfrak{V})$, is formed from the Chern classes of $\mathfrak{V}$, and is therefore an invariant of the almost-analytic structure. It has been defined by Hirzebruch [5] in the following manner. Let $c_k \in H^{2k}(\mathfrak{V}, Z)$ be the k-th Chern class of the variety $\mathfrak{V}$, and write formally

$$1 + c_1x + c_2x^2 + \cdots + c_nx^n = (1 + \alpha_1x)(1 + \alpha_2x) \cdots (1 + \alpha_nx).$$

Set $Q(x) = -x/(e^{-x} - 1)$, and consider the coefficient of x^n in the product $Q(\alpha_1x)Q(\alpha_2x) \cdots Q(\alpha_nx)$. The coefficient of x^n is obviously symmetric in $\alpha_1, \alpha_2, \cdots, \alpha_n$, and it may be expressed as a polynomial in $c_1, c_2, \cdots, c_n$. The coefficient of x^n thus determines an element of $H^{2n}(\mathfrak{V}, Z)$, and is therefore a multiple of the fundamental cocycle. This multiple, obviously a rational number, is defined to be the Todd genus $T(\mathfrak{V})$ of the variety $\mathfrak{V}$.

A problem of fundamental importance is that of determining the relationship between $\Pi(\mathfrak{V})$ and $T(\mathfrak{V})$.

Hirzebruch [5b] has shown that $\Pi(\mathfrak{V}) = T(\mathfrak{V})$ for algebraic varieties and the question remains whether $\Pi(\mathfrak{V}) = T(\mathfrak{V})$ more generally. Given an arbitrary compact almost-complex variety $\mathfrak{V}$, then, in terms of a particular almost-Hermitian structure, we can define

$$\Pi(\mathfrak{V}) = \sum_{\sigma=0}^{n} (-1)^\sigma \dim F^{0,\sigma}.$$

There are two questions: (i) Is Π independent of the particular almost-Hermitian structure chosen? (ii) If it is, does $\Pi(\mathfrak{V}) = T(\mathfrak{V})$?

BIBLIOGRAPHY

1. CARTAN, H. *Séminaire de topologie algébrique*, ENS IV. Paris, 1951–1952.
2. DOLBEAULT, P. *Sur la cohomologie des variétés analytiques complexes*, C. R. Acad. Sci. Paris 236 (1953), 175–177.
3. GAFFNEY, M. P. *The heat equation method of Milgram and Rosenbloom for open Riemannian manifolds*, Ann. of Math. 60 (1954), 458–466.
4. GARABEDIAN, P. R., AND SPENCER, D. C. *A complex tensor calculus for Kähler manifolds*, Acta Math. 89 (1953), 279–331.
5. HIRZEBRUCH, F. (a) *On Steenrod's reduced powers, the index of inertia, and the Todd genus*, Proc. Nat. Acad. Sci. U.S.A. 39 (1953), 951–956.
   —— (b) *Arithmetic genera and the theorem of Riemann-Roch for algebraic varieties*, Proc. Nat. Acad. Sci. U.S.A. 40 (1954), 110–114.
6. KODAIRA, K. *Harmonic fields in Riemannian manifolds (generalized potential theory)*, Ann. of Math. 50 (1949), 587–665.
7. —— *On cohomology groups of compact analytic varieties with coefficients in some analytic faisceaux*, Proc. Nat. Acad. Sci. U.S.A. 39 (1953), 865–868.
8. —— AND SPENCER, D. C. *On arithmetic genera of algebraic varieties*, Proc. Nat. Acad. Sci. U.S.A. 39 (1953), 641–649.
9. —— —— *On a theorem of Lefschetz and the lemma of Enriques-Severi-Zariski*, Proc. Nat. Acad. Sci. U.S.A. 39 (1953), 1273–1278.
10. DE RHAM, G., AND KODAIRA, K. *Harmonic integrals*. Princeton, 1950.
11. STEENROD, N. *The topology of fibre bundles*. Princeton, 1951.

PRINCETON UNIVERSITY

REMARKS ON RIEMANN SURFACES

L. V. AHLFORS

1. In this lecture I discuss the problem of constructing a harmonic function with prescribed singular behavior on an open Riemann surface. It is my purpose to present points of view rather than specific results.

In the classical problem one considers a closed Riemann surface W, and a finite number of points a_i on W. Let the a_i be contained in nonoverlapping parametric disks Δ_i. In each Δ_i, or rather in the corresponding punctured disk Δ_i', a harmonic singularity function s_i is given. The problem is to find a harmonic function u on W with the singularities s_i. This means that u is to be harmonic on the surface W' obtained by removing the points a_i, and that each $u - s_i$ has a harmonic extension to the whole disk Δ_i.

When this problem is analyzed, one becomes aware that it is more directly concerned with the open surface W' than with the originally given closed surface. The latter is involved only in the condition which the differences $u - s_i$ have to satisfy. Our aim is to replace this condition by more general ones.

2. We replace W' by an arbitrary open Riemann surface R, and the union of the punctured disks Δ_i' by a subset G with a compact complement. The set G plays the role of a neighborhood of the ideal boundary (the Alexander point in the one-point compactification). We give a singularity function s, which is harmonic in G, and ask for a harmonic function u on R with the property that $u - s$ is in some sense "regular" near the ideal boundary; that is to say, in G.

What precise sense can one give to this notion of regularity? In the case above, $u - s$ was regular if it had a harmonic extension. According to Riemann's theorem on removable singularities, this would be so if $u - s$ is bounded, or if it has a finite Dirichlet integral. These characterizations are independent of the imbedding in another surface, and could thus be used in the general case.

Let H be the linear space formed by all functions which are harmonic in G, and let H_0 denote a linear subspace of H. One can choose H_0 as the space of "regular" functions. The problem is then to find u so that $u - s \in H_0$. With another formulation, s determines a coset $S = H_0 + s$ of H_0, regarded as a subgroup of H, and we are required to find an element in S which has a harmonic extension to the whole surface R.

3. The alternating procedure of Schwarz has been adapted by L. Sario [1] to existence problems on open Riemann surfaces. His method applies to the general problem considered above, provided that the subspace H_0 is subject to certain restrictions which appear to be very natural. In the first place, it is required that the functions in H_0 satisfy the maximum principle in the sense that the maximum in G is attained on the relative boundary α. This guarantees the uniqueness of the solution. Secondly, I consider only the case in which all functions in H_0 have a vanishing flux along α. This is a reasonable condition, for a "regular" function would not be expected to have a source or sink on the ideal boundary. On the other hand, I am not able to show that this is a necessary condition for the problem to have a solution.

The nature of the problem is such that we can assume the boundary α to be analytic. With Sario, we consider a linear operator L which to continuous values v on α assigns a harmonic function Lv on $\bar{G}$ with the following properties:

(1) $$Lv = v \quad \text{on} \quad \alpha,$$

(2) $$L1 = 1, \qquad Lv \geqq 0 \quad \text{if} \quad v \geqq 0,$$

(3) $$\int_\alpha \frac{\partial Lv}{\partial n} \, ds = 0.$$

Such an operator determines a subspace H_0 formed by all functions u for which $Lu = u$. Conversely, if H_0 satisfies the conditions mentioned above and if, in addition, the Dirichlet problem has a solution in H_0 with given boundary values v on α, then this solution determines a linear operator with the properties (1)–(3). The two points of view are thus equivalent.

By use of the alternating procedure, Sario has proved that there exists a function u with $u - s = L(u - s)$ if and only if s has a zero flux. This means that $u - s$ is "regular" in the sense of belonging to the subspace H_0. The solution is obviously unique up to additive constants.

4. It would clearly be of great interest to determine all linear operators L which satisfy (1)–(3). They form a convex set, for if L_1 and L_2 are two such operators, then $(L_1 + L_2)/2$ has the same properties. Therefore, apart from topological considerations which are probably of a routine nature, the set is determined by its extremal elements, that is to say by the operators L which do not have any nontrivial representation in the form $(L_1 + L_2)/2$.

The general case may present serious difficulties, but if we assume that R has an analytic boundary β the solution is certainly within reach. For the region between α and β we determine the harmonic measure, i.e., the harmonic function which is 0 on α and 1 on β, and normalize it so that the period of the conjugate function along α becomes equal to 1. In terms of this conjugate function, let α and β be parametrized as $0 \leqq x \leqq 1$, $0 \leqq y \leqq 1$, respectively.

For given v on α, Lv has radial limits almost everywhere on β, and is determined by these limits. Thus we may consider L as a linear mapping from $C(0, 1)$ to $L^\infty(0, 1)$; we write $g(y) = Lf(x)$.

For each $f(x)$ the transform $g(y)$ is defined only outside of a null set which may depend on f. However, if we let f run through an everywhere dense set f_n, the corresponding $g_n(y)$ are defined outside of a fixed null set E_0. Letting f_n tend uniformly to f, we can then define $g(y)$ as the limit of $g_n(y)$ for every y outside of E_0. In other words, $g(y)$ exists outside of a fixed null set.

For fixed y we can now write, by Riesz's theorem,

$$g(y) = \int_0^1 f(x)\, d\mu(x, y).$$

By conditions (1) and (2) the mass is positive, and the total mass is one. It is fairly clear that the operator L will be extremal if and only if the mass $\mu(x, y)$ is concentrated in a point $x = Ty$ for almost every y. This would give $g(y) = f(Ty)$. Condition (3) is equivalent to

$$\int_0^1 f(x)\, dx = \int_0^1 g(y)\, dy = \int_0^1 f(Ty)\, dy;$$

in other words, Ty is a measure-preserving transformation.

5. The arguments presented above are of a heuristic nature, and I am not ready to give a precise proof. It is hoped, however, that these remarks can serve as a starting point for a more thorough investigation.

BIBLIOGRAPHY

1. Sario, L. *A linear operator method on arbitrary Riemann surfaces*, Trans. Amer. Math. Soc. 72 (1952), 281–295.

Harvard University

UNIVALENT FUNCTIONS AND LINEAR DIFFERENTIAL EQUATIONS*

ZEEV NEHARI

1. There exists a simple connection between the theory of univalent functions and that of linear differential equations of the second order. If $u(z)$ and $v(z)$ are two analytic functions defined in a region D, then the function

$$f(z) = \frac{u(z)}{v(z)} \tag{1}$$

will be univalent in D if, and only if, the equation

$$\frac{u(z)}{v(z)} = \alpha$$

has at most one solution in D for arbitrary complex values of α. If, as we shall assume, $u(z)$ and $v(z)$ have no common zeros, this is equivalent to the expression

$$Au(z) + Bv(z) \tag{2}$$

having at most one zero in D for arbitrary complex values of A and B.

Since $f(z)$, because of its univalence, is regular in D with the possible exception of a simple pole, $u(z)$ and $v(z)$ may both be assumed to be regular in D. Now, by the classical theory of linear differential equations, the expression (2) is the general solution of a homogeneous linear differential equation of the second order. Multiplying both $u(z)$ and $v(z)$ by a suitable regular and nonvanishing function, we may bring this equation into the form

$$u''(z) + p(z)u(z) = 0, \tag{3}$$

* This research was supported by the United States Air Force, through the Office of Scientific Research of the Air Research and Development Command.

where

(4) $$p(z) = \tfrac{1}{2}\{f(z), z\}, \qquad f(z) = \frac{u(z)}{v(z)},$$

and where

(5) $$\{w, z\} = \left(\frac{w''}{w'}\right)' - \frac{1}{2}\left(\frac{w''}{w'}\right)^2$$

is the Schwarzian derivative of the function $w = w(z)$. It follows that a univalent function in D can be written as the ratio of two linearly independent solutions of (3), where none of the solutions of this equation has more than one zero in D. Conversely, the ratio of two independent solutions of an equation with the latter property is a univalent function in D. Indeed, if $u(z)$ and $v(z)$ are such solutions and $Au(z) + Bv(z)$ does not vanish in D more than once, then $u(z)[v(z)]^{-1}$ does not take there the arbitrary value $-BA^{-1}$ more than once.

The theory of univalent functions in D is thus equivalent to the theory of the equation (3) whose coefficient $p(z)$ is regular in D and whose solutions do not vanish in D more than once. This equivalence provides a new approach to the investigation of univalent functions, since the methods available for the study of the zeros of the solutions of (3) are very different from those generally used in the theory of univalent functions. It is also worth noting that the results obtained in this way are independent of any particular normalization of the schlicht function, since the Schwarzian derivative is invariant with respect to a general linear transformation, i.e.,

$$\left\{\frac{\alpha w + \beta}{\gamma w + \delta}, z\right\} = \{w, z\}, \qquad \alpha\delta - \beta\gamma \neq 0.$$

In a previous paper, [6], the connection between schlicht functions and equation (3) was used to obtain two criteria of univalence. It was shown that $w = f(z)$ is schlicht in the unit disk—or, for short, that $f(z) \in S$—if either

(6) $$|\{w, z\}| \leqq \frac{2}{(1 - |z|^2)^2},$$

or

(7) $$|\{w, z\}| \leqq \frac{\pi^2}{2}.$$

The constants in both inequalities are the best possible (in the first case this was shown by E. Hille [4]), and the inequality (6) is also remarkable because of the fact that

$$|\{w, z\}| \leqq \frac{6}{(1 - |z|^2)^2}$$

is a sharp necessary condition for $w = f(z) \in S$ [6]. Generalizations of (6) and (7) are found in papers by V. V. Pokornyi [7] and C. Ryll-Nardzewski [8]. The objective of the present paper is the derivation of criteria of univalence of a somewhat different type.

2. If $\sigma(z)$ is regular and not zero on a connected set T in the domain of regularity of $u(z)$, then the function $v(z)$ defined by $u(z) = \sigma(z)v(z)$ has on T the same zeros as $u(z)$ and, in view of (3), it satisfies there the differential equation

$$(\sigma^2 v')' + (p\sigma^2 + \sigma\sigma'')v = 0. \tag{8}$$

Suppose now that $u(z)$—and thus also $v(z)$—vanishes at two points of S, say a and b. Multiplying (8) by $v^*(z)\,dz$ (the asterisk denoting the complex conjugate) and integrating from a to b along a path entirely in T, we obtain

$$[\sigma^2 v' v^*]_a^b - \int_a^b \sigma^2 |v'|^2\, dz^* + \int_a^b (p\sigma^2 + \sigma\sigma'')|v|^2\, dz = 0$$

and thus

$$\int_a^b \sigma^2 |v'|^2\, dz^* = \int_a^b (p\sigma^2 + \sigma\sigma'')|v|^2\, dz. \tag{9}$$

If along the entire integration path the differential $\sigma^2\, dz^*$ is of constant argument, we may conclude from (9) that

$$\int_a^b |\sigma|^2 |v'|^2 |dz| \leqq \int_a^b |p\sigma^2 + \sigma\sigma''|\, |v|^2 |dz|.$$

If $p(z)$ is now made subject to a condition which makes this inequality impossible, it will follow that we could not have had $u(a) = u(b) = 0$—or, what amounts to the same thing, $f(a) = f(b)$—in the first place.

We shall illustrate this procedure in the case in which T is the circumference $|z| = \rho$ $(\rho > 0)$. If we set $\sigma(z) = \sqrt{z}$, (9) will take the form

$$\int_a^b z\,|v'|^2\,dz^* = \int_a^b \left(zp - \frac{1}{4z}\right)|v|^2\,dz,$$

or, since $dz = iz\,d\theta$ $(z = \rho e^{i\theta})$,

$$\rho^2 \int_\alpha^\beta |v'|^2\,d\theta = \int_\alpha^\beta (\tfrac{1}{4} - z^2 p)\,|v|^2\,d\theta,$$

where $a = \rho e^{i\alpha}$, $b = \rho e^{i\beta}$, $\alpha < \beta$, and the integration is carried out along the shorter arc connecting a and b. Writing $v = U + iV$ (U, V real) and observing that $\rho^2\,|v'|^2 = U_\theta^2 + V_\theta^2$, we arrive at

$$\int_\alpha^\beta (U_\theta^2 + V_\theta^2)\,d\theta = \int_\alpha^\beta (\tfrac{1}{4} - z^2 p)(U^2 + V^2)\,d\theta. \tag{10}$$

Now both U and V vanish for $\theta = \alpha$ and $\theta = \beta$. It follows, therefore, from a well-known inequality (see [3, p. 184]) that

$$\int_\alpha^\beta U_\theta^2\,d\theta \geqq \frac{\pi^2}{(\beta - \alpha)^2}\int_\alpha^\beta U^2\,d\theta, \tag{11}$$

and similarly for V. Combining this with (10) and observing that $(\beta - \alpha)^2 \leqq \pi^2$, we find that

$$\int_\alpha^\beta (U^2 + V^2)\,d\theta \leqq \int_\alpha^\beta \operatorname{Re}\{\tfrac{1}{4} - z^2 p(z)\}(U^2 + V^2)\,d\theta;$$

equation (10) also shows that

$$\int_\alpha^\beta \operatorname{Im}\{\tfrac{1}{4} - z^2 p(z)\}(U^2 + V^2)\,d\theta = 0.$$

With the abbreviation $\tfrac{1}{4} - z^2 p(z) = A + iB$ (A, B real), we thus arrive at the inequality

$$\int_\alpha^\beta (A - 1 + \lambda B)(U^2 + V^2)\,d\theta \geqq 0,$$

where λ is an arbitrary real number.

If $A + iB$ is subject to the condition $A - 1 + \lambda B < 0$, this inequality cannot hold, and the assumption that $f(a) = f(b)$ leads to a contradiction. Now it is easily seen that the condition $A - 1 + \lambda B < 0$ is equivalent to $\operatorname{Re}\{(A - 1 + iB)e^{i\gamma}\} < 0$, where γ is a real number between $-\frac{1}{2}\pi$ and $\frac{1}{2}\pi$. In view of the definition of $A + iB$, it follows, therefore, that we cannot have $f(a) = f(b)$, $|a| = |b| = \rho$, if $p(z)$ satisfies the inequality

$$\text{(12)} \qquad \operatorname{Re}\{e^{i\gamma}[\tfrac{3}{4} + z^2 p(z)]\} > 0, \qquad |z| = \rho,$$

for some γ, $-\frac{1}{2}\pi < \gamma < \frac{1}{2}\pi$. Suppose now that $f(z)$ is not univalent in the entire disk $|z| < R$. Then there must exist a circumference $|z| = \rho$ $(0 < \rho < R)$ on which $f(z)$ takes the same value twice. In view of (4) and (12) we therefore arrive at the following result.

THEOREM 1. *If, for some* γ *such that* $-\frac{1}{2}\pi < \gamma < \frac{1}{2}\pi$,

$$\text{(13)} \qquad \operatorname{Re}\,(e^{i\gamma}[\tfrac{3}{2} + z^2\{f(z), z\}]) > 0, \qquad |z| < R,$$

where $f(z)$ *is single-valued and* $\{f(z), z\}$ *is the Schwarzian derivative of* $f(z)$, *then* $f(z)$ *is univalent in* $|z| < R$. *The constant* $\frac{3}{2}$ *in* (13) *is the best possible.*

That the constant $\frac{3}{2}$ cannot be improved upon is shown by the example $f(z) = z^2$, for which $z^2\{f(z), z\} = -\frac{3}{2}$.

3. In the last step of the proof of Theorem 1 we used the fact that a simply connected domain which is bounded by a Jordan curve is necessarily schlicht. In the case of a multiply connected domain it is, of course, in general not true that the domain will be schlicht if all its boundary components are Jordan curves. However, a simple argument shows that the conclusion will hold if the domain is free of branch points. This remark leads to the following extension of Theorem 1.

THEOREM 2. *If* $f(z)$ *is single-valued in the circular ring* $0 < r < |z| < R$ *and*

$$\text{(14)} \qquad \operatorname{Re}\,(e^{i\gamma}[\tfrac{3}{2} + z^2\{f(z), z\}]) > 0, \qquad r < |z| < R$$

for some γ *such that* $-\frac{1}{2}\pi < \gamma < \frac{1}{2}\pi$, *then* $f(z)$ *is univalent in* $r < |z| < R$.

Proof. If $f(z)$ is not schlicht in $r < |z| < R$, the same is true in $r + \epsilon \leqq |z| \leqq R - \epsilon$, where ϵ is positive and sufficiently small. By the foregoing remark, the mapping effected by $w = f(z)$ must have at least one of the following three properties: (i) the image of $|z| = r + \epsilon$ intersects itself; (ii) the same is true of the image of $|z| = R - \epsilon$; (iii) at some point z_0 $(r + \epsilon < |z_0| < R - \epsilon)$ we have

$f'(z_0) = 0$. By the proof of Theorem 1, (i) and (ii) are impossible if (14) holds. But (iii) is also excluded since, as one easily confirms, $\{f(z), z\}$ has a double pole at a zero of $f'(z)$ and this is incompatible with (14). This proves Theorem 2.

4. The proof of Theorem 1 may also be used to obtain an estimate for the number of times a function $f(z)$ may take the same value on a circumference. If $f(a_1) = f(a_2) = \cdots = f(a_n)$, where $a_\nu = re^{i\alpha_\nu}$, $\alpha_1 < \alpha_2 < \cdots < \alpha_n$, and the function $v(z) = U + iV$ is defined as before, it follows from (10) and (11) that

$$\frac{\pi^2}{(\alpha_\nu - \alpha_{\nu-1})^2} \leqq \max_{|z|=r} \operatorname{Re} \{\tfrac{1}{4} - z^2 p(z)\} = M, \qquad \nu = 1, 2, \cdots, n,$$

where $\alpha_0 = \alpha_n - 2\pi$. Hence

$$nM \geqq \pi^2 \sum_{\nu=1}^{n} \frac{1}{(\alpha_\nu - \alpha_{\nu-1})^2}.$$

It is easily verified that the sum on the right-hand side attains its minimum if $\alpha_1 - \alpha_0 = \alpha_2 - \alpha_1 = \cdots = \alpha_n - \alpha_{n-1} = 2\pi/n$. Therefore,

$$M \geqq \frac{n^2}{4},$$

and we have proved the following result.

THEOREM 3. *Let $w = f(z)$ be regular and single-valued, and $f'(z) \neq 0$, on the circumference $|z| = r$. If n is the number of times a particular value is taken by $f(z)$ on $|z| = r$, then*

$$n^2 \leqq 1 - 2 \min_{|z|=r} \operatorname{Re} [z^2\{w, z\}]. \tag{15}$$

The inequality is sharp, as is shown by the function $w = z^n$, for which $1 - 2z^2\{w, z\} = n^2$. We remark that the restriction $f'(z) \neq 0$ is necessary since (10) is valid only if $p(z)$ remains finite. It may be added that (15) will remain trivially true if $f'(z)$ vanishes at some point of $|z| = r$, the corresponding double pole of $\{w, z\}$ giving to the right-hand side of (15) the value $+\infty$.

5. Criteria of univalence of a different type are obtained if the differential equation (3) is replaced by the corresponding integral equation. It is well known, and easily verified, that a solution of (3) which vanishes at the points a and b satisfies the integral equation

$$u(\zeta) = \int_a^b p(z)g(z, \zeta)u(z)\,dz, \tag{16}$$

where the integration is performed along any rectifiable arc C which connects a and b and is contained in the domain of regularity of $p(z)$; ζ is any point of C other than a and b, and $g(z, \zeta)$ is the Green's function of the differential operator $L(u) \equiv u''$ associated with the arc C. If C_1 and C_2 denote the parts of C bounded by a, ζ and ζ, b, respectively, we have

$$g(z, \zeta) = \frac{(z - a)(b - \zeta)}{b - a}, \qquad z \in C_1;$$

$$g(z, \zeta) = \frac{(\zeta - a)(b - z)}{b - a}, \qquad z \in C_2.$$

If, in (16), we identify ζ with the point—or one of the points—of C on which $|u(z)|$ attains its maximum M on C, it follows that

$$M \leqq M \int_a^b |p(z)|\,|g(z, \zeta)|\,|dz|,$$

and thus

$$1 \leqq \max_{z,\zeta \in C} |g(z, \zeta)| \int_C |p(z)\,dz|.$$

If C is a convex arc, it is geometrically evident that $|g(z, \zeta)| \leqq |g(\zeta, \zeta)|$. In this case the preceding inequality may therefore be replaced by

$$1 \leqq \max_{\zeta \in C} |g(\zeta, \zeta)| \int_C |p(z)\,dz|.$$

We now assume that $p(z)$ is regular in $|z| \leqq 1$ and that there exists a solution of (3) which vanishes at the points $a = e^{i\alpha}$ and $b = e^{i\beta}$ (α, β real). It is clear that, for two given points on $|z| = 1$, α and β may always be so chosen that $0 < \beta - \alpha \leqq \pi$. Our choice for the arc C will be the intersection of $|z| \leqq 1$ and the circle orthogonal to $|z| = 1$ through a and b. By elementary geometric considerations it is easily shown that

$$\max_{\zeta \in C} |g(\zeta, \zeta)| = \frac{\sin \frac{1}{2}(\beta - \alpha)}{1 + \sin \frac{1}{2}(\beta - \alpha)} \leqq \tfrac{1}{2}. \tag{17}$$

Hence,

$$2 \leqq \int_C |\, p(z)\, dz \,|. \tag{18}$$

Our next step depends on the following result of Fejér and Riesz [2]: If $g(z)$ is regular in $|\, z \,| \leqq 1$, then

$$\int_{-1}^{1} |\, g(x) \,|\, dx < \tfrac{1}{2} \int_0^{2\pi} |\, g(e^{i\theta}) \,|\, d\theta, \qquad z = x + iy;$$

we may also write this in the form

$$\int_{C_0} |\, F(z)\, dz \,| < \tfrac{1}{2} \int_{|z|=1} |\, F(z)\, dz \,|, \tag{19}$$

where C_0 denotes the segment $-1 \leqq x \leqq 1$. Let now η be an arbitrary number such that $|\, \eta \,| < 1$ and let the function $h(z)$ be regular for $|\, z \,| \leqq 1$. If

$$w = \frac{z + \eta}{1 + \eta^* z}, \tag{20}$$

define the function $g(w)$ by

$$g(w) = \frac{(1 - \eta^* w)^2}{1 - |\, \eta \,|^2}\, h(w).$$

With this definition, we have

$$g\left(\frac{z + \eta}{1 + \eta^* z}\right) dz = g(w)\, \frac{(1 - |\, \eta \,|^2)}{(1 - \eta^* w)^2}\, dw = h(w)\, dw.$$

Now the substitution (20) maps $|\, z \,| = 1$ onto $|\, w \,| = 1$, and it will transform C_0 into one of the circular arcs C described above; in fact, by suitable choice of η it can be made to transform C_0 into any given arc C. Hence

$$\int_{C_0} \left| g\left(\frac{z + \eta}{1 + \eta^* z}\right) dz \right| = \int_C |\, h(w)\, dw \,|,$$

$$\int_{|z|=1} \left| g\left(\frac{z + \eta}{1 + \eta^* z}\right) dz \right| = \int_{|w|=1} |\, h(w)\, dw \,|$$

It follows therefore from (19) that

$$\int_C |\, h(w)\, dw \,| < \tfrac{1}{2} \int_{|w|=1} |\, h(w)\, dw \,|.$$

Applying this inequality to the right-hand side of (18), we find that

$$4 < \int_0^{2\pi} | p(e^{i\theta}) | \, d\theta. \tag{21}$$

Inequality (21) was derived under the assumption that equation (3) has a solution which vanishes twice on $|z| = 1$. As shown above, the existence of such a solution is equivalent to the condition that the function $f(z)$, for which

$$\{f(z), z\} = 2p(z),$$

take the same value twice on $|z| = 1$. The inequality (21) will therefore lead to the following criterion of univalence.

THEOREM 4. *If $f(z)$ is regular in $|z| < 1$ and*

$$\int_0^{2\pi} | \{f(z), z\} | \, d\theta \leqq 8, \qquad z = e^{i\theta}, \tag{22}$$

then $f(z)$ is univalent in $|z| < 1$.

The integral $\int_0^{2\pi} | g(e^{i\theta}) | \, d\theta$ for a function $g(z)$ regular in $|z| < 1$ means here, as usually, the limit for $\rho \to 1$ of the ascending function

$$A(\rho) = \int_0^{2\pi} | g(\rho e^{i\theta}) | \, d\theta.$$

The assumption of regularity for $|z| < 1$ instead of $|z| \leqq 1$ is justified by the fact that $\{f(\rho z), z\} = \rho^2 \{f(\rho z), \rho z\}$, and that $A(\rho)$ increases with ρ.

We add here a few remarks regarding the question whether the constant 8 in (22) may be the best possible. In view of (17), (21) cannot be sharp unless $\beta - \alpha = \pi$. Since a rotation will cause only trivial changes, we may therefore confine ourselves to the case in which the two zeros of $u(z)$ are situated at the points $z = \pm 1$. By a result which goes back to Liapounoff (see [1])—and which can also be easily deduced from (16)—we have in this case

$$\int_{-1}^{1} | p(x) | \, dx > 2, \tag{23}$$

where the constant 2 cannot be improved upon (see [5]). The constant $\frac{1}{2}$ in the Fejér-Riesz inequality (19) is also the best possible, and (21) is obtained—in this special case—by combining (19) and

(23) and setting $F(z) = p(z)$. The question whether (21) is sharp will therefore depend on the existence of functions $p(z)$ for which there will be "almost" equality in both (19) and (23) (actual equality is excluded in both cases).

6. The point of departure for the proof of Theorem 4 was the integral equation (16), which replaced differential equation (3). The same procedure may be applied to equation (8) with suitable functions $\sigma(z)$, and it will then yield criteria of univalence different from that given by Theorem 4. As an illustration, we treat the case $\sigma(z) = \sqrt{z}$, in which (8) takes the form

$$(zv')' + \left(zp - \frac{1}{4z}\right)v = 0. \tag{24}$$

If there exists a solution of (24) which vanishes at the points $z = a$, $z = b$, it will satisfy the integral equation

$$v(\zeta) = \int_a^b \left[zp(z) - \frac{1}{4z}\right] g(z, \zeta)v(z)\, dz, \tag{25}$$

where the integration is carried out along two rectifiable arcs C_1 and C_2 connecting, respectively, a with ζ and ζ with b. Here $g(z, \zeta)$ is the Green's function associated with the operator $L(v) \equiv (zv')'$, and its explicit form is

$$g(z, \zeta) = \frac{\log\left(\frac{z}{a}\right)\log\left(\frac{b}{\zeta}\right)}{\log\left(\frac{b}{a}\right)}, \qquad z \in C_1,$$

$$g(z, \zeta) = \frac{\log\left(\frac{\zeta}{a}\right)\log\left(\frac{b}{z}\right)}{\log\left(\frac{b}{a}\right)}, \qquad z \in C_2.$$

We now assume that $|a| = |b| = \rho$ and take $C_1 + C_2$ to be the shorter arc of $|z| = \rho$ connecting a and b. With $a = \rho e^{i\alpha}$, $b = \rho e^{i\beta}$, $z = \rho e^{i\theta}$, $\zeta = \rho e^{it}$, $0 < \beta - \alpha \leqq \pi$, we obtain

$$g(z, \zeta) = i\,\frac{(\theta - \alpha)(\beta - t)}{\beta - \alpha}, \qquad \alpha \leqq \theta \leqq t,$$

$$g(z, \zeta) = i\,\frac{(t - \alpha)(\beta - \theta)}{\beta - \alpha}, \qquad t \leqq \theta \leqq \beta.$$

It follows that

$$| g(z, \zeta) | \leqq \frac{(t - \alpha)(\beta - t)}{\beta - \alpha} \leqq \frac{\beta - \alpha}{4}.$$

Hence by (25)

$$| v(\zeta) | \leqq \frac{\beta - \alpha}{4} \int_\alpha^\beta | z^2 p(z) - \tfrac{1}{4} | \, | v(z) | \, d\theta.$$

Identifying ζ with the point at which $| v(z) |$ attains its maximum on $C_1 + C_2$, we find that

$$1 \leqq \frac{\beta - \alpha}{4} \int_\alpha^\beta | z^2 p(z) - \tfrac{1}{4} | \, d\theta. \tag{26}$$

If $C_1 + C_2$ is taken to be the longer arc of $| z | = \rho$ connecting a and b, we obtain similarly

$$1 \leqq \frac{2\pi - (\beta - \alpha)}{4} \int_\beta^{\alpha + 2\pi} | z^2 p(z) - \tfrac{1}{4} | \, d\theta.$$

Combining this with (26), we have

$$\int_0^{2\pi} | z^2 p(z) - \tfrac{1}{4} | \, d\theta \geqq 4 \left(\frac{1}{\beta - \alpha} + \frac{1}{2\pi - (\beta - \alpha)} \right) \geqq \frac{8}{\pi}.$$

This inequality was derived under the assumption that equation (8)—with $\sigma(z) = \sqrt{z}$—has a solution which vanishes twice on the circumference $| z | = \rho$. As shown before, this is equivalent to the function $f(z)$, for which $2p(z) = \{f(z), z\}$, taking there the same value twice. We are thus led to the following result.

THEOREM 5. *If*

$$\int_0^{2\pi} | z^2 \{f(z), z\} - \tfrac{1}{2} | \, d\theta < \frac{16}{\pi}, \qquad z = \rho e^{i\theta}, \qquad 0 < \rho < R,$$

then $f(z)$ *is univalent in* $| z | < R$.

In view of the remarks made in § 3, this result will also hold if the disk $| z | < R$ is replaced by the circular ring $0 < r < | z | < R$.

7. In the case of a nonunivalent function $f(z)$, the proof of Theorem 5 may be made to yield a result of the same type as Theorem 3.

If $f(\rho e^{i\alpha_1}) = f(\rho e^{i\alpha_2}) = \cdots = f(\rho e^{i\alpha_n})$, $\alpha_1 < \alpha_2 < \cdots < \alpha_n < \alpha_1 + 2\pi$, it follows from (26) that

$$\int_{\alpha_{\nu-1}}^{\alpha_\nu} | z^2 p(z) - \tfrac{1}{4} | \, d\theta \geqq \frac{4}{\alpha_\nu - \alpha_{\nu-1}} \qquad (\alpha_0 + 2\pi = \alpha_n),$$

and thus

$$\int_0^{2\pi} |z^2 p(z) - \tfrac{1}{4} | \, d\theta \geqq 4 \sum_{\nu=1}^{n} \frac{1}{\alpha_\nu - \alpha_{\nu-1}}.$$

The minimum of the right-hand side is attained if all the differences $(\alpha_\nu - \alpha_{\nu-1})$ are equal. Hence

$$\int_0^{2\pi} | z^2 p(z) - \tfrac{1}{4} | \, d\theta \geqq \frac{2n^2}{\pi}$$

and we have the following result.

THEOREM 6. *If $f(z)$ is regular and single-valued on the circumference $| z | = \rho$ and there takes a particular value n times, then*

$$n^2 \leqq \frac{\pi}{4} \int_0^{2\pi} | z^2 \{f(z), z\} - \tfrac{1}{2} | \, d\theta, \qquad z = \rho e^{i\theta}.$$

BIBLIOGRAPHY

1. BORG, G. *On a Liapounoff criterion of stability*, Amer. J. Math. 71 (1949), 67–70.

2. FEJÉR, L., AND RIESZ, F. *Über einige funktionentheoretische Ungleichungen*, Math. Zeit. 11 (1921), 305–314.

3. HARDY, G. H., LITTLEWOOD, J. E., AND PÓLYA, G. *Inequalities*. Cambridge Univ. Press, 1934.

4. HILLE, E. *Remarks on a paper by Zeev Nehari*, Bull. Amer. Math. Soc. 55 (1949), 552–553.

5. VAN KAMPEN, E. R., AND WINTNER, A. *On an absolute constant in the theory of variational stability*, Amer. J. Math. 59 (1937), 270–274.

6. NEHARI, Z. *The Schwarzian derivative and schlicht functions*, Bull. Amer. Math. Soc. 55 (1949), 545–551.

7. POKORNYI, V. V. *On some sufficient conditions for univalence*, C. R. (Doklady) Acad. Sci. URSS 79 (1951), 743–746.

8. RYLL-NARDZEWSKI, C. *Une extension d'un théorème de Sturm aux fonctions analytiques*, Ann. Univ. Mariae Curie-Sklodowska (Sec. A) 4 (1950), 5–7.

WASHINGTON UNIVERSITY
ST. LOUIS, MISSOURI

COUNTABILITY OF A RIEMANN SURFACE

ROLF NEVANLINNA

1. The problem. Let R be a Riemann surface and (U) a set of covering neighborhoods U, homeomorphic to a circular disk U_z: $|z| \leq 1$ in the complex plane. If the intersection of two neighborhoods U_1 and U_2 is not empty, the relation $z_1 \leftrightarrow z_2$ between two points of the parametric disks U_{z_1} and U_{z_2}, which correspond to the same point of R, is one-to-one and directly conformal. Radó proved in 1924 that every Riemann surface is *countable*: there exists a countable set of covering parametric disks U_z. This proof was based upon the main theorem of the theory of uniformization, which implies that the universal covering surface of a triangulable Riemann surface can be mapped onto the unit circle.

In a recent exposition of the theory of uniformization [3] I have given a more direct proof of the countability of a Riemann surface. The proof is based on the construction of a metric, defined by means of a certain potential function u in R. The existence of this potential can be established by the classical alternating method of Schwarz in the following way.

2. The alternating method. Let G_1 and G_2 be two open regions of R, with compact closures $G_1 + \Gamma_1$ and $G_2 + \Gamma_2$ in R. Suppose that the intersection G_1G_2 is nonempty. Let α_1 be the set of points of Γ_1 which lie outside of $G_2 + \Gamma_2$ and β_1 the set of points of Γ_1 inside of G_2, and let α_2 and β_2 be the corresponding sets with respect to Γ_2. The intersection $\gamma \equiv \Gamma_1\Gamma_2$ is assumed to be a *finite* set of points. We assume that the problem is solvable for both domains G_1 and G_2 with a boundary function f, which is bounded and continuous with the possible exception of a finite number of discontinuities; it follows from the principle of maximum and minimum that there exists only one bounded harmonic function (in G_1 or in G_2) with the given boundary values.

The problem of Schwarz seeks the solution of the Dirichlet problem in the union $G_1 + G_2$, which is bounded by the set $\alpha_1 + \alpha_2 + \gamma \equiv \Gamma$.

Following the method of Schwarz, we construct the sequences u_n and v_n of bounded harmonic functions in G_1 and G_2, respectively, determined by the boundary conditions

$$u_{n+1} = \begin{cases} f & \text{on} \quad \alpha_1 \\ v_n & \text{on} \quad \beta_1, \end{cases} \qquad v_n = \begin{cases} f & \text{on} \quad \alpha_2 \\ u_n & \text{on} \quad \beta_2, \end{cases}$$

$$(n = 0, 1, \cdots ; u_0 \equiv 0),$$

where f is a given bounded continuous function on Γ (with at most a finite number of discontinuities). Under these conditions the sequences u_n and v_n converge to two limits u and v, harmonic in G_1 and G_2, respectively, coinciding in G_1G_2, and taking the given boundary values on $\alpha_1 + \alpha_2$. For the proof we can restrict ourselves to the case $f \geqq 0$. The sequences u_n and v_n are increasing and $\leqq M \equiv \sup f$, as an immediate consequence of the maximum principle; the limits $\lim u_n = u$ and $\lim v_n = v$ are harmonic in G_1 and G_2, respectively, and the maximum and minimum principle shows that these functions have all the required properties.

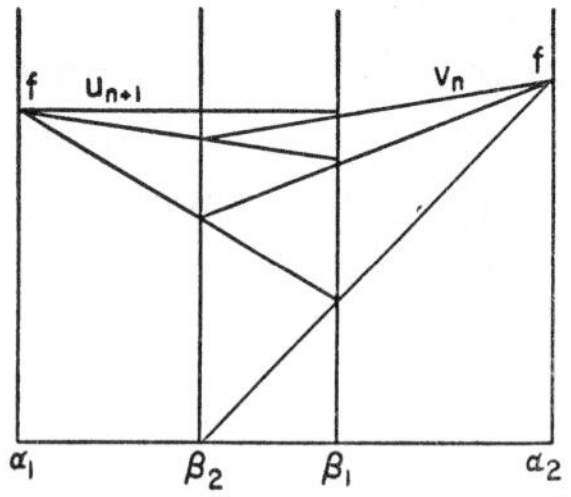

FIG. 1

In the one-dimensional case the process of Schwarz can be illustrated by the simple diagram shown in Figure 1: we must join two given points with the coordinates $(\alpha_1, f(\alpha_1))$ and $(\alpha_2, f(\alpha_2))$ by a straight-line segment, supposing that the corresponding construction is possible for the smaller intervals (α_1, β_1) and (β_2, α_2). The obvious properties of the (linear) functions u_n, v_n [monotonicity and convergence to the straight line joining the points $(\alpha_1, f(\alpha_1))$, $(\alpha_2, f(\alpha_2))$] can easily be proved by means of the maximum principle in the two-dimensional case; the harmonicity of the limit functions is a consequence of the elementary properties of the Poisson integral.

3. Circular domains. Consider on the Riemann surface R a compact domain D formed by the union of a finite number of circular disks or circular annuli (in a set of parametric circles U_z). Now the Dirichlet problem can be solved for a circle and for an annulus, and by the alternating method we are able to solve the problem for every "circular domain" D.

4. Construction of a particular potential function. From an arbitrary parametric circle U_z of the surface R we remove two small disjoint circular disks with circumferences α and β, and we consider the complementary part R_1 of R (Fig. 2). To show the countability of R it is sufficient to prove that this property holds for the surface R_1. Consider now the set of circular domains $D \subset R$, whose boundaries contain the two circles α and β. We construct a potential function u_D by the conditions $u_D = 1$ on α, $u_D = 0$ on $\bar{\alpha}$, where $\bar{\alpha}$ is the complement of α with respect to the boundary of D. The function $u(z) \equiv \sup_D u_D(z)$ $(0 \leqq u \leqq 1)$ is defined in every point z of R_1, and it is easy to show that u is harmonic[1] and equal to 1 on α and equal to 0 on β.

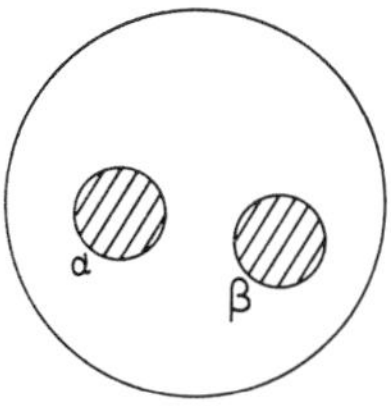

FIG. 2

5. Construction of a sequence z_n everywhere dense. Take now an arbitrary point $z = a \in R_1$; there exists then a sequence of circular domains $D_1, D_2, \cdots$ containing the point a such that

$$u_{D_n}(z) \longrightarrow u(z)$$

in the neighborhood of $z = a$. The corresponding countable set of parametric circles (U_z^n) is everywhere dense on R_1. In fact, should there be a point $z = b \in R_1$ and a circle $C_0 : |z - b| \leqq r$ $(r > 0)$ in the parametric disk U_b *outside* of the union (U_z) we could construct a potential function $v(z)$ in $R_0 - C_0$ with the boundary values 1 on α and 0 on $\bar{\alpha}$ and on the circle C_0. Obviously, $v(z) \leqq u(z)$. On the other hand, the maximum principle shows that $u_{D_n}(z) \leqq v(z)$, and for $n \rightarrow \infty$ we find $v(z) \geqq u(z)$. Consequently $u \equiv v$. But this is impossible, since $u > 0$ on C_0 while v vanishes there. Thus the sequences D_n and U_z^n are everywhere dense on R_1. It follows that there exists a countable set of *points* z_n, everywhere dense in R_1.

6. Construction of a metric. We introduce now in R_1 the invariant line-element

$$ds_z \equiv |\operatorname{grad} u(z)| \, |dz| .$$

The corresponding metric obviously determines the same topology as the topology given by the definition of R as a two-dimensional mani-

---

[1] For a simple proof see my monograph [3]. A similar proof is given by L. Ahlfors [1].

fold. The set z_n, constructed above, is everywhere dense also in the sense of the metric ds_z, and now it easily follows [2, p. 80] that the surfaces R_1 and R are countable.

BIBLIOGRAPHY

1. Ahlfors, L. *Complex analysis*. New York, 1953.

2. Alexandroff, P., and Hopf, H. *Topologie*, vol. I. Berlin, 1935.

3. Nevanlinna, R. *Uniformisierung*. Berlin, 1953.

University of Zurich

POLYGONAL REPRESENTATION OF RIEMANN SURFACES

ROLF NEVANLINNA

1. A closed Riemann surface can be represented by a polygonal domain with certain identifications between the edges. A similar statement applies to a general Riemann surface, except that the "polygonal domain" may have infinitely many edges on its boundary.

We study here the local problem of the structure of a Riemann surface in the neighborhood D of a boundary element. The neighborhood D is assumed to be represented by a Jordan domain bounded by a Jordan curve PQ_2Q_1P, with analytical identifications between the edges Q_z^1: PQ_1 and L_z^2: PQ_2, so that points on these edges are interior points of D, while P and the arc Q_1Q_2 are on the boundary (see Fig. 1). We are interested in the structure at P.

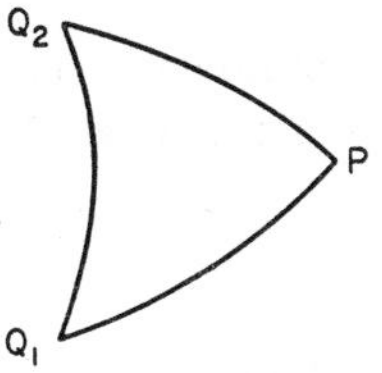

FIG. 1

After the identification, the domain D is doubly-connected, and can hence be mapped onto an annular domain: $1 \leqq |\omega| < \rho \leqq \infty$, with Q_1Q_2 mapping onto $|\omega| = 1$ and the boundary P corresponding to $|\omega| = \rho > 1$. We term P hyperbolic or parabolic according as $\rho < \infty$ or $\rho = \infty$.

2. EXAMPLE. We can choose D as the half-strip $k > 0$, $0 \leqq y \leqq 1$ with $(x_1, 0)$ and $((1 + \epsilon)x_1, 1)$ identified, ϵ being a constant $\geqq 0$, and P being at ∞. If $\epsilon = 0$, the mapping onto the ω-plane is given by

$$\omega = e^{2\pi z};$$

the image domain is the exterior of the unit circle and P is parabolic.

If $\epsilon > 0$, there is a dilatation. We can verify that

$$\rho = \exp\,[\pi^2/\log(1 + \epsilon)],$$

so that P is hyperbolic. The curves L_z^1, L_z^2 correspond to a spiral L_ω in the ω- plane.

3. In general, let L_z^1, L_z^2 map on a curve L_ω which goes from one boundary of the annulus to the other. If we cut the annulus along L_ω, then $\log \omega$ is analytic in the complement; $w = u + iv = (1/2\pi) \log \omega$ maps on a domain bounded by the segment: $u = 0$, $0 \leqq v \leqq 1$, two curves L_w^1 and L_w^2 and possibly a segment $u = (\log \rho)/2\pi$, $0 \leqq v \leqq 1$. There is now an identification between w_1 and $w_2 = w_1 + 1$.

We can also map the original domain D onto a rectangle, $s \geqq 0$, $0 \leqq t < \beta$ in an st-plane by a map of class C' in such a way that equivalent points z_1, z_2 on L_w^1, L_w^2 map on points $(s, 0)$, (s, β) of the

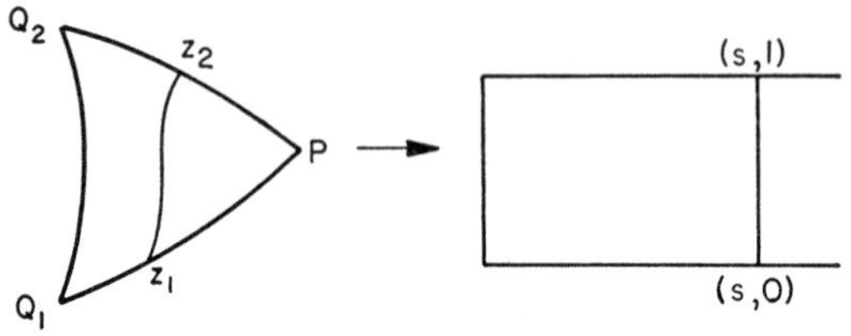

FIG. 2

boundary. The inverse image of a line $s = $ const is a curve λ_s joining z_1, z_2 (see Fig. 2). Now we have

$$1 \leqq \left(\int_{\lambda_s} |dw|\right)^2 = \left(\int_0^1 \left|\frac{dw}{dz}\right| \sqrt{\Delta} \frac{ds}{dt\sqrt{\Delta}} dt\right)^2,$$

where

$$\Delta = \frac{\partial(x, y)}{\partial(s, t)} > 0.$$

Hence by the Schwarz inequality

$$1 \leqq l(s) \int_0^1 \left|\frac{dw}{dz}\right|^2 \Delta\, dt.$$

where

$$l(s) = \int_0^1 \left(\frac{|dz|}{dt}\right)^2 \frac{dt}{\Delta}$$

If we divide by $l(s)$ and integrate, we obtain:

$$\int_0^\sigma \frac{ds}{l(s)} \leqq \int_0^\sigma \int_0^1 \left|\frac{dw}{dz}\right|^2 \Delta\, dt\, ds = A_\sigma$$

The integral on the right gives the area of the region in the w-plane corresponding to the shaded region of Figure 3. If the integral on the left diverges, $A_\sigma \to \infty$ and P is parabolic. Hence a sufficient condition for the parabolic case is

$$\int_0^\infty \frac{ds}{l(s)} = \infty .$$

4. We can give a geometric interpretation of $l(s)$. A small circle of radius dt and center (s, t) corresponds to a small ellipse of semiaxes a and b in D. Now the integrand for $l(s)$ is

$$\left|\frac{dz}{dt}\right|^2 \frac{1}{\Delta} = \frac{|dz|^2}{dt^2}\frac{dt^2}{ab},$$

since

$$\Delta = \frac{ab}{dt^2}.$$

But $|dz| \leqq a$, the greater semiaxis. Hence the integrand is at most

$$\frac{a}{b} = d(s, t),$$

the dilatation ratio, and $l(s)$ is less than the mean value of the dilatation ratio $d(s, t)$ on the segment $s =$ const. We can majorize this by using the maximum dilatation ratio $\delta(s)$ on the segment:

$$l(s) \leqq \delta(s) \int_0^1 dt = \delta(s).$$

Hence

$$\int^\infty \frac{ds}{\delta(s)} = \infty$$

is also a sufficient condition for the parabolic case.

5. If, in particular, the curves λ_s are line segments, and z_1 is identified with $z_2 = z_1 + \zeta(s)$, we can write

$$l(s) = \frac{\left|\log \dfrac{d\tau_2}{d\tau_1}\right|}{|d\tau_2 - d\tau_1|} \cdot |\zeta(s)|\, ds,$$

where $d\tau_1$ and $d\tau_2$ are as shown in Figure 3.

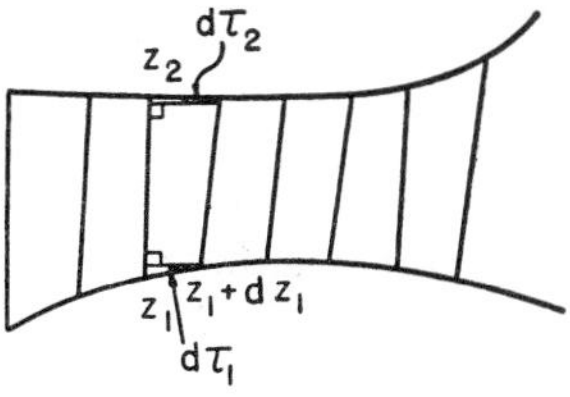

FIG. 3

Now in general for $a \geqq 0$, $b \geqq 0$,

$$\frac{\left|\log \dfrac{a}{b}\right|}{|a-b|} \leqq \frac{1}{\min(a, b)}.$$

Hence

$$l(s) \leqq \frac{1}{d\tau} |\zeta| \, ds, \qquad d\tau = \min(d\tau_1, d\tau_2)$$

and

$$\frac{ds}{l(s)} \geqq \frac{d\tau}{|\zeta|}.$$

Hence we obtain

$$\int^{\infty} \frac{d\tau}{|\zeta(s)|} = \infty$$

as sufficient condition for the parabolic case.

6. Example. Let D be given as the strip $x > 0$, $0 \leqq y \leqq 1$ with z_1 identified with $z_2 = z_1 + \zeta(s)$, and assume x_2 to be an increasing function of x_1. Then we can write

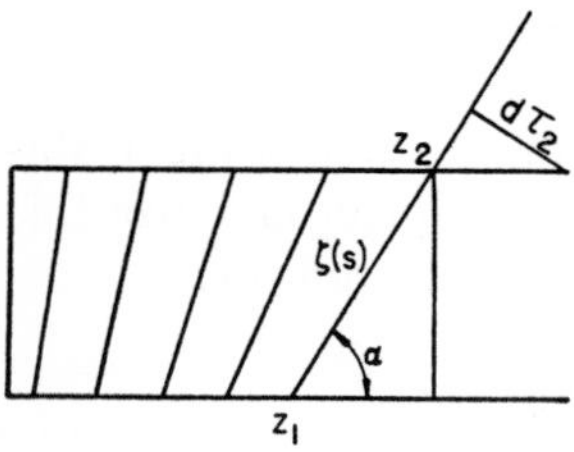

Fig. 4

$$\frac{1}{|\zeta(s)|} = \sin \alpha,$$

as shown in Figure 4, and also

$$\frac{d\tau_1}{dx_1} = \frac{d\tau_2}{dx_2} = \sin \alpha,$$

so that

$$\frac{d\tau}{|\zeta|} = \sin^2 \alpha \, dx_1,$$

and

$$\int^{\infty} \sin^2 \alpha \, dx_1 = \infty$$

is again a sufficient condition for the parabolic case. This is the same as

$$\int^{\infty} \frac{dx_1}{1 + (x_2 - x_1)^2} = \infty.$$

7. For instance, if we take $x_2 - x_1 \equiv \phi(x_1) = x_1^{\lambda}$ $(\lambda > 0)$, it follows that the ideal element $s = \infty$ is parabolic for $\lambda \leqq \frac{1}{2}$. The example of § 2 shows that $\lambda = 1$ corresponds to the hyperbolic case. It remains to determine the type for the values $\frac{1}{2} < \lambda < 1$.[1]

It is natural to try to maximize the integral

$$\int_0^{\infty} \frac{ds}{l(s)}$$

by using appropriate families $l(s)$, following classical methods in the calculus of variations.

8. The analysis above leads to an extension of the Ahlfors-Grötzsch distortion theorem. Consider a rectangle

$$\mathcal{G}: 0 \leqq s \leqq \alpha \leqq \infty, \qquad 0 \leqq t \leqq \beta \leqq \infty$$

in the plane of $\zeta = s + it$ and a map $z = z(s)$ (of class C') in the complex z-plane with the determinant $\Delta > 0$. The image $\mathcal{G}_z$ is a domain $ABCD$ bounded by four arcs $AB, \cdots, DA$; the points $A, \cdots, D$ correspond respectively to $(0, 0)$, $(\alpha, 0)$, (α, β), $(0, \beta)$. As in § 3, we define

$$l_1(s) = \int_0^{\beta} \left|\frac{\partial z}{\partial t}\right|^2 \frac{dt}{\Delta} \leqq \int_0^{\beta} d(s, t)\, dt \leqq \beta\delta_1(s),$$

where $d(s, t)$ is the dilatation quotient of the map $(s, t) \to z$ and $\delta_1(s)$ denotes the maximum of $d(s, t)$ on the segment $s =$ const. In a similar way we have

$$l_2(t) = \int_0^{\alpha} \left|\frac{\partial z}{\partial s}\right|^2 \frac{ds}{\Delta} \leqq \int_0^{\alpha} d(s, t)\, ds \leqq \alpha\delta_2(t).$$

Here $\delta_2(t)$ is the maximum of d on the segment $t =$ const.

9. If $z = z(s, t)$ is a conformal map of $\mathcal{G}_z$ onto a rectangle $(w = u + iv)$

$$\mathcal{G}_w: 0 \leqq u \leqq a, \qquad 0 \leqq v \leqq b,$$

[1] It has been proved by Miss Eva Wirth (February, 1954) that for every λ $(\frac{1}{2} < \lambda \leqq 1)$ there exists a surface of hyperbolic type.

we find

$$\int_0^\alpha \frac{ds}{l_1(s)} \leqq \frac{a}{b} \leqq \frac{1}{\displaystyle\int_0^\beta \frac{dt}{l_2(t)}}.$$

This double inequality can be used for determination of the type of a Riemann surface.

10. The Ahlfors distortion theorem can be stated in the following form ($l_1 = l$, $b = 1$).

If

$$\int_{s_1}^{s_2} \frac{ds}{l(s)} > 2,$$

then

$$m_1(s_2) - m_2(s_1) > \int_{s_1}^{s_2} \frac{ds}{l(s)} - 4.$$

Here $m_1(s)$ is the minimum and $m_2(s)$ the maximum of the real part $u = u(s, t)$ for $s =$ const.

If the curves λ_s (images of the lines $s =$ const in the z-plane) are straight segments, we have (see § 5)

$$\int \frac{ds}{l(s)} = \int \frac{d\tau}{|\zeta(s)|}.$$

If the λ_s are parallel to the y-axis, we find the Ahlfors theorem.

UNIVERSITY OF ZURICH

RINGS OF ANALYTIC FUNCTIONS

SHIZUO KAKUTANI

1. Introduction and main theorems. Let D be a schlicht domain in the Gaussian plane, simply connected or not. Let

(1.1) $A(D)$ = the ring of all single-valued analytic functions on D,

(1.2) $B(D)$ = the ring of all single-valued bounded analytic functions on D.

When we discuss the ring $B(D)$, it is always assumed that D is bounded and has the following property:

(1.3) for any $\zeta \in \bar{D} - D$ (boundary of D), there exists a function $f \in B(D)$ for which ζ is an unremovable singularity.

A bounded domain D with the property (1.3) is called a *Δ-domain.*

Two domains D, D' are said to be *conformally equivalent* to each other (notation: $D \sim D'$) if there exists a single-valued analytic function $z' = \phi(z)$ which maps D conformally onto D'. Two rings $A(D)$, $A(D')$ are said to be *isomorphic* with each other (notation: $A(D) \sim A(D')$) if there exists a one-to-one ring isomorphism $g = \Phi(f)$ of $A(D)$ onto $A(D')$ which satisfies $\Phi(\alpha) = \alpha$ for every complex number α. In a similar way, we can define the ring isomorphism $B(D) \sim B(D')$ of two rings $B(D)$ and $B(D')$.

It is easy to see that $D \sim D'$ implies $A(D) \sim A(D')$ and $B(D) \sim B(D')$. In fact, if $z' = \phi(z)$ is a single-valued analytic function which maps D conformally onto D', then $g = \Phi(f)$, where $g(z') = f[\phi^{-1}(z')]$, is a one-to-one ring isomorphism of $A(D)$ onto $A(D')$ [of $B(D)$ onto $B(D')$] which satisfies $\Phi(\alpha) = \alpha$ for every complex number α. We shall prove that the converse is also true:

THEOREM 1. *$A(D) \sim A(D')$ [$B(D) \sim B(D')$] implies $D \sim D'$; more precisely, if $g = \Phi(f)$ is a ring isomorphism of $A(D)$ onto $A(D')$ [of $B(D)$ onto $B(D')$] which satisfies $\Phi(\alpha) = \alpha$ for every complex number α, then there exists a one-to-one conformal mapping $z' = \phi(z)$ of D onto D' such that $g(z') = f[\phi^{-1}(z')]$ for every $z' \in D'$, if $g = \Phi(f)$.*

This theorem was first proved by C. Chevalley and S. Kakutani (unpublished) in 1942 for $B(D)$, and by L. Bers in 1948 [1] for $A(D)$. The result obtained by Bers is more general than Theorem 1 since he does not assume that $\Phi(\alpha) = \alpha$ for every complex number α. It was proved by him that a ring isomorphism $g = \Phi(f)$ of $A(D)$ onto $A(D')$ is obtained either by $g(z') = f[\phi^{-1}(z')]$, where $z' = \phi(z)$ is a conformal mapping of D onto D', or by $g(z') = \overline{f[\psi^{-1}(z')]}$, where $z' = \psi(z)$ is an inversely conformal mapping of D onto D'. In the second case, it is clear that $\Phi(\alpha) = \bar{\alpha}$ for every complex number α. Recently, W. Rudin gave a simpler proof for $B(D)$ (unpublished).

A proper ideal M of $A(D)$ [of $B(D)$] is called a *maximal ideal* if there is no proper ideal of $A(D)$ [of $B(D)$] which contains M as a proper subideal. For each complex number $\alpha \in D$, let $M(\alpha)$ be the set of all functions $f \in A(D)$ [$f \in B(D)$] which satisfy $f(\alpha) = 0$.

LEMMA 1.1. *$M(\alpha)$ is a principal ideal of $A(D)$ [of $B(D)$] generated by the function $f_\alpha(z) = z - \alpha$.*

The proof is clear.

LEMMA 1.2. *$M(\alpha)$ is a maximal ideal of $A(D)$ [of $B(D)$], and the factor ring $A(D)/M(\alpha)$ [$B(D)/M(\alpha)$] is isomorphic with the field K of complex numbers.*

Proof. For every $f \in A(D)$ [$f \in B(D)$], there exists a complex number $\beta = f(\alpha) \in K$ such that $f - \beta \in M(\alpha)$. This shows that the factor ring $A(D)/M(\alpha)$ [$B(D)/M(\alpha)$] is isomorphic with K. The maximality of $M(\alpha)$ follows from this immediately.

$M(\alpha)$ is called a *maximal ideal of* $A(D)$ [of $B(D)$] *of type* I. All other maximal ideals of $A(D)$ [of $B(D)$] are called *maximal ideals of type* II.

THEOREM 2. *In order to prove Theorem* 1 *it suffices to show that the maximal ideals of $A(D)$ [of $B(D)$] of type I can be characterized in purely algebraic terms.*

Proof. Assume that the maximal ideals of $A(D)$ [of $B(D)$] of type I can be characterized in purely algebraic terms. Let $g = \Phi(f)$ be a ring isomorphism of $A(D)$ onto $A(D')$ [of $B(D)$ onto $B(D')$] which satisfies $\Phi(\alpha) = \alpha$ for any complex number α. Then, to every maximal ideal $M(\alpha)$ of $A(D)$ [of $B(D)$] of type I there corresponds a maximal ideal $M'(\alpha')$ of $A(D')$ [of $B(D')$] of type I. If we put $\alpha' = \phi(\alpha)$, then $z' = \phi(z)$ gives a one-to-one mapping of D onto D'. In order to prove that $z' = \phi(z)$ is a conformal mapping of D onto D', let us put $g_0(z) = z$ on D'. Then $g_0 \in A(D')$ $[\in B(D')]$. Let $f_0 = \Phi^{-1}(g_0) \in A(D)$ $[\in B(D)]$ be a function on D which corresponds to g_0 by the isomorphism Φ. It is then easy to see that, for any $\alpha \in D$, $f_0(z) - f_0(\alpha) \in M(\alpha)$ and hence $g_0(z) - f_0(\alpha) = z - f_0(\alpha) \in M'(\alpha') = M'[\phi(\alpha)]$. This shows that $\phi(\alpha) = f_0(\alpha)$ and consequently $z' = \phi(z)$ is a conformal mapping of D onto D'.

Algebraic characterizations of maximal ideals of $A(D)$ and $B(D)$ of type I will be given in § 2 and § 3 (Theorems 4, 5, 6). It is possible to determine all maximal ideals of $A(D)$ (Theorem 3),[1] but the same problem is still open for $B(D)$.[2,3]

2. Discussion of the ring $A(D)$. Let D be a schlicht domain in the Gaussian plane, and let $A(D)$ be the ring of all single-valued analytic functions on D. We first want to determine all maximal ideals of $A(D)$.

A subset S of D is said to be *discrete* if S has no limiting point in D. A discrete subset of D is either finite or countably infinite.

LEMMA 2.1. *Let* $\{\alpha_k \mid k = 1, 2, \cdots\}$ *be a discrete sequence of points in* D. *Let* $\{m_k \mid k = 1, 2, \cdots\}$ *be a sequence of positive integers, and let* $\{\beta_{k,p} \mid p = 0, 1, \cdots, m_k - 1; k = 1, 2, \cdots\}$ *be a system of complex numbers. Then there exists a function* $f \in A(D)$ *such that*

$$(2.1)\quad f^{(p)}(\alpha_k) = \beta_{k,p}\,,\ p = 0, 1, \cdots, m_k - 1;\ k = 1, 2, \cdots.$$

Because of its simplicity, the proof is omitted.

For each function $f \in A(D)$, let $N(f)$ be the set of all zero points of f in D; $N(f)$ is clearly a (finite or countably infinite) discrete subset of D.

LEMMA 2.2. *Let* f_1, f_2 *be two functions of* $A(D)$ *which do not vanish at the same point in* D; *i.e.,* $N(f_1)$ *and* $N(f_2)$ *are disjoint. Then, for*

---

[1] P. C. Rosenbloom pointed out that the ring of all entire functions was discussed by M. Henriksen [2], who determined all maximal ideals of this ring. This ring is nothing but the ring $A(D)$ when D is the entire Gaussian plane.

[2] A. Beurling remarked that he had investigated (unpublished) the structure of the normed ring of all complex-valued functions $f(z)$ defined and continuous for $|z| \leqq 1$ and analytic for $|z| < 1$, where the norm is given by $\|f\| = \max |f(z)|$, $|z| \leqq 1$, and that he found that there exists a closed ideal in this ring which is not an intersection of maximal ideals.

[3] S. B. Myers asked whether there is any known algebraic characterization of those rings which are isomorphic with the ring $A(D)$ or $B(D)$. The answer to this interesting question is apparently not known.

every function $h \in A(D)$, *there exist two functions* $g_1, g_2 \in A(D)$ *such that* $h = f_1 g_1 + f_2 g_2$.

Proof. Let $N(f_1) = \{\alpha_k \mid k = 1, 2, \cdots\}$ be the zero points of f_1 in D. Let m_k be the multiplicity of zero point α_k, $k = 1, 2, \cdots$. It suffices to prove that there exists a function g_2 in $A(D)$ such that $h - f_2 \cdot g_2$ has zero points of multiplicity at least m_k at α_k, $k = 1, 2, \cdots$, i.e., $(d^p/dz^p)\,[h(z) - f_2(z) \cdot g_2(z)] = 0$ for $p = 0, 1, \cdots, m_k - 1$ at $z = \alpha_k$, $k = 1, 2, \cdots$.

Let

$$
\begin{aligned}
\frac{h(z)}{f_2(z)} &= \beta_{k,0} + \beta_{k,1}(z - \alpha_k) + \frac{\beta_{k,2}}{2!}(z - \alpha_k)^2 + \cdots \\
&\quad + \frac{\beta_{k,m_k-1}}{(m_k - 1)!}(z - \alpha_k)^{m_k-1} + \cdots
\end{aligned}
\tag{2.2}
$$

be the Taylor expansion of $h(z)/f_2(z)$ at $z = \alpha_k$. This expansion is possible since $f_2(\alpha_k) \neq 0$. Let g_2 be a function of $A(D)$ which satisfies $g_2^{(p)}(\alpha_k) = \beta_{k,p}$, $p = 0, 1, \cdots, m_k - 1$; $k = 1, 2, \cdots$. The existence of such a function follows from Lemma 2.1. Then

$$
\frac{d^p}{dz^p}\left(\frac{h(z)}{f_2(z)}\right) = \frac{d^p}{dz^p}(g_2(z))
$$

for $p = 0, 1, \cdots, m_k - 1$ at $z = \alpha_k$, $k = 1, 2, \cdots$, and this implies

$$
\frac{d^p}{dz^p}[h(z) - f_2(z) \cdot g_2(z)] = \frac{d^p}{dz^p}\left[h(z) - f_2(z)\frac{h(z)}{f_2(z)}\right] = 0
$$

for $p = 0, 1, \cdots, m_k - 1$ at $z = \alpha_k$, $k = 1, 2, \cdots$.

LEMMA 2.3. *Let* f_1, f_2 *be two functions in* $A(D)$. *Then there exist two functions* g_1, g_2 *in* $A(D)$ *such that* $N(f_1 \cdot g_1 + f_2 \cdot g_2) = N(f_1) \cap N(f_2)$.

Proof. If $N(f_1)$ and $N(f_2)$ are disjoint, then Lemma 2.3 is reduced to Lemma 2.2 with $h(z) = 1$.

Assume that $N(f_1)$ and $N(f_2)$ are not disjoint. Let $N(f_1) \cap N(f_2) = \{\alpha_k' \mid k = 1, 2, \cdots\}$ be the common zero points of f_1 and f_2 in D. Let m_k'', m_k''' be the multiplicity of zero point α_k' in f_1 and f_2, respectively, and put $m_k' = \max(m_k'', m_k''')$. Further, let h be a function in $A(D)$ with $N(h) = N(f_1) \cap N(f_2)$ and such that the multiplicity of zero point α_k' is exactly m_k', $k = 1, 2, \cdots$. We want to show that there exist two functions g_1, g_2 in $A(D)$ such that $h = f_1 \cdot g_1 + h_2 \cdot g_2$.

We first observe that we may assume, without loss of generality,

$m_k' = m_k'' = m_k'''$, $k = 1, 2, \cdots$. In fact, it is possible to find two functions f_1^*, f_2^* in $A(D)$ such that (i) f_1^*, f_2^* do not vanish outside $N(f_1) \cap N(f_2)$, (ii) the multiplicity of α_k' in f_1^* and f_2^* is $m_k' - m_k''$, $m_k' - m_k'''$, respectively, $k = 1, 2, \cdots$. It is then clear that $N(f_1 \cdot f_1^*) = N(f_1)$, $N(f_2 \cdot f_2^*) = N(f_2)$ and that $f_1 \cdot f_1^*$ and $f_2 \cdot f_2^*$ have the same multiplicity m_k' of zero at each α_k', $k = 1, 2, \cdots$.

Let now $f_1, f_2, h \in A(D)$ be three functions with the property: (i) $N(f_1) \cap N(f_2) = N(h) = \{\alpha_k' \mid k = 1, 2, \cdots\}$, (ii) f_1, f_2, h have the same multiplicity m_k' of zero at each α_k'. We want to show that there exist two functions g_1, g_2 in $A(D)$ such that $h = f_1 \cdot g_1 + f_2 \cdot g_2$. Let $N(f_1) - N(f_1) \cap N(f_2) = \{\alpha_k \mid k = 1, 2, \cdots\}$ be the zero points of f_1 which are not zero points of f_2. Let m_k be the multiplicity of zero point α_k in f_1, $k = 1, 2, \cdots$. It suffices to show that there exists a function g_2 in $A_2(D)$ such that $h - f_2 \cdot g_2$ has zero points of multiplicity at least m_k at α_k, $k = 1, 2, \cdots$, i.e.,

$$\frac{d^p}{dz^p}(h(z) - f_2(z)\, g_2(z)) = 0 \quad \text{for } p = 0, 1, \cdots, m_k - 1$$

at $z = \alpha_k$, $k = 1, 2, \cdots$. This can be shown exactly as in the proof of Lemma 2.2.

Let Σ be a family of nonempty discrete subsets S of D; Σ is called a *dual ideal* if the following conditions are satisfied:

(2.3) if $S_1, S_2 \in \Sigma$, then $S_1 \cap S_2 \in \Sigma$;

(2.4) if $S_1 \in \Sigma$ and if S_2 is a discrete subset of D such that $S_1 \subset S_2$, then $S_2 \in \Sigma$.

A dual ideal Σ of discrete subsets of D is said to be *maximal* if there is no larger dual ideal of discrete subsets of D which contains Σ as a proper subfamily. The existence of a maximal dual ideal follows from Zorn's lemma. It is easy to see that if Σ is a maximal dual ideal of discrete subsets of D, then

(2.5) for every discrete subset S_1 of D which does not belong to Σ, there exists a discrete set $S_2 \in \Sigma$ such that $S_1 \cap S_2$ is empty.

A maximal dual ideal Σ of discrete subsets of D is called a *maximal dual ideal of type* I if there exists a point $\alpha \in D$ such that $\alpha \in S$ for all $S \in \Sigma$. All other maximal dual ideals of discrete subsets of D are called *maximal dual ideals of type* II. In this case every member of Σ is a countably infinite subset of D.

THEOREM 3. *For every maximal dual ideal Σ of discrete subsets of*

D, $M(\Sigma) = \{f \mid f \in A(D), N(f) \in \Sigma\}$ is a maximal ideal of $A(D)$. Conversely, for every maximal ideal M of $A(D)$, $\Sigma(M) = \{N(f) \mid f \in M\}$ is a maximal dual ideal of discrete subsets of D. The mappings $\Sigma \to M(\Sigma)$ and $M \to \Sigma(M)$ give a one-to-one correspondence between all maximal dual ideals Σ of discrete subsets of D and all maximal ideals M of $A(D)$. Σ is a maximal dual ideal of type I or type II according as the corresponding M is a maximal ideal of type I or type II.

Proof. Let Σ be a dual ideal of discrete subsets of D. Then it is clear that $M(\Sigma) = \{f \mid f \in A(D), N(f) \in \Sigma\}$ is an ideal of $A(D)$. Assume that Σ is a maximal dual ideal. We want to show that $M(\Sigma)$ is a maximal ideal of $A(D)$. If $M(\Sigma)$ is not a maximal ideal of $A(D)$, then there exists an ideal I of $A(D)$ such that $M(\Sigma) \subsetneqq I \subsetneqq A(D)$. Let $f \in I - M(\Sigma)$ be a function such that $N(f)$ does not belong to Σ. Since Σ is a maximal dual ideal, it follows that there exists a discrete subset $S \in \Sigma$ such that $S \cap N(f)$ is empty. Let $g \in M(\Sigma)$ be a function such that $N(g) = S$. Then both f and g belong to I, and $N(f)$ and $N(g)$ are disjoint. Hence from Lemma 2.2 it follows that $I = A(D)$. Since this is a contradiction, $M(\Sigma)$ must be a maximal ideal of $A(D)$.

Conversely, let M be an ideal of $A(D)$. Then $\Sigma(M) = \{N(f) \mid f \in M\}$ is a dual ideal of discrete subsets of D. In fact, it is clear that (2.4) is satisfied by $\Sigma(M)$, and (2.3) for $\Sigma(M)$ follows from Lemma 2.3. Assume that M is a maximal ideal. We want to show that $\Sigma(M)$ is a maximal dual ideal. If $\Sigma(M)$ is not a maximal dual ideal, then there exists a dual ideal Σ' of discrete subsets of D which contains $\Sigma(M)$ as a proper subfamily. Let us consider the ideals $M[\Sigma(M)] = \{f \mid f \in A(D), N(f) \in \Sigma(M)\}$, and $M(\Sigma') = \{f \mid f \in A(D), N(f) \in \Sigma'\}$. Then $M \subseteqq M(\Sigma(M)) \subsetneqq M(\Sigma') \subsetneqq A(D)$. This is a contradiction to the fact that M is a maximal ideal of $A(D)$. Consequently, $\Sigma(M)$ must be a maximal dual ideal.

It is now easy to see that $\Sigma \to M(\Sigma)$ and $M \to \Sigma(M)$ give a one-to-one correspondence between all maximal dual ideals Σ of discrete subsets of D and all maximal ideals M of $A(D)$. The rest of the proof of Theorem 3 is easy, and consequently omitted.

THEOREM 4. *A maximal ideal M of $A(D)$ is of type I if and only if the factor ring $A(D)/M$ is isomorphic with the field K of complex numbers.*

Proof. The "only if" part of this theorem was proved in Lemma 1.2. In order to show the "if" part, let $f_0(z) = z$. Then $f_0(z) \in A(D)$ and $f_0 - \beta$ never belongs to any maximal ideal of $A(D)$ of type II. (This follows from the fact that every discrete subset of D belonging to a maximal dual ideal of type II is an infinite set and hence every function in a maximal ideal M of $A(D)$ of type II vanishes on an infinite discrete set.) This shows that the factor ring $A(D)/M$ is not isomorphic with the field K of complex numbers, if M is a maximal ideal of $A(D)$ of type II. This completes the proof of Theorem 4. (Note that we always consider isomorphisms which preserve the scalar product by complex numbers.)

Theorem 4 gives a purely algebraic characterization of maximal ideals of $A(D)$ of type I. Because of Theorem 2, this shows that Theorem 1 holds for the ring $A(D)$.

It is possible to demonstrate that the factor ring $A(D)/M$ is infinite dimensional over the field K of complex numbers if M is a maximal ideal of $A(D)$ of type II. (The interesting problem of determining the structure of this factor ring $A(D)/M$ is not discussed here.)

We also observe that maximal ideals $M(\Sigma)$ of $A(D)$ of type II are in one-to-one correspondence with the points p_Σ of the Čech compactification $\beta(D)$ of D such that $p_\Sigma \in \beta(D) - D$ and $p_\Sigma \in \bar{S}$ for some discrete infinite subset S of Σ, where $\bar{S}$ denotes the closure of S in $\beta(D)$.

3. Discussion of the ring $B(D)$. Let D be a Δ-domain, i.e., a bounded domain which satisfies the condition (1.3) of § 1. Let $B(D)$ be the ring of all single-valued bounded analytic functions on D. Then $B(D)$ is a normed ring with unit 1 (i.e., a constant function 1) with respect to the norm:

$$\|f\| = \sup_{z \in D} |f(z)|. \tag{3.1}$$

It is well known that every proper ideal of $B(D)$ is contained in a maximal ideal of $B(D)$. Further, every maximal ideal M of $B(D)$ is closed in the norm topology, and the factor ring $B(D)/M$ is isomorphic with the field K of complex numbers. For any function $f \in B(D)$ and for any maximal ideal M of $B(D)$, there exists a complex number β such that $f - \beta \in M$. If we put $\beta = (f, M)$, then

$f \to (f, M)$ is a continuous homomorphism of $B(D)$ onto the field K of complex numbers and

$$(3.2) \qquad |(f, M)| \leqq \|f\|,$$

$$(3.3) \qquad M = \{f \mid f \in B(D), (f, M) = 0\}.$$

The set $\mathfrak{M}$ of all maximal ideals M of $B(D)$ is a compact Hausdorff space with respect to the weak topology of $\mathfrak{M}$ in which a defining neighborhood $V(M_0; f_1, \cdots, f_n; \epsilon)$ of an $M_0 \in \mathfrak{M}$ is given by

$$(3.4) \qquad \begin{aligned} &V(M_0; f_1, \cdots, f_n; \epsilon) \\ &\quad = \{M \mid M \in \mathfrak{M}, |(f_i, M) - (f_i, M_0)| < \epsilon, i = 1, \cdots, n\}, \end{aligned}$$

where $f_1, \cdots, f_n \in B(D)$ and $\epsilon > 0$. For each $f \in B(D)$, (f, M) is a continuous function on $\mathfrak{M}$ and

$$(3.5) \qquad \|f\| = \max_{M \in \mathfrak{M}} |(f, M)|.$$

This follows from the fact that $\|f^2\| = \|f\|^2$ for any $f \in B(D)$.

Let us put $f_0(z) \equiv z$. Then $f_0 \in B(D)$ since D is bounded by assumption. For any $M \in \mathfrak{M}$, let us put $\tau(M) = (f_0, M)$. This means that $\alpha = \tau(M)$ is a complex number such that $f_0 - \alpha = z - \alpha \in M$.

Lemma 3.1. *$M \to \tau(M)$ is a continuous mapping of $\mathfrak{M}$ onto $\bar{D}$, where $\bar{D}$ is the closure of D in the Gaussian plane.*

Proof. It is clear that $\tau(M) = (f_0, M)$ is continuous on $\mathfrak{M}$. We first show that $\alpha = \tau(M)$ belongs to $\bar{D}$ for any $M \in \mathfrak{M}$. In fact, if $\alpha = \tau(M)$ does not belong to $\bar{D}$ for some $M \in \mathfrak{M}$, then $g_\alpha(z) = (z - \alpha)^{-1}$ is a single-valued bounded analytic function on D and hence belongs to $B(D)$. This is a contradiction to the fact that $f_\alpha(z) = z - \alpha$ belongs to a maximal ideal M. Thus $\tau(M) \in \bar{D}$ for all $M \in \mathfrak{M}$.

We shall next show that, for any complex number $\alpha \in \bar{D}$, there exists a maximal ideal M of $B(D)$ such that $\tau(M) = \alpha$. This is clear if $\alpha \in D$, since obviously $\tau[M(\alpha)] = \alpha$. Thus it suffices to consider the case $\alpha \in \bar{D} - D$. Let $\alpha \in \bar{D} - D$ and let $I(\alpha) = \{f \mid f \in B(D), \lim_{z \to \alpha} f(z) = 0\}$. Then $I(\alpha)$ is a proper ideal of $B(D)$ and hence there exists a maximal ideal M of $B(D)$ which contains $I(\alpha)$. It is then easy to see that $\tau(M) = \alpha$. This follows from the fact that $f_\alpha(z) = z - \alpha \in I(\alpha) \subset M$.

LEMMA 3.2. *The complex number* $\tau(M)$ *belongs to* D *if and only if* M *is a maximal ideal of* $B(D)$ *of type I.*

Proof. It suffices to prove the "only if" part of this lemma. Let us assume that $\alpha = \tau(M) \in D$. Let $M(\alpha)$ be the principal maximal ideal of $B(D)$ generated by $f_\alpha(z) = z - \alpha$. Since $f_\alpha(z)$ belongs to M, it follows that $M(\alpha)$ is a subset of M. However, this is possible only if $M = M(\alpha)$.

Let $\mathfrak{M}_I = \{M(\alpha) \mid \alpha \in D\}$ be the set of all maximal ideals of $B(D)$ of type I.

LEMMA 3.3. $\mathfrak{M}_I$ *is an open subset of* $\mathfrak{M}$ *which is homeomorphic with* D *by means of the correspondence* $M(\alpha) \leftrightarrow \alpha$.

Proof. Let $M(\alpha_0) \in \mathfrak{M}_I$ (i.e., $\alpha_0 \in D$), and let $V[M(\alpha_0); f_0; \epsilon]$ be a neighborhood of $M(\alpha_0)$ in $\mathfrak{M}$ defined by

$$\begin{aligned} (3.6)\qquad & V[M(\alpha_0); f_0; \epsilon] \\ &\qquad = \{M \mid M \in \mathfrak{M}, \mid (f_0, M) - (f_0, M(\alpha_0)) \mid < \epsilon\}, \end{aligned}$$

where $f_0(z) \equiv z$ and ϵ is chosen so small that the circular disk $\{\alpha \mid \mid \alpha - \alpha_0 \mid < \epsilon\}$ is contained in D. If $M \in V[M(\alpha_0); f_0; \epsilon]$, then $\mid (f_0, M) - (f_0, M(\alpha_0)) \mid < \epsilon$ or, equivalently, $\mid \tau(M) - \alpha_0 \mid < \epsilon$, and consequently $\tau(M) \in D$ and hence $M \in \mathfrak{M}_I$. This shows that $\mathfrak{M}_I$ is an open subset of $\mathfrak{M}$.

Again let $M(\alpha_0) \in \mathfrak{M}_I$ (i.e., $\alpha_0 \in D$) and let $V[M(\alpha_0); f_1, \cdots, f_n; \epsilon]$ be a neighborhood of $M(\alpha_0)$ in $\mathfrak{M}$ which is contained in $\mathfrak{M}_I$. We may write

$$\begin{aligned} (3.7)\qquad & V[M(\alpha_0); f_1, \cdots, f_n; \epsilon] \\ &\qquad = \{M(\alpha) \mid \alpha \in D, \mid f_i(\alpha) - f_i(\alpha_0) \mid < \epsilon, i = 1, \cdots, n\}. \end{aligned}$$

Let $\delta > 0$ be so small that $\mid \alpha - \alpha_0 \mid < \delta$ implies $\alpha \in D$ and $\mid f_i(\alpha) - f_i(\alpha_0) \mid < \epsilon$, $i = 1, \cdots n$. Then $\mid \alpha - \alpha_0 \mid < \delta$ implies $M(\alpha) \in V[M(\alpha_0); f_1, \cdots, f_n; \epsilon]$. From this it follows that $\alpha \rightarrow M(\alpha)$ is a continuous mapping of D onto $\mathfrak{M}_I$. It is clear that the inverse mapping $M(\alpha) \rightarrow \alpha = \tau[M(\alpha)]$ is continuous. Thus $\alpha \leftrightarrow M(\alpha)$ gives a homeomorphism between D and $\mathfrak{M}_I$.

It is an interesting problem to determine all maximal ideals of $B(D)$ of type II. This problem is open even in the simplest case, when $D = \{z \mid \mid z \mid < 1\}$ is the interior of the unit circle. Our next objective is to find a purely algebraic characterization of maximal ideals of $B(D)$ of type I.

We state some conjectures:

Conjecture 1. A maximal ideal M of $B(D)$ is of type I if and only if $\mathfrak{M}$ satisfies the first countability axiom at M.

Conjecture 2. A maximal ideal M of $B(D)$ is of type I if and only if M has a neighborhood in $\mathfrak{M}$ which is homeomorphic with the interior of the unit circle.

Conjecture 3. A maximal ideal M of $B(D)$ is of type I if and only if it is a principal ideal.

We shall first prove that Conjecture 3 is true if D is a finitely connected Δ-domain.

THEOREM 5. *Let D be a finitely connected Δ-domain. Then a maximal ideal M_0 of $B(D)$ is of type* I *if and only if M_0 is a principal ideal.*

Proof. It suffices to show that, in case D is a finitely connected Δ-domain, every principal maximal ideal of $B(D)$ is of type I. We may assume, without loss of generality, that D is of this form:

$$D = C_0 - (\bar{C}_1 \cup \cdots \cup \bar{C}_m), \tag{3.8}$$

where $\bar{C}_1, \cdots, \bar{C}_m$ are mutually disjoint closed circular disks all contained in an open circular disk C_0.

Let M_0 be a principal maximal ideal of $B(D)$ generated by a function $f_0(z) \in B(D)$. It is clear that $\inf_{z \in D} |f_0(z)| = 0$. We divide our argument into two cases: (i) $f_0(\alpha) = 0$ for some $\alpha \in D$; (ii) $f_0(z) \neq 0$ for all $z \in D$.

In the first case it is easy to see that $M_0 = M(\alpha)$ and hence $M_0 \subseteqq M(\alpha)$. In the second case, there exists a sequence $\{\alpha_n \mid n = 1, 2, \cdots\}$ of points in D such that $\lim_{n\to\infty} f_0(\alpha_n) = 0$. We may assume, without loss of generality, that $\lim_{n\to\infty}\alpha_n = \alpha \in \bar{D} - D$. Since M_0 is a principal ideal of $B(D)$ generated by f_0, it follows that $\lim_{n\to\infty} f(\alpha_n) = 0$ for any $f \in M_0$. From this it follows that for each f in $B(D)$ $\lim_{n\to\infty} f(\alpha_n) = \beta$ exists and $f \in M_0$ if and only if $\beta = 0$. This is an immediate consequence of the fact that, for any $f \in B(D)$, there exists a complex number $\beta = (f, M_0)$ such that $f - \beta \in M_0$.

Let us consider the function $g_0(z) = [f_0(z)]^{\frac{1}{2}}$; $g_0(z)$ is bounded and analytic on D, but is not necessarily single-valued. It is, however, easy to see that if we take a suitable system of complex numbers $\gamma_{i_1}, \cdots, \gamma_{i_p}$, where $1 \leqq i_1 < \cdots < i_p \leqq m$ and γ_{i_k} is the center of the closed circular disk $\bar{C}_{i_k}$, $k = 1, \cdots, p$, then

$$h_0(z) = \{f_0(z)(z - \gamma_{i_1}) \cdots (z - \gamma_{i_p})\}^{\frac{1}{2}} \tag{3.9}$$

is single-valued, bounded, and analytic on D, and hence $h_0(z) \in B(D)$. It is clear that $\lim_{n \to \infty} h_0(\alpha_n) = 0$ and hence $h_0 \in M_0$. However, this is a contradiction since, on the one hand, $h_0(z)/f_0(z)$ must be bounded (because h_0 belongs to the principal ideal of $B(D)$ generated by f_0), while on the other hand we have

$$\lim_{n\to\infty} \left| \frac{h_0(\alpha_n)}{f_0(\alpha_n)} \right| = \lim_{n\to\infty} \left\{ \frac{| \alpha_n - \gamma_{i_1} | \cdots\cdot | \alpha_n - \gamma_{i_p} |}{| f_0(\alpha_n) |} \right\}^{\frac{1}{2}} = \infty. \tag{3.10}$$

Thus case (ii) cannot happen. This completes the proof of Theorem 5.

If D is a general Δ-domain, the situation does not seem to be so simple. The following algebraic characterization of maximal ideals of $B(D)$ of type I is due to C. Chevalley:

THEOREM 6. *Let D be a Δ-domain. Then a maximal ideal M_0 of $B(D)$ is of type I if and only if the following conditions are satisfied:* (i) *M_0 is a principal maximal ideal of $B(D)$ generated by a function $g_0 \in B(D)$*; (ii) *there exists a neighborhood $V(M_0)$ of M_0 in $\mathfrak{M}$ which is mapped homeomorphically onto a circular disk $\{w \mid | w | < \epsilon\}$ in the Gaussian plane by the mapping: $M \to (g_0, M)$*; (iii) *for every function $f \in B(D)$, the corresponding function (f, M) defined on $\mathfrak{M}$ can be expanded into a power series*

$$(f, M) = \textstyle\sum_{k=0}^{\infty} a_k[(g_0, M)]^k, \tag{3.11}$$

which converges on $V(M_0)$, where a_k are complex numbers which satisfy: $a_k = 0$, $k = 0, 1, 2, \cdots$ if and only if $f(z) \equiv 0$.

Proof. The necessity of conditions (i), (ii), and (iii) is almost immediately clear if we observe that $\mathfrak{M}_I$ and D are homeomorphic with each other (Lemma 3.3). In fact, if $M_0 = M(\alpha)$, for some $\alpha \in D$, then we have only to take $g_0(z) = z - \alpha$. The formula (3.11) is nothing but the Taylor expansion of a function $f(z) \in B(D)$ in a power series in $z - \alpha$ in a neighborhood of $z = \alpha$.

Thus in order to prove Theorem 6 it suffices to show that a maximal ideal M_0 of $B(D)$ satisfying conditions (i), (ii), and (iii) is a maximal ideal of type I. Let us take the function $f_0(z) = z$. Because of condition (iii), we have a power-series expansion

$$(f_0, M) = \sum_{k=0}^{\infty} b_k[(g_0, M)]^k \tag{3.12}$$

which is convergent in a neighborhood $V(M_0)$ of M_0. Since $f_0(z)$ is not a constant function, there exists a positive integer $k \geqq 1$ such that $b_k \neq 0$. From condition (ii) it follows that the set $\{(g_0, M) \mid M \in V(M_0)\}$ contains a circular disc $\{w \mid |w| < \epsilon\}$ and hence the formula (3.12) shows that the set $\{(f_0, M) \mid M \in V(M_0)\}$ contains a circular disk around the point $b_0 = (f_0, M_0)$. Hence $\alpha = \tau(M_0) = (f_0, M_0)$ is an interior point of $\{(f_0, M) \mid M \in \mathfrak{M}\}$, which is equal to $\bar{D}$ by Lemma 3.1. But this does not necessarily mean that $\alpha = \tau(M_0)$ is a point of D. The proof of Theorem 6 is completed if we can prove that $\alpha \in D$. (See Lemma 3.2.)

We shall next show that $b_1 \neq 0$ in the expansion (3.12). In fact, if $b_1 = b_2 = \cdots = b_{n-1} = 0$ and $b_n \neq 0$ for some $n \geqq 2$, then there exists a $\delta > 0$ such that for every complex number β with $0 < |\beta - \alpha| < \delta$, the equation $\beta = (f_0, M)$ has exactly n different solutions in $V(M_0)$. Since $\alpha \in \bar{D}$, this implies that there exist a complex number $\beta \in D$ and n maximal ideals $M_1, \cdots, M_n$ $(n \geqq 2)$ in $V(M_0)$ such that $\beta = (f_0, M_1) = \cdots = (f_0, M_n)$. This is a contradiction of the fact that for any complex number $\beta \in D$ there exists one and only one maximal ideal $M = M(\beta)$ which satisfies $(f_0, M) = \beta$.

Thus we have shown that $b_1 \neq 0$. Hence we can invert the formula (3.12) and obtain

$$(g_0, M) = \sum_{k=0}^{\infty} c_k[(f_0, M)]^k, \qquad c_1 \neq 0, \tag{3.13}$$

which is convergent if (f_0, M) is sufficiently near to $\alpha = (f_0, M_0)$. If we combine (3.11) and (3.13), we see that (f, M) is an analytic function of (f_0, M) in a small neighborhood of $\alpha = (f_0, M)$. Since there exists, by assumption, for every boundary point ζ of D, a single-valued function $f \in B(D)$ for which ζ is an unremovable singularity, this implies that α is an interior point of D. This completes the proof of Theorem 6.

Remark. It is to be observed that these conditions (i), (ii), and (iii) are algebraic properties of the ring $B(D)$. It is true that the notions of topology and analysis appear in (ii) and (iii), but all of these properties can be obtained from the algebraic structure of our ring $B(D)$. Because of Theorem 2, this shows that Theorem 1 holds for the ring $B(D)$.

BIBLIOGRAPHY

1. BERS, L. *On rings of analytic functions*, Bull. Amer. Math. Soc. 54 (1948), 311–315.

2. HENRIKSEN, M. *On the ideal structure of the ring of entire functions*, Pacific J. Math. 2 (1952), 179–184.

YALE UNIVERSITY

TOPOLOGIES ON THE BOUNDARY AND HARMONIC MEASURE

MARCEL BRELOT

1. The theory of functions of a complex variable, chiefly studied for itself, has been for a long time much in advance of the theory of harmonic functions. Thus the famous theorem of Picard (1879) was worked upon a great deal, whereas the study of the singularities of harmonic functions, strangely enough, was neglected; elementary but fundamental theorems on this topic published by Schwarz (1872) and Poincaré and Bôcher (around 1900) were not mentioned in the classical treatises on analysis. It was only in 1923 and the following years that a number of papers on this subject began to appear, the first ones among them showing little knowledge of the previous work; nor did they exhaust a subject which has still not developed enough to treat Picard's theorem (see [1]).

It was at the same time, thirty years ago, that the Dirichlet problem, thanks chiefly to Perron [2] and Wiener [3], took a new form that led later to theorems of a somewhat definitive aspect, after so many imperfect solutions. It was also at this time that F. Riesz [4], analyzing a theorem of Hardy on the means of the modulus of a holomorphic function, evolved the notion of subharmonic function, of which this modulus is a particular case; he gave to this notion a generality such that he could identify it locally with a potential (logarithmic or Newtonian potential of negative masses) plus some harmonic function (see [5]). Everyone knows the considerable subsequent development of the theory of subharmonic functions (see [6] and [15]) and of the potential (see [7] and [16]). But if potential theory owes its revival partly to the theory of functions of a complex variable, it has largely rewarded this theory, in the way pointed out by F. Riesz (see [8]). It is now used at every step, and I believe that it will always have more to offer. However, the modern extensive development of potential theory would have come to an early halt without the systematic use of the topological methods, which here, as elsewhere, give new life to the old questions of analysis.

2. One of the more usual tools in the theory of a complex variable is *harmonic measure* [9], the subject of this lecture. An example of its application will show the value of this concept. Let us consider in a bounded plane domain Ω a holomorphic function $f(z)$. If f vanishes on a part of the boundary which is a rectifiable arc, or only on a set E of length not zero on this arc, then, as has been known for a long time, and proved by conformal mapping on the circle, f must be zero. Similarly and more generally, if $f_n(z)$ are functions whose moduli are uniformly bounded, if each f_n possesses a limit ϕ_n on E, and if the sequence ϕ_n converges, then there will be convergence of f_n in Ω (uniformly locally) (see the works of the Riesz brothers, Montel, Privaloff, Khinchin, and so on (see [10])). Now it is sufficient that E be not of classical harmonic measure zero, and the preceding results will remain true even if certain more refined definitions, which improve the properties, are chosen for harmonic measure [11]. The proofs are very short, without conformal mapping, as applications of the modern theory of the Dirichlet problem, valid for all dimensions $n \geqq 2$.

Actually, the study of harmonic measure is the same as that of the *Dirichlet problem.* It would take too long and, I believe, be of little use to give here a historical account of this problem [12], which was first considered toward 1830, was still, after many famous papers, the object of the twentieth question of Hilbert, in 1900, and gave rise thereafter to a considerable bibliography, in the midst of the development of potential theory. Because of this complex history, I shall try instead to give a modern synthesis, necessarily not exhaustive. I shall only outline the question from the contemporary point of view which seems to me the most useful basis at the present time and in the order of proofs which I find the most simple.

We are concerned with a boundary-value problem. The boundary was first assumed to be in Euclidean space, but it became necessary to study various modes of approach—that is to say, convergence in the sense of new topologies. Thus new boundaries were introduced, obtained solely from the given domain by means of theorems which yield compact or complete topological structures relative to this domain. Then it became natural to consider, as we shall do, manifolds more general than Euclidean domains, such as locally Euclidean spaces or Riemann surfaces. Now the Dirichlet problem, which associates a certain solution with given boundary values, includes also the study of this solution near the boundary. In the more general study of harmonic and subharmonic functions near the Euclidean boundary, as in potential theory, it is convenient to use a tool closely connected with the old notion of irregular point: the weakest topology which makes the subharmonic functions continuous (the so-called fine topology of H. Cartan). We shall examine it also.

3. Let us study the Dirichlet problem first, in order to separate the difficulties, in a bounded domain Ω of the Euclidean space R^n (of dimension $n \geqq 2$) [13]. Let f be a finite continuous real function on the boundary $\overset{*}{\Omega}$. Let us consider, in almost the same manner as did Perron [2], the class of all subharmonic functions in Ω, for which at every boundary point P the upper limit is at most $f(P)$. Their upper envelope, denoted by $\underline{H}_f^\Omega$, or, briefly, by $\underline{H}_f$ (that is to say, the function equal to the least upper bound at every point), is harmonic, as may be quickly shown: Let us notice that u remains in the same class if, in a circular or spherical domain D, it is changed into the corresponding Poisson integral I_u. As $I_u \geqq u$, these I_u have in D the same upper envelope as the u. Moreover, they form a filtering family ordered with respect to increasing; the upper envelope, or limit corresponding to the filter of the sections, is harmonic; for we may take limits under the integral sign in every spatial mean condition which expresses harmonicity. In the same way, we define $\bar{H}_f$ with superharmonic functions and opposite inequalities; of course, $\bar{H}_f = -\underline{H}_{(-f)}$.

In order to compare $\underline{H}_f$ and $\bar{H}_f$, let us use the following elementary form of the maximum principle: if u is subharmonic and has at every boundary point an upper limit $\leqq 0$, then $u \leqq 0$. We find at once: $\underline{H}_f \leqq \bar{H}_f$. The opposite inequality may be established, also, in a simple way: It is indeed almost obvious when f may be extended continuously to Ω as a subharmonic function; in the general case we may use, for a continuous extension of f, Poincaré's idea of approximation by a difference of two finite continuous subharmonic functions. Thus we get the Wiener equality: $\underline{H}_f = \bar{H}_f$ [3c].

With every f we associate this common envelope, denoted by H_f. At every point M, H_f is a linear increasing functional of f (that is to say, of the general finite continuous function on the compact set $\mathring{\Omega}$). Therefore *this functional defines a Radon measure* $\geqq 0$ (according to a theorem of F. Riesz, now commonly taken as a definition). *It is the harmonic measure* at the point M. We denote it by μ^M and write $H_f(M) = \int f\, d\mu^M$. It is not difficult to see that the condition that a boundary set have harmonic measure zero does not depend on the point M; the same is true for the summability of a function on the boundary, relative to the harmonic measure.

Let us study now the idea of envelope, for any given real function, finite or not, on the boundary. We introduce the restriction that every subharmonic function considered be bounded above, and we enlarge the set of these functions by adjoining the function $-\infty$. There will be an envelope $\underline{H}_f$ which is $+\infty$, $-\infty$, or harmonic (by the same argument as appears above). (Let us notice that, if f may be continued as a subharmonic function F in an open set containing the closure of Ω, $\underline{H}_f$ is the upper envelope of the class of subharmonic functions in Ω for which the continuation by F is subharmonic.) We shall introduce also $\bar{H}_f$, and, because of the restriction to the classes of subharmonic or superharmonic functions, we get $\underline{H}_f \leqq \bar{H}_f$. We now have the main theorem (see [13a]): *These envelopes are equal and finite* (at one point and hence everywhere)—*in other words, f is "resolutive"—if and only if f is summable with respect to the harmonic measure.* (The proof is easily deduced from the theorem that, if f_n is continuous and tends decreasingly to f_0, H_{f_n} tends to $\underline{H}_{f_0}$.) As has been known for a short time, this may be demonstrated in a simple manner, without studying the behavior of $\underline{H}_f$, $\bar{H}_f$ at the boundary and without potential theory. Therefore we get for the common envelope H_f the expression $H_f = \int f\, d\mu^M$. Let us deduce from this the following improved form of the maximum principle: If the subharmonic function u is bounded above and has an upper limit $\leqq 0$ at every boundary point, except on a set of harmonic measure zero, then $u \leqq 0$.

Up to this point we have used only elementary properties of harmonic and subharmonic functions, properties including the general Poisson integral and its behavior at the boundary, but *if we wish to study H_f near the boundary*, the shortest way is to call upon the power and subtleties of *potential theory*. We shall therefore recall from this theory some notions extracted from a development of it, which we cannot stop to outline here, independent of the Dirichlet problem.

4. In classical potential theory it is often assumed, in order to obtain simple results, that the potential is continuous and the boundary somewhat smooth. Now general extensions of the theory can be given, with the same simplicity of language, by changing topology and employing, instead of the Euclidean one, a stronger topology, one which makes the potentials continuous where they are well-defined, or, to be more precise, the weakest topology which makes the subharmonic functions continuous [14]. This so-called *fine topology* is included in a certain fine topology studied by Cartan on the class of nonnegative measures having potentials not everywhere infinite; for the subclass of those measures which reduce to the mass 1 at a point, this latter topology corresponds to our fine topology in Euclidean space, the only case we consider. It will be convenient to designate the corresponding topological notions by adding to the usual terms the words "fine" or "finely" or the index ϕ in formulas.

The complements of the *fine neighborhoods* of a point O are completely characterized as sets E, not containing O and such that there exists in the Euclidean neighborhood of O a subharmonic function whose value at O is greater than its upper limit at O on E. Such a set E, or E plus O, is called *thin at O*. Its section by a circumference or sphere whose center is at O subtends at O an angle tending to zero with the radius. It is this last property, much weaker than indicated in the definition, which led, after long study, precisely to the thin sets and later to the fine topology. It is easy to form examples of thin sets consisting of small circles or spheres converging to O but sufficiently sparse. In ordinary space, let us recall the famous example of Lebesgue, which differs only slightly from the following one: the spine of revolution around Ox, defined by the meridian region $|y| \leqq e^{-1/x}$ $(x > 0)$. In the plane there is nothing of this kind; it is always possible to describe around O curves (even circumferences) which are arbitrarily small and do not cut E (Lebesgue-Beurling; see Brelot [14a]). I must emphasize such a rare property, which differentiates the plane from spaces of higher dimension in potential theory, as does the behavior at infinity of log $(1/r)$ or r^{2-n}; however, I shall not take space here for a discussion of the criteria which characterize thin sets.

The concept of thin set is closely connected with that of *polar set*, which is also essential. A polar set may be defined as a set such that there exists locally a subharmonic function $\leqq 0$ and equal to $-\infty$ at least on the set (this is equivalent to the property of advanced potential theory that the set has outer capacity zero). It can also be characterized as a set which is thin at every point, or, even (as is equivalent), only at each of its points; that is to say, every point of the set is finely isolated. Furthermore, the finely isolated points of any set form a polar set. But these results (see Brelot [14b]) can be deduced only from an advanced potential theory—for instance, from the basic convergence theorem, whose definitive form, given by Cartan, reads as follows: For a family of subharmonic functions, uniformly bounded above, the upper envelope is quasi-subharmonic, that is to say, is equal to a subharmonic function except on a polar set.

For a function f defined on a set E we know the meaning of the notion of fine limit, called also pseudolimit, at a point O of the fine closure of E but not in E. If the value is λ, we may write

$$\lim_{\phi} \underset{M\to O, M\neq O, M\in E}{f} = \lambda.$$

It is easy to deduce, as Cartan observed (see Deny [17]), from a criterion of thinness that existence of such a limit signifies the existence of a fine neighborhood in which, inside E and outside O, f approaches λ in the ordinary Euclidean sense. If f is bounded and defined in a whole ordinary neighborhood of O, except at O, then its mean on a circumference or sphere whose center is O tends to λ when the radius tends to zero. However, the notion of fine limit is much more precise than such previously used notions founded upon means.

5. Let us return to our *Dirichlet problem*. On the boundary we shall distinguish the finely isolated points of the complement of Ω; they are called *irregular points*. These are the points at which the complement of Ω is thin; together they form a polar set. The other boundary points are called *regular*. Now with the aid of the main convergence theorem (a less powerful tool would be sufficient), it is easy to prove that, for any boundary point O, the solution H_{OM} (where OM is subharmonic) vanishes or does not vanish at O according to whether O is regular or not. As application, let us point out a local criterion of regularity which has served generally as a definition of regularity and whose importance will be indicated below: the criterion is the existence in a neighborhood of O, but only in Ω, of a superharmonic positive function vanishing at O; this implies existence of such a function, even of a harmonic function, whose greatest lower bound outside every neighborhood of O is > 0 (which is almost the same as the so-called barrier of Lebesgue).

Let f first be supposed to be finite and continuous on the boundary. Then H_f admits at every regular point P a limit (in the ordinary sense) equal to $f(P)$; it is known since the work of Kellogg and Evans (1933, an important date in the history of the Dirichlet problem) that H_f is the only harmonic bounded function which has the limit $f(P)$ at the regular points. This follows at once from the theorem that the set of irregular points is polar, either by a simple direct argument or because any polar set is of harmonic measure zero and because of the improved maximum principle.

As to *the behavior of* H_f *for any resolutive* f, a general and easily proved result is that the upper limit of H_f, or even of $\bar{H}_f$, at a regular point is not greater than the upper limit of f at P (and even the maximum in harmonic measure at P), provided that f is bounded above on the whole boundary; at the irregular points important results are partly contained in the following fundamental property (see [18]): For any superharmonic function $u > 0$ there is a fine limit at every irregular boundary point; moreover, $u/\log OM$ or $u \cdot OM^{n-2}$ has also a fine limit which is finite.

I cannot examine here the subtle theory of subharmonic functions at the boundary and its special ramifications concerning holomorphic functions, but I shall show, as an example, how *potential theory and the fine topology may improve the maximum principle* (see [19]): The previous condition lim sup $u \leqq 0$ for u bounded above and subharmonic may be understood in the sense of the fine topology, though only at the points of the fine boundary; moreover, the condition may be omitted at the points of a set of harmonic measure zero. Thus we see that the points of the ordinary boundary which are not on the fine boundary are neglected, but in fact they form a set of harmonic measure zero.

I shall complete this preliminary account by some words about the Green's function. A definition which will be convenient for later extensions is the following: $G_P(M)$ is the least positive superharmonic function in Ω whose associated masses contain the mass 1 at the pole P. The continuation by zero, with a suitable change at the irregular points, is subharmonic outside P; the associated masses which are entirely on the boundary define a measure which is precisely the harmonic measure at the pole. In other words, this measure at P is gotten by the sweeping out in Ω of the mass 1 at P. I must pass over this phase of potential theory, which provides further properties of the harmonic measure.

Finally, I wish to emphasize that the regular boundary points are those where G approaches zero. Therefore it is interesting to introduce the sets defined by $G < \epsilon$. They describe a basis of a filter. This filter, the *Green filter*, does not depend on the pole. As an application, let us consider f, finite and continuous on the boundary, and any finite continuous extension F in Ω; H_f is the only harmonic bounded function ϕ such that $\phi - F$ tends to zero according to the Green filter (that is to say, $\phi - F \to 0$ with G).

6. Now in all this study the definitions and difficulties have a chiefly local character and, moreover, in the plane the basic notions are invariant under conformal mapping. Therefore they may be considered on Riemann surfaces, where potential theory has recently been considerably investigated, chiefly by Finnish and Japanese mathematicians, as one may see in the thesis of Parreau [20]. In the three-dimensional case one may think first of locally Euclidean spaces, analogous to Riemann surfaces; Evans and a number of his pupils have recently made some endeavors in this direction [21].

It is always preferable in a theory to introduce particular hypotheses as late as possible. Consequently, in a recent paper published in collaboration with Choquet [13c], $\mathcal{E}$-spaces were introduced and characterized as follows:

(1) The space $\mathcal{E}$ is a connected Hausdorff space; (2) for every point P there is a homeomorphism of a neighborhood $\mathcal{V}_P$ on an open subset of a fixed Euclidean space R^n; (3) if $\mathcal{V}_P$ and $\mathcal{V}_Q$ intersect, the intersection has two images the correspondence between which is isometric or, in the two-dimensional case, conformal. We don't assume the correspondences to be orientation-preserving; thus, in addition to Riemann surfaces, there will be analogous nonorientable manifolds.

Moreover, let us recall that a detailed study (not trivial for $n \geqq 3$) has been developed of the concepts of harmonic functions, subharmonic functions, and so on, in the neighborhood of the point at infinity of R^n, with suitable definitions and the same form for the essential properties (see [13b]). We therefore add this point at infinity and consider the new compact space $\bar{R}^n$. For a domain of this space having a nonpolar complement, the theory of the Dirichlet problem remains valid in the same general terms, without consideration of the special position of the point at infinity. However, for $n \geqq 3$, this point has special properties; with a suitably extended terminology, it forms a set which is nonpolar, always regular on a boundary, and with a harmonic measure which can be positive.

We shall now understand our definition of $\mathcal{E}$-space to permit the homeomorphism of $\mathcal{V}_P$ to be on an open subset of the compact space $\bar{R}^n$. Thus there may be points at infinity in our space with isometric structure; they are countable. They may and will be avoided in the two-dimensional space of conformal structure.

Our general space $\mathcal{E}$, which is of course locally compact, is metrizable and has, therefore, a countable base and is a countable union of compact sets; in the case of conformal structure, it is possible to choose a metric generated by a ds^2, which on the local image is the Euclidean ds^2 up to a factor of class C^∞.

7. Following various authors who have recently studied the *Dirichlet problem* on Riemann surfaces, let us outline *an extension in our $\mathcal{E}$-space.* We take first a relatively compact domain (having a nonpolar complement if $\mathcal{E}$ is compact). We introduce $\underline{H}_f$ and $\bar{H}_f$ in the same way as before. But in order to prove their equality when f is finite and continuous on the boundary, we cannot easily achieve an approximation by a difference of two subharmonic functions; it is simpler to see that $\underline{H}_f$ and $\bar{H}_f$ tend to $f(P)$ at the regular points and to prove the equality with the aid of the following maximum principle, which is a consequence of previous local studies:

If u is bounded above and subharmonic and has an upper limit $\leqq 0$ at every regular boundary point, then $u \leqq 0$.

The theory then proceeds as indicated above to obtain the harmonic measure and the resolutivity theorem.

Let us now take any subdomain Ω of $\mathcal{E}$. First we add to $\mathcal{E}$, if it is not compact, an Alexandroff point $\mathcal{A}$; thus we have always a compact space $\mathcal{E}'$, which is, moreover, metrizable, and we adopt its topology until we fix another convention. Therefore the boundary of Ω will be compact and $\mathcal{A}$ may be a boundary point. But any research would be trivial if every subharmonic function bounded above were constant. It is a theorem (published by Ohtsuka for the case of Riemann surfaces) that *the existence of a positive nonconstant superharmonic function is equivalent to the existence of a minimal positive superharmonic function with associated masses reducing to the mass* 1 *in a given point;* that is to say, to the existence of the Green's function. Consequently, we shall term *Green space* any $\mathcal{E}$-space having a Green's function. A subdomain Ω of $\mathcal{E}$ is a Green space (and will be called a Green subdomain) only if $\mathcal{E}$ is a Green space or if the complement of Ω is nonpolar. It would be interesting to know criteria for establishing that an $\mathcal{E}$-space be a Green space.

Now our theory of the Dirichlet problem may be developed for *any Green subdomain* of a given $\mathcal{E}$. There is some difficulty in proving that a finite continuous f is resolutive, because of the Alexandroff point $\mathcal{A}$; the difficulty may be overcome by use of a relatively compact approximating domain. Beyond this, there is no change in the method of obtaining the general resolutivity theorem. Of course the results depend, for a given Ω, on the containing $\mathcal{E}$-space, but actually they depend only on the closure $\bar{\Omega}$ in such a space. As to the study of H_f near the boundary, it is, for the neighborhood of any point different from $\mathcal{A}$, included in the previous local studies; in fact, if we call F the boundary function f and its continuation by H_f^{Ω}, and if ω is a subdomain of Ω, the solution H_F (understood for this ω in $\mathcal{E}$) is equal to H_f^{Ω} in ω. But *the point* $\mathcal{A}$ *is quite different* from the other boundary points, and it may form the whole boundary. To take this into account one must change tools in the study of the boundary. It is convenient to introduce the sequences of points on which $G \to 0$ (called regular sequences) and, more generally, to introduce regular filters: that is to say, filters finer than the Green filter (defined as indicated above, by the sets $G < \epsilon$). Then for such a regular filter which converges toward a point Q (for instance $\mathcal{A}$) and for any f bounded above, the upper limit of $\bar{H}_f$ according to this filter is not greater than the upper limit of f at Q. We have also the same characterization of H_f as before, for f finite and continuous, using a continuation of f and the Green filter.

Furthermore, *the point* $\mathcal{A}$ *enables us to speak in simple terms.* Let us take in the space $\mathcal{E}$ a nonpolar compact set K, with a connected complement. In order that $\mathcal{E}$ be a Green space, it is necessary and sufficient that it be not compact and that the harmonic measure of $\mathcal{A}$ be > 0 relative to the subdomain $\mathcal{E} - K$. Let us notice that these last conditions express, for a Riemann surface, the definition of the hyperbolic case or the case of positive boundary in the sense of Nevanlinna. And the theorem expresses, for Riemann surfaces, the Myrberg criterion for existence of a Green's function.

8. In order to extend the previous Dirichlet problem (which will be called the ordinary Dirichlet problem), we are led to decompose the point $\mathcal{A}$ as has been done in various ways for open Riemann surfaces. Moreover, the earlier theory is obviously insufficient in comparison with that obtained by conformal mapping of a simply connected domain and subsequent use of the Poisson integral. About 1935–1937 Perkins and then de la Vallée Poussin distinguished at every accessible boundary point of a Euclidean domain various paths of approach, grouped in equivalence classes, and they dealt with a Dirichlet problem for given values on these classes, values continuous in a certain sense; de la Vallée Poussin emphasized, as a key lemma, that the nonaccessible points form a set of harmonic measure zero, and therefore it is not surprising that they disappear. Later general topology led to simplifications and interpreted the equivalence classes as real points of a new boundary; a corresponding Dirichlet problem, called the ramified problem, was developed as far as the previous one and brought, in the particular case of a simply connected domain, precisely the same results as conformal mapping and the Poisson integral.

An accurate analysis of this research and of later improvements has led to a very simple axiomatic theory (see [13c]), which may be summarized thus:

Let us take a Green space $\mathcal{E}$, forget the Alexandroff point $\mathcal{A}$, but consider in $\mathcal{E}$ a distance compatible with the topology. We complete $\mathcal{E}$ and get a space $\hat{\mathcal{E}}$ formed of $\mathcal{E}$ and a boundary $\overset{*}{\mathcal{E}}$. We shall assume as essential the existence in $\mathcal{E}$ of a set of filters $\mathfrak{F}$ converging in $\hat{\mathcal{E}}$ toward boundary points and satisfying two fundamental conditions. These filters may be generated by the traces on $\mathcal{E}$ of the neighborhoods of some boundary points; they may be the filters associated with some sequences of points, or separately formed from a filter basis the elements of which are the terminal arcs of a Jordan arc end-ing at a boundary point. We assume the following conditions to be satisfied:

CONDITION A (condition in the large, or maximum principle). If a subharmonic u is bounded above and has an upper limit $\leqq 0$ according to every filter $\mathfrak{F}$, then $u \leqq 0$.

CONDITION B (local condition, generalizing the barrier of Lebesgue). For every filter $\mathfrak{F}$ there exists a neighborhood $\mathcal{W}$ of the limit point Q and a superharmonic positive function v on $\mathcal{W} \cap \mathcal{E}$ such that v tends to zero according to $\mathfrak{F}$ and such that its greatest lower bound is > 0 outside any neighborhood of Q.

This is sufficient for developing the Dirichlet problem nearly as before. With the conditions at the boundary, understood in the topology of $\hat{\mathcal{E}}$, we introduce the envelopes $\underline{\mathcal{H}}_f$, $\overline{\mathcal{H}}_f$, which are as before $+\infty$, $-\infty$, or harmonic; the maximum principle (A) gives $\underline{\mathcal{H}}_f \leqq \overline{\mathcal{H}}_f$. Then, because of condition (B),

$$\limsup_{\mathfrak{F}} \overline{\mathcal{H}}_f \leqq \text{lim sup of } f \text{ at } Q.$$

Because of (A), we get the equality $\underline{\mathcal{H}}_f = \overline{\mathcal{H}}_f$ for f bounded and continuous. The common value or solution $\mathcal{H}_f$ is the unique harmonic bounded function which has the limit $f(Q)$ at every boundary point Q, according to every filter $\mathfrak{F}$ converging to Q. It is also the limit of $H_\Phi^{\Omega_n}$, where Φ is a bounded continuous continuation of f in $\mathcal{E}$ and where Ω_n is a domain relatively compact in $\mathcal{E}$ and increasing to $\mathcal{E}$ as $n \to \infty$.

Our $\mathcal{H}_f$ is at every point M a linear increasing functional of the bounded continuous function f. But the boundary is not generally locally compact and $\mathcal{H}_f$ does not therefore define a Radon measure. However, the class of continuous bounded f and this functional $\mathcal{H}_f(M)$ provide the definition of a Daniell integral because, if f_n decreases to zero, $\mathcal{H}_{f_n} \to 0$. The corresponding measure is the *generalized harmonic measure* relative to $\hat{\mathcal{E}}$. Afterwards we get, just as before, the resolutivity theorem which reads: $\underline{\mathcal{H}}_f$ is equal to $\overline{\mathcal{H}}_f$ and is finite, if and only if f is summable. We write the common value as $\mathcal{H}_f = \int f \, d\mu^M$.

Let us emphasize that, for a boundary set e of characteristic function ϕ_e, the condition that the harmonic measure be zero is equivalent to $\overline{\mathcal{H}}_{\phi_e} = 0$ and to the existence of a superharmonic positive function tending to $+\infty$ at the points of e; a change of f on such a set does not change $\underline{\mathcal{H}}_f$ and $\overline{\mathcal{H}}_f$.

We remark that the filters $\mathfrak{F}$ are only auxiliary tools; the results depend only on the metric chosen and, even, only on the corresponding uniform structure.

Let us notice also that, if we suppress a boundary set of harmonic measure zero, the filters which do not converge toward points of this set satisfy both fundamental conditions. The reduced boundary may be used for developing a similar theory; the corresponding new harmonic measure is equal to the old one on the reduced boundary.

We shall now *compare the results for two different metrics in a given Green space* $\mathcal{E}$. We assume that the uniform structure of one, which gives a complete space $\mathcal{E}_1$, is weaker than the structure of the other, which gives a complete space $\mathcal{E}_2$. Then the neighborhoods in $\mathcal{E}_2$ of a point Q of $\mathcal{E}_2 - \mathcal{E}$ determine on $\mathcal{E}$ a filter which converges in $\mathcal{E}_1$ toward a point $\underset{*}{Q}$ of $\mathcal{E}_1 - \mathcal{E}$ called support of Q. The mapping $Q \to \underset{*}{Q}$ is continuous. One can then assert:

(1) The points of $\mathcal{E}_1 - \mathcal{E}$ which are not supports form a set of harmonic measure zero.

(2) Let f_1 be a function on $\mathcal{E}_1 - \mathcal{E}$; let us take on $\mathcal{E}_2 - \mathcal{E}$ a function which is at each point Q equal to the value of f_1 at the support of Q. Then the envelope $\underline{\mathcal{H}}_{f_1}$ with the first topology is equal to the envelope $\underline{\mathcal{H}}_{f_2}$ with the second one. Consequently, if a set e of $\mathcal{E}_1 - \mathcal{E}$ admits a harmonic measure, its inverse image on $\mathcal{E}_2 - \mathcal{E}$ admits relative to $\mathcal{E}_2$ a harmonic measure equal to the first one.

9. Although this theory is simple, technical difficulties appear in the applications in proving that the axiomatic conditions are satisfied. We shall disregard these difficulties in the *following examples:*

(i) Let Ω be a Green subdomain of the $\mathcal{E}$-space. Let us consider for Ω the *ordinary Dirichlet problem,* using the metrizable space $\mathcal{E}'$, which is $\mathcal{E}$ if $\mathcal{E}$ is compact and is otherwise $\mathcal{E} \cup \{\mathcal{A}\}$, where $\mathcal{A}$ is the Alexandroff point of $\mathcal{E}$.

Let us take in Ω a metric compatible with the uniform structure of $\mathcal{E}'$ and take as filters $\mathfrak{F}$ the elementary filters associated with the regular sequences of points; the axiomatic conditions are satisfied and the corresponding Dirichlet problem is precisely the ordinary one, which is thus included in the general scheme.

(ii) Now let us introduce a stronger uniform structure on Ω; it will be unnecessary here that the subdomain Ω of the $\mathcal{E}$-space be a Green subdomain. We define, from the metric chosen in the previous $\mathcal{E}'$, the following Mazurkiewicz metric: the new distance between two points of Ω is the greatest lower bound of the diameters of the Jordan arcs which join these points in Ω. The corresponding *uniform structure*, called *ramified*, is compatible with the topology of Ω and results directly from the unique uniform structure of the compact space $\mathcal{E}'$. By completion we get the ramified boundary. Its points are in one-to-one correspondence with certain equivalence classes of Jordan arcs converging in $\mathcal{E}'$ to points of the ordinary boundary. If we compare the two boundaries, we see that the supports of the ramified boundary points are the accessible points of the ordinary boundary.

Let us observe that, for the particular case in which Ω is the whole noncompact $\mathcal{E}$-space, the point $\mathcal{A}$ is replaced by a ramified boundary which is compact; when $\mathcal{E}$ is an open Riemann surface, it is precisely the ideal boundary of Kerékjártó-Stoïlow.

We come now to the generalized Dirichlet problem for a Green subdomain Ω of $\mathcal{E}$.

The ramified structure satisfies the axiomatic conditions and leads to a *ramified harmonic measure* which we may therefore compare with the ordinary one. This implies that the nonaccessible points of the ordinary boundary form a set of harmonic measure zero; this can be proved without the ramified theory.

I wish to emphasize a *particular case*. Let us take for $\mathcal{E}$ the complex plane and for Ω a simply connected Green subdomain which a classical transformation T maps onto the unit circular domain D. The ramified structure of Ω is stronger than the uniform structure S which provides the prime ends (we call it "the prime end structure") and which, as we know, corresponds under T to the Euclidean structure of D. If we compare the ramified structure with S, we see that the ramified boundary points have as supports certain prime ends; moreover, this correspondence is one-to-one. These supports are said to be prime ends possessing a ramified or accessible point; the other prime ends form a set whose image on the circumference (after continuation of T) has a length zero. Let f be a function on the prime ends; let us use the same notation for the corresponding functions on the circumference and on the ramified boundary. We may pose a Dirichlet problem with the topology and the boundary of the prime ends; the envelopes we get are of course equal, at the corresponding point, to the $\underline{H}_f$, $\bar{H}_f$ of the circle; these latter can be proved to be equal to the envelopes $\underline{\mathcal{H}}_f$, $\overline{\mathcal{H}}_f$ of the ramified problem. Thus conformal mapping followed by use of the Poisson integral gives precisely the ramified theory; the classical *conformal measure* of a set of prime ends, which is the corresponding measure on the circumference, is, within a factor 2π, nothing other than the ramified harmonic measure of the corresponding ramified set at the inverse image of the center.

(iii) Let us go a little further, with a still stronger uniform structure on Ω, but assuming that Ω is a bounded subdomain of R^n or, more generally, a Green subdomain, relatively compact in an $\mathcal{E}$-space without point at infinity. From the local Euclidean ds^2 or from the ds^2 chosen as in the case of the conformal structure, we shall take as distance between two points the greatest lower bound of the lengths of the arcs joining these points. With this *metric*, called *geodesic*, we can verify the axiomatic conditions, develop a so-called *geodesic problem* and compare the geodesic harmonic measure with the previous ones. The points of the ordinary or ramified boundary which are not accessible by a path of finite length form a set of corresponding harmonic measure zero. Examples prove the successive theories to be refinements. However, in the particular case of a bounded simply connected domain, the ramified points are not decomposed by the geodesic structure; that is, those which are accessible by a path of finite length are in one-to-one correspondence with the geodesic boundary points. Thus the geodesic measure is in this case the same as the ramified one.

Furthermore, as a consequence of the work of Beurling and Dufresnoy, the prime ends which are not "supports" of geodesic boundary points form a set the circular image of which has capacity zero; I shall return to this in the following lecture.

10. I have not given here any proof of the axiomatic conditions or any indication of the choice of filters in the two new problems. It is convenient to use to this end the Green lines: that is, the orthogonal trajectories of the surfaces or curves G = const, or the orthogonal trajectories of analogous level surfaces. In addition, by means of these lines, limit conditions may obviously be expressed as boundary conditions without a boundary, and in a more refined way than that described above; the measure on the set of these lines, defined as the flux of a bundle, is in close relation to the previous harmonic measures and will appear as a more powerful tool, which provides improvements in many applications—in particular, those on holomorphic functions mentioned at the beginning of this lecture. Another analogous tool is provided by the Martin extension of the Poisson-Stieltjes integral. These new tools, which are natural continuations of the harmonic measure, require much development, raise many unsolved questions, and seem rich in hope and consequences. Their study is the subject of the lecture that follows.

BIBLIOGRAPHICAL NOTES

(The following notes, referred to in the text by numbers in brackets, supplement the text and provide bibliographical references.)

1. For a historical account of this question, see:

Brelot, M. *Über die Singularitäten der Potentialfunktionen und der Integrale der Differentialgleichungen vom elliptischen Typus*, Berlin Math. Ges. Sitzungsber. 31 (1932), 46–54.

2. Perron, O. *Eine neue Behandlung der ersten Randwertaufgabe für* $\Delta u = 0$, Math. Zeit. 18 (1923), 42–54.

3. Wiener, N. (a) *Certain notions in potential theory*, J. Math. Phys. 3 (1924), 24–51.

—— (b) *The Dirichlet problem*, J. Math. Phys. 3 (1924), 127–146.

—— (c) *Note on a paper of O. Perron*, J. Math. Phys. 4 (1925), 21–32.

4. Riesz, F. *Über subharmonische Funktionen und ihre Rolle in der Funktionentheorie und in der Potentialtheorie*, Acta Univ. Szeged 2 (1925), 87–100.

5. Riesz, F. *Sur les fonctions subharmoniques et leur rapport à la théorie du potentiel*, Acta Math. 48 (1926), 329–343, and 54 (1930), 321–360.

6. Brelot, M. (a) *Étude des fonctions sousharmoniques au voisinage d'un point*. Actualités Scientifiques et Industrielles, No. 134. Paris, 1934.

Radó, T. *Subharmonic functions*. Ergebnisse der Mathematik, Bd. 5, Heft 1. Berlin, 1937.

Privaloff, J. *Subharmonic functions*. (In Russian.) Moscow, 1937.

For more recent accounts and proofs of some fundamental properties of subharmonic functions, see:

BRELOT, M. (b) *Fonctions sousharmoniques, presque sousharmoniques ou sousmédianes*, Ann. Univ. Grenoble Sec. Sci. Math. Phys. 21 (1945), 75–90.

SCHWARTZ, L. *Théorie des distributions*, vol. II. Actualités Scientifiques et Industrielles, No. 1122. Paris, 1951.

Besides this notion of subharmonic function, essential for the theory of functions of one complex variable, see for a related notion, similarly useful for functions of several complex variables, the following:

LELONG, P. *Les fonctions plurisousharmoniques*, Ann. École Norm. 62 (1945), 301–308.

7. Concerning old research and bibliography on potential theory, see:

KELLOGG, O. D. *Foundations of potential theory*. Berlin, 1929.

FROSTMAN, O. *Potentiel d'équilibre et capacité des ensembles*, Meddel. Lunds Univ. Mat. Sem. 3 (1935), 1–115.

VASILESCO, F. *La notion de capacité*. Actualités Scientifiques et Industrielles, No. 571. Paris, 1937.

EVANS, G. C. *Modern methods of analysis in potential theory*, Bull. Amer. Math. Soc. 43 (1937), 481–502.

DE LA VALLÉE POUSSIN, C. J. (a) *Les nouvelles méthodes de la théorie du potentiel et le problème généralisé de Dirichlet*. Actualités Scientifiques et Industrielles, No. 578. Paris, 1939.

—— (b) *Le potentiel logarithmique, balayage et représentation conforme*. Paris, 1949.

I shall mention in the notes below only a few recent fundamental papers, useful here, among all the works on the basis of which a new account of the theory would now have to be written.

8. For old applications, see the books of Privaloff [6], Frostman [7], and the following:

NEVANLINNA, R. *Eindeutige analytische Funktionen*. Berlin, 1936.

Characteristic examples, with some bibliography, can be found in the following:

BRELOT, M. (a) *Quelques applications aux fonctions holomorphes de la théorie du potentiel et du problème de Dirichlet*, Bull. Soc. Roy. Sci. Liége 1939 (1939), 385–391.

—— (b) *Sur l'approximation et la convergence dans la théorie des fonctions harmoniques ou holomorphes*, Bull. Soc. Math. France 73 (1945), 55–70. (Contains some theory and bibliography concerning a Dirichlet problem for compact sets.)

Among the many recent works are a book, now in press, by J. Lelong-Ferrand, on conformal mapping, and a study by Parreau [20] about Riemann surfaces.

For applications to functions of several complex variables, see first:

LELONG, P. *Sur quelques problèmes de la théorie des fonctions de deux variables complexes*, Ann. École Norm. 58 (1941), 83–177.

9. The importance of this concept in that theory, even twenty years ago, is to be seen in the book of Nevanlinna cited in [8].

10. LAVRENTIEFF, M. A. *Sur les fonctions d'une variable complexe représentables par des séries de polynomes*. Actualités Scientifiques et Industrielles, No. 441. Paris, 1936.

11. See Brelot [8b]. The proofs are the same for generalized harmonic measures.

12. For old history and bibliography, see the book by Kellogg cited in [7] and the following:

BOULIGAND, G. *Fonctions harmoniques—Principes de Picard et de Dirichlet*. Mémorial des Sciences Mathématiques, No. 11. Paris, 1926.

KELLOGG, O. D. *Recent progress with the Dirichlet problem*, Bull. Amer. Math. Soc. 32 (1926), 601–625.

EVANS, G. C. *The logarithmic potential, discontinuous Dirichlet and Neumann problems*. Amer. Math. Soc. Colloquium Publications, No. 6. New York, 1927.

BRELOT, M. *Le problème de Dirichlet sous sa forme moderne*, Mathematica 7 (1933), 147–166.

VASILESCO, F. (a) *Le problème généralisé de Dirichlet*, Acad. Roy. Belgique Cl. Sci. Mem. 16 (1937), 1–55.

—— (b) *La notion de point irrégulier dans le problème de Dirichlet*. Actualités Scientifiques et Industrielles, No. 660. Paris, 1938.

More recent papers are mentioned in the note below.

13. The method outlined here is taken from the following:

BRELOT, M. (a) *Familles de Perron et problème de Dirichlet*, Acta Univ. Szeged 9 (1939), 133–153.

—— (b) *Sur le rôle du point à l'infini dans la théorie des fonctions harmoniques*, Ann. École Norm. 61 (1944), 301–332.

—— AND CHOQUET, G. (c) *Espaces et lignes de Green*, Ann. Inst. Fourier Grenoble 3 (1951), 199–263.

14. Concerning thin sets and fine topology, see the following:

BRELOT, M. (a) *Points irréguliers et transformations continues en théorie du potentiel*, J. Math. Pures Appl. (9) 19 (1940), 319–337.

—— (b) *Sur les ensembles effilés*, Bull. Sci. Math. 68 (1944), 12–36.

CARTAN, H. *Théorie générale du balayage en potentiel newtonien*, Ann. Univ. Grenoble Sec. Sci. Math. Phys. 22 (1946), 221–280.

15. BRELOT, M. *Sur la théorie autonome des fonctions sousharmoniques*, Bull. Sci. Math. 65 (1941), 72–98.

16. CARTAN, H. *Théorie du potentiel newtonien, énergie, capacité, suites de potentiels*, Bull. Soc. Math. France 73 (1945), 74–106.

17. DENY, J. *Les potentiels d'énergie finie*, Acta Math. 82 (1950), 107–183.

18. BRELOT, M. *Étude générale des fonctions harmoniques ou surharmoniques positives au voisinage d'un point frontière irrégulier*, Ann. Univ. Grenoble Sec. Sci. Math. Phys. 22 (1946), 205–219.

19. BRELOT, M. (a) *Sur l'allure des fonctions harmoniques et sousharmoniques à la frontière*, Math. Nachr. 4 (1950–1951), 298–307.

Concerning special properties of holomorphic functions, see results and bibliography in:

BRELOT, M. (b) *Le problème de Dirichlet ramifié*, Ann. Univ. Grenoble Sec. Sci. Math. Phys. 22 (1946), 167–200.

20. PARREAU, M. *Sur les moyennes des fonctions harmoniques et analytiques et la classification des surfaces de Riemann*, Ann. Inst. Fourier Grenoble 3 (1951), 103–197.

21. EVANS, G. C. *Lectures on multiple-valued harmonic functions in space*, Univ. California Publ. Math. 1 (1951), 281–340.

UNIVERSITY OF GRENOBLE

TOPOLOGY OF R. S. MARTIN AND GREEN LINES

MARCEL BRELOT

1. Harmonic functions in the circle or sphere and the Poisson integral have been studied intensively for a long time, as one can see in the book by G. C. Evans on the logarithmic potential (1927) [1]. Of course, because of their relation to conformal mapping, they are extremely useful for problems in the plane, problems about functions of a complex variable, and, in particular, problems of hydrodynamics. But the method of mapping evades the difficulties instead of really resolving them, is ineffective in the case of infinite connectivity, and gives few ideas for extensions to space. It was therefore necessary to try to extend the theory of the circle directly to general domains. We have seen that the Dirichlet problem has been developed very far. But this is not true of two other matters which I shall discuss here—and I shall perhaps have more questions to ask than fundamental theorems to state.

Although we know little about the most general harmonic functions in the circle, we do know that the differences of two positive harmonic functions are the functions given by the Poisson-Stieltjes integral. In order to extend this powerful theorem, R. S. Martin [2] twelve years ago introduced, for a general Euclidean domain, a well-suited ideal boundary in a new topology, and an integral with a kernel which replaces the Poisson-Stieltjes integral. Martin, however, died shortly afterwards, and this fundamental work has not inspired much research until now, in spite of its promise. Moreover, all the properties of radial limits of harmonic and subharmonic functions in the circle can be transformed to a simply connected domain, as is done in the book by Evans; under a conformal mapping, the concentric circles become lines $G =$ const and the radii become the orthogonal trajectories. It was therefore natural to study such trajectories, called Green lines, directly in the general case, even in space; essential properties have been given by Choquet and myself in a recent paper [3]. The first applications [3], [11] leave hope for many others and for a systematic adaptation of the radial properties. Furthermore, as both these notions, the Martin topology and the Green lines, are purely harmonic ones, in contrast to previously suggested topologies, they probably have close relations which would be the key to a larger and fairly definitive theory.

2. We shall take at once, as a domain in which harmonic functions are studied, a Green space. A Green space may be defined as a connected Hausdorff space with the following properties: there exists a homeomorphism of an open neighborhood of every point onto an open set of the Euclidean space R^n (or even $\bar{R}^n$, compactified by a point at infinity); the images of the intersection of two such neighborhoods are in isometric correspondence or, in the two-dimensional case, in conformal correspondence; a Green's function exists.

The theory by Martin that I shall outline was first developed in Euclidean space, but is valid in our Green space after extension of certain notions of potential theory, as Parreau [4] observed for Riemann surfaces. We start as does Martin with the following remark:

Let us consider a Green space Ω with its Alexandroff point, and inside Ω a harmonic or superharmonic positive function u. It is the limit of an increasing sequence of Green potentials, as follows. Let us introduce a compact set α_n increasing with n and tending to Ω. Let us solve the Dirichlet problem for the domains of $\Omega - \alpha_n$ with boundary values equal to u on the boundary $\overset{*}{\alpha}_n$ of α_n and equal to 0 at the Alexandroff point of Ω. We get in $\Omega - \alpha_n$ a function v_n; the continuation of u in α_n by v_n is quasi-superharmonic: that is to say, becomes a superharmonic function U_n when values are appropriately changed on a polar set of $\overset{*}{\alpha}_n$. Moreover, U_n is exactly a Green potential: $U_n(P) = \int G(M, P)\, dm^{(n)}$.

These masses $m^{(n)}$ are $\geqq 0$ and lie only on $\overset{*}{\alpha}_n$ if u is harmonic. Let us study this case further, and start from the formula:

$$u(P) = \int G(M, P)\, dm^{(n)}$$

valid for P interior to α_n.

Let us choose a fixed point P_0 and introduce $K(M, P) = G(M, P)/G(M, P_0)$ and the masses $d\mu^{(n)} = G(M, P_0)\, dm^{(n)}$, the sum of which is $u(P_0)$ (for n great enough). Then

$$u(P) = \int K(M, P)\, d\mu_M^{(n)}.$$

For every point P we should be able to choose a subsequence for which we can pass to the limit under the integral sign, if the function $K(M, P)$ of M (which is bounded outside neighborhoods of P and P_0) were defined continuously in a larger compact space, that is to say in Ω and a suitable compact boundary. There would be in the neighborhood of this boundary a uniform structure for which K would be uniformly continuous. Therefore let us introduce in Ω two compact sets: σ_0 containing P_0 and σ whose interior contains σ_0. We shall choose the weakest uniform structure on $\Omega - \sigma$ for which all the K corresponding to the P in σ_0 are uniformly continuous in the ordinary sense as functions of M in $\Omega - \sigma$. This structure admits a metric—for instance, that defined by the distance $\sup_{P\in\sigma_0} | K(M_1, P) - K(M_2, P) |$.

This structure or metric can be continued in Ω, in compatibility with the topology of Ω. We complete the space and get a space $\hat{\Omega}$ or Martin space, formed by Ω and a boundary Δ called Martin boundary. The sets $\hat{\Omega}$, Δ are compact and independent of P_0, σ_0, σ. The function $K(M, P)$ becomes defined for M in Δ as a harmonic limit of $K(M, P)$ for M in Ω. There is a one-to-one correspondence between the Martin space and all the $K(M, P)$ functions of P. We have realized what we wanted, and our harmonic function u has a representation $\int K(M, P)\, d\mu_M$, where μ_M is a Radon measure on Δ.

It is much more difficult to define a subset Δ_0 of Δ such that there is for every harmonic positive u a unique measure μ with $\mu(\Delta - \Delta_0) = 0$, called the measure associated with u. To this end, Martin introduces the so-called *minimal harmonic functions;* they are the harmonic positive functions u such that every harmonic positive function which is smaller than u is proportional to u. Martin proves that every minimal function equal to 1 at P_0 is a $K(M, P)$ (M in Δ). The set of these points M, called minimal points, is the desired subset Δ_0. It is a countable intersection of open sets, which can in fact be different from Δ.

Let us observe that among the harmonic positive functions h equal to 1 at P_0, the minimal functions are equivalently defined by the condition that they cannot be expressed as a sum of the form $\alpha h_1 + \beta h_2$ $(\alpha > 0, \beta > 0, \alpha + \beta = 1, h_1 \neq h_2)$; that is to say, they are the extremal points of the set of these h functions. Similarly, the $K(M, P)$ functions for M in Ω are the extremal points of the set of the Green potentials of positive masses, equal to 1 at P_0. From this some interesting remarks can be deduced for our problem, but the theory of the extremal points in vector spaces is not developed enough—and thus offers a subject for research—to provide the whole theorem of Martin as a particular case.

3. Too little is known about the Martin topology and the minimal functions. Therefore, *particular cases* are to be emphasized:

(i) In the case of a *domain with sufficiently regular boundary* in the Euclidean space R^n, previously studied by de la Vallée Poussin [5], the Martin uniform structure is the Euclidean one; and the $K(M, P)$ are all minimal and proportional to

$$\frac{dG(M, P)}{dn_M} \bigg/ \frac{dG(M, P_0)}{dn_M};$$

in the circle or sphere we get again the Poisson kernel. But even for the simple domain between two internally tangent spheres, the point of tangency, as Bouligand remarked, is decomposed, and provides an infinity of limits for $G(M, P)/G(M, P_0)$. With an infinite connectivity, even in the plane, examples show that the Martin structure is not comparable with the Euclidean one or the ramified or geodesic ones; not only can it decompose a ramified point, but it can also merge two distinct ones [6].

(ii) If Ω is a *simply connected domain of the plane*, the Martin structure is that of the prime ends; we could make certain extensions of this to relatively compact domains in an $\mathcal{E}$-space or to finitely connected plane domains.

(iii) Let us consider the uniform structure of the compact space $\Omega \cup \{\mathfrak{A}\}$ ($\mathfrak{A}$ being the Alexandroff point of Ω) and the corresponding ramified structure. Then the Martin structure is stronger than the ramified one; therefore every Martin boundary point has a ramified support; the Martin points which have the same support form a connected closed set. Thus the ramified boundary points (which for Riemann surfaces are, as we know, the *ideal points of Kerékjártó-*

Stoïlow) are in one-to-one correspondence with the *connected components of the Martin boundary* (partly according to Parreau [4]).

4. Now, with the Martin topology and boundary, one could pose a *Dirichlet problem;* for a simply connected plane domain it is precisely the problem with the prime-ends topology, equivalent, as we know, to the ramified problem; but in general this has still to be developed.[1] Let us introduce at least the measure ν_0 on Δ_0 associated to the constant 1, called *Martin measure*, which for a simply connected plane domain is equivalent to the conformal or ramified measure and which could, perhaps, be in general just as useful as the harmonic measure.

Let us consider $\int K(M, P)\, f(M)\, d\nu_0(M)$, where f is ν_0-summable.

How could this generalization of the Poisson integral be interpreted as a solution of some Dirichlet problem? Let us observe at any rate, with Parreau [4], that this integral for $f \geqq 0$ represents all the harmonic functions that are limits of increasing sequences of positive harmonic bounded functions. Furthermore, every harmonic positive function u is the sum of a v of this kind and of another harmonic positive function w (called singular) for which inf $(1, w)$ is a Green potential; this seems to be new even in the case of the circle.

5. Although we know little about the minimal functions—for instance, we do not know whether they are necessarily unbounded for a bounded Euclidean domain—we can provide a characterization which gives the real form of the so-called *principle of positive singularities* [7].

Let us consider our Green space Ω to be imbedded in a larger space Ω_1 and let us say for a harmonic function u that it is associated to zero at a boundary point Q if the following condition is satisfied: there exists an open neighborhood ω of Q in Ω_1 such that in every open component δ of $\omega \cap \Omega_1$, u is equal to H_ϕ^{δ}, where ϕ is equal to u in Ω and equal to 0 at the Alexandroff point of Ω, and H_ϕ^{δ} is the solution of the ordinary Dirichlet problem in subdomains of Ω. We ask whether there are harmonic positive functions associated to zero at every point of the boundary except *one*, Q_0. If there exist such functions

[1] Since this lecture, a Martin-Dirichlet problem has been posed, solved, and generalized, as indicated in a note by the author: "Le problème de Dirichlet avec la frontière de Martin," *C. R. Acad. Sci. Paris* 240 (1955), 142–144.

and if they are proportional, it is said that the principle of positive singularities is true at Q_0. This principle, well formulated and investigated by Bouligand in Euclidean space, is not true in general with the Euclidean topology or the ramified or geodesic one that we have studied. But with the Martin topology there exist required functions only if Q_0 is minimal, and these functions are proportional to $K(Q_0, P)$. Moreover, this minimal function $K(Q_0, P)$ is equal to H_ϕ^ω for *every* subdomain ω of which Q_0 is not a point of closure in the Martin space and for ϕ equal to this K in Ω and to zero at the Alexandroff point of Ω.

6. As a second application of the Martin theory I shall examine *certain extensions of the existence and uniqueness theorems of Cauchy.*

Let us consider a harmonic function u in a Euclidean domain ω and suppose that u vanishes on a part γ of the boundary, which we suppose only to be sufficiently smooth (for instance, with continuous curvatures). It is known that the derivatives of u possess limits on γ. If $du/dn = 0$, it is easy to see that the continuation of u by 0 is harmonic. Therefore, $u = 0$ and we have concluded without analytic hypothesis a classical Cauchy theorem on uniqueness. Let us notice that the Green's function G of ω has a normal derivative $dG/dn > 0$ on γ; thus the hypothesis $du/dn = 0$ on γ may be replaced by $u/G \to 0$. This may be done without γ being smooth; in a precise way, let us consider u harmonic in a domain ω and a point Q_0 on the boundary of the exterior of ω. If in a neighborhood of Q_0 u is bounded and if $u/G \to 0$, then $u = 0$ [8]. This uniqueness theorem can be improved; but it has been established in the Euclidean space by use of potential theory and of masses on the boundary. Other methods are necessary to get extensions in any Green space Ω. In this general case, let us consider a subdomain ω, the complement of which is compact, and a harmonic function u in ω which is the solution of an ordinary Dirichlet problem for bounded boundary values equal to zero at the Alexandroff point of Ω. It is easy to see that u is equal, outside a compact set β, to a Green potential

$$\int G(M, P)\, dm(P),$$

where the masses m are on β. Then

$$u(M)/G(M, P_0) \to \int K(M_0, P)\, dm(P)$$

when the point M tends to a point M_0 which is on the Martin boundary. This limit will be called the slope of u at M_0. Will u be zero if the slope is equal to zero everywhere or at least at the minimal points? This is so if Ω is relatively compact in an $\mathcal{E}$-space with $\mathcal{E} - \bar{\Omega}$ not empty, by the same argument as in a Euclidean domain [6]. It would be interesting to get a better result and to reduce the set where the slope is supposed to be zero—for instance, to a set of Martin-measure zero. One may also consider the limit condition for functions more general than our solutions of a Dirichlet problem.

As to an *existence theorem*, let us give a finite continuous function ϕ on a compact subset of Δ. It is possible to find (as in [6]) in a neighborhood of the Martin boundary a harmonic function u with slope approaching ϕ arbitrarily and uniformly; u may even be of the form $\sum_i \lambda_i G(M, P_i)$ (finite sum), where the P_i are in an open set arbitrarily chosen. However, such a "solution," as the solution of a Cauchy problem, has an unstable character, that is to say, two very different functions u may have neighboring slopes.

7. If we go back now to the Poisson-Stieltjes integral and to the circular case, we observe that after the first steps their study uses as essential the notion of *radial limit;* we can see in the book by Evans systematic extensions of this notion by means of conformal mapping, which introduces naturally the lines $G =$ const and their orthogonal trajectories. Later, de la Vallée Poussin [9] also studied these trajectories together with conformal mapping, and suggested an analogous use in three-dimensional space.

A fundamental remark by Evans concerning the simply connected plane domain is that $\text{grad}^2 G$ is summable outside a neighborhood of the pole, as follows from Green's formula. A consequence is that the length of every trajectory is summable relative to the arc of a small level curve $G =$ const; therefore, almost all trajectories are finite in length and consequently have a limit point (Carathéodory theorem). This argument of Evans appeared to have possible extensions in any domain, even in space, and that possibility is the origin of the *recent research on the Green lines* [3], [11], which I now intend to discuss. I shall omit a detailed development concerning particular domains, but shall outline the foundations of a general theory.

Let us take a general Green space Ω and a certain pole P. We shall have to use the classical formulas of Green; they are valid in the large, not merely locally, because of the invariance of the differential element in a conformal correspondence. We shall consider the domain D_P^λ: $G > \lambda$ and its boundary, which is the level line or surface $\sum_P^\lambda$ $(G = \lambda)$, the so-called Green sphere.

The ordinary Dirichlet problem for the subdomain D_P^λ of Ω is understood, as we know, with an Alexandroff point $\mathfrak{A}$ adjoined to Ω. Essential properties for the demonstrations will be that $\mathfrak{A}$ forms a set of harmonic measure equal to zero (as do the points at infinity located on $\sum_P^\lambda$), that the Green function of D_P^λ is $G - \lambda$, and that for D_P^λ the harmonic measure at P of a set e of $\sum_P^\lambda$ is proportional to $\int_e (dG/dn)\, d\sigma$ (with the Lebesgue area or length $d\sigma$). Now let us call *Green arc* an open Jordan arc (without point at infinity), defined with a parameter in such a way that there is locally at every point a tangent vector not equal to zero, parallel to grad G, assumed to be different from zero along this arc. We term *Green line* a *maximal Green arc.* It is easy to study the Green lines first *in the neighborhood of the pole P.* We suppose, for instance, that P is not a point at infinity.

The Green lines tend to P when $G \to \infty$ and there is a tangent at P. For every direction issuing from P there is a unique Green line admitting it as tangent at P. If we consider any small Green sphere $\sum_P^\lambda$, there is a homeomorphism between the points of $\sum_P^\lambda$ and the directions issuing from P, the correspondence being determined by the Green lines cutting the Green sphere. Let us take a Borel set on $\sum_P^\lambda$; its harmonic measure at P relative to the domain D_P is equal to the angular measure of the corresponding set of directions issuing from P, divided by the area or length of the unit sphere or circle. This harmonic measure or reduced angular measure will be called the Green measure of the corresponding set of Green lines. We should have similar properties with the pole P at infinity. On the set of Green lines issuing from P we choose a topology, given by the topology on a small Green sphere or on the set of the tangent half-lines.

Now let us study the Green lines issuing from P and cutting any fixed Green sphere $\sum_P^\lambda$. They form an open set. There is between these lines and the traces on $\sum_P^\lambda$ a homeomorphism which equalizes the Green measure and the harmonic measure. But not all the Green lines issuing from P necessarily cut $\sum_P^\lambda$, unlike the situation in the case of the simply connected plane domain. Some may approach points at infinity, or points where grad $G = 0$. Some may go out of any compact set of Ω without cutting $\sum_P^\lambda$. However, almost all the lines considered cut $\sum_P^\lambda$. To get this main result, the three exceptional eventualities must be studied, with the aid of the Green formulas for small tubes of Green arcs and the summability of $\text{grad}^2 G$ outside a neighborhood of the pole.

Let us call *regular* a Green line issuing from P on which the greatest lower bound of G is equal to zero. If we consider a sequence $\lambda_n \to 0$, we conclude that almost all the Green lines considered will cut all the Green spheres—that is to say, they are regular.

8. *Let us inquire about the possible convergence of these lines for* $G \to 0$. For a simply connected plane domain, every Green line is regular and converges toward a prime end, with obviously one-to-one correspondence; it is known that for every ramified boundary point, there is one Green line converging to this point. In order to study the general case, we choose in Ω a bounded continuous function Φ (outside the points at infinity) such that $\int \Phi^2 \, dv$ is finite; dv is the volume or area and it is supposed that, in the case of conformal structure of the space, we have chosen a compatible ds^2, already considered in the preceding lecture. Every Green line will have a generalized length $\int_l \Phi \, ds$, and every Green sphere a generalized area or length.

In the case where the structure is isometric and the whole volume or area finite, we may take $\Phi = 1$, and the previous notions become the ordinary length and area. Then the generalized length of the Green lines issuing from P is summable for the Green measure, and the generalized area or length of the Green sphere is λ-summable.

Therefore, almost all regular Green lines have a finite generalized length and consequently have for $G \to 0$ a limit point in the following topologies: if Ω is a subdomain of an $\mathcal{E}$-space, we may first take the topology of our ordinary Dirichlet problem, that is to say the topology of $\mathcal{E}$ if $\mathcal{E}$ is compact, or the topology of the space $\mathcal{E}'$ deduced by addition of the Alexandroff point. We may consider also the corresponding ramified space or the geodesic one. Almost all regular Green lines converge in these spaces.

Let us choose a small Green sphere around P and consider on it the exceptional points for which the Green lines issuing are not regular or are not of finite generalized length. They form a set of harmonic measure equal to zero, that is to say, of length or area equal to zero on the level curve or surface. Now from works of Dufresnoy [10] we deduce at once that in the case of a simply connected plane domain, the set corresponding to the Green lines of infinite length is polar. The same improvement is to be hoped for the general set of our exceptional points.

9. Let us next obtain an *important maximum principle* and outline some applications [3], [11]. Let u be subharmonic in a Green space Ω. Let us consider a fixed pole P and the ordinary Dirichlet problem for a subdomain D_P^λ with boundary values u. (We need not assign a boundary value at the Alexandroff point of Ω, which forms a set of harmonic measure equal to zero.) If u is bounded above, there is a solution $U_\lambda \geqq u$; U_λ increases when λ decreases, and tends to a harmonic limit U. The same is true, and I must emphasize this though it is not all obvious, if u, instead of being bounded above, possesses a finite Dirichlet integral.

In order to bring together both cases, we shall say in general that u is *minor* if the following conditions are satisfied: (1) for any λ, the solution U_λ exists and is $\geqq u$; (2) U_λ, which necessarily increases when λ decreases, has a finite limit U, necessarily harmonic. Then the same will hold for any other pole and the limit U is independent of the pole; we call U the *best harmonic majorant* because of the coincidence with an old notion of this name in elementary cases. Let us notice that $U_\lambda(P) = \int u_\lambda(l)\, dg$, where dg is the Green measure and $u_\lambda(l)$ is equal to u on the Green line l and the Green sphere $\sum_P^\lambda$.

In addition, let us define for a Borel-measurable function v in Ω a *radial function* $\phi(l)$ on the set $\mathfrak{L}$ of the regular lines as one, if it exists, such that $\int | v_\lambda(l) - \phi(l) |\, dg \to 0$ as $\lambda \to 0$, in obvious notation. We shall say briefly that v converges in the mean toward ϕ (and this may be extended to the case of complex v and ϕ). Two such radial functions are equal almost everywhere on $\mathfrak{L}$.

Moreover, ϕ will be said to be only a *radial majorant* of v if $\int [v_\lambda(l) - \phi]^+\, dg \to 0$. We shall use these notions also for any subset α of $\mathfrak{L}$ with integral taken only over α.

Now we can state a *new maximum principle:* If u is subharmonic and minor and admits 0 as a radial majorant, then $u \leqq 0$.

This implies the following form, more intuitive but less powerful, which we may get directly from the expression for U_λ : If u is subharmonic and bounded above and has an upper limit $\leqq 0$ along almost all the regular lines, then $u \leqq 0$.

As an application, let us first go back to *our generalized Dirichlet problem;* we may now prove that the axiomatic conditions are verified for the ramified or geodesic case if we take as filters those corresponding to the regular and convergent Green lines with a finite generalized length. This is evident for the first axiomatic condition, which is almost the same as our last maximum principle, but the second and local condition requires some technical study.

10. Our new maximum principle suggests also the posing of a Dirichlet problem as follows:

Let ϕ be a function on the set $\mathfrak{L}$ of all the regular Green lines. Let us consider the functions which are $-\infty$ or subharmonic and which, for instance, are minor and admit ϕ as radial majorant. There is an upper envelope, $-\infty$, $+\infty$, or harmonic, denoted by $\underline{\mathcal{G}}_\phi$. We introduce the analogous envelope $\overline{\mathcal{G}}_\phi$ equal to $-\underline{\mathcal{G}}_{(-\phi)}$.

From the maximum principle, $\underline{\mathcal{G}}_\phi \leqq \overline{\mathcal{G}}_\phi$; we should get similar results with u bounded above and with a limit condition on every regular line; the new envelopes would enclose the previous ones. But in spite of the weakness of the first limit conditions, our envelopes $\mathcal{G}$ are not necessarily equal even for a bounded continuous ϕ. One may easily form an example with a Riemann surface, like that of Tôki [12], which has a Green function but no harmonic nonconstant functions. Therefore, we cannot develop the suggested Dirichlet problem in the same way as the others, and the *Green measure is not similar to a harmonic measure.*

11. Let us *compare the Green measure to the various harmonic measures.* For a simply connected plane domain, it is obvious that the Green measure, the Martin or conformal measure, and the ramified or geodesic measure in P_0 are all the same. Let us consider a generalized Dirichlet problem (according to our axiomatic theory) for which almost all the Green lines converge, and let us choose a boundary set e with harmonic measure. The regular Green lines which tend toward points of e form a set possessing a Green measure. These harmonic and Green measures are equal. But the Green measure of a set of lines is not generally equal to the generalized harmonic measure of the limit points. One may construct examples for which at every point of a convenient geodesic boundary set two and only two symmetrical Green lines converge. Thus the Green measure appears to be a more refined tool than the previous harmonic measures.

We may appreciate this at once through *some properties of subharmonic functions relating to the behavior along the Green lines.* Let us express the results in the case of $\log |f(z)|$ which is $-\infty$ or subharmonic, if f is holomorphic. We shall improve the theorems on vanishing or convergence which I gave at the beginning of the preceding lecture, using then harmonic measure.

Let us consider on a hyperbolic Riemann surface α a set of regular Green lines issuing from P, with a Green measure different from zero. Let $f(z)$ be holomorphic and bounded. If $|f(z)|$ converges on α in the mean to 0, then $f = 0$.

Let $f_n(z)$ be a sequence uniformly bounded; we suppose that every f_n converges in the mean on α to a function ϕ_n, and we suppose that ϕ_n converges in the mean, that is to say, $\int_\alpha |\phi_{n+p} - \phi_n| \, dg \to 0$ as $n \to \infty$. Then $f_n(z)$ converges in Ω, uniformly locally. Of course, the hypotheses are satisfied if f or f_n converges along every line of α and if ϕ_n converges simply. Let us note that these stronger limit conditions are much better than those used with harmonic measure.

12. For another application, let us go back to the better form of the *maximum principle.* We shall say that u (harmonic) is *indifferent* if u and $-u$ are minor, that is to say, if the solution H_u in D_P^λ exists and is equal to u. Therefore, harmonic functions which are bounded or which have a finite Dirichlet integral are indifferent (they are even differences of two positive indifferent functions). Let us notice that for a minor subharmonic function the best harmonic majorant is the smallest indifferent harmonic majorant.

Then, by the maximum principle, *there is at most one indifferent harmonic function which possesses a given radial function* ϕ.

The problem arises whether and when there is one for a given summable ϕ. Studies of this kind appear in the book by Evans [1] and lead to some positive replies for certain plane domains even of infinite connectivity. Unfortunately, there is not always a solution. That is a consequence of our previous research on a Dirichlet problem with Green lines; besides, a counterexample is easy to form with the complement in the plane of a linear Cantor set. But it is interesting to examine some important and general cases, as we shall now do.

In our various Dirichlet problems and even in any generalized one for which almost all the Green lines l converge, the solution is indifferent and admits a radial function; and this function of l is almost everywhere equal to the value of the given function at the boundary point where the line l converges. Conversely, this important result on the behavior of the solution gives a solution to our problem in the case for which the given function is deduced by such a correspondence from a certain boundary function summable with respect to the generalized harmonic measure.

13. The second case of existence which I shall examine is closely connected to the *Dirichlet principle* [13]. Let us call the norm of a function in a domain the square root of the Dirichlet integral. It has been known for a long time that for a bounded Euclidean domain with a sufficiently smooth boundary (for instance, with continuous curvatures) and for a sufficiently smooth function f on the boundary (for instance, such that it may be continued as a continuously differentiable function F), there is, among the functions which are finite and continuous in the closure of Ω and continuously differentiable in Ω with finite norm, one and only one which takes the given values f on the boundary and has the smallest norm. This function is the solution of the Dirichlet problem with boundary values f; it is also the only harmonic function with finite norm, defined up to an additive constant, which minimizes the norm of $u - F$. Zaremba and Nikodym [14] carried out research on this minimizing harmonic function for more general F. Recently Bochner [15] went further in the particular case of a domain limited by several spheres. He proved that for every function F in Ω, continuously differentiable or only piecewise smooth and with finite norm, but not at all defined on the boundary, there is for every limiting sphere a quadratic mean limit calculated on concentric neighboring spheres. And among the functions of this kind, the previous minimizing harmonic function is the only function which has the same mean limits and the smallest norm.

Thus, but with the aid of spherical expansions, Bochner got a form of the principle which does not require the direct intervention of the boundary and solves a new Dirichlet problem. Precisely this research has led to our radial functions; we replace concentric spheres by Green spheres, we take a simple mean instead of a quadratic one, and we get a similar but general form of the Dirichlet principle.

Of course we take a general Green space Ω. Then we shall consider on Ω *better functions than the piecewise smooth ones;* the most convenient seem to be functions studied by Deny [16], being more precise than the (BL) functions of Beppo Levi and Nikodym (see [14b]), which, besides, are defined only on a Euclidean space and depend, as Deny observed, on the chosen axes. We will call them (BLD) *functions* and denote them by δ.

They may be defined, in our Green space Ω, as limit quasi-everywhere finite and also as limit according to the norm of functions continuously differentiable (outside of the points at infinity) and possessing a finite norm. Within a constant or a change on any polar set, they form a Hilbert space with scalar product $\int \text{grad } \delta_1 \text{ grad } \delta_2 \, dv$. They admit a radial function (for every pole), and a powerful property is that, if δ_n converges quasi-everywhere and according to the norm, to a function quasi-everywhere finite, necessarily also (BLD), the radial function of δ_n converges in the mean to the radial function of the limit.

First one may prove, using the Hilbert space as Nikodym did, that for a given δ there is a harmonic function of finite norm, unique up to a constant, minimizing the norm of $u - \delta$. Then let us consider the ordinary Dirichlet problem in the subdomain D_P^λ (for $\lambda \to 0$), or in domains Ω_n which are relatively compact and increasing toward Ω, with boundary values equal to δ (and suitably defined at the points at infinity if necessary); the solution has a limit U which is the minimizing function. This U is the unique (BLD) function admitting the same radial function as δ or the smallest norm. Moreover, if δ is subharmonic, U is the *best* and also the *smallest* harmonic majorant.

Thus *we have generalized the Dirichlet principle and we have obtained an existence theorem as follows:* For any given function on $\mathfrak{L}$, radial function of a (BLD) function, there is a harmonic function admitting this radial function and a finite norm; one may deduce an existence theorem for any summable function on $\mathfrak{L}$ in the two-dimensional case and with important restrictions, such as finite connectivity. Moreover, *we notice that any (BLD) function may be decomposed in a unique way*, as the sum of a (BLD) function of radial function zero and of a (BLD) harmonic function. Now all the (BLD) functions of radial function zero are all the (BLD) functions which are the limit quasi-everywhere and in norm of (BLD) functions equal to zero outside a compact set. And it is fairly obvious that any such (BLD) function is orthogonal to any (BLD) harmonic function. Thus in the Hilbert space of the (BLD) functions, two orthogonal closed and complementary manifolds are determined in accordance with the decomposition theorem. In fact, this is, in substance, a result given by Ahlfors-Deny (see [16]) for a Euclidean domain and then established with the aid of Schwartz distributions.

14. From a survey of the Green lines theory one may observe that the proofs are founded upon the use of the Green formulas for tubes of lines between two level surfaces. Therefore, *it is possible to extend the theory to more general lines*. Let K be a compact set in our Green space Ω and V the solution of the ordinary Dirichlet problem for the subdomain $\Omega - K$, with value 0 at the Alexandroff point of Ω and 1 on the boundary of K. We may consider the level surfaces or curves $V =$ const, and the orthogonal trajectories may replace the Green lines in a similar theory.

This suggests an examination in potential theory of the sweeping-out process of the flux and of the ways followed by the swept masses.

But I should prefer to conclude by emphasizing more precise and urgent questions. As to the behavior of the potential functions along the Green lines, the Fatou theorem would first have to be extended, at least as a theorem of existence of a radial limit function for any bounded harmonic function. The most important thing would be, perhaps, *to find close connections with the Martin theory*, which I have intentionally outlined in this lecture. Would the function of P: $G(M, P)/G(M, P_0)$ have a limit when M describes a regular Green line—that is to say, would such Green lines, or at least almost all, have unique limit points in the Martin space, as is true in the simply connected plane domains? And then, which relationship would the Green measure have to the Martin measure?

BIBLIOGRAPHICAL NOTES

1. EVANS, G. C. *The logarithmic potential.* Amer. Math. Soc. Colloquium Publications, No. 6. New York, 1927.

2. MARTIN, R. S. *Minimal positive harmonic functions*, Trans. Amer. Math. Soc. 49 (1941), 137–172.

3. BRELOT, M., AND CHOQUET, G. *Espaces et lignes de Green*, Ann. Inst. Fourier Grenoble 3 (1951), 199–263.

4. PARREAU, M. *Sur les moyennes des fonctions harmoniques et analytiques et la classification des surfaces de Riemann*, Ann. Inst. Fourier Grenoble 3 (1951), 103–197.

5. DE LA VALLÉE POUSSIN, C. J. *Propriétés des fonctions harmoniques dans un domaine ouvert limité par des surfaces à courbures bornées*, Ann. Scuola Norm. Super. Pisa 2 (1933), 167–197.

6. BRELOT, M. *Sur le principe des singularités positives et la topologie de R. S. Martin*, Ann. Univ. Grenoble Sec. Sci. Math. Phys. 23 (1947), 113–138.

7. A historical account is given in the following:

DENY, J. *Le principe des singularités positives de G. Bouligand et la représentation des fonctions harmoniques positives dans un domaine*, Rev. Sci. 14 (1947), 866–872.

A new form of the principle is given in [6].

8. BRELOT, M. *Sur l'allure des fonctions harmoniques et sousharmoniques à la frontière*, Math. Nachr. 4 (1951), 298–307.

9. DE LA VALLÉE POUSSIN, C. J. *Le potentiel logarithmique, balayage et représentation conforme.* Paris, 1949.

10. DUFRESNOY, J. (a) *Sur les fonctions méromorphes et univalentes dans le cercle unité*, Bull. Sci. Math. 69 (1945), 21–36.

—— (b) *Remarques complémentaires sur deux propriétés de la représentation conforme*, Bull. Sci. Math. 69 (1945), 117–121.

Paper (a) is corrected in (b).

11. In the text of the present lecture I give, and even improve and complete, some essential results of [3] and of the following papers:

BRELOT, M. (a) *Principe et problème de Dirichlet dans les espaces de Green*, C. R. Acad. Sci. Paris 235 (1952), 598–600.

—— (b) *Lignes de Green et problème de Dirichlet*, C. R. Acad. Sci. Paris 235 (1952), 1595–1597.

In paper (b) the last sentence of the final theorem must be corrected by the additional condition that the two-dimensional domain Ω has, for example, finite connectivity.

Since this lecture these papers (a) and (b) have been developed in the following articles by the author:

—— (c) *Majorantes harmoniques et principe du maximum,* Arch. Math. 5 (1954), 429–440.

—— (d) *Étude et extensions du principe de Dirichlet,* Ann. Inst. Fourier Grenoble 5 (1953–1954), 371–419.

12. Tôki, Y. *On the classification of open Riemann surfaces,* Osaka Math. J. 4 (1952), 191-201.

13. For a bibliography of the Dirichlet principle, to which [14] and [15] should be added, see:

Courant, R. *Dirichlet's principle, conformal mapping and minimal surfaces.* New York, 1950.

14. Zaremba, S. *Sur un problème toujours possible comprenant à titre de cas particulier de problème de Dirichlet et celui de Neumann,* J. Math. Pures Appl. (9) 6 (1927), 127-163.

Nikodym, O. (a) *Sur un théorème de M. S. Zaremba concernant les fonctions harmoniques,* J. Math. Pures Appl. (9) 12 (1933), 95–108.

—— (b) *Sur une classe de fonctions considérées dans l'étude du problème de Dirichlet,* Fund. Math. 21 (1933), 129-150.

15. Bochner, S. *Dirichlet problem for domains bounded by spheres.* Annals of Mathematics Studies, No. 25. Princeton, 1950.

16. Deny, J. *Les potentiels d'énergie finie,* Acta Math. 82 (1950), 107-183.

University of Grenoble

CONJUGATE NETS ON AN OPEN RIEMANN SURFACE

JAMES JENKINS AND MARSTON MORSE

1. Introduction. Let Q be an open, connected, locally Euclidean surface. Such a surface is defined as is an open, connected Riemann surface, except that the homeomorphism between two Euclidean coordinate regions *admissibly* representing the same region in Q is not required to be conformal but merely topological and sense-preserving. Families of curves F and G, defined on Q, are *admissible* if locally conditioned as in [5] and [6]. A pair $[F, G]$ of admissible families is called a *conjugate net* on Q if for any sufficiently small neighborhood H of a point q of Q, the curves in $F \mid H$ and $G \mid H$ are level curves on H of $\mathcal{R} f_H$ and $\mathcal{I} f_H$, respectively, where

$$w = f_H(p) \mid (p \in H)$$

is an interior map of H into the w-plane. If Q has a conformal structure and if each f_H is analytic, $[F, G]$ is termed *isothermal* on Q. If $[F, G]$ is a conjugate net on Q and if $[F, G]$ becomes isothermal for *some* conformal structure on Q, then $[F, G]$ is said to be *isothermally realizable.* Not every conjugate net $[F, G]$ on Q is isothermally realizable, as we shall show by example in § 3. We seek necessary and sufficient conditions on $[F, G]$ of a topological nature that $[F, G]$ be isothermally realizable.

Suppose that a conjugate net $[F, G]$ gives the nonsingular level loci, respectively, of $\mathcal{R} f$ and $\mathcal{I} f$, where $w = f(p) \mid (p \in Q)$ is an interior map of Q into the w-plane. We say then that $[F, G]$ *contours* f. If Q is topologically equivalent to a finite z-plane, $[F, G]$ always contours some single-valued interior map f of Q into the w-plane. Let M be the universal covering surface of Q and Γ its cover group. If Γ is not trivial, a conjugate net $[F, G]$ on Q contours an interior map $w = f(p)$ of Q only exceptionally. As an example, let Q be a surface Σ^* formed from a z-sphere Σ by deleting a north pole N: $(z = \infty)$ and south pole S: $(z = 0)$. The family $[F_0, G_0]$ on Σ^* in which F_0 is the family of meridians and G_0 the family of parallels of constant latitude contours no interior map of Σ^* into the w-plane. However, $\log z$, which is single-valued on M, is contoured by $[F_0, G_0]$. This suggests the introduction of a basic class of interior maps λ of M into the plane as follows.

Class A. This class shall consist of all interior maps

$$w = \lambda(p) \mid (p \in M)$$

of M into the w-plane such that for each topological map $g \in \Gamma$ of M onto M

$$\lambda g(p) = a_g \lambda(p) + b_g + ib_g' \qquad (p \in M) \quad (a_g \neq 0), \tag{1.1}$$

where a_g, b_g and b_g' are real constants uniquely determined by g and λ.

The significance of Class A is shown by the following two theorems, established in §§ 2, 3.

Theorem 1.1. *A necessary and sufficient condition that a conjugate net* $[F, G]$ *on* Q *be isothermally realizable is that there exist an interior map* $\lambda \in A$ *which is contoured by* $[F, G]$.

Theorem 1.2. *Each interior map* $\lambda \in A$ *defines in a canonical way* (see § 2) *a conformal structure on* Q, *and each conformal structure on* Q *can be canonically defined by suitable choice of* $\lambda \in A$.

If $[F, G]$ contours a $\lambda \in A$, and if M_λ is a copy of M conformally structured in a canonical way by λ, then λ becomes analytic on M_λ and $[F, G]$ isothermal on M_λ. We are thus led to consider the following basic problems.

(i) Given a curve family F admissible on Q, when does there exist a family G such that $[F, G]$ is a conjugate net on Q? (See [3].)

(ii) Under what topological conditions on a conjugate net $[F, G]$ on Q does $[F, G]$ contour an interior map $\lambda \in A$?

(iii) If $[F, G]$ contours $\lambda \in A$, how are the coefficients a_g, b_g, b_g' in (1.1) limited by the topological characteristics of $[F, G]$? When does $(a_g, b_g, b_g') = (1, 0, 0)$?

(iv) If $[F, G]$ contours $\lambda \in A$, and λ canonically defines a conformal structure on Q, how do the resulting numerical conformal invariants of Q (when they exist) depend on the topological characteristics of $[F, G]$?

We are able to answer these questions rather completely under the assumption that Γ is generated by one element g. This is to be regarded not as a special case but as a basic one preliminary to answering these questions in general. Investigations not reported in this paper point to the great applicability in general of the results in the case of one generator.

Let us suppose that Q admits some conformal structure. One could equivalently assume that the Class A is not empty. Let M^g be formed from M by identifying points p and $g(p)$ in M. The resulting surface M^g is topologically equivalent to the punctured sphere Σ^* described above. The universal covering surface of M^g is again M. We are thus led to study the problem in which $Q = \Sigma^*$. In Part I we shall establish Theorems 1.1 and 1.2. In the remainder of the paper we shall be mostly concerned with Σ^*. However, we return to a study of a general separable Q in §§ 9, 10.

Part I. General Theorems

2. Maps $\lambda \in A$ and conformal structure on Q. Let R be a region in the z-plane and f a map of R into the w-plane. We say that f is *interior* at $z = z_0 \in R$ if in some neighborhood H of z_0, f has the form $f = \phi\psi$, where ψ maps H topologically with preservation of sense onto a neighborhood of z_0, leaving z_0 fixed, and where ϕ is analytic at z_0. We say that f is interior over R, if interior at each point of R.

In the definition of interiority of f at z_0 one need only use analytic functions of the form $\phi(z) = c + (z - z_0)^n$, where n is a positive integer and c a complex constant. We term n the *index* of f at z_0. When $n = 1$, f is termed *nonsingular* at z_0, and when $n > 1$, *singular*. Suppose that f has the index n at z_0 and that in some neighborhood H of z_0, f is contoured by $[F_H, G_H]$. We say that z_0 is a singular point of $[F_H, G_H]$ of index n when $n > 1$. When the index n of z_0 exceeds 1 the inverse of the map $w = f(p) \mid (p \in H)$ is single-valued on an n-sheeted branch element with branch point at $w = f(z_0)$, provided H is properly restricted. The singular points of f on R are isolated in R.

Let p_0 be a point of M and let R in the z-plane be the domain of a distinguished representation $p = k(z) \mid (z \in R)$ of a neighborhood $k(R) \subset M$ of p_0. Let $w = \lambda(p) \mid (p \in M)$ be a map of M into the w-plane. Let $\lambda k(z) = f(z) \mid (z \in R)$. We say that λ is *interior* at p_0 if f is interior over some neighborhood of $z = a = k^{-1}(p_0)$ in R. It is clear that the interiority of λ at p_0 is independent of the particular distinguished representation of a neighborhood of p_0 which is used. We say that λ is interior over M if interior at each point of M. An interior map of Q or of a subregion of Q into a w-plane is similarly defined.

A conformal structure on Q canonically defined by λ. Given a map $\lambda \in A$ of M into the w-plane a pair $(w, p) = (\lambda(p), p) \mid (p \in M)$ will be represented by the point w on the w-sphere. The pair (w, p) is not the point w, but rather the point w with a tag p attached. The union W of the pairs $(w, p) = (\lambda(p), p)$ so represented is in one-to-one correspondence with M, where $p \in M$ corresponds to $(w, p) = (\lambda(p), p)$ in W. We assign a topology to W by agreeing that this mapping Θ of W onto M shall be topological. The neighborhoods of points (w_0, p_0) on W are now well-defined. If p_0 is an ordinary point of λ, (w_0, p_0) has a neighborhood K which projects in a one-to-one way onto a neighborhood of w_0 in the w-sphere. For K we choose w as a conformal parameter and the projection of w into (w, p) as the distinguished representation. If p_0 is a singular point of λ of index $n > 1$ there is a neighborhood K of (w_0, p_0) relative to W which is an n-sheeted branch element E. The classical representation of the point (w, p) of E in terms of a uniformizing parameter t becomes (by our choice) a distinguished representation of E as element of W. These distinguished representations define a consistent conformal structure for W. We carry this conformal structure over to M under Θ. With this conformal structure added, denote M by M_λ.

Let g be an element in the cover group Γ of M, with g not the identity. Under g, M is mapped topologically onto M, the points p and $g(p)$ in M covering the same point in Q. On M_λ, g is *directly conformal* as well as topological. To see this, examine g in a neighborhood of a nonsingular point p_0 of λ. In a sufficiently restricted neighborhood H of p_0, the map $w = \lambda(p)$ is topological. Set $\lambda(p) \mid (p \in H) = \lambda_0(p)$. Relative to the conformal structure of M_λ, $p = \lambda_0^{-1}(w)$ is a distinguished representation of $p \in H$ in terms of a conformal parameter w. Similarly, the inverse of

$$w' = \lambda(p) \mid (p \in g(H))$$

is a distinguished representation of $p \in g(H)$ in terms of a conformal parameter w'. Points w and w' which represent congruent points p

and $g(p)$ respectively stand in the relation

$$w' = a_g w + b_g + ib_g' \qquad (w \in \lambda(H))$$

by virtue of (1.1). This relation is directly conformal, so that g is directly conformal at each point p_0 of M_λ excepting, at most, the singular points p_0 of λ. Since these singular points are isolated and g is topological, we can conclude that g is directly conformal without exception.

To define a conformal structure on Q, recall that Q is obtained from M by identifying all pairs of congruent points p and $g(p)$, for $p \in M$ and for each $g \in \Gamma$. Let H be a neighborhood of p_0 on M_λ so restricted that H contains no pair of points congruent under any transformation of Γ. A point $p \in M$ covers a point p_Q in Q. We assign the conformal structure of H to its projection H_Q on Q, using the projection $p \to p_Q$ to carry over the distinguished representations in terms of conformal parameters. The conformal structure of $g(H)$ in M_λ so projected will yield the same conformal structure on H_Q, since g is a directly conformal map of H onto $g(H)$. Thus projecting the conformal structure of M_λ into a conformal structure on Q yields, not many, but one consistent conformal structure on Q. This is the conformal structure on Q *canonically defined* by λ.

This first affirmation of Theorem 1.2 is thereby established. To establish the concluding affirmation of the theorem we reason as follows.

According to Behnke and Stein [1], when Q has a conformal structure S_1, there exists a single-valued nonconstant analytic map $w = f(p) \mid (p \in Q)$ of Q into the w-plane. Analyticity is relative to S_1. There clearly then exists a unique $\lambda \in A$ such that for each point $q \in M$ and projection q_Q in Q, $\lambda(q) = f(q_Q)$. In (1.1) the constants (a_g, b_g, b_g') are (1, 0, 0). The map λ serves to define canonically a second conformal structure S_2 on Q. Let Q_i be Q with the conformal structure S_i, $i = 1, 2$. Let T map Q_1 onto Q_2 under the identity. The map T is directly conformal at each point p_0 of Q which is a nonsingular point of f. For the inverse of $w = f(p)$, taken over a sufficiently restricted neighborhood H of p_0, is a distinguished representation of H in terms of the conformal parameter w, both in the structure S_1 and in the structure S_2. This is not true if p_0 is not an ordinary point of f, but such exceptional points are isolated, and T is topological. Hence T is directly conformal.

The conformal structures S_1 and S_2 are thus equivalent and Theorem 1.2 is true.

Given $\lambda \in M$, let M_λ and Q_λ be respectively the surfaces M and Q, with the conformal structures canonically defined by λ. We state the following theorem.

THEOREM 2.1. *A mapping λ of Class A is analytic on M_λ, and the conjugate net $[F, G]$ on Q which projects into a net $[F_M, G_M]$ which contours λ is isothermal on Q_λ.*

The proof of this theorem is implied by the definitions involved. Let p_0 be a nonsingular point of λ. In a sufficiently restricted neighborhood H of p_0 in M_λ, the inverse of $w = \lambda(p) \mid (p \in H)$ is single-valued and is a distinguished representation $p = \psi(w) \mid (w \in \lambda(H))$ of H in terms of a conformal parameter w. If $\phi(p) \mid (p \in H)$ is single-valued on H, ϕ is analytic on M_λ at p_0 if $\phi\psi$ is analytic in the w-plane at $w_0 = \lambda(p_0)$. In particular, λ is analytic on M_λ at p_0 since $\lambda\psi(w) = w$ for $w \in \lambda(H)$. Thus λ is analytic on M_λ. For λ is continuous on M_λ, and analytic at all except the isolated singular points of λ.

To show that $[F, G]$ is isothermal on Q_λ, let H be any disk-type neighborhood on Q_λ with a homeomorphic covering H_M on M_λ. Then $\lambda \mid H_M$ projects into a single-valued function f on H, analytic on $Q_\lambda \mid H$ and contoured by $[F, G] \mid H$.

The theorem follows.

Pseudoharmonic functions. Our definition of a map of M or Q into a w-plane which is interior is paralleled by a definition of a function u which is PH (pseudoharmonic) over a subregion K of M or Q. Let p_0 be a point of K and let R in the z-plane be the domain of a distinguished representation $p = k(z) \mid (z \in R)$ of a neighborhood $k(R) \subset K$ of p_0. Then u is termed PH on K at p_0 if uk is PH in the sense of [7, § 2] in a neighborhood of $k^{-1}(p_0)$ in the z-plane. The function u is PH over K if PH at each point of K.

3. Conjugate nets $[F, G]$ isothermally realized. We shall establish Theorem 1.1.

To that end, let Q' be Q with a conformal structure, and let $[F, G]$ be an isothermal net on Q'. Let M' be M with a conformal structure which projects into that of Q'. Let $[F_M, G_M]$ be the isothermal net on M' which projects into $[F, G]$. The net $[F_M, G_M]$ is invariant under each map $g \in \Gamma$. By virtue of the definition of an isothermal net, each point $q \in M'$ has a neighborhood H_q in which $[F_M, G_M]$ contours a function f_q analytic on H_q. For q fixed, two functions f_q and ϕ_q analytic on H_q and contoured by $[F_M, G_M]$ on H_q satisfy a linear relation

$$f_q(p) = a_q\phi_q(p) + b_q + ib_q' \qquad (a_q \neq 0, p \in H_q), \tag{3.1}$$

where the constants (a_q, b_q, b_q') are real. This is proved when q is a nonsingular point of $[F_M, G_M]$ as follows.

Take $w = \phi_q(p) \mid (p \in K_q)$ as a conformal parameter over a connected restricted neighborhood $K_q \subset H_q$ of q, and in terms of this parameter set $f_q(p) = h(w)$. If $w = u + iv$ it appears that the values of $\mathcal{R}h$ and $\mathcal{I}h$ depend only on u and v respectively and are real for real values of u and v. It follows from the Cauchy-Riemann differential equations that $h(w) = a_q w + b_q + ib_q'$ for $w \in \phi_q(H_q)$, where $a_q \neq 0$, and a_q, b_q, b_q' are real. Thus a relation (3.1) holds for an ordinary point q of $[F_M, G_M]$, and hence for any point $q \in M$.

On H_{q_0} let λ equal a fixed associated function f_{q_0}. One can continue λ analytically over M'. This follows from the monodromy law provided one can continue λ from q_0 along any sensed simple arc k in M'. But there can be no limiting point r on k such that λ can be continued along k into any neighborhood of r but cannot be continued over a whole neighborhood of r. For f_r exists and is linearly related to λ in a part at least of a neighborhood H_r of r. It follows from the preceding that λ and f_r satisfy a linear relation such as (3.1) in a part and hence (with proper extension of λ) in the whole of some neighborhood H_r of r. Hence λ is continuable over H_r, and so over all of M'.

To show that λ satisfies relations of the form (1.1), recall that the map $g \in \Gamma$ is a directly conformal map of M' onto M' and carries the net $[F_M, G_M]$ into itself. Hence λg is analytic over M', and λg and λ are both contoured by $[F_M, G_M]$. Hence a relation of the type (1.1) must hold in some neighborhood H_q of the point q of M'. On continuing λ and λg over M' it follows that the satisfaction of (1.1) in H_q implies its satisfaction over all of M'.

There thus exists a map $\lambda \in A$ contoured by a net $[F, G]$ given as isothermal on a conformally structured copy Q' of Q.

This shows that the condition of Theorem 1.1 is necessary. That it is sufficient follows from Theorem 2.1. This establishes Theorem 1.1.

Counterexample. We shall exhibit a simple conjugate net which cannot be realized isothermally. Let $Q = \Sigma^*$ be the w-sphere with a south pole S: $(w = 0)$ and a north pole N: $(w = \infty)$ deleted. The family F on Σ^* shall be without singularities. Let (α, θ) be the latitude and longitude of a point on Σ^*. The family F shall include two parallels on which $\alpha = \pm a$, where $0 < a < \pi/2$. The central annulus bounded by these two circles in F shall be filled with asymptotes to these two parallels of the form

$$\theta = \theta_0 - \frac{1}{\alpha^2 - a^2} \qquad (-a < \alpha < a) \tag{3.2}$$

where θ_0 is constant on each asymptote and $0 \leqq \theta_0 < 2\pi$. The annulus on which $a < \alpha < \pi/2$ shall be filled with asymptotes of the form

$$\theta = \theta_0 - \frac{1}{(\alpha - a)^2} \qquad (a < \alpha < \pi/2). \tag{3.3}$$

Each such ray has a limiting end point at N and tends asymptotically to the parallel $\alpha = a$ as $\alpha \downarrow a$. The annulus on which $-a > \alpha > -\pi/2$ shall be filled by curves obtained by reflecting the north annulus in the equatorial plane of the w-sphere. Let G be the curve family of trajectories orthogonal to the curves in F.

So defined, $[F, G]$ is a conjugate net on Σ^*. However, it will follow from Theorem 8.2 that there is no $\lambda \in A$ contoured by $[F, G]$, hence by Theorem 1.1 no conformal structure on Σ^* under which $[F, G]$ is isothermal. The fact that θ is bounded below on each asymptote in F in the central annulus, and bounded above on each asymptote in the north and south annuli, excludes F from the class of *restricted* curve families to which reference is made in Theorem 8.2.

To consider questions (i) to (iv) as proposed in § 1 we introduce the surface M^g defined as follows.

The surface M^g. Let g be any element in Γ not the identity. Let M^g be formed from M by identifying the points p and $g(p)$ for each $p \in M$. The surface M projects into M^g, each point $p \in M$ corresponding to the collection of points $g^n(p)$, $n = 0, \pm 1, \cdots$ in M regarded as a single point in M^g. From the point of view of M, this projection is locally one-to-one, and we assign M^g a topology, by agreeing that each neighborhood in M which contains no two points congruent under the subgroup of Γ generated by g, shall project topologically into its image on M^g. We state the following lemma.

LEMMA 3.1. *If the Class A of maps* λ *is not empty,* M^g *is the topological image of the doubly punctured sphere* Σ^*.

Since there exists a $\lambda \in A$, M can be replaced by M_λ, identical with M except that M_λ has the conformal structure canonically defined by λ. We suppose M^g has been assigned the conformal structure implied by the projection of M_λ onto M^g, recalling that g is a directly conformal map of M_λ onto M_λ.

According to the classical uniformization theorem, M_λ can be mapped directly conformally either onto the finite w-plane (Case I) or the unit disk D: $\{|w| < 1\}$ (Case II). Points p and $g(p)$ on M_λ will go thereby into points w and w' such that $w' = L_g(w)$, where L_g is a translation of the w-plane in Case I, and fractional linear in Case II, mapping D onto D. In Case I, M^g is homeomorphic to a strip in the w-plane bounded by a straight line h and by $L_g(h)$, with identification of points on h and $L_g(h)$ which are congruent under L_g. In Case II, M is homeomorphic to a region in D bounded by a circle C orthogonal to the boundary βD of D, and by $L_g(C)$, with identification of points on C and $L_g(C)$ which are congruent under L_g. In both cases M^g appears homeomorphic to Σ^*.

This establishes the lemma.

In Part II we shall study an admissible curve family F on Σ^*. Let F_M be the curve family on M covering F [6, § 2]. We seek a function u which is PH on M and F_M-admissible in the sense that the elements of F_M are level lines of u. We shall find topological conditions on F which are necessary and sufficient that such functions u exist and satisfy a relation of the form

$$u(p^{(1)}) = au(p) + b \qquad (a \neq 0), \tag{3.4}$$

where a and b are real. Here p and $p^{(1)}$ are points on M which project into the same point of Σ^* but on M have longitudes θ and $\theta + 2\pi$ respectively.

In Part III we shall study families F and their conjugates G on Σ^*, admitting just those families F (termed *restricted*) which contour a function u on M which is PH on M and satisfies (3.4) for some pair of real constants (a, b) $(a \neq 0)$. These restricted families have been characterized purely topologically in Part II.

We show that a restricted family F *on* Σ^* *always has a restricted conjugate* G.

In Part IV we shall start with a restricted conjugate net $[F, G]$ and establish the existence of at least one map $\lambda \in A$ contoured by $[F, G]$. In the case of Σ^*, the covering group Γ of M is generated by one map g of M onto M, namely a map which carries p in M into $p^{(1)}$ as defined above. The condition (1.1) on a map $\lambda \in A$ corresponding to the generator g of Γ takes the form

$$\lambda(p^{(1)}) = a\lambda(p) + b + ib' \qquad (a \neq 0), \tag{3.5}$$

where a, b, and b' are real constants. General results are obtained. A special case of particular interest occurs when $a = 1$.

Module $b + ib'$. In case $a = 1$ in (3.5), a map $\lambda \in A$ is like an integral in that it has the *module* $b + ib'$. We refer to a module $b + ib'$ of $\lambda \in A$ only when $a = 1$. On the metric side, the values of both b and b' naturally fall into three classes: B_1 with arbitrary values, B_2 with null values only, B_3 with arbitrary nonnull values. The modules $b + ib'$ thereby fall into nine classes given by the respective products $B_i \times B_j = B_{ij}$ $(i, j = 1, 2, 3)$ with $b \in B_i$ and $b' \in B_j$. The classes B_{ij} are of course not disjoint, but restricted conjugate nets which contour some $\lambda \in A$ with a module fall into nine disjoint classes C_{ij}, where C_{ij} is a maximal class of restricted conjugate nets such that $[F, G] \in C_{ij}$ implies that $[F, G]$ contours a $\lambda \in A$ with prescribed module $b + ib'$ in B_{ij}. The classes C_{ij} are characterized purely topologically, by properties such as the existence of asymptotes in F^* or G^*, or curves joining N to S, and so on, and the integral values of our indices $\nu(F)$, $\nu(G)$, $\mu(F)$, $\mu(G)$ are determinative. These results on modules yield necessary and sufficient conditions that a restricted net $[F, G]$ contour a $\lambda \in A$ whose projection on Q is *single-valued*.

Conformal invariants of Σ_λ^*. Given a restricted conjugate net $[F, G]$ on Σ^*, there always exists a $\lambda \in A$ contoured by $[F, G]$. By Theorem 1.2 a conformal structure can then be canonically defined on Σ^* by λ. So structured, Σ^* can be directly conformally mapped onto a circular ring of one of the known conformal types in the w-plane. The dependence of the conformal module of this ring upon $[F, G]$ through the mediation of λ is of maximum interest. We shall present results concerning this in a later paper.

Part II. Restricted Families F

4. Formulation of Problem I and definitions. We shall make use of the notation and results of [6]. In particular, reference is made to the universal covering surface M of $\Sigma^* = \Sigma - N - S$ and its representation in terms of latitude and longitude [6, § 12]. Let p be a point in M with latitude α and longitude θ, and let $p^{(n)} \in M$ be the point congruent to p with latitude α and longitude $\theta + 2n\pi$, $n = 0, \pm 1, \pm 2, \cdots$. Since M is simply connected, there exists a function u which is PH over M, for which the curves in F_M are level curves, where F_M projects into F on Σ^* [6, § 2]. We say that such a u is *F_M-admissible* on M, and say that u is *invariant under a transformation* $T(a, b)$ if for each $p \in M$

$$u(p^{(1)}) = au(p) + b \qquad (a \neq 0), \tag{4.1}$$

where a and b are real constants.

In Part II we shall obtain the complete solution of the following problem.

PROBLEM I. *What are the necessary and sufficient conditions (if any) on F^* and on $T(a, b)$ that there exist a function u which is F_M-admissible on M and invariant under $T(a, b)$?*

When a meridian [6, § 3] exists in F^*, we shall show that there always exists a transformation $T(a, b)$ and a function u which is F_M-admissible on M and invariant under $T(a, b)$. In this case the solution of Problem I is given by the determination of the transformations $T(a, b)$ realizable with a family F^*. When there is no meridian in F^*, there may exist no transformation $T(a, b)$ for which a function u exists as above.

The solution of Problem I consists then of conditions on F^* and associated conditions on (a, b). The conditions on F^* involve the distribution and nature of asymptotes and inner cycles in F^*. In all cases the admissible choices of the constants (a, b) are conditioned by the value of the index $\nu(F)$ defined in [6, § 10]. When a meridian exists, the values of (a, b) are conditioned further by the value of a second integral index $\mu(F)$, which we now define.

The index $\mu(F)$ shall be the maximum number of disjoint *meridional units* in a decomposition of Σ^* as now defined. In the absence of meridional regions [6, § 12] there are by definition no meridional units. If a doubly connected meridional region R exists we regard Σ^* as a special meridional unit. In any other case we refer to the decomposition of Σ^* as given in [6, Theorem 12.1(a)]. In the circular sequence of disjoint canonical polar sectors whose Ûnion is Σ^*, each meridional sector is separated from each other such meridional sector (if any exists) by canonical sectors of the other types. By a *meridional unit* Z we shall mean the $\hat{\text{U}}$nion of a sequence of consecutive, distinct, canonical sectors which begins and ends with a sector of meridional type and is such that on an F-guide g the number of reversing points, in the $\hat{\text{U}}$nion of the canonical sectors between any two successive sectors of meridional type in Z, is even. Further, we require that Z be not a proper subset of another such $\hat{\text{U}}$nion. We admit the possibility that a meridional unit may consist of a single sector of meridional type.

Coverings in M. The mapping t. For us a connected set shall be an arcwise connected set. Let E be connected in Σ^*. By a covering $E_M \subset M$ of E is meant any maximal connected set in M which projects onto E. Let t be the mapping of M onto itself which carries $p \in M$ into $p^{(1)}$. Given $K \subset M$, set $t^n K = K^{(n)}$, $n = 0, \pm 1, \pm 2, \cdots$. If E is homotopic to zero in Σ^*, E_M projects homeomorphically onto E. In this case the sets $E_M{}^{(n)}$ are disjoint. A special case of importance in which E_M is invariant under t $(E_M = E_M{}^{(n)})$ is that in which E is an annulus A with boundaries which are carriers of elements in Φ [6, § 7]. Then A_M is a simply connected region on M invariant under t. If $h \in F^*$ and h_M is invariant under t, then h must be a topological circle in F^*.

Functions F-admissible. A function u defined over an open set $R \subset \Sigma^*$ will be termed F-admissible over R if u is PH over R and has the level lines $F^* \mid R$, and will be termed F-admissible over $\bar{R} \cap \Sigma^*$ if F-admissible over R and continuous over $\bar{R} \cap \Sigma^*$; F_M-admissibility is similarly defined.

The method of establishing the existence of a function u, conditioned as in Problem I, will involve the decomposition of M into basic disjoint regions R covering the canonical regions given in [6]. We seek to define a function u which is F_M-admissible over each $\bar{R}$, under boundary conditions which imply that u is F_M-admissible over all of M. To that end we introduce a new concept.

Concept of k-compatibility of functions u_1 and u_2. Let R_i, $i = 1, 2$, be disjoint subregions of M and set

$$H = \hat{\text{U}}\text{nion}\,(R_1, R_2), \qquad \beta R_1 \cap \beta R_2 = k.$$

We make the assumption that k is an open arc in $F_M{}^* \mid H$. Suppose u_i, $i = 1, 2$, are F_M-admissible on R_i and continuous on $R_i \cup k$. Noting that u_i is constant on k, we suppose further that $u_1(k) =$

$u_2(k) = c$, introducing c. The functions u_i determine a function u defined on H by setting

$$(4.2) \qquad u \mid R_i = u_i, \qquad u \mid k = u_i \mid k \qquad (i = 1, 2).$$

Such a function u is continuous over H. Let p be an arbitrary nonsingular point of k, and let K be an F_M-neighborhood of p. Set $k \cap R_i = K_i$. We say that u_1 and u_2 are *compatible* at p if the signs of the functions

$$(u - c) \mid K_1, \qquad (u - c) \mid K_2$$

are opposite. If u_1 and u_2 are compatible at p, u is clearly PH over $K \cap H$.

It is a capital fact that the compatibility of u_1 and u_2 at any one nonsingular point $p \in k$ implies the compatibility of u_1 and u_2 at any other nonsingular point of k. This is a consequence of the facts that k is connected and in H, and that the number of F_M-sectors [6, § 2] in R_i, $i = 1, 2$, and incident with a singular point $p \in k$ has a parity dependent on p but independent of i. With this understood, we refer to the k-compatibility of u_1 and u_2, meaning thereby the compatibility of u_1 and u_2 at each nonsingular point of k.

If u_1 and u_2 are not k-compatible, and if one defines a function u_2^* by setting

$$u_2^* - c = -(u_2 - c),$$

then $u_2^*(k) = c$, and u_1 is k-compatible with u_2^*.

We shall make repeated use of the following lemma.

LEMMA 4.1. *Let R_i, $i = 1, 2$, be disjoint regions in M. Set $\widehat{\text{Union}}$ $(R_1, R_2) = H$ and suppose that $\beta R_1 \cap \beta R_2$ is a connected element $k \in F_M^* \mid H$. Let u_i be F_M-admissible in R_i and continuous on $R_i \cup k$. Then if u_1 and u_2 are k-compatible, the function u defined on H in* (4.2) *is* PH *on H.*

The preceding discussion shows that u is PH at all nonsingular points of k. Since it is continuous at the singular points on k (if any exist), it is PH at them by [2, Lemma 2.1].

An F-guide g [6, § 10] enters into our study of functions F_M-admissible on M by way of its covering g_M on M.

The function $u \mid g_M$. Let the covering g_M of the F-guide be sensed so that the longitude $\theta \uparrow \infty$ as g_M is traced in its positive sense. Let

u be a function F_M-admissible on M. On g_M, u is locally strictly monotone except at reversing points. At such points $u \mid g_M$ changes its type of monotonicity. In particular, on the intersection k of g_M with a primitive, $u \mid g_M$ changes its type of monotonicity just once, at the unique reversing point in k [6, Theorem 10.2].

5. A meridian in F^*. The terms meridian, meridional sector, primitive, and so on, originally defined for F^* and Σ^*, are carried over without further comment to the maximal connected coverings on M of these sets.

When a meridian exists in F^*, the condition $\mu(F) = 0$ on F implies loop coverage [6, § 9] on Σ^*, while the condition $\nu(F) = 0$ implies the existence of a doubly connected meridional region [6, Theorem 11.2(b)]. With this understood, we shall prove the following lemma.

LEMMA 5.1. *If a meridian exists in F^* and u is F_M-admissible over M, then the following is true.*

(1) *On the two meridian boundaries in M of a polar sector X of primitive type, or of a maximal cut sector Y, u assumes just one value.*

(2) *On the two meridian boundaries of a meridional unit or sector R, u assumes two different values.*

(3) *If p is a nonreversing point in g_M (g an F-guide), the types of monotonicity of $u \mid g_M$ at p and at $p^{(1)}$ are the same or opposite according as $\nu(F)$ is even or odd.*

(4) *If $\mu(F) = 0$, u has the same value on each meridian in M.*

(5) *If $\nu(F) = 0$, and if p is a point on a meridian h, $u(p^{(1)}) \neq u(p)$.*

Proof of (1). Let p and q be any two points in βX. If $e > 0$ is prescribed, there exists a nonsingular loop ϕ_e in X which meets e-neighborhoods of p and q. The equality $u(p) = u(q)$ is then implied by the constancy of u over $| \phi_e |$ and the continuity of u at p and q.

The two meridian limits of Y either intersect or are connected by an arc of $F_M^* \mid Y$. The constant values of u on these two limits are thus equal.

Proof of (2). If R is a meridional sector, u is strictly monotone on $g_M \mid R$. Hence u assumes different values on the two meridian boundaries of R.

If R is a meridional unit, the number of reversing points in g_M between any two successive meridional sectors in R is even, so that the type of monotonicity of $u \mid g_M$ in each meridional sector in R is the same. Taken with (1), this implies that the resultant algebraic change in u along $g_M \mid R$ is not zero.

Proof of (3). This statement follows directly from the definition of $\nu(F)$.

Proof of (4). If $\mu(F) = 0$, a meridian h is either in the boundary of an unbounded primitive or in the closure of a maximal cut sector Y. Because of (1), $u(h)$ has the same value for all meridian boundaries of sectors of primitive type or of maximal cut sectors. There remains the case of a meridian in $\bar{Y}$ but not in βY. However such a meridian h meets βY or else an element in $F_M^* \mid Y$ incident with βY, so that $u(h) = u(\beta Y)$.

Proof of (5). If $\nu(F) = 0$, $u \mid g_M$ is strictly monotone. Then for an arbitrary point $q \in g_M$, $u(q^{(1)}) \neq u(q)$. But the given meridian h in F_M^* bearing p meets g_M in some point q, and $h^{(1)}$ meets g_M in $q^{(1)}$ and bears $p^{(1)}$. Thus

$$u(q) = u(p), \qquad u(q^{(1)}) = u(p^{(1)}), \qquad u(q^{(1)}) \neq u(q),$$

from which (5) follows.

We come to a major theorem.

THEOREM 5.1. *If there is at least one meridian in F^*, and if there exists a function u which is F_M-admissible over M and invariant under a transformation $T(a, b)$, then*

(i) *$a > 0$ or $a < 0$ according as $\nu(F)$ is even or odd;*
(ii) *The conditions $\mu(F) = 1$ and $a = 1$ imply $b \neq 0$;*
(iii) *The conditions $\mu(F) = 0$ and $a = 1$ imply $b = 0$.*

Proof of (i). Let p and r be distinct points on a transverse subarc of g_M. Then $p^{(1)}$ and $r^{(1)}$ are on a congruent transverse subarc of g_M. It follows from Lemma 5.1(3) that $u(p) - u(r)$ and $u(p^{(1)}) - u(r^{(1)})$ have the same or opposite signs according as $\nu(F)$ is even or odd. But

$$u(p^{(1)}) = au(p) + b, \qquad u(r^{(1)}) = au(r) + b$$

so that

$$a = \frac{u(p^{(1)}) - u(r^{(1)})}{u(p) - u(r)}. \tag{5.1}$$

Thus (i) holds.

Proof of (ii). By hypothesis $a = 1$ so that

$$u(p^{(1)}) - u(p) = b \qquad (p \in M). \tag{5.2}$$

If $\nu(F) = 0$, $u \mid g_M$ is strictly monotone, so that $b \neq 0$ in (5.2), and (ii) is established in this case.

If $\nu(F) \neq 0$, a decomposition of Σ^* into disjoint canonical sectors is given in [6, Theorem 12.1(a)]. If Z is a meridional unit, there is no meridional sector not in Z, since $\mu(F) = 1$. Let h and k be meridian boundaries of Z_M, with $h < k$ in the sense of [6, § 12]. On h and k, u assumes different values c_1 and c_2 respectively (Lemma 5.1(2)). The region between k and $h^{(1)}$ will be the Union of disjoint canonical sectors of primitive type or maximal cut sectors. On the meridian limits of these canonical sectors u will assume the value $u(k) = c_2$ (Lemma 5.1(1)). In particular, $u(h^{(1)}) = c_2$. In (5.2), then, $b = c_2 - c_1$. Thus $b \neq 0$, as stated in (ii).

Proof of (iii). Here $\mu(F) = 0$. If h is any meridian, $u(h) = u(h^{(1)})$ by Lemma 5.1(4). Since $a = 1$ by hypothesis, (5.2) implies that $b = 0$.

This establishes Theorem 5.1.

To show that the conditions on F^* and $T(a, b)$ in Theorem 5.1 are sufficient for the existence of a function u which is F_M-admissible over M and invariant under $T(a, b)$, two lemmas will now be established. Note first that if h is a meridian on M, then $h \cap h^{(1)} = \emptyset$. Otherwise h and $h^{(1)}$ would be identical open arcs in F_M^*. The projection of h on Σ^* would then carry a topological circle in F^*, which is impossible.

LEMMA 5.2. *Let h be a meridian in M. Let R be the region in M bounded by h and $h^{(1)}$. In $T(a, b)$ suppose that $a > 0$ or $a < 0$ according as $\nu(F)$ is even or odd. If u is F_M-admissible over $\bar{R}$ and assumes values c and c_1 on h and $h^{(1)}$ respectively such that $c_1 = ac + b$, then u admits an extension over M which is F_M-admissible over M and invariant under $T(a, b)$.*

Set $h^{(1)} = k$. Let u, defined over $\bar{R}$, be extended over $H = R \cup k \cup R^{(1)}$ by setting

$$u(p^{(1)}) = au(p) + b \qquad (p \in R). \tag{5.3}$$

So extended, u is continuous over H since $c_1 = ac + b$ and $u(h^{(1)}) =$

c_1. We shall show that the functions

$$u \mid (R \cup k), \qquad u \mid (R^{(1)} \cup k) \tag{5.4}$$

are k-compatible.

Let g be an F-guide. Since longitude θ takes all values on g_M, there exists a point p in $g_M \cap h$ at which g_M passes from the negative to the positive side of h [6, § 12]. Then p is not a reversing point on g_M. Let g_1 be the sensed subarc of g_M between p and $p^{(1)}$. Let λ and μ be respectively initial and final transverse subarcs of g_1 and let η be a transverse subarc of g_M following g_1. The point $p^{(1)}$ is a final end point of μ and an initial end point of η. The type of monotonicity of $u \mid \lambda$ is or is not that of $u \mid \mu$ according as $\nu(F)$ is even or odd, and is or is not that of $u \mid \eta$ according as $a > 0$ or $a < 0$. Hence the type of monotonicity of $u \mid \mu$ is that of $u \mid \eta$. The k-compatibility of the two functions in (5.4) follows, and Lemma 4.1 implies that u is PH over H.

We now extend u over all of M by requiring that (5.3) hold without exception. Each point in M has a neighborhood which is congruent to a neighborhood in H, so that the lemma follows from the fact that u is PH over H.

LEMMA 5.3. *Let h_1 and $h_1^{(1)}$ be meridians on M bounding a Union R of canonical sectors. Let w be a function F_M-admissible over M. If there exists a meridional sector H in R, there exists a function u, F_M-admissible over M and such that*

$$u(h_1) = w(h_1), \qquad u(h_1^{(1)}) = w(h_1^{(1)}) + ed, \tag{5.5}$$

where d is an arbitrary constant $\geqq 0$, and $e = +1$ or -1, according as w is increasing or decreasing on $g_M \mid H$.

Let h_2 and h_3 be two nonsingular meridians in H. If $h_2 < h_3$ then $h_1 < h_2 < h_3 < h_4 = h_1^{(1)}$. Let R_{23} be the region in M bounded by h_2 and h_3, let R_2 be the region in M bounded by h_2 which contains h_1, and let R_3 be the region in M bounded by h_3 which contains h_4. With μ a positive constant, set

$$u \mid \bar{R}_2 = w \mid \bar{R}_2, \tag{5.6}$$

$$u \mid \bar{R}_{23} = w(h_2) + \mu[w - w(h_2)] \mid \bar{R}_{23}, \tag{5.7}$$

$$u \mid \bar{R}_3 = u(h_3) + [w - w(h_3)] \mid \bar{R}_3, \tag{5.8}$$

where it is understood that $u(h_3)$ in (5.8) is defined by (5.7). One sees that u is continuous over M. Further, $u \mid \bar{R}_2$ and $u \mid \bar{R}_{23}$ are h_2-compatible since the type of monotonicity of $w \mid \bar{R}_2$ on g_M at the point $g_M \cap h_2$ is that of $\mu w \mid \bar{R}_{23}$ on g_M at the same point. Similarly $u \mid \bar{R}_{23}$ and $u \mid \bar{R}_3$ are h_3-compatible. Finally

$$u(h_1^{(1)}) = (\mu - 1)[w(h_3) - w(h_2)] + w(h_1^{(1)})$$

so that u satisfies the lemma if μ is properly chosen.

The second principal theorem of this section follows.

THEOREM 5.2. *If there is a meridian in F^*, and if $T(a, b)$ satisfies the necessary conditions of Theorem 5.1 but is otherwise arbitrary, there exists a function u which is F_M-admissible over M, and invariant under $T(a, b)$.*

We distinguish three cases:

Case I. $\mu(F) = 0$. This is the case of loop coverage [6, § 9].

Case II. $\mu(F) = 1$. In this case if $\nu(F) = 0$ there exists a doubly connected meridional region. If $\nu(F) > 0$ there exists a meridional sector [6, § 12].

Case III. $\mu(F) > 1$. This is the general case.

Proof for Case I. Choose c so that $c = ac + b$. Such a constant exists if $a \neq 1$. If $a = 1$ then $b = 0$ by hypothesis in Case I (Theorem 5.1 (iii)), so that c is arbitrary when $a = 1$. Let w be F_M-admissible. Let h be a meridian in F_M^*. By virtue of Lemma 5.1(4) we can assume that $w(h) = w(h^{(1)}) = c$. Let R be the region in M bounded by h and $h^{(1)}$. It follows from Lemma 5.2 that $w \mid \bar{R}$ admits an extension over M which satisfies Theorem 5.2.

Proof for Case II. Let c_1 and c be any two constants such that $c_1 \neq c$ and $c_1 = ac + b$. Such constants exist since $(a, b) \neq (1, 0)$ by hypothesis when $\mu(F) = 1$ (Theorem 5.1 (ii)). If $\nu(F) = 0$, let h be an arbitrary meridian. If $\nu(F) > 0$, let h be a meridian boundary of a meridional sector. It follows from Lemma 5.1(5) and from Lemma 5.3, respectively, that there is a function w which is F_M-admissible over M and assumes different values on h and $h^{(1)}$. Without loss of generality we may suppose that $w(h) = c$ and $w(h^{(1)}) = c_1$. Indeed, the fact that $c \neq c_1$ and $w(h) \neq w(h^{(1)})$ implies the existence of real constants A and B not both zero such that $Aw(h) + B = c$ and $Aw(h^{(1)}) + B = c_1$. Let R be the region bounded by h and

$h^{(1)}$. It follows from Lemma 5.2 that $w \mid \bar{R}$ admits an extension over M which satisfies Theorem 5.2.

Proof for Case III. Let c be a constant and set $c_1 = ac + b$. Since $\mu(F) > 1$, there exist disjoint meridional sectors on Σ^* in which the types of monotonicity on g_M of an arbitrary F_M-admissible function PH on M are different. Let h be a meridian boundary of a canonical sector. Let w be F_M-admissible over M and such that $w(h) = c$. It follows from Lemma 5.3 that there exists a function $\tilde{u}$, F_M-admissible over M, such that $\tilde{u}(h) = w(h)$ and $\tilde{u}(h^{(1)}) = w(h^{(1)}) + d$, where d is an arbitrary constant. Hence we may assume that $\tilde{u}(h) = c$ and $\tilde{u}(h^{(1)}) = c_1$. Let R be the region in M bounded by h and $h^{(1)}$. It follows from Lemma 5.2 that $\tilde{u} \mid \bar{R}$ admits an extension u over M which satisfies Theorem 5.2.

COROLLARY 5.1. *Suppose that a meridian exists in F^*. A function u which is F-admissible over Σ^* fails to exist when $\mu(F) = 1$ or when $\nu(F)$ is odd, and exists in all other cases.*

6. No meridian in F^*. Necessary conditions. We now turn to the solution of Problem I in case there is no meridian in F^*. The conditions on F^* and $T(a, b)$ depend upon a separation of Case I, in which there is at least one asymptote in F^*, from Case II, in which there is no such asymptote. We begin with the following lemma.

LEMMA 6.1. *In a spiral or concave annulus A filled with asymptotes* [6, §§ 5, 8] *there is an F-guide g without reversing point.*

We begin by mapping A conformally onto a ring R on Σ^* bounded by two parallels or by a parallel and one pole. We then map R topologically onto Σ^* so that parallels in R go into parallels. The elements in $F \mid A$ are all asymptotes without singularity. In case A is a spiral annulus they tend in one sense to a point on that F^*-cycle or pole boundary of A which is not an asymptotic limit. In any case, they are carried into a family F_1 of open arcs on Σ^* each of which is an F_1-meridian. There accordingly exists an F_1-guide on Σ^* without reversing point [6, Theorem 11.2], so that an F-guide without reversing point exists in A.

THEOREM 6.1. *When there is no meridian in F^*, $\nu(F) = 0$ or 2 according as there exists at least one asymptotic F^*-ray or no asymptotic F^*-ray.*

We begin by proving the following assertion:

(i) *If there is no meridian or asymptotic F^*-ray, $\nu(F) = 2$.*

When there is no asymptotic F^*-ray there is no spiral annulus in Σ^*, since such annuli are covered with asymptotic F^*-rays [6, Theorem 8.2]. Hence in this case

$$\Sigma^* = \hat{\text{U}}\text{nion } (U_N, C, U_S),$$

where C is a central annulus, U_N an N-cap, and U_S an S-cap. The annulus C cannot be empty since there is no meridian in F^*. Moreover, C must be covered with inner F^*-cycles [6, Theorem 8.1].

An F-guide g might lie in or meet any one of the sets U_N, C, U_S. If g is in C it is clear that $\nu(F) = 2$. If g is in U_N, U_N would necessarily be an annulus with an S-concave [6, § 3] south boundary F^*-cycle, and one sees that g would meet at least two of the N-primitives whose Ûnion is U_N. (See [6, Theorem 10.2].) In this case $\nu(F) = 2$, since there is a 2-transverse topological circle in C.

If g meets U_N but does not lie in U_N, g would meet at least one N-primitive in U_N and so bear a reversing point in this primitive. The intersection of g with Ûnion (C, U_S) would bear at least one other reversing point, so that $\nu(F) = 2$ as before. One can interchange U_N and U_S in the preceding argument. Hence $\nu(F) = 2$.

The theorem follows from (i) and Lemma 6.1.

An element $h \in F^*$ which bears at least one asymptotic ray will now be called simply an *asymptote*.

Let u be F_M-admissible on M. The values of u on congruent asymptotes in M and on a limiting cycle are conditioned as follows.

LEMMA 6.2. *Let A be a concave or spiral annulus in Σ^* bounded on the north by an asymptotic cycle $\phi \in \Phi$. Let u be F_M-admissible in A_M and let h be an element in $F \mid A$ asymptotic to $\phi+$ $[\phi-]$. Let B_N be the north boundary of A_M. Set $h_n = [h_M]^{(n)}$. The values $u(h_n) = u_n$ define a strictly monotone function over the set of rational integers, and u can be continuously extended over $A_M \cup B_N$ if and only if the sequence*

$$u_{-1}, u_{-2}, \cdots \qquad [u_1, u_2, \cdots]$$

converges. The analogous statement with north replaced by south holds.

According to Lemma 6.1, there exists an F-guide g in A without reversing point. Set $p_0 = g_M \cap h_M$ and $p_n = (p_0)^{(n)}$. Then $p_n =$

$g_M \cap h_n$ and the values $u_n = u(p_n)$ must vary strictly monotonically with n since the points p_n appear on g_M in the order of n, and g_M bears no reversing points. Recall that h is nonsingular.

Let λ be a sensed transversal which is in A_M with a nonsingular point $p \in B_N$ as limiting terminal point. For definiteness, suppose that h is asymptotic to $\phi+$ and refer to [6, Lemma 4.1]. If r is a sufficiently large fixed integer and if $n < -r$, h_n will meet λ in a point q_n such that $q_n \to p$ as $n \downarrow -\infty$ and such that the order of the points q_n on λ is the order of the integers n. Recall that u is strictly monotonic on λ.

If then u admits a continuous extension over $A_M \cup B_N$, the sequence $u_{-1}, u_{-2}, \cdots$ must converge to the value $u(p) = u(B_N)$. Conversely, if the sequence converges to a value c, we shall show that u admits a continuous extension over $A_M \cup B_N$ with $u(B_N) = c$.

For $n < -r$ let λ_n be the open subarc of λ between q_n and p, and let E_n be the subarc of h_n with end points q_n and $q_{n-1}^{(1)}$. Let Q_n be the limited subregion of A_M bounded in A_M by the open arc

$$\lambda_n E_n \lambda_{n-1}^{(1)}.$$

The projection of Q_n on Σ^* lies in A, and so contains no singular point. The range of values of u on Q_n is the range of values of u on λ_n. Indeed, an element $\alpha \in F_M$ which meets Q_n meets λ_n, since βA_M is concave toward A_M and h_n is nonsingular. Moreover, the maximum distance of points of Q_n from βA_M tends to zero as $n \downarrow -\infty$. If, then, $u_{-1}, u_{-2}, \cdots$ converges to a finite value c, the inf and sup of values of u on λ_n and hence on Q_n tend to c, and it follows that u admits a continuous extension over $A_M \cup B_N$ in which $u(B_N) = c$.

Asymptote of type (e_1, e_2). An F^*-ray π asymptotic to $\phi+$ or to $\phi-$, where ϕ is a cycle in Φ, will be said to be asymptotic of *type* $e = +$ or $e = -$, respectively. An element in F^* which is divided by a point into two asymptotic F^*-rays of types e_1 and e_2 respectively will be said to be an *asymptote of type* (e_1, e_2). An F^*-cycle ψ to which an F^*-ray is asymptotic will be called a *limit cycle,* and any loop carried by $|\psi|$ and sensed as in ψ will be called a *limit loop.*

The invariant value c. When $a \neq 1$, the transformation $T(a, b)$ may be written in the form

$$u(p^{(1)}) - c = a[u(p) - c] \qquad (c = b/(1 - a)), \tag{6.1}$$

so that $T^n(a, b)$ has the form

$$(6.2) \quad u(p^{(n)}) - c = a^n[u(p) - c], \qquad n = 0, \pm 1, \pm 2, \cdots.$$

We term c the *invariant value* of $T(a, b)$. If u is F_M-admissible over the closure of a region $R \subset M$ and invariant under a transformation $T(a, b)$ for which $a \neq 1$, then u takes the invariant value c of $T(a, b)$ on any self-congruent element in $F_M^* \mid \bar{R}$.

When $a = 1$, there exists a constant c such that $c = ac + b$ if and only if $b = 0$. When $a = 1$ and $b = 0$, every value of c is an invariant value. When $a = 1$,

$$(6.3) \qquad u(p^{(n)}) = u(p) + nb.$$

Theorem 6.2 gives the necessary and sufficient (§ 8) conditions sought in Problem I, provided there is no meridian in F^*:

THEOREM 6.2. *In the case in which there is no meridian in F^*, suppose that there exists a function u which is F_M-admissible over M and invariant under $T(a, b)$. Let Case* I *be the case in which there is at least one asymptote in F^* and let Case* II *be the complementary case.*

(i) *In Case* I, *$a > 0$ and $a \neq 1$. Each asymptotic F^*-ray π is of type $+$ or $-$ according as $a > 1$ or $a < 1$, and each cycle $\phi \in \Phi$ is isolated in Φ. If c is the invariant value of $T(a, b)$, $u(\pi_M) \neq c$, and if h is any component of $\mid \phi \mid$ in Σ^*, $u(h_M) = c$ whenever ϕ is in Ψ* [6, § 8].

(ii) *In Case* II, *$a = 1$ and $b = 0$. Moreover*

$$(6.4) \qquad \Sigma^* = \hat{\mathrm{U}}\mathrm{nion}\,(U_N, C, U_S),$$

where C is a central annulus filled with topological circles in F^*.

Proof of (i). Suppose that π is asymptotic to $\psi \in \Phi$. On setting $(\pi_M)^{(n)} = \pi_n$ and $u(\pi_n) = u_n$, $n = 0, \pm 1, \pm 2, \cdots$, we have

$$(6.5) \qquad u_n = u_0 + nb, \quad \text{if} \quad a = 1,$$

$$(6.6) \qquad u_n - c = a^n[u_0 - c], \quad \text{if} \quad a \neq 1.$$

Let k be a component of $\mid \psi \mid$ in Σ^*. According to Lemma 6.2, u_{-1}, u_{-2}, $\cdots$ converges in strictly monotone fashion to $u(k_M)$. It follows that (6.5) cannot hold, and that, in (6.6), $u_0 \neq c$, $a > 1$, and $u_n \to c$ as $n \downarrow -\infty$. Hence $u(k_M) = c$. If π is asymptotic to $\psi-$, it similarly follows that $u_0 \neq c$, $0 < a < 1$, and $u(k_M) = c$.

Let ϕ now be arbitrary in Φ. Let $h \in F^*$ be a component of $\mid \phi \mid$ in Σ^*. If ϕ is an inner cycle, h_M is self-congruent, and since $a \neq 1$

in Case I, we infer that $u(h_M) = c$. Hence inner cycles are isolated in Φ. It follows that every cycle ϕ in Ψ is a limit cycle in Case I, and from the results of the preceding paragraph $u(h_M) = c$ if h is a component of $|\phi|$ in Σ^*.

Proof of (ii). For any point p in M on the covering of an inner cycle, $u(p) = u(p^{(1)})$, and if $a \neq 1$, by (6.1), $u(p) = c$. When there are no asymptotes there are no spiral annuli, so that when no meridian and no asymptotes exist, there must be a central annulus C filled with inner cycles. If, then, $a \neq 1$, $u(p) = c$ for each $p \in C_M$. Since this is impossible, we infer that $a = 1$. From the relation $u(p^{(1)}) = u(p)$, for $p \in M$ on the covering of an inner cycle, and from (6.3) we conclude that $b = 0$. Thus $a = 1$ and $b = 0$.

Since there are no spiral annuli in Case II, the decomposition (6.4) follows.

Notation $k(r_1, r_2)$. We adopt the following convention. Let k be an arc or open arc in M or in Σ^* and let r_1 and r_2 be points in k. If $r_1 \neq r_2$, let $k(r_1, r_2)$ be the subarc of k with end points r_1 and r_2. If $r_1 = r_2$, let $k(r_1, r_2) = r_1 = r_2$.

7. Concave annuli. In showing that the conditions on F^* and $T(a, b)$ given in Theorem 6.2 are sufficient for the existence of a function u conditioned as in Problem I, we shall define u separately on concave annuli, spiral annuli, and caps. We begin with a concave annulus $A(\phi_1, \phi_2)$ bounded by cycles ϕ_1 and ϕ_2 in Φ with $\phi_1 < \phi_2$. We suppose A filled with asymptotes of type (e, e).

LEMMA 7.1. *There exists a topological circle g in A which is an F-guide without reversing point, and an arc k which is in A except for nonsingular end points r' and r'' in $|\phi_1|$ and $|\phi_2|$ respectively and which is the union of two F-transverse arcs k' and k'' which meet g in a reversing point Q and join r' to Q on the south side of g and Q to r'' on the north side of g.*

It follows from Lemma 6.1 that there is an F-guide g in A without reversing points. Let λ' and λ'' be two nonintersecting arcs in $\bar{A}$ such that λ' is incident with r' in $|\phi_1|$, λ'' with r'' in $|\phi_2|$, $\lambda' - r'$ and $\lambda'' - r''$ are in A and F-transverse. There exists an asymptote μ in F which meets λ' in a point q' near r' south of g, and λ'' in a point q'' near r'' north of g. We start with the composite arc

$$\lambda'(r', q')\mu(q', q'')\lambda''(q'', r'')$$

joining r' to r'', and replace $\mu(q', q'')$ by a 2-transverse arc $\gamma(q', q'')$ which joins q' to q'', taking $\gamma(q', q'')$ in A on the opposite side of μ from r' and r''. We can suppose that $\gamma(q', q'')$ meets g in just one point Q, a reversing point of $\gamma(q', q'')$. If one sets

$$k' = \lambda'(r', q')\gamma(q', Q), \qquad k'' = \gamma(Q, q'')\lambda''(q'', r''),$$

the lemma is satisfied.

Concept of μ-mapping. We shall have occasion to map various sensed arcs h in a metric space I onto various sensed arcs k in a metric space II. To that end we refer both h and k to their μ-lengths [7, § 27] as parameters measured from their initial points, making points on h and k correspond which divide h and k in the same ratio with respect to μ-length. We term this mapping of h onto k a μ-mapping.

The mapping f of the ring H onto A. The annulus A is the directly conformal image of a ring H in the z-plane, on which $0 < \rho_1 < |z| < \rho_2 < \infty$, under a map f of H onto A. We can suppose f extended to a map defined over $\bar{H}$ and continuous. (Cf. the proof of Theorem 3.1 in [6].) We can also suppose that f maps the circle $\{|z| = \rho_2\}$ onto the set $|\phi_2|$ and the circle $\{|z| = \rho_1\}$ onto $|\phi_1|$. Such a map is locally one-to-one in a neighborhood (relative to $\bar{H}$) of each point of βH whose f-image is in Σ^*. If ϕ_1 [ϕ_2] meets S [N] the f-antecedent of S [N] in βH is a closed, nowhere dense set on the circle on which $|z| = \rho_1$ [$|z| = \rho_2$].

The model family $\mathfrak{F}_H$ on H. The universal covering surface of the ring is represented by the strip

$$K: 0 < \rho_1 < \rho < \rho_2 \qquad (-\infty < \alpha < \infty)$$

in the (ρ, α) plane, where the point (ρ, α) in K projects into the point $z = \rho e^{-i\alpha}$ in H. We introduce a model function V, PH on K, continuous on $\bar{K}$, and of the form

$$V(\rho, \alpha) = e^{c_1\alpha} \sin \pi \left(\frac{\rho - \rho_1}{\rho_2 - \rho_1}\right) + c, \tag{7.1}$$

where c and c_1 are real constants with $c_1 > 0$. Note that $V(\rho_1, \alpha) = V(\rho_2, \alpha) = c$. The function V has no critical points on $\bar{K}$. Moreover,

$$V(\rho, \alpha + 2\pi) - c = a[V(\rho, \alpha) - c] \qquad (a = e^{2\pi c_1}). \tag{7.2}$$

For variable choice of $c_1 > 0$, a is arbitrary and > 1. The model family $\mathfrak{F}_K$ of open level arcs of $V \mid K$ is composed of asymptotes, each divided by a point into two rays asymptotic respectively to the straight lines on which $\rho = \rho_1$ and $\rho = \rho_2$, these lines having the sense of increasing α. Let $\mathfrak{F}_H$ denote the projection of the curve family $\mathfrak{F}_K$ onto H.

The given family F_H. On H we introduce also the family of asymptotes

$$F_H = f^{-1}(F \mid A) \qquad (A = A(\phi_1, \phi_2)).$$

LEMMA 7.2. *If the family $F \mid A$ is composed of asymptotes of type (e, e), where $e = \pm$, there exists a topological map Ω_e of $\bar{H}$ onto $\bar{H}$ leaving the boundaries of the ring pointwise invariant in case $e = +$, reflecting each boundary in the axis of reals if $e = -$, and such that*

$$F_H = \Omega_e \mathfrak{F}_H, \qquad F \mid A = f\Omega_e \mathfrak{F}_H. \tag{7.3}$$

The arcs k_F and g_F. We return to Lemma 7.1 and set

$$f^{-1}g = g_F, \qquad f^{-1}Q = Q_F, \qquad f^{-1}k = k_F.$$

The arc k_F is in the ring H except for end points q_1 and q_2 such that $f(q_1)$ and $f(q_2)$ are nonsingular points of ϕ_1 and ϕ_2 respectively. It is such that k_F is the union of two F_H-transverse arcs k_F' and k_F'' which meet in an F_H-reversing point Q_F of k_F and which join q_1 to Q_F and Q_F to q_2, respectively. We can suppose that q_1 and q_2 are points in $\bar{H}$ with polar coordinates $(\rho_1, 0)$ and $(\rho_2, 0)$ respectively. No generality is lost thereby in the proof of Lemma 7.2, if one takes account of our freedom to choose the axis in the z-plane on which the polar angle α equals 0.

The arc k_F is 2-transverse relative to the family F_H. Relative to the family $\mathfrak{F}_H$, we analogously introduce the radial arc

$$k_{\mathfrak{F}} : \{\rho_1 \leqq \rho \leqq \rho_2, \alpha = 0\}$$

in $\bar{H}$, composed of two $\mathfrak{F}_H$-transverse arcs

$$k'_{\mathfrak{F}} : \{\rho_1 \leqq \rho \leqq (\rho_1 + \rho_2)/2, \alpha = 0\}$$

$$k''_{\mathfrak{F}} : \{(\rho_1 + \rho_2)/2 \leqq \rho \leqq \rho_2, \alpha = 0\}$$

meeting in a point $Q_{\mathfrak{F}}$ which is the unique $\mathfrak{F}_H$-reversing point of $k_{\mathfrak{F}}$ in H. Let $g_{\mathfrak{F}}$ be the circle in H on which $\rho = \frac{1}{2}(\rho_1 + \rho_2)$. The circle $g_{\mathfrak{F}}$ is transverse to $\mathfrak{F}$.

The definition of Ω_e. Suppose first that $e = +$ in the lemma. Consider the open topological rectangle $R_{\mathfrak{F}}$ in H bounded by $k_{\mathfrak{F}}''$, $g_{\mathfrak{F}}$ and the circle $[\rho = \rho_2]$, and the open topological rectangle R_F in H bounded by k_F'', g_F and the circle $[\rho = \rho_2]$. Under Ω_+, let $g_{\mathfrak{F}}$ be cut at the point $Q_{\mathfrak{F}}$ and positively sensed, and then μ-mapped onto g_F, cut at Q_F, and positively sensed. Map the circle $\rho = \rho_2$ onto itself under the identity. Take each maximal $\mathfrak{F}_H$-vector in the closure of $R_{\mathfrak{F}}$, and each maximal F_H-vector in the closure of R_F in the sense of its asymptotic continuation on the north side of $g_{\mathfrak{F}}$ and g_F respectively. Let a point r trace $g_{\mathfrak{F}}$ once in its negative sense starting from $Q_{\mathfrak{F}}$, and continue by tracing $k_{\mathfrak{F}}''$. Let the maximal $\mathfrak{F}_H$-vector X_r in the closure of $R_{\mathfrak{F}}$ with initial point r (the initial vector being omitted when $r = Q_{\mathfrak{F}}$) be μ-mapped onto the maximal F_H-vector in the closure of R_F with initial point $\Omega_+(r)$. This map defines $\Omega_+(q_r)$ at the terminal point q_r of X_r, and since q_r sweeps out $k_{\mathfrak{F}}''$ in advance of r, $\Omega_+(r)$ continues to be defined as r traces $k_{\mathfrak{F}}''$. The map Ω_+ is thereby defined over the part of the ring H on which $\frac{1}{2}(\rho_1 + \rho_2) \leqq |z| \leqq \rho_2$. It is similarly defined over the remainder of the ring. So defined, Ω_+ satisfies the lemma when $e = +$.

In case $e = -$, a reflection J of F_H in the axis of reals gives a curve family F_H' over H consisting of asymptotes of type $(+, +)$. There exists, as above, a topological map Ω_+' of $\bar{H}$ onto $\bar{H}$ such that $F_H' = \Omega_+'\mathfrak{F}_H$. If one sets $\Omega_- = J\Omega_+'$, then (7.3) holds and Ω_- has the required character.

This establishes the lemma in all cases.

We now state the first of several lemmas concerned with the existence of a function u in Problem I when there is no meridian in F^*.

LEMMA 7.3. *In the case in which cycles in* Φ *are isolated and in which asymptotic* F^**-rays exist and are of one type e, let C be a nonempty central annulus. Corresponding to any transformation* $T(a, b) \mid (a > 0)$ *in which* $a > 1$ *or* $a < 1$ *according as the asymptotes are of type* $(+, +)$ *or* $(-, -)$, *there exists a function u,* F_M*-admissible over* C_M, *continuous on* $\bar{C}_M$, *invariant under* $T(a, b)$ *and taking the invariant value c of* $T(a, b)$ *on* βC_M *(unless the latter is void).*

Consider first the case in which C consists of a single concave annulus A filled with asymptotes of type (e, e). The function V defined in (7.1) over the strip $\bar{K}$ is $\mathfrak{F}_K$-admissible over K, continuous on $\bar{K}$, and satisfies (7.2). There exists a topological map θ_e of $\bar{A}_M$

into $\bar{K}$ related to the map $f\Omega_e$ of $\bar{H}$ onto $\bar{A}$ as follows. If $P \in \bar{A}_M$ goes into $Q \in \bar{K}$ under θ_e, and if P covers $p \in \bar{A}$ and Q covers $q \in \bar{H}$, then $p = f\Omega_e(q)$. The function $u = V\theta_e$ is defined over $\bar{A}_M$ and satisfies the lemma when $C = A$. In particular, u takes the value c on βA_M, where c is the invariant value of $T(a, b)$, since V assumes the value c on βK.

In the general case, C_M has the form

$$C_M = \hat{\text{U}}\text{nion } \{A^r\}_M$$

where r is a rational integer with a range which may be $(-\infty, \infty)$, $(0, \infty)$, $(-\infty, 0)$, or a finite range $(0, m)$. Here A^r is a nonempty concave annulus filled with asymptotes of type (e, e), where e equals $\pm$ and is independent of r; no two annuli A^r meet and the north boundary of A^r is the south boundary of A^{r+1}, when the latter exists. Let U_r be a function defined on $Cl\{A^r\}_M$ and satisfying the lemma when A^r is read in place of C. It follows from Theorem 6.2(i) that $U_r(p) \neq c$ for $p \in \{A^r\}_M$. We can suppose that the sign of $U_r - c$ on $\{A^r\}_M$ is $(-1)^r$. Indeed, either U_r or else the function U_r^* such that

$$U_r^* - c = -[U_r - c]$$

has this property. A function u which equals U_r on $Cl\{A^r\}_M$ will be defined over $\bar{C}_M$ and satisfy the lemma (compare with Lemma 4.1).

LEMMA 7.4. *If a central annulus C is filled with inner cycles, then there is a function U which is F-admissible over C, bounded and continuous over $\bar{C}$, and which takes on different values on different inner cycles of $F^* \mid C$. The function u induced on C_M by U is invariant under $T(a, b)$ if and only if $a = 1$, $b = 0$.*

For any point $p \in C$, let h_p be the topological circle in F^* meeting p. Let $U(p)$ be the maximum distance of a point of h_p from S. Then U is continuous over C and takes on different values on different topological circles in F^*. Clearly U is PH over C. Referring to [6, § 7], set

$$\phi_1 = \inf \phi \mid (|\phi| \subset C), \qquad \phi_2 = \sup \phi \mid (|\phi| \subset C).$$

Then U becomes continuous over $\bar{C}$ if and only if one sets

$$U(\phi_1) = \inf U(p) \mid (p \in C), \qquad U(\phi_2) = \sup U(p) \mid (p \in C).$$

The last statement of the lemma is evident.

8. No meridian in F^*. Sufficient conditions. The conditions on F^* and $T(a, b)$ given in Theorem 6.2 as necessary for the existence of a function u, F_M-admissible on M and invariant under $T(a, b)$, will be proved sufficient. The nature of a solution on a central annulus has been considered in § 7. We turn now to a spiral annulus.

LEMMA 8.1. *Let W_N be a nonempty N-spiral annulus, U_N an N-cap (necessarily nonannular and possibly empty), and set*

$$X_N = \hat{\text{U}}\text{nion } (U_N, W_N).$$

Corresponding to a $T(a, b)$, $a > 0$, in which $a > 1$ or $a < 1$ according as the asymptotic F^*-rays on W_N are of $+$ or $-$ type (§ 6), there exists a function u, F_M-admissible on $\bar{X}_{NM}$, invariant under $T(a, b)$ and taking the invariant value c of $T(a, b)$ on βX_{NM}.

The lemma also holds if N is replaced by S.

There exists a nonsingular element $h \in F^*$ in W_N with limiting initial point in N, and with h asymptotic to $\psi_N\pm$ [6, Theorem 8.2]. Let w be a function F_M-admissible over M. Let π on M cover h and let K be the closure of the region on M bounded by π and $\pi^{(1)}$. Set $u(p) = w(p) + c_1$ for $p \in K$, and choose c_1 so that

$$u(\pi^{(1)}) - c = a[u(\pi) - c]. \tag{8.1}$$

This is possible since $a \neq 1$. Let u be further defined on X_{NM} so as to be invariant under $T(a, b)$. So defined, u is continuous on X_{NM}. That u is PH on X_{NM} is seen as follows. By Lemma 6.1 there is an F-guide g in W_N without reversing point. The type of monotonicity of u on $g_M \cap K$ is that on $g_M \cap K^{(1)}$, since $a > 0$. It follows that u is PH at each point of $\pi^{(1)}$ (compare with Lemma 4.1). Hence u is PH on X_{NM} and invariant under $T(a, b)$.

It remains to show that u can be continuously extended over $\bar{X}_{NM}$ by setting $u(\beta X_{NM}) = c$. Set $u(\pi^{(n)}) = u_n$ for each rational integer n. Then

$$u_n - c = a^n[u_0 - c] \tag{8.2}$$

since u is invariant under $T(a, b)$. Hence $u_n = c$ for no n; otherwise $u_n = c$ for every integer n, contrary to Lemma 6.2. It follows from (8.2) that $u_{-1}, u_{-2}, \cdots$ or $u_1, u_2, \cdots$ converges to c according as $a > 1$ or $a < 1$ respectively, and so by Lemma 6.2 u can be continuously extended over $\bar{X}_{NM}$ by setting $u(\beta X_{NM}) = c$.

LEMMA 8.2. *Let R be a nonempty N-cap annulus [S-cap annulus] with ϕ_N S-concave [ϕ_S N-concave]. Corresponding to any transformation $T(a, b)$ with $a > 0$ and having an invariant value c, there exists a function u, F_M-admissible on $\bar{R}_M$, invariant under $T(a, b)$, and taking the value c on βR_M. When $a = 1$, $b = 0$ and every value c is an invariant value of $T(a, b)$.*

In accordance with (m) in the proof of Theorem 6.3 in [6], there exists an open arc $h \in F_M^* \mid R_M$ with limiting initial point r in βR_M and projection on Σ^* with limiting terminal point N [S]. Necessarily $h \cap h^{(1)} = \emptyset$. Let H be the region on R_M bounded by h and $h^{(1)}$. A function w, F_M-admissible on $\bar{R}_M$, will be constant on βR_M and will be assumed to have the invariant value c there. Let $u = w \mid \bar{H}$. We define u over $\bar{R}_M - \bar{H}$ so as to be invariant on $\bar{R}_M$ under $T(a, b)$. So defined, u is continuous on $\bar{R}_M$ and PH on $H^{(n)}$ for every integer n.

We shall show that u is PH at points of $h^{(1)}$ by showing that $u \mid H$ and $u \mid H^{(1)}$ are $h^{(1)}$-compatible. The number of local F_M-rays in R_M incident with a singular point in $\beta R_M \cap \beta H$ is even because ϕ_N is S-concave [ϕ_S is N-concave]. Let q be a nonsingular point in h on a nonsingular subarc of h incident with r. Let k be the arc obtained by tracing h from q to r, then $\mid \phi_{NM} \mid$ from r to $r^{(1)}$, and finally $h^{(1)}$ from $r^{(1)}$ to $q^{(1)}$. The number of F_M-rays in H incident with points of k is odd. Recalling that $u(q) = u(q^{(1)}) = c$, one sees then that the signs of $u(p) - c$, for $p \in H$ sufficiently near q and $q^{(1)}$, respectively, are opposite; moreover, since $a > 0$, the sign of $u(p) - c$ for p sufficiently near q in H is the same as the sign for p sufficiently near $q^{(1)}$ in $H^{(1)}$. Hence u is PH in R_M at points in $h^{(1)}$. See Lemma 4.1.

It follows that u is PH in R_M and so satisfies the lemma.

LEMMA 8.3. *Let R be a nonempty, bounded, nonannular N-cap [S-cap] with ϕ_N S-concave [ϕ_S N-concave]. Let X be the union on M of the coverings of the components of R. Let A be an annulus on Σ^* such that the north (south) boundary of A_M is βX, and let u be a function F_M-admissible on $\bar{A}_M$ and invariant under a transformation $T(a, b)$. Then u can be extended over $\hat{U}$nion (X, A_M) so as to be F_M-admissible over this $\hat{U}$nion and invariant under $T(a, b)$.*

Let $K_1, K_2, \cdots$ be a maximal sequence (possibly finite) of disjoint noncongruent components of X. The boundary of K_i carries a loop in F_M^* which is concave toward its exterior. For each fixed i, u can be extended over K_i so as to be F_M-admissible over $\hat{\text{U}}\text{nion}$ (K_i, A_M). For each i, let u then be extended over

$$K_i^* = \hat{\text{U}}\text{nion}_n\, K_i^{(n)},$$

$n = 0, \pm 1, \pm 2, \cdots$ so as to be invariant under $T(a, b)$. Since u is given on $\bar{A}_M$ as invariant under $T(a, b)$ it is clear that u so extended satisfies the lemma.

In the case in which there is a meridian in F^*, the solution of Problem I is given by Theorems 5.1, 5.2. When there is no meridian in F^*, necessary conditions for the existence of a function u conditioned as in Problem I are given in Theorem 6.2. The concluding theorem of this sequence is the following one.

THEOREM 8.1. *In the case in which there is no meridian in F^*, the conditions on F^* and $T(a, b)$ necessary for the existence of a function u, F_M-admissible over M and invariant under $T(a, b)$ as given in Theorem* 6.2 *are sufficient.*

The decomposition of Σ^* given in [6, Theorem 8.3] must satisfy the conditions on F^* of Theorem 6.2. We have

$$\Sigma^* = \hat{\text{U}}\text{nion}\, (U_N, W_N, C, W_S, U_S),$$

where C is a central annulus, W_N and W_S are N- and S-spiral annuli, and U_N and U_S, N- and S-caps, respectively. Some of these sets may be empty, but in any case $\hat{\text{U}}\text{nion}$ (W_N, C, W_S) is not empty, since there is no meridian. We find it convenient to set

$$\text{(8.3)} \quad \hat{\text{U}}\text{nion}\, (U_N, W_N) = X_N, \qquad \hat{\text{U}}\text{nion}\, (U_S, W_S) = X_S.$$

The proof of Theorem 8.1 distinguishes Case I, in which asymptotes are present, from the complementary Case II. Let $\emptyset$ be the empty set. In Case I the subcases $C \neq \emptyset$ and $C = \emptyset$ are distinguished.

Case I, $C \neq \emptyset$. In this situation let u be defined over $\bar{C}_M$ in accordance with Lemma 7.3, noting that $T(a, b)$ in Lemma 7.3 satisfies the condition $a > 1$ or $0 < a < 1$, according as the asymptotes are of type $(+, +)$ or $(-, -)$, in agreement with Theorem 6.2, and that the invariant value c is unique.

If $W_N \neq \emptyset$ let u be further extended over $\bar{X}_{NM}$ in accordance with Lemma 8.1. Note that Lemma 8.1 requires that u equal c on

$$k = \beta X_{NM} = \beta X_{NM} \cap \beta C_M.$$

One can suppose that the functions

$$u_1 = u \mid \bar{C}_M, \qquad u_2 = u \mid \bar{X}_{NM}$$

are k-compatible, and then apply Lemma 4.1. If u_1 and u_2 were not k-compatible, one could replace u_2 by a function u_2^* such that

$$u_2^* - c = -[u_2 - c].$$

This function u_2^* would satisfy Lemma 8.1 with u_2, and be k-compatible with u_1. The extended u will be F_M-admissible over Ûnion (X_{NM}, C_M) and invariant under $T(a, b)$.

Suppose then $W_N = \emptyset$. If $U_N \neq \emptyset$ and is annular, one admissibly extends u over U_{NM} with the aid of Lemma 8.2. If $U_N \neq \emptyset$ and is not annular, U_N is in general not connected and U_{NM} not defined. As in Lemma 8.3, let X be the union of the coverings in M of components of U_N. One can then extend $u \mid \bar{C}_M$ over Ûnion (X, C_M), as in Lemma 8.3. If U_N is empty, nothing more is required.

Further extension of u over the coverings of the components of X_S in M is made in similar fashion.

Case I, $C = \emptyset$. In this situation not both W_N and W_S are empty, since there is no meridian in F^*. Suppose $W_S \neq \emptyset$. One then defines u over $\bar{X}_{SM}$ as in Lemma 8.1, and admissibly extends this u over X_{NM} as in the case $C \neq \emptyset$.

Case II. In Case II there are no asymptotes, so that $W_N = W_S = \emptyset$ and $C \neq \emptyset$. One defines u over $\bar{C}_M$ as in Lemma 7.4. If $U_N = U_S = \emptyset$ we are through. If U_N is not empty and annular, we define u over $\bar{U}_{NM}$ as in Lemma 8.2, requiring that the value assigned to u on $k = \beta U_{NM}$ in Lemma 8.2 be the value of u on k considered as the north boundary of C_M, and that $u \mid U_{NM}$ be so defined that

$$u \mid \bar{C}_M \qquad u \mid \bar{U}_{NM}$$

are k-compatible. If U_N is not empty and not annular, one extends $u \mid \bar{C}_M$ over the coverings in M of the components of U_N as in Lemma 8.3. One treats U_S similarly.

Thus in every case we obtain a u defined over M, F_M-admissible and invariant under $T(a, b)$.

COROLLARY 8.1. *If there is no meridian in F^*, then a function u which is F-admissible over Σ^* exists if and only if there are no asymptotes in F^*.*

There is a function u which is F-admissible over Σ^* if and only if there is a function which is F_M-admissible over M and invariant under a $T(a, b)$ in which $a = 1$ and $b = 0$. According to Theorem 6.2 and Theorem 8.1, this is possible if and only if there are no asymptotes in F^*.

As indicated in § 3, we term an admissible curve family F defined over Σ^* a *restricted* curve family if there exists a transformation $T(a, b) \mid (a \neq 0)$ and a function u, F_M-admissible over M and invariant under $T(a, b)$. The following theorem characterizes a restricted curve family.

THEOREM 8.2. *A curve family F admissibly defined over Σ^* is restricted if and only if it satisfies the following conditions. Relative to F^* the cycles in Φ are isolated without exception, or else there are no asymptotes in F^*. Asymptotic F^*-rays (if any exist) are all of one asymptotic type e.*

This theorem follows from Theorems 5.1, 5.2, 6.2, 8.1.

Part III begins with theorems that hold on our surface Q of § 1, with the additional condition that Q is required to be separable. In the remainder of Part III we are concerned with *restricted* curve families F and G on Σ^*.

PART III. TRANSVERSE CURVE FAMILIES F AND G

9. Global and local definitions of F on Q. In Part II we have solved the problem formulated in § 4, and we have given a topological characterization of a restricted curve family in Theorem 8.2. Let F be a restricted curve family defined over Σ^*. In Part III we shall seek a curve family G which is defined over Σ^* and conjugate to F. A curve family G, conjugate to a restricted family, is not necessarily restricted; but we shall eventually show that G can be chosen so as to be restricted.

The proof of the existence of a curve family G conjugate to F will be facilitated by making the definition of an admissible curve family purely local in character. In this section we shall show that this is possible. Other conceptions of more novelty must be introduced so as to bring out the essential duality of the relations between F and G. In particular G-coboundaries will be defined.

Q separable. In § 9 and § 10 we shall suppose that our surface Q of § 1 is separable. Since Q is locally Euclidean it follows that Q

is metrizable. We can suppose Q provided with a bounded distance function. One shows readily that there exists a sequence $\{Q_n\}$ of compact subsets of Q such that $Q_n \subset Q_{n+1}$ and Union $Q_n = Q$.

Disk families of index n, disk transversals, sectors and cosectors. Let D be the open disk $|z| < 1$ in the complex z-plane and let n be a positive integer. The open level arcs of $\Re z^n$ in $D - 0$, where 0 is the origin in D, include $2n$ *disk rays* incident with 0. When $n > 1$ [$n = 1$] the family of open level arcs of $\Re z^n \mid (D - 0)$, [$\Re z \mid D$] will be termed the *disk family of index n.* We distinguish the $2n$ *disk transversals* on which

$$(9.1) \qquad 0 < |z| < 1, \qquad \text{arc } z = \frac{r\pi}{n}, \qquad (r = 0, 1, \cdots, 2n - 1),$$

respectively. A subregion of $D - 0$ bounded by two successive rays is called a *disk sector of index n,* a subregion of $D - 0$ bounded by two disk transversals a *disk cosector of index n.*

Our curve families F as previously defined on Q may be termed globally admissible. Recall that the singular points of an admissible curve family F form a discrete subset ω_F of points of Q, and that each point of ω_F is given with an F-index $n > 1$. Every other point is given with an index $n = 1$. In the definition of F there is associated with each point $p \in Q$ of F-index n at least one F-neighborhood X_p of p ([3], [5], [6]) such that $\bar{X}_p \cap \omega_F = p \cap \omega_F$, and there is given a homeomorphic map f_p of $\bar{D}$ onto $\bar{X}_p$ under which the origin in D goes into p, and the maximal open arcs of the disk family of index n go into the maximal open arcs of $F \mid X_p$. The images under f_p of disk rays, transversals, sectors, and cosectors, respectively, are called F-rays, F-transversals, F-sectors, and F-cosectors defined by f_p. They are said to be of *index n* and *incident* with p.

The global definition of F included more than this local characterization. The open arcs and topological circles in F were given as complete entities. The μ-mappings we now introduce will serve to define F purely locally in an intrinsic manner. Their usefulness extends beyond this first application.

The μ-mappings f_p^e of span e. A sense-preserving homeomorphic map f_p^e of $\bar{D}$ into Q, carrying the origin into $p \in Q$, and the disk family of index n into a curve family $F_p^e \mid f_p^e(D)$, is called a μ-mapping of span $e > 0$ if the following is true. Each F_p^e-ray and F_p^e-transversal in $X_p^e = f_p^e(D)$ induced by f_p^e has the μ-length e, and is

μ-mapped under $(f_p^e)^{-1}$ onto its image in D. Let λ be an F_p^e-transversal defined by f_p^e. Let q be a point of λ at μ-distance s from p on $\lambda \cup p$, and let α_q be the open arc of F_p^e meeting q. This α_q is divided by q into two open arcs α_q' and α_q'', lying respectively in the F_p^e-cosectors preceding and following λ. We suppose that the μ-lengths of α_q' and α_q'', as measured from q, equal $e - s > 0$, and that α_q' and α_q'' are μ-mapped under $(f_p^e)^{-1}$ onto their images in D. We then term X_p^e a μ-neighborhood of p of span e, f_p^e a μ-mapping of span e, and F_p^e a curve family of span e and index n.

Let F be a curve family given as globally admissible over Q, and let n be the F-index of $p \in Q$. Let $\lambda_1, \cdots, \lambda_{2n}$ be arbitrary F-transversals incident with p, chosen so as to lie in different F-sectors of some F-neighborhood of p and to follow each other in the positive circular order about p determined by the orientation of Q. If $e > 0$ is a sufficiently small positive constant, there exists a μ-mapping f_p^e of span e of a disk family of index n into a family F_p^e defined on $X_p^e = f_p^e(D)$, in which $\lambda_i \cap X_p^e$ is the i-th F_p^e-transversal incident with p defined by f_p^e and

$$F \mid X_p^e = F_p^e.$$

The specific definition of f_p^e is readily made starting with a μ-mapping of the $2n$ disk transversals in D onto initial subarcs of μ-length e of the respective transversals λ_i. If e is sufficiently small, the definition of f_p^e can be completed in a unique manner determined by F. We say that a mapping f_p^e so defined is *consistent* with F.

Consistent μ-mappings f_p^e. We shall arrive at a curve family F by inference from a consistent ensemble of μ-mappings f_p^e. There is given a priori a closed discrete set of points ω_F in Q, with each point p of which is associated an integer $n > 1$ to be termed the F-index of p. With every other point of Q is associated the F-index 1. With each point p of Q there shall be associated a nonempty set σ of μ-mappings f_p^e with the F-index of p and neighborhoods $X_p^e = f_p^e(D)$, such that the inclusion of f_p^e in σ implies the inclusion in σ of each μ-mapping $f_q^{e_1}$ into X_p^e which is consistent with F_p^e. Further, let p and r be distinct points of Q, f_p^e and f_r^η μ-mappings in σ. Suppose that

$$f_p^e(D) \cap f_r^\eta(D) = R \neq \emptyset.$$

If q is any point in R and f_q^a a μ-mapping consistent with F_p^e and such that

$$f_q^a(\bar{D}) \subset R,$$

then f_q^a shall be consistent with F_r^η in the sense just defined. Such a set σ of μ-mappings f_p^e will be termed complete and consistent.

Given a curve family F, globally defined over Q in the earlier sense, there clearly exists a complete and consistent ensemble of μ-mappings each consistent with F. The converse will now be established.

LEMMA 9.1. *Corresponding to a complete and consistent family σ of μ-mappings f_p^e into Q, there exists a curve family F which is globally admissible over Q and such that each μ-mapping f_p^e in σ is consistent with F.*

We must define the elements of F.

Let $W_1, W_2, \cdots$ be a sequence of neighborhoods on Q whose union is Q, which have the form

$$W_i = f_{p_i}^{e_i}(D) \qquad (i = 1, 2, \cdots),$$

where $f_{p_i}^{e_i}$ is one of the given μ-mappings, and which are such that any compact subset of Q is met by at most a finite subset of the neighborhoods W_i. The sequence W_i exists by virtue of the separability and local compactness of Q. For brevity, set $F_{p_i}^{e_i} = F_i$.

Let p_0 be a point in $Q - \omega_F$. Then p_0 is in $W_{n(0)}$ for some integer $n(0)$. Let a_0 be the open arc of $F_{n(0)}$ meeting p_0. Give a_0 an arbitrary sense and let p_1 then be the final end point of a_0. If p_1 is in ω_F, a_0 shall be its own continuation in its positive sense. In any other case, let $W_{n(1)}$ contain p_1. There is an element b_1 in $F_{n(1)}$ meeting p_1. By virtue of the consistency of the family of μ-mappings, the set $a_0 \cap b_1$ includes an open subarc of a_0 preceding p_1. Let b_1 take its sense from a_0 and let a_1 be the open subarc of b_1 following p_1. Let p_2 be the final end point of a_1, and, if p_2 is not in ω_F, define a_2 using a_1 in the manner in which a_0 was used in defining a_1. One thus gets a sequence $a_0, a_1, a_2, \cdots$ (finite or infinite) of open arcs. Taken with the end points $p_1, p_2, \cdots$, this sequence continues a_0 in its positive sense. One can similarly continue a_0 sensed oppositely.

One thus arrives at a sequence

$$(9.2) \qquad \cdots, a_{-2}, a_{-1}, a_0, a_1, a_2, \cdots$$

which may be finite in either or both senses.

If a_{i+m} meets a_i for some $m > 0$, the a_j are carried by a nonsingular topological circle g. In any other case the a_j and the intermediate points p_i are carried by a nonsingular open arc g. The open arc or topological circle g is uniquely determined by any one of its points by virtue of the consistency of the mappings f_p^e. The set of these open arcs and topological circles constitutes F.

The intersection of g with any one of the given neighborhoods X_p^e is a union of elements of the corresponding family F_p^e. Otherwise, the construction of g would imply that a ray π on g would lie in X_p^e and have a limiting end point in X_p^e. This is impossible since only a finite number of the neighborhoods W_i meet $\bar{X}_p^e$.

The lemma follows.

It should be observed that no analogue of Lemma 9.1 would be possible (see § 11(i)) if the open arcs in F were required to be the homeomorphic images of an open interval rather than only one-to-one continuous images.

The μ-mappings above are particularly useful in treating curve families near boundaries.

G-coboundaries. Let R be a region in Q. We can regard R as an admissible surface, so that the concept of a curve family G defined over R is immediate. However, the set of singular points of G on R shall be a set which has no cluster point in Q. Let g be an open arc in βR. To each point $p \in g$ we assign a G-index $n(p, g, R)$ which shall be 1 except at most at a subset of points of g without cluster point in Q. At each exceptional point, $n(p, g, R)$ shall be prescribed as an integer exceeding 1. Let η_G denote the set of points of g of boundary G-index $n(p, g, R) > 1$.

The open arc g of βR with its indices $n(p, g, R)$ will be called a *G-coboundary* of R if corresponding to each point $p \in g$ there exists a homeomorphic mapping f_p of the closure of the union E of $n(p, g, R)$ consecutive cosectors of a disk family of index exceeding $n(p, g, R)/2$ onto the closure of a neighborhood X_p of p relative to $R \cup g$, such that

$$\bar{X}_p \cap \eta_G = p \cap \eta_G .$$

We require also that the origin in D shall go into p, and that the two disk transversals on βE shall go into open subarcs of g incident with p, while the open arcs of the disk family in E shall go into the open arcs of G in $f_p(E)$.

We state a composition lemma.

LEMMA 9.2. *Let R be a region in Q divided by an open arc or topological circle g in R into regions R_0 and R_1. Let G_0 and G_1, respectively, be curve families globally admissible on R_0 and R_1 such that g is a G_0-coboundary of R_0 and a G_1-coboundary of R_1. Let the G_0-index $n(p, g, R_0)$ and the G_1-index $n(p, g, R_1)$ at each point $p \in g$ be such that*

$$n(p, g, R_0) + n(p, g, R_1) \tag{9.3}$$

is even. Then there exists a unique curve family G, admissible over R and such that

$$G \mid R_0 = G_0, \qquad G \mid R_1 = G_1.$$

Let p be an arbitrary point of g. Set m equal to the index sum in (9.3). Note that for $e > 0$ and sufficiently small there exists a μ-mapping f_p^e of span e and index $m/2$ such that $f_p^e(D)$ is a neighborhood X_p^e of p relative to R with the following properties. The set $R_i \cap X_p^e$ $(i = 0, 1)$ is the union of $n(p, g, R_i)$ G_i-cosectors in R_i incident with p, and the curve family F_p^e defined by f_p^e is such that

$$F_p^e \mid (X_p^e \cap R_i) = G_i \mid (X_p^e \cap R_i) \qquad (i = 0, 1).$$

The lemma follows from Lemma 9.1. The curve family G is defined by a family of consistent μ-mappings which includes the mappings f_p^e just defined with vertices p in g, and also all μ-mappings f_p^e into R_0 and R_1 which are consistent with G_0 and G_1 respectively.

10. Transverse curve families on Q. Let R be an open subset of the surface Q of § 9. Let F and G be curve families admissible over R. We say that G is *transverse* to F over R if each element in G is an F-transversal. (See [6, § 2].) If G is transverse to F, we shall see that G is conjugate to F in the sense of § 1. A basic lemma follows.

LEMMA 10.1. *Let F and G be curve families which are nonsingular in a neighborhood R of a point p_0 of Q and such that the elements of G are F-transversals. Let $z = x + iy$. There exists a topological map of a square neighborhood X of the origin in the z-plane of the form $|x| < e$, $|y| < e$, onto a neighborhood Y of p_0 in R such that the im-*

ages in Y of the open arcs in X on which x and y respectively are constant, are open subarcs of elements of F and G.

Let (u, v) and (m, n) be canonical coordinates [6, § 2], relative to G and F respectively, of right neighborhoods of p_0. Let pairs (u, v) and (m, n) correspond which represent the same point of R. This correspondence becomes topological with a form

$$(10.1) \qquad m = \phi(u, v), \qquad n = \psi(u, v)$$

for $|u| < e_0$, $|v| < e_0$, provided $e_0 > 0$ is sufficiently small. An open arc $\{u = \text{constant} = c, |v| < e_0\}$ with $|c| < e_0$ represents an F-transversal by hypothesis. Such a transversal can meet an element of F (m constant) in at most one point in a simply connected subregion of R [5, Corollary 7.5]. Hence for c and d prescribed, with $|c| < e_0$, $|d| < e_0$, the equation

$$\phi(c, d) = \phi(c, v)$$

has but one solution, $v = d$, with $|v| < e_0$. It follows that $\phi(c, v)$ varies strictly monotonically with v for $|c| < e_0$ and $|v| < e_0$. The relation $m = \phi(u, v)$ taken for $|u| < e_0$, $|v| < e_0$ accordingly admits a unique continuous solution $v = \theta(u, m)$ for $|u| < e_1$ and $|m| < e_1$, provided $e_1 < e_0$ is sufficiently small. If one sets $u = y$ and $m = x$, the mapping

$$(10.2) \quad m = x, \qquad n = \psi(y, \theta(y, x)) \qquad \{|x| < e_1, |y| < e_1\}$$

carries a point $z = x + iy$ into a point in R with parameters (m, n), and with $e = e_1$ satisfies the lemma.

THEOREM 10.1. *If F and G are curve families admissibly defined over an open subset $R \subset Q$, and if G is transverse to F in R, then G is conjugate to F in R.*

Let U and V be PH functions which are F- and G-admissible respectively over some open simply connected subset $R_0 \subset R$. Each point p_0 of R is in some such set R_0. We shall show that the map of R_0 into the w-plane in which $p \in R_0$ corresponds to the point $w = U(p) \pm iV(p) = \psi(p)$ is interior if the sign $\pm$ is properly chosen.

From the definition of G transverse to F we can infer that $\omega_F \subset \omega_G$, but a priori not necessarily the reverse inclusion. Let p_0 be a G-nonsingular point of R_0. Under ψ, the mapping of a sufficiently small neighborhood H of p_0 is topological as a consequence of Lemma

10.1. If $p = k(z) \mid (z \in R)$ is a distinguished topological map of a region R in the z-plane onto a neighborhood of p_0 in H, then ψ is interior at p_0 in our sense, if $w = \psi k(z)$ is sense-preserving. Clearly, ψk will be sense-preserving for proper choice of the sign $\pm$ in the definition of $\psi(p)$ as $U(p) \pm iV(p)$. Moreover, the choice of the sign $\pm$ is independent of p_0 in $R_0 - \omega_G$, since $R_0 - \omega_G$ is connected, and since the choice of the sign $\pm$ cannot change as p_0 varies in $R_0 - \omega_G$.

Suppose the sign $\pm$ chosen so that ψ is interior at each point of $R_0 - \omega_G$. Then ψ is also interior at each point $p_0 \in R_0 \cap \omega_G$. Indeed, ψ is interior in some neighborhood of p_0 relative to R_0, possibly excluding p_0, and continuous without exception. If D is an admissible plane coordinate region for a sufficiently small neighborhood of p_0 in Q, ψ is represented by a map θ from D into the w-plane. It follows from Lemma 2.1 [2] that θ is interior at the point in D representing p_0 and thus that ψ is interior at p_0.

This establishes the theorem.

COROLLARY 10.1. *If G is transverse to F over R, then the F-index and G-index of any point $p \in R$ are equal.*

Since $[F, G]$ is a conjugate net in R by Theorem 10.1, $[F, G]$ contours in some neighborhood N_0 of p_0 an interior map f of N_0 into the w-plane. The F-index and G-index of p_0 are then one half the number of level lines of $\mathcal{R}f$ and $\mathcal{I}f$, respectively, incident with p_0. Hence these indices are equal.

COROLLARY 10.2. *If the curve family G is transverse to F over R, then F is transverse to G over R.*

Corollary 10.1 shows that $\omega_F = \omega_G$. With this established, Corollary 10.2 follows from Lemma 10.1.

We shall need an extension of Corollary 10.1 of the following form.

LEMMA 10.2. *Let G be transverse to F over a region R, with $k \in F^*$ a G-coboundary of R. Let p_0 be a point in k. There is then one and only one G-ray incident with p_0 in each F-sector in R incident with p_0.*

Let N_0 be a neighborhood of p_0 relative to $\bar{R}$ such that $\bar{N}_0$ is the closure of the union of r F-sectors of the same span e incident with p_0. Let $\bar{N}_0$ be carried by a topological map Θ onto the closure of the union of r consecutive disk sectors of a disk family of index r. The closure of the union of these latter sectors is a semidisk E. In this way we obtain families

$$F' = \Theta F \mid N_0 \qquad G' = \Theta G \mid N_0$$

on E. Reflecting E, F', G' in the diameter of E, we obtain families F_D and G_D defined on a disk D. Both F_D and G_D are admissible in that the number of F_D- or G_D-sectors incident with the origin 0 in D is even. Moreover, G_D is transverse to F_D in D. Then, by Theorem 10.1, F_D and G_D are conjugate, so that Lemma 10.2 holds.

A basic existence lemma follows. It concerns a curve family F, admissibly defined over Σ^*. The universal covering surface of Σ^* is denoted by M, as previously.

LEMMA 10.3. *Let R be a region on the universal covering surface M of Σ^* which is invariant under t. Suppose that h and $h^{(1)}$ are nonintersecting open arcs in $F_M \mid R$ such that h divides R. Let R_0 denote the subregion of R bounded by h and $h^{(1)}$. Suppose $R_0 \cap R_0^{(1)} = \emptyset$. Let G_0 be a curve family, admissibly defined over R_0 and transverse to F_M with h and $h^{(1)}$ G_0-coboundaries of R_0. There then exists a curve family J admissibly defined over R, transverse to $F_M \mid R$, invariant under t, and such that*

$$J \mid R_0 = G_0. \tag{10.3}$$

Denote $R_0^{(1)}$ by R_1 and $G_0^{(1)}$ by G_1. We shall apply Lemma 9.2, taking g and R of Lemma 9.2 as $h^{(1)}$ and $R_{01} = \hat{\text{U}}\text{nion } R_0R_1$ respectively. The index condition (9.2) is verified as a consequence of Lemma 10.2 and the t-invariance of F_M. By Lemma 9.2 there exists a curve family I admissible over R_{01} and such that

$$I \mid R_0 = G_0, \qquad I \mid R_1 = G_1.$$

It is clear that I is transverse to $F_M \mid R_{01}$. Since $G_1 = G_0^{(1)}$, we can extend I over the region R of Lemma 10.3 to obtain a curve family J, admissible over R, invariant under t and satisfying (10.3). Finally J is transverse to $F_M \mid R$, and the proof is now complete.

We shall need a special modification of Lemma 10.3 as follows.

LEMMA 10.4. *Relative to a restricted curve family F, let X_N and X_S be defined as in* (8.3) *and set $W = W_N$, $X = X_N$, or alternately set $W = W_S$, $X = X_S$. If $W \neq \emptyset$, there exists a curve family G extensibly transverse* (§ 11) *to F over X.*

Let ϕ be the F^*-cycle in Φ [6, § 7] bounding X. On the covering surface M let K be transverse to F_M. Let q be a nonsingular point of βX_M. We can suppose K modified in a sufficiently small right neighborhood T of q, so that for a subneighborhood $T_0 \subset T$

$$K \mid T_0^{(1)} = [K \mid T_0]^{(1)},$$

while $T \cap T^{(1)} = \emptyset$, K remains unchanged outside of T, and K remains transverse to F_M over all of M.

In $X_M \cap T_0$ let λ be an open subarc of an element of K, with λ's final end point at q. Let k_M be a nonsingular sensed element in $F_M^* \mid X_M$ [6, Theorem 8.2] for which k is asymptotic to ϕe ($e = \pm$), meeting $\bar{\lambda}$ in one point $p \in T_0$; we can suppose p is λ's initial point. The initial point of k is N if $X = X_N$ and S if $X = X_S$. Let g be the sensed open arc consisting of k_M up to and including p, followed by λ. Let R_0 be the subregion of X_M bounded by k_M and $k_M^{(1)}$. Using constructions similar to those in the proof of Lemma 10.3, we see that there exists a curve family J, admissible on X_M, invariant under t, extensibly transverse to F_M over X_M, reducing to K over R_0. The projection of K on X will yield the required family G.

11. Transverse families on concave annuli on Σ^*. Whenever the general surface Q of §§ 1 and 2 is separable, its universal covering surface M is topologically equivalent to a finite z-plane. In particular, this is trivially true when Q is Σ^*. A family F admissibly defined over Q is covered on M by a family F_M. To F_M our basic theorem in [3], Theorem 6.1, applies and we can infer that there exists an admissible curve family K defined over all of M and transverse to F_M. For a logically correct application of the theorem in [3] to F_M it was necessary that no a priori condition be put on the family F in [3] and [5] that its elements which are open arcs be homeomorphic images of open intervals. Otherwise, the assumption that the elements in F on a general Q are not so limited would then have led a priori to a family F_M to which we would not yet have shown that the theorem of [3] would apply.

(i) *On a sphere from which four or more points have been deleted these "recurrent" elements may exist in F, as will be shown by example in a separate note.*

From this point on we suppose that F is defined over Σ^* and, except in Theorem 14.2, is restricted. We begin this section by extending certain lemmas concerning an F-guide as defined in [6, § 10].

Lemma 11.1. *Relative to the curve family F on Σ^*, any two distinct nonsingular points P and Q in Σ^* can be joined by an m-transverse arc g such that m is finite and minimal.*

The points P and Q can be included in a simply connected subregion $R \subset \Sigma^*$. The mode of proof of the existence of an FL-guide [6, Lemma 10.2] suffices to show the existence of an m-transverse arc joining P to Q on R for which m is finite. An m-transverse arc g for which m is minimal accordingly exists.

Corollary 11.1. *If A is a concave annulus of the form $A(\phi_1, \phi_2)$ filled with topological circles in F, there exists an F-transverse arc g which meets each element in A once and only once and is in A except for prescribed nonsingular end points $P \in |\phi_1|$ and $Q \in |\phi_2|$.*

The arc g affirmed to exist in Lemma 11.1 satisfies the corollary. In fact, g cannot meet the north side of any component ψ of ϕ_2. Otherwise there would be an open subarc g_1 of g on the north side of ψ, with end points on ψ. There would then be at least one reversing point on g [6, Theorem 2.3] and by a simple construction [6, Lemma 10.3] one would replace g by an n-transverse arc joining P and Q with $P \cap |\phi_2| = P$ and $n < m$. Similarly, g meets the south side of no component of ϕ_1. An analogous use of [6, Theorem 2.3] shows that g meets no element of F^* in $A(\phi_1, \phi_2)$ in more than one point. It follows that $g \cap |\phi_1| = P$, $g \cap |\phi_2| = Q$ and the corollary is established.

The ring H and family $\mathcal{G}_H$. In § 7, $A(\phi_1, \phi_2)$ appears as the directly conformal image of a ring H, in the z-plane, of the form

$$H: 0 < \rho_1 < |z| < \rho_2 < \infty,$$

under a map f from H to A. As in § 7 we suppose f extended over $\bar{H}$ so as to be continuous. On H we introduce the family of circles

$$\mathcal{G}_H : \{|z| = \rho\} \qquad (\rho_1 < \rho < \rho_2),$$

and state the following lemma.

Lemma 11.2. *If F is such that $F \mid A$ is composed of topological cir-*

cles, there exists a topological map Ω_0 *of the ring* $\bar{H}$ *onto* $\bar{H}$ *leaving* βH *pointwise fixed, and such that*

(11.1) $$F \mid A = f\Omega_0 \mathcal{J}_H .$$

Definition of Ω_0. We introduce the family of topological circles

$$J_H = f^{-1}(F \mid A)$$

on the ring H. Let g be the transverse arc affirmed to exist in Corollary 11.1, and set $f^{-1}g = h$. The arc h is transverse to the family J_H and joins a point q_1 at which $\mid z \mid = \rho_1$ to a point q_2 at which $\mid z \mid = \rho_2$. Let h^* be an arc which joins q_1 to q_2 in H, with h^* transverse to $\mathcal{J}_H$. Under Ω_0, let h^* be μ-mapped onto h, giving each the sense from q_1 to q_2. Let p^* be any point in $h^* - q_1 - q_2$ and set $\Omega_0(p^*) = p$. Let $\alpha(p^*)$ be the open arc of the circle in $\mathcal{J}_H$ which meets p^*, cutting this circle at p^* to obtain $\alpha(p^*)$. For $p \in h - q_1 - q_2$ let $\eta(p)$ be the open arc of the topological circle in J_H meeting p, cutting this topological circle at p to obtain $\eta(p)$. Under Ω_0 let $\alpha(p^*)$ be μ-mapped onto $\eta(p) \mid (p = \Omega_0(p^*))$, both arcs in the counterclockwise sense. As p tends to q_i $(i = 1, 2)$ on h, $\eta(p)$ tends in the sense of Fréchet to the circular arc obtained by cutting the circle $\{\mid z \mid = \rho_i\}$ at q_i. (See the proof of Theorem 4.1 in [3].) It follows that the map of H onto H admits a continuous extension over $\bar{H}$ which leaves βH pointwise fixed. Clearly (11.1) holds, and the proof is complete.

G extensibly transverse to F over R. Let R be a subregion of Σ^* bounded in Σ^* by a set of disjoint elements in F^*. A curve family G will be termed extensibly transverse to F over R if G is transverse to F over R and if each element g of F^* in βR is a G-coboundary.

COROLLARY 11.2. *If the curve family* $F \mid A$ *is composed of topological circles, then there exists a family* K_A *extensibly transverse to* F *over* A *and of the form*

$$K_A = f\Omega_0\mathcal{K}_H ,$$

where $\mathcal{K}_H$ *is the family of open radial arcs in* H *on which* $\rho_1 < \mid z \mid < \rho_2$.

LEMMA 11.3. *If* C *is a central annulus filled with topological circles in* F, *there exists a nonsingular curve family* G, *extensibly transverse to* F *over* C, *such that each element of* G *has an arc closure, in* C *except for* *one end point on the north boundary of C, and one on the south boundary of C.*

Let Φ_F denote the space associated with F in [6, § 7] and there denoted by Φ.

The central annulus C may be a concave annulus A, in which case Lemma 11.3 follows from Corollary 11.2. Again, C may have no boundary in Σ^*. In this case C may be represented as the $\hat{\text{U}}$nion of a countable set of disjoint concave annuli whose boundaries form a doubly infinite sequence of F^*-cycles ordered as in Φ_F, converging in one sense in Φ_F to $\mathfrak{N}$ and in the other to $\mathcal{S}$. Finally, if C has but one boundary cycle $\phi \in \Phi_F$, C may be similarly regarded as the $\hat{\text{U}}$nion of a sequence of disjoint concave annuli whose boundaries converge in Φ_F either to $\mathfrak{N}$ or to $\mathcal{S}$, with ϕ the first F^*-cycle in the sequence.

On each annulus A in these $\hat{\text{U}}$nions let G be defined as K_A in Corollary 11.2. Thus defined, G is admissibly extendible over C by virtue of Lemma 9.2, and extensibly transverse to F over C. The concluding affirmation of the lemma follows from the construction of G.

LEMMA 11.4. *If $F \mid A(\phi_1, \phi_2)$ is a family of asymptotes of type (e, e), where $e = \pm$, then there exists a curve family G_A, extensibly transverse to F over A, which includes a topological circle g separating ϕ_1 from ϕ_2 in A, and which is such that $A - g$ is filled with G^*-rays, asymptotic to g of type e, with one such ray entering A from each point of βA in Σ^*.*

Let $\mathfrak{F}_H$ be the family of asymptotes of type $(+, +)$ as defined in the ring H in § 7. In accordance with Lemma 7.1, $F \mid A = f\Omega_e\mathfrak{F}_H$. In the ring H let $\mathcal{G}_H$ be the family of orthogonal trajectories of $\mathfrak{F}_H$. The lemma is satisfied by the family $G_A = f\Omega_e\mathcal{G}_H$. In particular, the topological circle g of the lemma is the $f\Omega_e$ image of the circle in H on which $|z| = (\rho_1 + \rho_2)/2$.

COROLLARY 11.3. *Relative to a restricted curve family F, let C be a central annulus in which the F^*-cycles in Φ_F are discrete, and asymptotes in F are of type (e, e). Then there exists a curve family G, extensibly transverse to F over C and such that $G \mid A$ has the character described in Lemma 11.4 whenever $A \subset C$ is a concave annulus filled with asymptotes in F.*

One defines G as in Lemma 11.4 whenever $A \subset C$ is a concave annulus filled with asymptotes in F. A curve family G extensibly transverse to F over C is thereby determined in accordance with Lemma 9.2.

The following lemma has several applications.

LEMMA 11.5. *Let A be an annulus in Σ^* one of whose two boundary curves is an F^*-cycle $\phi \in \Phi_F$ such that $\phi e \mid (e = \pm)$ is the asymptotic limit of an F^*-ray π in A. Let a curve family K be transverse to $F \mid A$ and possess at least one element in A with limiting end point s on $\mid \phi \mid \cap \Sigma^*$. Then there exists a closed curve γ on A which is both an F-guide and a K-guide, which bears no F- or K-reversing points, and which traced in its e-sense crosses the elements of K in the same sense as does π.*

Without loss of generality, we can suppose A free from singular points of F and K. Indeed, ϕ is one of the boundaries of an F-concave or F-spiral annulus on which F has no singular point and which includes all points of A within a prescribed small distance of $\mid \phi \mid$.

Suppose for definiteness that $e = +$ in the lemma. By hypothesis there exists in $K_M^* \mid A_M$ an element λ with limiting end point s_M covering the point $s \in \mid \phi \mid$. A suitably chosen covering π_M of π and image $\pi_M^{(1)}$ meet λ in points p and q respectively, delimiting a K_M-vector $[p, q] = h$ on λ of so small a diameter that (under the assumption that $e = +$) $p^{(1)}$ follows q on $\pi_M^{(1)}$. One knows that $h \cap \pi_M = p$ and $h \cap \pi_M^{(1)} = q$. There will be a K_M-vector $[r, p^{(1)}] = k$ which is a subarc of $\lambda^{(1)}$ and joins $p^{(1)}$ to some point $r \in \pi_M$. This K_M-vector will be such that

$$k \cap \pi_M = r, \qquad k \cap \pi_M^{(1)} = p^{(1)}, \qquad k \cap h = \emptyset.$$

We consider also the F_M-vectors $\{p, r\}$ and $\{q, p^{(1)}\}$ respectively on π_M and $\pi_M^{(1)}$. A curvilinear quadrilateral Z with successive vertices $p, q, p^{(1)}, r$ is thereby defined, bounded by two F_M- and two K_M-vectors.

There exists a unique F_M-vector A_j joining an arbitrary point j of $[p, q]$ to a point of $[r, p^{(1)}]$ and reaching thereby each point on $[r, p^{(1)}]$ once and only once. Let the K_M-vector $[p, q]$ be parametrized by μ-length and let the μ-parameter u of j on $[p, q]$ be assigned to each point of A_j. There exists also a unique K_M-vector B_t joining a point t of $\{p, r\}$ to a point of $\{q, p^{(1)}\}$, reaching thereby each point of $\{q, p^{(1)}\}$ once and only once. Let $\{p, r\}$ be μ-parametrized and let the μ-parameter v of t be assigned to each point of B_t. In this way coordinates (u, v) will be uniquely assigned to each point of Z. In terms of these coordinates let the point p be joined to $p^{(1)}$ on Z by a "straight" arc. The projection γ of this straight arc in A will satisfy the lemma when $e = +$.

The case $e = -$ is similar.

The following lemma shows that the family G_A constructed as transverse to F in A in Lemma 11.4 is essentially the only type of family G which is extensibly transverse to F over A.

LEMMA 11.6. *Let $A(\phi_1, \phi_2)$ be a concave F-annulus bounded by F^*-cycles ϕ_1 and ϕ_2, $[\phi_1 < \phi_2$ in $\Phi_F]$, and filled with F-asymptotes of type (e, e). If G is extensibly transverse to F over A there is in A a unique nonsingular G^*-cycle ψ in Φ_G, and $A - |\psi|$ is filled with G^*-rays asymptotic to ψe of type e.*

A nonsingular G^*-ray π entering A from a nonsingular point of ϕ_2 cannot meet ϕ_1 without meeting some F^*-asymptote in A in two points. Since π is an F-transversal this is impossible [6, Theorem 2.3]. Similarly, π (open) cannot meet ϕ_2. Hence π must be asymptotic to a G^*-cycle $\psi\pm$ in $\bar{A}$ $(\psi \in \Phi_G)$ [6, Theorem 4.1].

That $|\psi| \cap \beta A = 0$ may be seen as follows. By Lemma 11.5 there exists a G-guide γ, without G-reversing point in A, and so near to $|\phi_2|$ that $\pi \cap \gamma \neq \emptyset$. Thus π crosses from the north to the south side of γ. It can meet γ but once, so that $|\psi| \cap |\phi_2| = \emptyset$.

If one interchanges the roles of ϕ_2 and ϕ_1 in the preceding, one infers the existence of an asymptotic limit G^*-cycle ϕ in A with

$$|\phi| \cap |\phi_1| = \emptyset,$$

and with $|\phi| = |\psi|$ or with ϕ south of ψ. There cannot, however, be two distinct G^*-cycles ϕ and ψ in A, since one could then infer the existence of an F^*-cycle in the annulus $A(\phi, \psi)$. Hence there is a unique nonsingular G^*-cycle $\psi \in \Phi_G$ in A.

To show that the G^*-rays π asymptotic to ψ or $\psi-$ in A must be of type e, let g be an F^*-asymptote in A. Let Ig_M be that subregion of M bounded by g_M which does not contain βA_M. The ray π_M, if properly chosen on M as a covering of π, will enter Ig_M. On

$$Ig_M \cap |\psi|$$

the latitude θ will be bounded below or above according as $e = +$ or $-$. Hence θ will be bounded below or above on a terminal ray of π_M according as $e = +$ or $-$.

Finally, it is readily established that each element of $G \mid A$ is nonsingular, is asymptotic to ψe in one sense, and tends to a point of $\mid \phi_1 \mid$ or $\mid \phi_2 \mid$ as limiting end point in the other sense. This completes the proof of the lemma.

LEMMA 11.7. *Suppose that F and G are restricted and transverse on Σ^*. If there exists an asymptotic F^*-ray of $+$ type [$-$ type], then there exists no asymptotic G^*-ray of $-$ type [$+$ type].*

Let us suppose, for example, that there is an asymptotic F^*-ray of $+$ type. If there exists a concave F-annulus the lemma is immediate. Indeed, F is restricted so that all F^*-rays are of $+$ type. By Lemma 11.6 there exists an asymptotic G^*-ray of $+$ type and, since G is restricted, no asymptotic G^*-ray of $-$ type.

There remains the case where there is just one F^*-cycle $\phi \in \Phi_F$ which is an asymptotic limit. Let g be a nonsingular element in F^* asymptotic to ϕ. (See Theorem 8.2 of [6].) The element g must have one limiting end point at N or S, say S. Let R be the region in M bounded by g_M and not containing the covering in M of any component of $\mid \phi \mid$. Because g is of $+$ type, any continuous determination of the longitude θ on R is bounded below on any subset of R whose Σ^* projection is bounded from N and S.

Let h be a nonsingular element in G^* meeting a point of $\mid \phi \mid \cap \Sigma^*$. We shall show that h is either a G-meridian or bears an asymptotic G^*-ray of $+$ type.

The south side of ϕ. Let π' be the G^*-ray on h with initial subarc on the south side of ϕ. The ray π_M', if properly chosen on M, will enter R and cannot leave R by [6, Theorem 2.3]. If π' were an asymptotic G^*-ray of $-$ type, there would exist a continuous determination of θ along π', and a set of points on π' bounded from N and S at which θ would not be bounded below. This is impossible since π_M' is in R. As in the proof of Lemma 11.6, π' cannot intersect $\mid \phi \mid$ nor have a limiting end point on $\mid \phi \mid$. Thus π' either has a limiting end point at S or is a G^*-ray of $+$ type.

The north side of ϕ. Let π'' be the G^*-ray on h with initial subarc on the north side of ϕ. If there is a nonsingular element in F^* asymptotic to ϕ on the north side of ϕ, then the preceding argument shows that π'' either has N as limiting end point or is a G^*-ray of $+$ type. In any other case $\mid \phi \mid$ bounds an N-cap and π'' necessarily has N as limiting end point.

Thus in any case h either carries a G^*-ray of $+$ type or is a G-

meridian. A G-meridian excludes all asymptotic G^*-rays, while a G^*-ray of $+$ type excludes a G^*-ray of $-$ type, because G is restricted.

12. Modifying a G transverse to F. The methods used up to this point to derive a curve family transverse to a given restricted curve family F are not adequate to show that G can be chosen so as to be restricted. In this section we shall introduce certain supplementary concepts and methods.

We shall need to modify a family G_M near a nonsingular open subarc σ of an element in F_M. To this end we introduce a coordinate neighborhood of σ as follows.

(i) Let R be a subregion of M and J a curve family transverse to F_M over R. Let σ (open) be a nonsingular J-coboundary of R, in an $\alpha \in F_M$.

(ii) *A Δ-coordinate system based on σ.* Let Δ be a closed simplex in the (x, y)-plane with vertices $A_1 = (-1, 0)$, $A_2 = (0, 1)$, $A_3 = (1, 0)$. Let b be the open base A_1A_3 of Δ. Suppose that Θ maps $\Delta - A_1 - A_3$ topologically into $R \cup \sigma$ so that $\Theta(b) = \sigma$. Set

$$\Theta(\Delta - A_1 - A_3) = \Delta_R(\sigma). \tag{12.1}$$

Under Θ arcs in Δ in which parallels to the x and y-axes meet Δ shall go respectively into nonsingular arcs of $F_M \mid \Delta_R(\sigma)$ and $J \mid \Delta_R(\sigma)$. The mapping Θ shall be uniformly continuous in the sense that the diameter on M of an image set under Θ shall tend to zero uniformly with the diameter in the (x, y)-plane of the antecedent set.

If p is a point in $\Delta_R(\sigma)$ and (x, y) its antecedent under Θ, x and y will be termed Δ-coordinates of $p \in \Delta_R(\sigma)$.

The set $\Delta_R(\sigma)$ may be closed in M. This will be the case if σ covers a meridian in Σ^*. The uniform continuity of Θ then implies the following. If z in $\Delta - A_1 - A_3$ tends to an end point of b, the projection of $\Theta(z)$ into Σ^* tends to one of the two poles. We shall also be concerned with the case in which σ has just one limiting end point q in M. Then $\Delta_R(\sigma)$ is closed in M by adding q, and the map Θ can be continuously extended so as to be defined at one of the points A_1 and A_3, say A, and so extended, $\Theta(A) = q$.

LEMMA 12.1. *Under the conditions* (i) *on R, J, σ, F_M there exists a subset $\Delta_R(\sigma)$ of $R \cup \sigma$ with Δ-coordinates (x, y).*

Let T be a right neighborhood relative to F_M whose principal transversal [5, § 2] λ lies in R and has a limiting end point in σ. Let $R(T)$ be the band [5, § 8] of nonsingular elements $\alpha \in F_M$ which meet λ. Then σ is an open subarc on $\beta R(T)$. Let $\bar{\lambda}$ be parametrized by the values u, $0 \leqq u \leqq 1$, the value 0 corresponding to the end point of λ in σ. Extend the domain of u to define a function U on $\bar{R}(T)$ by setting $U(p) = u$, $p \in \bar{R}(T)$, if $p \in \alpha$, $\alpha \in F_M$ and α meets $\bar{\lambda}$ at the point with parameter u.

Let σ be given as the one-to-one continuous image of an interval $s_0 < s < s_1$. Let $\phi(s)$ be the point on σ with parameter s. There is a maximal open arc h_s on an element of J with limiting initial point $\phi(s)$ and lying in $R(T)$. Let $\mu(s)$ denote the μ-length of h_s. The function μ is readily seen to be lower semicontinuous [5, § 4], so that there exists a positive continuous function μ_1 defined over the interval (s_0, s_1) with values $\mu_1(s) < \mu(s)$. Without loss of generality we may suppose that the interval (s_0, s_1) includes the value 0, and that $\mu_1(s_0+) = \mu_1(s_1-) = 0$. Let k_s be the initial subarc of h_s with μ-length $\mu_1(s)$.

Let $[0, \theta(s)]$ be the interval of values of U on k_s. Then $\theta(s)$ varies continuously with s on (s_0, s_1). Clearly there exists a function $\theta_1(s) \leqq \theta(s)$, defined and continuous over (s_0, s_1), strictly increasing for $s < 0$, strictly decreasing for $s > 0$, with limits

$$\theta_1(s_0+) = \theta_1(s_1-) = 0.$$

Let $c > 0$ be a constant such that $c\theta_1(0) = 1$.

Let L_s be the subarc of k_s on which $0 \leqq U \leqq \theta_1(s)$. The union of the arcs L_s will be our choice for $\Delta_R(\sigma)$. We define Θ as follows. The Θ-antecedent of L_s shall be that arc intercepted by Δ parallel to the y-axis on which x has the sign of s when $s \neq 0$, and which has the length $c\theta_1(s)$. A point $p \in L_s$ $(s_0 < s < s_1)$ in $\Delta_R(\sigma)$ shall correspond to a point (x, y) such that $y = cU(p)$. Recall that for $p \in L_s$, $U(p)$ ranges from 0 to $\theta_1(s)$. The uniform continuity of Θ, as defined above, follows from the restrictions on $\mu_1(s)$, and the nature of μ-length on Σ and of θ_1.

The map Θ so defined satisfies the lemma.

We shall state and prove a lemma concerning the possibility of linearizing the boundary values of a PH function on a boundary arc such as σ.

LEMMA 12.2. *Let R be a subregion of M, J a curve family transverse to $F_M \mid R$ and σ as in* (i) *a J-coboundary of R. Let v be J-admissible* *over R, bounded and continuous on $R \cup \sigma$. Let ϕ map an interval (s_0, s_1) onto σ in a one-to-one continuous manner. Then there exists a function w which is* PH *on R, bounded and continuous on $R \cup \sigma$, has a level curve family I transverse to F_M on R and such that σ is an I-coboundary, equals v on $R - \Delta_R(\sigma)$, has the range of v on σ, and is such that $w(\phi(s))$ is linear in $s \in (s_0, s_1)$.*

Let L be the linear function of s over (s_0, s_1) which has the limiting end values of $v \mid \sigma$. Let E be the maximal open arc in $R \cap \beta\Delta_R(\sigma)$. Set $w = v$ on $R - \Delta_R(\sigma)$. If p is a point in E, the level line of w incident with p shall join p to the point on σ at which $L(s) = v(p)$ by a path in $\Delta_R(\sigma)$ which is straight in terms of the Δ-coordinates (x, y). The resulting function w satisfies the lemma.

13. Lemmas of §§ 10, 11, and 12 applied. We begin with the following lemma.

LEMMA 13.1. *If F_M includes a nonsingular meridian g, there exists a restricted curve family G, transverse to F.*

Definition of G. There exist a function U F_M-admissible over M [5] and a function V bounded and continuous on M and pseudoconjugate to U [3]. The family K of nonsingular level lines of V is transverse to F_M over M. Let R_0 be the region in M bounded by g and $g^{(1)}$, and set $K \mid R_0 = G_0$. By Lemma 10.3 there exists a t-invariant curve family J, transverse to F_M over M, with $J \mid R_0 = G_0$. Let G be the projection of J in Σ^*. Then G is transverse to F and is either restricted or becomes restricted if G_0 is properly modified, as we shall see.

Set $v = V \mid \bar{R}_0$. Let the value of $v(p)$ at an arbitrary point $p \in g$ be denoted by s, and set $p = \phi(s)$. Let (s_0, s_1) be the range of v on g. We apply Lemma 12.2, taking σ therein as $g^{(1)}$ and R as R_0. It follows that we can suppose v so chosen that $v[\phi^{(1)}(s)] = L(s)$, where L is linear in s over (s_0, s_1).

If v has this character, there will be an asymptotic limit G^*-cycle ψ at most if $L(s) \not\equiv s$ and if for some $c \in [s_0, s_1]$, $L(c) = c$. If, then, $L(s) \not\equiv s$ there is at most one such value c, and hence at most one such limit cycle $\psi \in \Phi_G$. If c exists, $L(s) - c = m(s - c)$, and if $L(s) \not\equiv s$, $m \neq 1$. If $c = s_0$ or s_1 the cycle ψ (if such exists) is at most a limit of asymptotic G^*-rays from one side only. In this case asymptotic G^*-rays are trivially of one asymptotic type e. If c is in the open interval (s_0, s_1), it follows from the form $L(s) - c = m(s - c)$ of L, with $m \neq 1$, that the G^*-rays π asymptotic to $\psi\pm$ (if ψ exists) are of one type regardless of the side of ψ on which π lies.

This establishes the lemma. In this lemma, F is automatically "restricted."

Relative to a restricted curve family F, let X_N and X_S be defined as in (8.3) and set $W = W_N$, $X = X_N$, or alternatively set $W = W_S$, $X = X_S$.

LEMMA 13.2. *If $W \neq \emptyset$ and if the asymptotic F^*-rays in W are of type e, then there exists a curve family G extensibly transverse to F over X, such that there is at most one limit G^*-cycle in X and the G^*-rays asymptotic to any such cycle are of type e.*

Definition of k and K. Let ϕ be the F^*-cycle in Φ_F bounding X. There exists a sensed nonsingular element $k \in F^* \mid X$ asymptotic to ϕe [6, Theorem 8.2]. According to Lemma 10.4 there exists a curve family K extensibly transverse to F over X. One could take G in Lemma 13.2 as K, except that the concluding conditions on G^*-cycles and G^*-rays would not in general be satisfied. Because of this it is necessary to modify K as follows.

Definition of K_1. In Lemma 11.5, let the annulus A be a subregion of X, let ϕ be the F^*-cycle just discussed, and let the F^*-ray π be taken on k as defined above. Then Lemma 11.5 implies the existence of a closed curve γ on A which is an F- and K-guide without F- or K-reversing points. Let A_1 and A_2 be the annuli into which γ divides X, with A_1 bounded by γ and ϕ. Since A can be chosen so as to consist of points of X within a prescribed arbitrarily small positive distance of $\mid \phi \mid$, we can suppose that there are no singular points of F on A_1, and that at least one element in $K \mid A_1$ has limiting end points on γ and $\mid \phi \mid$. Set $K \mid A_1 = K_1$. It follows that each element in K_1 has limiting end points on γ and $\mid \phi \mid$. Note that γ is a K_1-coboundary of A_1. Each point p of γ has a boundary K_1-index $n(p, \gamma, A_1) = 1$.

Definition of K_2. We have defined K_1 over A_1. We shall define K_2 over A_2, modifying $K \mid A_2$. Let v be K_M-admissible on X_M and bounded. Set $k_M \cap A_{2M} = g$ and let R be the subregion of A_{2M} bounded in A_{2M} by g and $g^{(1)}$. We shall apply Lemma 12.2 to R taking σ in Lemma 12.2 as $g^{(1)}$. We suppose $v \mid R$ replaced by w, defined over R as in Lemma 12.2 in terms of $v \mid R$. In particular, if p is an arbitrary point of g and if one sets $v(p) = s$, then $w(p^{(1)})$ will be a linear form $L(s)$ in s giving the values of $w \mid g^{(1)}$ with the same range of values as $v \mid g^{(1)}$, while $w(p) = v(p)$ for $p \in g$ and, more generally, for $p \in R - \Delta_R(\sigma)$. Let J be the invariant curve family on A_{2M} obtained from the level lines of w on R in accordance with Lemma 10.3. Let K_2 be the projection of J on Σ^*. The family K_2 is extensibly transverse to F over A_2, and γ is a K_2-coboundary of A_2 with the K_2-index $n(p, \gamma, A_2) = 1$ at each point p of γ. This follows from the fact that γ is a $K \mid A_2$-coboundary with a boundary index 1 at each point of γ. The alteration of $K \mid A_2$ near $g^{(1)}$ to define K_2 has preserved these essential properties of $K \mid A_2$.

K_2-asymptotes in A_2.* Let r be the terminal point of g on γ_M. We can suppose that w is increasing as r is approached on g. For definiteness, suppose that $e = +$. In accordance with Lemma 11.5, w will then continue to increase as γ_M is traced from r to $r^{(1)}$, so that $w(r^{(1)}) > w(r)$. It follows that $L(s) \not\equiv s$. If $L(c) = c$ for some value c on the range $[s_0, s_1]$ of values of s, then $L(s) - c = m(s - c)$. Since $L(s) = w(r^{(1)})$ when $s = v(r) = w(r)$,

$$m = \frac{w(r^{(1)}) - c}{w(r) - c} > 1 \qquad (\text{in case } e = +).$$

Since $L(c) = c$ has at most one solution c, there is at most one limit K_2*-cycle $\psi \in \Phi_{K_2}$ in $\bar{A}_2$, and since $m > 1$, the asymptotic K_2*-rays in A_2 are all of type $+$. The case in which $e = -$ is similar.

Definition of G. Take G in the lemma so that

$$G \mid A_1 = K_1, \qquad G \mid A_2 = K_2.$$

Such a G is well-defined over $X - \gamma$. Further, γ is a K_1-coboundary of A_1 and a K_2-coboundary of A_2, while a point p of γ has a K_1-index $n(p, \gamma, A_1)$ and a K_2-index $n(p, \gamma, A_2)$ equal to one. By virtue of Lemma 9.2, G can be admissibly extended over X. The definition of K_1 and K_2 in terms of K is such that G, like K, is transverse to F over X, and G is extensibly transverse to F over X, since K_1 is extensibly transverse to F over A_1.

This completes the proof of the lemma.

We conclude this section with two lemmas on caps.

LEMMA 13.3. *Relative to F let $U = U_N$ or U_S. If U is a cap annulus, then there exists a curve family G, extensibly transverse to F over U and such that there is no limit G*-cycle or nonsingular G*-cycle in $\bar{U}$.*

Let K be transverse to F_M over M. It follows from (m) in the proof of Theorem 6.3 in [6] that there exists an element $h \in F_M^* \mid U_M$ with limiting terminal point on βU_M, and such that the projection of h in Σ^* has a limiting initial point which is N or S according as U is U_N or U_S. Necessarily, $h \cap h^{(1)} = \emptyset$. Let R_0 be the subregion of U_M bounded by h and $h^{(1)}$. Set $K \mid R_0 = G_0$. Then h and $h^{(1)}$ are G_0-coboundaries of R_0. By Lemma 10.3, there exists a curve family J defined and transverse to F_M over U_M, invariant under t and such that $J \mid R_0 = G_0$. Let G be the curve family on U into which J projects.

Then G is transverse to F over U, since J is transverse to F_M over U_M. That G is extensibly transverse to F over U follows from the fact that βU_M is a J-coboundary of U_M, and that J and U_M are invariant under t.

A nonsingular inner G^*-cycle in $\bar{U}$ (if such existed) would be an F-guide without reversing point, and could not exist in $\bar{U}$. If a limit G^*-cycle ϕ met U, then there would exist, on one side of ϕ and arbitrarily close to ϕ, an F-guide without reversing point (Lemma 11.5) which would meet U. Since this is impossible, ϕ cannot exist.

This completes the proof of the lemma.

LEMMA 13.4. *Relative to F let R be a component of a nonempty nonannular cap. Then there exists a curve family G extensibly transverse to F over R.*

Let J be transverse to F_M over M. The projection of $J \mid R_M$ onto R is a family G defined over R and satisfying the lemma.

14. Restricted transverse curve families F and G. We are supposing that F is a restricted curve family defined over Σ^*. If G is constructed as transverse to F over Σ^*, G may fail to be restricted. We shall construct G so that G is restricted.

The cases $\nu(F) > 0$. Recall that $\nu(F) > 0$ if Σ^* includes any unbounded primitives or cut sectors, or is a union of primitives. For in any such case an F-guide h must meet at least one primitive, and so contain at least one reversing point [6, Theorem 10.2]. If the F^*-cycles are not discrete and if F is restricted as we are supposing, Σ^* includes a central annulus filled with F^*-cycles and no spiral annuli, (Theorem 8.2). In this case, $\nu(F) = 2$ (Theorem 6.1).

The cases $\nu(F) = 0$. If there is a meridian in F^* and if $\nu(F) = 0$, then none of the cases described in the preceding paragraph occurs, and Σ^* contains a doubly connected region in which nonsingular F-meridians are everywhere dense [6, Theorem 11.1]. There remains the case in which there is no meridian in F^* and in which the F^*-cycles are discrete in Φ_F (Theorem 8.2). In this case there is at least one asymptotic F^*-ray so that $\nu(F) = 0$ (Lemma 6.1). We state the following corollary of Lemma 11.5.

COROLLARY 14.1. *If F is a restricted curve family defined over Σ^*, and if G is transverse to F over Σ^*, then G fails to be restricted at most if $\nu(F) = \nu(G) = 0$.*

If G fails to be restricted, there must exist an asymptotic G^*-ray and so $\nu(F) = \nu(G) = 0$ by Lemma 11.5.

THEOREM 14.1. *Corresponding to an arbitrary restricted curve family F defined over Σ^*, there exists a restricted curve family G, transverse to F over Σ^*.*

If F includes a nonsingular meridian the theorem has been established in Lemma 13.1. We begin by establishing (i).

(i) *If there exists a meridian $h \in F^*$ but no nonsingular meridian, then G exists as stated in Theorem* 14.1.

Let g be a meridian in F_M^*. Let K be transverse to F_M over M. Let R_0 be the region in M bounded by g and $g^{(1)}$ and set $K \mid R_0 = G_0$. It follows from Lemma 10.3 that there exists a curve family G on Σ^* which is the projection on Σ^* of G_0. Such a G is transverse to F.

If G were not restricted, $\nu(F) = 0$ by Corollary 14.1. But $\nu(F) = 0$ only if there exists an asymptotic F^*-ray or a doubly connected F-meridional region. An asymptotic F^*-ray cannot coexist with the meridian g, and an F^*-meridional region, by the definition in [6, § 11], always contains a nonsingular meridian of F^*, contrary to the hypothesis of (i). Thus G is restricted and (i) is true.

(ii) *If there exists no meridian in F^*, G exists as stated in Theorem* 14.1.

We distinguish Case I, in which there exist asymptotic F^*-rays, from Case II, in which no such asymptotic F^*-rays exist. The decomposition of Σ^* into annuli C, W_N, W_S and caps U_N, U_S of [6, Theorem 8.3] holds.

Case I. Suppose $C \neq \emptyset$. Define G over C as in Corollary 11.3. If $W_N \neq \emptyset$, define G over X_N as in Lemma 13.2. If $W_N = \emptyset$ but $U_N \neq \emptyset$, define G over U_N as in Lemma 13.3 or in Lemma 13.4, according as U_N is annular or nonannular. Define G over X_S similarly in case $X_S \neq \emptyset$. So defined, G can be admissibly extended over the $\hat{\text{U}}$nion of these regions in accordance with Lemma 9.2. The index condition (9.3) is verified as a consequence of Lemma 10.2, applied to each point $p_0 \in \Sigma^*$ of a common boundary of two regions in the $\hat{\text{U}}$nion specified. This completes the definition of G.

F-transversality of G. Lemma 10.2 also implies that the total G-index of p_0 equals its total F-index. Since G is extensibly transverse to F over each of the component regions, G is transverse to F over Σ^*. This transversality has to be verified merely at the nonsingular points of F.

The restrictedness of G. In Case I, inner G^*-cycles are discrete, and all asymptotic G^*-rays are of the same type e as the asymptotic F^*-rays, in accordance with the constructions used. For a G^*-ray in Case I crosses one of the boundaries separating two component regions at most once [6, Theorem 2.3], and so bears a G^*-subray in one of the component regions of the $\hat{\text{U}}$nion. Thus G is restricted.

Suppose $C = \emptyset$. Since there is no meridian by hypothesis in (ii), $\hat{\text{U}}\text{nion}(W_N, W_S) \neq \emptyset$, and one defines G over an $X_N \neq \emptyset$ or an $X_S \neq \emptyset$ as in the case $C \neq \emptyset$.

Case II. Here $W_N = W_S = \emptyset$. Since there is no meridian, $C \neq \emptyset$ [6, § 9], and C is filled with a family of nonsingular F^*-cycles. One defines G over C as in Lemma 11.3. The definition of G over a nonempty U_N or U_S is as in Lemma 13.3 or Lemma 13.4, according as these caps are annular or nonannular. Such a G can be admissibly extended over Σ^* (Lemma 9.2).

So extended, G is transverse to F. Since C is filled with a family of F^*-cycles, $\nu(F) = 2$ (Theorem 6.1). Hence there are no asymptotic G^*-rays (Lemma 11.5), so that G is restricted.

This establishes the theorem.

The following theorem supplements Theorem 14.1. Since no use will be made of Theorem 14.2, our proof of this theorem is omitted.

THEOREM 14.2. *Corresponding to an arbitrary curve family F admissibly defined over Σ^*, there exists a curve family G transverse to F over Σ^*.*

PART IV. INTERIOR TRANSFORMATIONS

15. Restricted pairs $[F, G]$. We suppose F and G admissibly defined over Σ^*, restricted and mutually transverse. The decomposition of Σ^*, relative to F, into polar sectors as in [6, Theorem 12.1], into annuli and caps as in [6, Theorem 8.3], into primitives as in [6, § 9] in the case of loop coverage of Σ^*, or as in [6, Theorem 11.2 (b)], will be termed an *F-decomposition* of Σ^*. A *G-decomposition* of Σ^* is similarly defined. A canonical region in an F-decomposition, such as a meridional region, primitive, primitive sector, cut sector, central annulus, spiral annulus, or cap, will be distinguished, when necessary, from a canonical region in a G-decomposition by placing F or G before the technical name of the region. Thus one has F-meridional regions, FN-primitives, FS-primitives, and so on.

If F and G are restricted and mutually transverse, we term the pair $[F, G]$ *restricted*. An interior transformation λ defined on M and contoured by $[F_M, G_M]$ will be called *$[F_M, G_M]$-admissible*. If λ satisfies a relation of the form

$$\lambda(p^{(1)}) = a\lambda(p) + b + ib' \tag{15.1}$$

with a, b, b' real and $a \neq 0$, we say that λ is *invariant* under $T(a, b, b')$ and that $[F, G]$ is *associated* with $T(a, b, b')$.

In Part II we have characterized a restricted family F, and in Part III we have shown that, given a restricted family F, there exists a restricted family G transverse to F. In this section we will discuss the relationship of the families in a restricted pair. In general, the F-decomposition conditions but does not determine the nature of the G-decomposition. For example, if F is composed entirely of ordinary semicircular meridians, G can be taken as the family of parallel circles at constant latitude. However, G can also be taken so that Σ^* is the union of a finite sequence of unbounded G-primitives, alternatingly N- and S-primitives.

We shall here treat this problem from the point of view of determining the maximal class of transformations $T(a, b, b')$ associated with a given restricted pair $[F, G]$. In a later paper we shall discuss in more detail the many topological restrictions on F and G implied by the relationship of F and G in $[F, G]$. An interior transformation λ, defined on M with $\lambda = u + iv$, is invariant under $T(a, b, b')$ if and only if u is invariant under $T(a, b)$ and v is invariant under $T(a, b')$.

Thus our first step is to recapitulate certain results from Part II in the following form.

We shall say that a class H of restricted curve families and a class K of transformations $T(a, b)$ are *associated* if corresponding to each $F \in H$ and $T(a, b) \in K$ there exists a function u, F_M-admissible on M, and invariant under $T(a, b)$. It is natural to distinguish the following seven classes H_i, $i = 1, \cdots, 7$ of restricted curve families and associated classes K_i of transformations $T(a, b)$. Here π denotes the open half (a, b)-plane in which $a > 0$.

$$\begin{cases} H_1: \nu(F) \text{ even, positive, } \mu(F) > 1. \\ K_1: (a, b) \text{ arbitrary in } \pi. \end{cases}$$

$$\begin{cases} H_2: \nu(F) \text{ even, positive, loop coverage.} \\ K_2: (a, b) \text{ arbitrary in } \pi, \text{ excluding every point but } (1, 0) \text{ on the} \\ \quad \text{line } a = 1. \end{cases}$$

$$\begin{cases} H_3: \nu(F) \geqq 0, \text{ even, } \mu(F) = 1. \\ K_3: (a, b) \text{ arbitrary in } \pi, \text{ excluding the point } (1, 0). \end{cases}$$

$$\begin{cases} H_4: \text{asymptotic } F^*\text{-rays of type } + \text{ exist.} \\ K_4: 1 < a < \infty, b \text{ arbitrary.} \end{cases}$$

$$\begin{cases} H_5: \text{asymptotic } F^*\text{-rays of type } - \text{ exist.} \\ K_5: 0 < a < 1, b \text{ arbitrary.} \end{cases}$$

$$\begin{cases} H_6: \text{no meridian or asymptotic } F^*\text{-ray exists.} \\ K_6: (a, b) = (1, 0). \end{cases}$$

$$\begin{cases} H_7: \nu(F) \text{ odd.} \\ K_7: (a, b) \text{ arbitrary in the half-plane } a < 0. \end{cases}$$

The justification of this classification is given by the following lemma. We note that no two classes K_i are identical.

LEMMA 15.1. *Each restricted curve family F is in a unique class H_i, $i = 1, \cdots, 7$. Each curve family $F \in H_i$ is associated with each $T(a, b)$ in K_i and with no other transformations. Given K_i, H_i is the maximal class of curve families for which this is true.*

These statements follow directly from Theorems 5.1, 5.2, 6.2, 8.1, and 8.2.

Let H_{ij} denote the class of restricted pairs $[F, G]$ with $F \in H_i$, $G \in H_j$. We term H_{ji} *conjugate* to H_{ij}. With H_{ij} we shall associate the class T_{ij} of transformations $T(a, b, b')$ defined as follows. Let A_i be the set of points (a, b, b') in which (a, b) ranges over the values for which $T(a, b) \in K_i$ and b' is arbitrary. Similarly, let

A_i' be the set of points (a, b, b') in which (a, b') ranges over the values for which $T(a, b') \in K_i$ and b is arbitrary. Set $A_{ij} = A_i \cap A_j'$ and let T_{ij} be the set of transformations $T(a, b, b')$ in which (a, b, b') ranges over A_{ij}. The conditions on b and b' that a point (a, b, b') be in A_{ij} are independent and the range of the projection of these points on the b and b'-axes respectively is determined independently by K_i and K_j. However, A_{ij} may restrict the range of a on the a-axis more than does A_i or A_j separately.

In order to determine the maximal class of transformations $T(a, b, b')$ associated with any restricted pair $[F, G]$ it is sufficient to determine which of the classes H_{ij} are nonempty and then to describe the sets A_{ij} corresponding to these. First of all we need the following lemma.

LEMMA 15.2. *If F and G are restricted and mutually transverse, then $\nu(F)$ and $\nu(G)$ have the same parity.*

Suppose that, contrary to the statement of the lemma, $\nu(G)$ is odd but $\nu(F)$ is even, say. In accordance with Theorems 5.2 and 8.1, there exist a pair of real constants a and b, of which $a > 0$, and a function u, F_M-admissible over M and such that

$$u(p^{(1)}) = au(p) + b \qquad (p \in M). \tag{15.2}$$

According to Theorem 5.2 there exists also a function v, G_M-admissible over M and such that

$$v(p^{(1)}) = -av(p) \qquad (p \in M). \tag{15.3}$$

As in the proof of Theorem 10.1, for proper choice of the sign $\pm$, $u \pm iv = f$ is an interior map of M into a complex plane. Since v can be replaced by $-v$ without affecting the validity of (15.3), we can suppose that $u + iv = f$ is interior. From (15.2) and (15.3) it follows that

$$\bar{f}(p^{(1)}) = af(p) + b \qquad (p \in M). \tag{15.4}$$

Let $p^{(1)}$ be regarded as a function of $p \in M$ with values $p^{(1)} = \theta(p)$. The map θ is a sense-preserving map of M onto M. Set $f(p^{(1)}) = f(\theta(p)) = H(p)$. Then H is a sense-preserving interior map of M into the complex plane, contrary to (15.4) which implies that H is a sense-inverting map of M into the complex plane. This contradiction proves the lemma.

For our purposes, crucial characteristics of an $F \in H_i$ include the values of $\nu(F)$ and $\mu(F)$, the arrangement in the corresponding F-decomposition of Σ^* of meridional or maximal cut sectors, N- or S-primitives, the existence of central or spiral annuli, or N- and S-caps, the existence of asymptotes, and so forth. Restricted pairs $[F, G]$ in H_{ij} will not in general exist which combine arbitrary characteristics of an $F \in H_i$ with arbitrary characteristics of a $G \in H_j$. In fact some of the classes H_{ij} are empty. A particular instance of the limitation of the a priori characteristics of an $F \in H_i$ and $G \in H_j$ when $[F, G]$ is in H_{ij} is that when $[F, G]$ is in any one of the classes H_{43}, H_{53}, H_{63}, $\nu(G) = 0$, although there exists $G \in H_3$ in which $\nu(G)$ is an arbitrary even integer. If it happens that whenever $[F, G]$ is in H_{ij}, $\nu(F) = n$ and $\nu(G) = m$, where n and m are fixed integers, we shall write $H_{ij} = H_{ij}^{nm}$. In proving Lemma 15.3 we shall see that $H_{43} = H_{43}^{00}$, $H_{53} = H_{53}^{00}$, $H_{63} = H_{63}^{20}$. The value of the first superscript corresponds merely to the definition of H_4, H_5, and H_6 respectively. Similarly, $H_{34} = H_{34}^{00}$, $H_{35} = H_{35}^{00}$, $H_{36} = H_{36}^{02}$. It is trivial that $H_{44} = H_{44}^{00}$, $H_{55} = H_{55}^{00}$.

LEMMA 15.3. *The nonempty classes H_{ij} of restricted pairs $[F, G]$ are as follows: H_{ii}, $i = 1, 2, 3, 4, 5, 7$; H_{ij}, $i, j = 1, 2, 3$; H_{43}^{00}, H_{53}^{00}, H_{63}^{20}, and the conjugate classes H_{34}^{00}, H_{35}^{00}, H_{36}^{02}.*

We first verify the correctness of the exclusions.

The classes H_{7j} and H_{j7} are empty unless $j = 7$. Indeed $\nu(F)$ and $\nu(G)$ have the same parity (Lemma 15.2).

If F is in H_6, an F-decomposition includes a central annulus C which is not empty; otherwise, $\Sigma^* = \widehat{\text{U}}\text{nion}\ (U_N, U_S)$ and an F-meridian would exist contrary to the definition of H_6. The annulus C is filled with nonsingular F^*-cycles [6, Theorem 8.1] so that $\nu(F) = 2$ (Theorem 6.1). Since these F^*-cycles are G-guides, $\nu(G) = 0$. There cannot be asymptotic G^*-rays, since this would imply $\nu(F) = 0$ (Lemma 11.5). Hence G must be in H_3 if $[F, G]$ is a restricted pair. Thus H_{6j} is empty unless $j = 3$, and $H_{63} = H_{63}^{20}$. Similarly with H_{j6}.

If F is in H_4, $\nu(G) = 0$ by Lemma 11.5, so that H_{4j} is empty if $j = 1, 2, 6, 7$. H_{45} is empty by Lemma 11.7. Similarly, H_{5j} is empty for $j = 1, 2, 4, 6, 7$. Clearly, $H_{43} = H_{43}^{00}$, $H_{53} = H_{53}^{00}$.

This accounts for all the classes H_{ij} excluded in Lemma 15.3. That the classes included in Lemma 15.3 are *not empty* will now be shown by simple constructions using nonsingular F and G.

H_{13} : Let F determine an F-decomposition which includes two meridional sectors each filled with ordinary semicircular meridians. Let these meridional sectors be separated by an FN-primitive sector π_1 and an FS-primitive sector π_2. Let $F \mid \pi_1$ be the image of the level curves of $\mathcal{R}(1/(1 - z))$ under a conformal mapping of $\{\mid z \mid < 1\}$ onto π_1, so that the point $z = 1$ corresponds to N. Let $F \mid \pi_2$ be given similarly except that $z = 1$ corresponds to S. The family G of orthogonal trajectories will be composed of meridians. Here $\nu(F) = \mu(F) = 2$, $\nu(G) = 0$, $\mu(G) = 1$.

H_{12} : Take F as in the preceding example but with the FS-primitive sector replaced by a second FN-primitive sector. The family G of orthogonal trajectories will decompose into two GN-primitives. There will be just two meridians in G.

H_{11} : Take F as in the preceding example. Modify G in that example by replacing the two meridians in G by narrow meridional regions, appropriately narrowing the two GN-primitives.

H_{22} : Take F as a pencil of circles meeting N, deleting S and N, and take G as the family of orthogonal circles.

H_{33} : A pair in this class, in which $\nu(F) = \nu(G) = 0$, is easily constructed with F and G each consisting of nonsingular meridians. From the example $[F_0, G_0]$ in H_{22} one can obtain a pair $[F, G]$ in H_{33} by replacing one of the meridians in F_0 by a narrow F-meridional sector and one of those in G_0 by a narrow G-meridional sector. In this example, $\nu(F) = 2$, $\nu(G) = 2$. From the example $[F_1, G_1]$ in H_{23} which follows one can obtain a pair in H_{33} by replacing one of the meridians in F_1 by a narrow meridional sector. In this example, $\nu(F) = 2$, $\nu(G) = 0$. By an obvious extension of these constructions one can obtain an $[F, G]$ in H_{33} in which $\nu(F)$ and $\nu(G)$ are arbitrary even positive integers.

H_{23} : Cover one hemisphere of Σ^* with a pencil of circles meeting N. Reflect these circles in the center of Σ to get the remaining elements in F. The family G of orthogonal trajectories will consist of meridians.

H_{44}, H_{55} : These classes are immediately realized by using appropriate annuli bounded by parallels of constant latitude.

H_{43}^{00}, H_{53}^{00}: Take G as the family of ordinary meridians. Let F include the equator and consist otherwise of an N- and an S-spiral annulus.

H_{63}^{20}: Compose G of ordinary meridians and F of their orthogonal trajectories.

H_{77} : That H_{77} is realizable follows from the fact that H_7 is not empty, and that to an $F \in H_7$ there corresponds a restricted transverse family G (Theorem 14.1). The family G must be in H_7 (Lemma 15.2).

Evidently the classes conjugate to those listed above are also not empty.

We next determine the classes T_{ij} associated with the nonempty classes H_{ij}. To simplify the notation it is convenient to introduce the three classes of values of a real variable b:

$$B_1 : b \text{ arbitrary}, \qquad B_2 : b = 0, \qquad B_3 : b \neq 0,$$

and the classes B_{ij} of pairs (b, b') such that $b \in B_i$ and $b' \in B_j$. In terms of these the sets A_{ij} are described in the following lemma.

LEMMA 15.4. *Points (a, b, b') in A_{ij} corresponding to a nonempty class H_{ij} are such that for A_{ij} $(i, j = 1, 2, 3)$ $a > 0$; for A_{34}, A_{44}, A_{43}, $1 < a < \infty$; for A_{35}, A_{55}, A_{53}, $0 < a < 1$; for A_{36}, A_{63}, $a = 1$; for A_{77}, $a < 0$. The pair (b, b') in each case runs over B_{11} except that for A_{36}, A_{63}, $(b, b') \in B_{32}$, B_{23}, respectively, and when $a = 1$* for *A_{ij} $(i, j = 1, 2, 3)$ (b, b') runs over B_{ij}.*

This follows directly from Lemma 15.1.

We summarize these results in the following theorem.

THEOREM 15.1. *The nonempty classes H_{ij} of Lemma 15.3 of restricted pairs $[F, G]$ of transverse curve families and the associated classes T_{ij} of transformations $T(a, b, b')$ are such that each pair $[F, G]$ in H_{ij} is associated with each transformation $T(a, b, b')$ in T_{ij}. These classes H_{ij} are disjoint and include all restricted pairs $[F, G]$, and the classes T_{ij} include each transformation associated with a pair in H_{ij}.*

COROLLARY 15.1. *To each restricted curve family F defined over Σ^* there correspond restricted curve families G transverse to F. For each such pair $[F, G]$ there exists an interior map λ of M into a complex plane such that λ is $[F_M, G_M]$-admissible and invariant under some transformation $T(a, b, b')$. Thus every restricted pair $[F, G]$ is isothermally realizable.*

The first statement follows from Theorem 14.1. The second is a consequence of the fact that the class T_{ij} associated with a nonempty class H_{ij} is itself nonempty. The last statement then follows from Theorem 1.1.

COROLLARY 15.2. (i) *In Corollary* 15.1 *the map* λ *can be chosen so that*

$$\lambda(p^{(1)}) = \lambda(p) + b + ib' \qquad (p \in M), \tag{15.5}$$

for some choice of (b, b') *if and only if* F *or* G *includes a meridian, neither* F *nor* G *includes an asymptotic ray, and* $\nu(F)$ *and* $\nu(G)$ *are even.* (ii) *A map contoured by* $[F, G]$ *has a module* $b + ib'$ *if and only if* $[F, G]$ *is in a class entered in the following table in some* i*-th row and* j*-th column, with* $b \in B_i$ *and* $b' \in B_j$.

$b \diagdown b'$	B_1	B_2	B_3
B_1	H_{11}	H_{12}	H_{13}
B_2	H_{21}	H_{22}	$H_{23} \cup H_{63}^{20}$
B_3	H_{31}	$H_{32} \cup H_{36}^{02}$	H_{33}

(iii) *There exists a map* λ *which projects into a single-valued map of* Σ^* *into a complex plane if and only if* F *and* G *contain meridians, both* $\nu(F)$ *and* $\nu(G)$ *are even and positive, and neither* $\mu(F)$ *nor* $\mu(G) = 1$.

By Lemma 15.4, the classes T_{ij} of transformations $T(a, b, b')$ for which a triple $(1, b, b')$ is admissible are the classes T_{ij}, $i, j = 1, 2, 3$, T_{36}, and T_{63}. The corresponding conditions on (b, b') when $a = 1$, are given in Lemma 15.4. The corresponding classes H_{ij} are those listed in the table above.

Proof of (iii). Of these classes T_{ij} those with $i, j = 1, 2$ are those for which b and b' can vanish in (15.5). A restricted pair $[F, G]$ is in one of the associated classes H_{ij}, $i = 1, 2$, if and only if the conditions of (iii) are satisfied.

BIBLIOGRAPHY

(See [2], [3], [5], and [6] for references to papers by W. Kaplan, S. Stoïlow, and G. T. Whyburn.)

1. BEHNKE, H., AND STEIN, K. *Entwicklung analytischer Funktionen auf Riemannschen Flächen*, Math. Ann. 120 (1947–1949), 430–461.

2. JENKINS, J., AND MORSE, M. *Contour equivalent pseudoharmonic functions and pseudoconjugates*, Amer. J. Math. 74 (1952), 23–51.

3. —— —— *The existence of pseudoconjugates on Riemann surfaces*, Fund. Math. 39 (1952), 269–287.

4. —— —— *Conjugate nets, conformal structure and interior transformations on open Riemann surfaces*, Proc. Nat. Acad. Sci. U.S.A. 39 (1953), 1261–1268.

5. —— —— *Topological methods on Riemann surfaces*. Annals of Mathematics Studies, No. 30, pp. 111–139. Princeton, 1953.

6. —— —— *Curve families F^* locally the level curves of a pseudoharmonic function*, Acta Math. 9 (1954), 1–42.

7. MORSE, M. *Topological methods in the theory of functions of a complex variable*. Annals of Mathematics Studies, No. 15. Princeton, 1947.

JOHNS HOPKINS UNIVERSITY *and*
INSTITUTE FOR ADVANCED STUDY

THE GROWTH OF ENTIRE AND SUBHARMONIC FUNCTIONS

W. K. HAYMAN

1. Introduction and notation. Let $f(z)$ be a nonconstant entire function and set

$$u(z) = \log |f(z)|. \tag{1}$$

I should like to discuss certain problems relating to the growth and behavior of $u(z)$. Now the function $u(z)$ is subharmonic,[1] and many of the results in question remain true for general subharmonic functions $u(z)$. In such a case we shall say that the result holds for subharmonic functions; otherwise, that it holds for entire functions. This lecture is intended to be in the nature of a survey, for the field is an interesting one and has been actively considered by mathematicians in many countries in recent years. My principal aim is to concentrate on results that have been obtained recently and on problems that constitute a present challenge.

We define

$$A(r) = \max_{|z|=r} u(z), \qquad B(r) = \min_{|z|=r} u(z),$$

$$k = \limsup_{r\to\infty} \frac{\log B(r)}{\log r}, \qquad \lambda = \liminf_{r\to\infty} \frac{\log B(r)}{\log r}.$$

The numbers k, λ are defined to be the *order*, *lower order* of $u(z)$, respectively [23]. Here $B(r)$ is an increasing convex function of $\log r$. One problem of interest is the relative behavior of $A(r)$, $B(r)$ as $r \to \infty$. Clearly $A(r) = -\infty$ whenever $u(z) = -\infty$ for some z on $|z| = r$. For a general subharmonic function this may happen for a dense set of values of r; for a function of type (1) it happens whenever a zero of $f(z)$ lies on $|z| = r$. On the other hand, if $f(z)$ is the sum of a gappy power series in (1), of which a single term is dominant for certain values of r, $A(r)$ may be nearly as large as

[1] For general properties of subharmonic functions, see [19].

$B(r)$ for such r. In these circumstances we can only hope to prove that $A(r)$ cannot in general, i.e., for all large r or for almost all large r, in some sense, be less than a certain definite function of r, related to $B(r)$.

According to a fundamental theorem of F. Riesz [20], we can associate with the subharmonic function $u(z)$ a positive mass distribution, $\mu(e)$, defined and additive over bounded Borel sets, and such that, if D is a bounded domain,

$$u(z) = \int_D \log |\zeta - z| \, d\mu(e_\zeta) + v(z), \tag{2}$$

where $v(z)$ remains harmonic in D. In the case (1), $\mu(e)$ reduces to the number of zeros of $f(z)$ on e. The decomposition (2) of $u(z)$ into a potential and a harmonic function enables us to extend many of the notions and results obtained previously for entire functions. We accordingly define

$$n(r) = \mu[\,|\zeta| < r], \qquad N(r) = \int_1^r n(t) \frac{dt}{t}, \qquad r > 1;$$

$$u^+(z) = \max [u(z), 0], \qquad u^-(z) = \min [u(z), 0],$$

$$T(r) = \frac{1}{2\pi} \int_0^{2\pi} u^+(re^{i\theta}) \, d\theta, \qquad m(r) = -\frac{1}{2\pi} \int_0^{2\pi} u^-(re^{i\theta}) \, d\theta.$$

As soon as $B(r) > 0$ and $R > r > 0$, we have the inequalities

$$T(r) \leqq B(r) \leqq \frac{R + r}{R - r} T(R),$$

from which it follows that the order k and lower order λ defined above have the same value if defined in terms of $T(r)$ instead of $B(r)$.

If (1) holds, $T(r)$ is the characteristic function of $f(z)$ in Nevanlinna's original form [16]. The first fundamental theorem is

$$T(r) = m(r) + N(r) + \text{constant}, \qquad 1 < r < \infty, \tag{3}$$

and this remains true for general subharmonic functions. It follows in particular that, for functions of order $k < \infty$, $N(r) = O(r^{k+\epsilon})$ and $n(r) = O(r^{k+\epsilon})$ for every $\epsilon > 0$ as $r \to \infty$.

2. Functions of order less than one. The simplest subharmonic functions $u(z)$ are those of order $k < 1$. If we assume further the normalization $u(0) = 0$, we can use the decomposition (2) in the small to obtain the formula

$$u(z) = \int_{|\zeta|<\infty} \log \left| 1 - \frac{z}{\zeta} \right| d\mu(e_\zeta),$$

valid in the whole plane. For entire functions this reduces to the Weierstrass product formula

$$| f(z) | = \prod_{n=1}^{\infty} \left| 1 - \frac{z}{z_n} \right|.$$

To study the behavior of $u(z)$, we compare it with

$$u^*(z) = \int_0^\infty \log \left| 1 + \frac{z}{t} \right| dn(t) = \operatorname{Re} \left\{ z \int_0^\infty \frac{n(t)\, dt}{t(t+z)} \right\}.$$

The function $u^*(z)$ determines the same values for $n(r)$, $N(r)$ as $u(z)$ and also the same order. However, all the mass lies on the negative real axis for $u^*(z)$, and so $u^*(z)$ is harmonic in the rest of the plane. If we take the special case $n(t) = t^k$, $0 < k < 1$, we obtain easily

$$u^*(z) = \frac{\pi}{\sin \pi k} r^k \cos k\theta, \quad \text{if } z = re^{i\theta}, \quad |\theta| \leqq \pi.$$

Some further elementary calculations give the following results:

$$A(r) = \pi r^k \cot \pi k, \; B(r) = \pi r^k \operatorname{cosec} \pi k, \; N(r) = \frac{r^k - 1}{k}, 1 < r < \infty;$$

$$m(r) = 0, \; T(r) = \frac{r^k}{k}, k \leqq \tfrac{1}{2};$$

$$m(r) = \frac{\operatorname{cosec} \pi k - 1}{k} r^k, \; T(r) = \frac{\operatorname{cosec} \pi k}{k} r^k, k \geqq \tfrac{1}{2}.$$

The above example leads to the conjecture, first proposed by Littlewood [15] for entire functions, that

$$A(r) > (\cos \pi k - \epsilon) B(r) \tag{4}$$

holds for some arbitrarily large r and any function of order $k < 1$. Littlewood established the result with $\cos 2\pi k$ instead of $\cos \pi k$. Proofs of (4) were given almost simultaneously by Valiron [22] and Wiman [24]. A simple argument shows that it is sufficient to consider the functions $u^*(z)$.

We may also mention some extensions and refinements. Thus Beurling [3] has shown that, if $k \leqq \frac{1}{2}$ and $B(r) = o(r^k)$ as $r \to \infty$, we can replace ϵ by zero in (4). It was shown by Besicovitch [2] that if the entire function $f(z)$ has order $k' < k$, (4) holds with $\epsilon = 0$ on a set of upper density at least $1 - k'/k$, and this lower bound for the density is best possible. This result also extends to subharmonic functions. A consequence is that for entire functions of order $k < 1$ (4) holds on some arbitrarily large annuli of the type $R < r < R + R^\delta$, provided that $\delta < 1 - k$. This is of course false for subharmonic functions.

The case $k = \frac{1}{2}$, where $\cos \pi k = 0$, is clearly a turning point, and here much more is known. For instance, the result of Beurling, first proved by Wiman when $k = \frac{1}{2}$, has been sharpened by Heins [10] in this case to state that, if $A(r)$ is bounded above,

$$\lim_{r\to\infty} \frac{B(r)}{r^{\frac{1}{2}}} = \alpha; \qquad \lim_{r\to\infty} \frac{T(r)}{r^{\frac{1}{2}}} = \lim_{r\to\infty} \frac{N(r)}{r^{\frac{1}{2}}} = 2 \lim_{r\to\infty} \frac{n(r)}{r^{\frac{1}{2}}} = \frac{2}{\pi}\, \alpha,$$

where $0 < \alpha \leqq \infty$. Thus if α is finite, $u(z)$ has perfectly regular growth. Further, $u(z)$ has lower order at least $\frac{1}{2}$ in this case. No result of comparable precision is known for other values of k. In particular, it is not known whether k may be replaced by the lower order λ in (4) provided that $\lambda < 1$.[2]

Typical of another type of result is the following theorem of Pólya [18]. If for an entire function $A(n^2)$ is bounded above for $n = 1, 2, 3, \cdots$, then either $\liminf_{r\to\infty} r^{-\frac{1}{2}} B(r) > 0$ or the function is constant. Although a number of much more general theorems of this type are known, there is none which is at the same time general and as precise as this one. We should also mention the theorems of Valiron [22], which make it possible to deduce the asymptotic behavior of the functions $n(r)$, $T(r)$, etc., from the asymptotic behavior of $u^*(re^{i\theta})$ for a fixed θ. The converse problem of deducing the behavior of $u^*(z)$ from that of $n(r)$ is relatively trivial.

3. Functions of order greater than one. No result as precise as (4) is known when $k > 1$. If we are prepared to give up the best

[2] B. Kjellberg has now proved this for the functions $u^*(z)$ in his paper "A relation between the maximum and minimum modulus of a class of entire functions," *C. R. 12. Cong. Math. Scand. Lund* (1954), pp. 135–138. For a more detailed historical account of related problems, see [13].

possible constant $\cos \pi k$ in (4), we can extend the result and even replace k by λ. We have in fact for any function of lower order $\lambda < \infty$

$$A(r) > -[C(\lambda) + \epsilon]B(r) \tag{5}$$

for some arbitrarily large r, where the constant $C(\lambda)$ depends only on λ. This result was proved by Littlewood as a corollary of his $\cos 2\pi k$ theorem, with k instead of λ.

The deduction is very simple. Let n be a positive integer, $\lambda/n < \frac{1}{2}$, ω an nth root of unity, and put

$$v(z) = u(z) + u(\omega z) + \cdots + u(\omega^{n-1}z).$$

Then v is clearly a subharmonic function of $\zeta = z^n$ of lower order $\lambda/n < \frac{1}{2}$. Thus by the Wiman-Heins theorem, $A(r, v) > 0$ for some arbitrarily large r, and hence for the same values of r,

$$A(r, u) > -(n - 1)B(r, u).$$

This proves (5). A refinement of the argument also allows us to extend (4) to the case $k = 1$.

The correct value of $C(\lambda)$ is not known for any $\lambda > 1$. It was conjectured by Wiman [25] that (5) holds with $C(\lambda) = 1$ for an arbitrary entire function. He proved this result for harmonic functions $u(z)$, that is, in the case of (1) when $f(z) \neq 0$. Beurling [4] has shown further that for any fixed θ and any nonconstant subharmonic function $u(z)$ we have

$$u(re^{i\theta}) > -(1 + \epsilon)B(r)$$

for some arbitrarily large r. This proves the conjecture for functions which attain their minimum on a ray through the origin, such as the ones we have considered in § 2.

I have recently proved [8] that Wiman's conjecture is nevertheless false, and that the correct order of magnitude of $C(\lambda)$ is $\log \lambda$, as $\lambda \to +\infty$. A similar result holds if we replace λ by the order k or consider only entire functions instead of general subharmonic functions. The corresponding result for functions of infinite order is that

$$A(r) > -C_0 B(r) \log \log B(r)$$

holds on a set of r of positive lower logarithmic density, provided

$C_0 > 2.19 \cdots$. The result need not hold for any r if $C_0 \leqq .09$ even for entire functions. The positive theorems take rather long to prove, but I give a simple counterexample below to show how the behavior I have described is possible. The functions concerned attain their minimum in certain bounded regions or pits, each of which contains a large amount of mass and such that each circle $|z| = r$ intersects some pit somewhere. In fact, on any continuum Γ stretching to infinity there exist some arbitrarily large $z = re^{i\theta}$ such that

$$u(z) > -C_1B(r),$$

where C_1 is an absolute constant. This theorem, which is a less precise generalization of Beurling's theorem about rays, shows that functions with $A(r) < -C_1B(r)$, cannot attain their minimum on any single curve.

The results raise a number of other questions. First, is it possible to find the correct lower bounds of the constants C_0, C_1? If the lower bound of C_1 is 1, we should have a direct generalization of Beurling's theorem. Secondly, is Wiman's conjecture perhaps true for orders only slightly greater than one, or is the best possible value of $C(k)$ a strictly increasing function of k?

4. Asymptotic values. Suppose that $\gamma_1, \cdots, \gamma_p$ are p Jordan curves stretching from the origin to ∞ and having no other common point.

Let $f(z)$ be an entire function such that $f(z) \to w_\nu$ as $z \to \infty$ along γ_ν. If the values w_ν are all different, it follows from the Phragmén-Lindelöf principle that $f(z)$ must be unbounded between two adjacent curves γ_ν. The values w_ν are called asymptotic values of $f(z)$. If $p = 1$, $A(r)$ is bounded above and it follows from the Wiman-Heins theorem that $\alpha = \lim r^{-\frac{1}{2}}B(r)$ exists and is positive or $+\infty$.

It was first conjectured by Denjoy [6] and proved by Ahlfors [1] that if $f(z)$ has p asymptotic values, then

$$\alpha_p = \liminf_{r\to\infty} \frac{B(r)}{r^{p/2}} > 0. \tag{6}$$

For a subharmonic function $u(z)$ it is sufficient to assume $u(z)$ bounded above on each curve γ_ν and unbounded above in the intermediate domains. With this hypothesis Heins [11] proved not only that $\alpha_p > 0$ but also that if $\alpha_p < \infty$, then $u(z)$ has order $\frac{1}{2}p$, i.e.,

$$B(r) = O\{r^{\frac{1}{2}p+\epsilon}\}, \qquad \text{as } r \to \infty,$$

for every $\epsilon > 0$. It is not always true for $p \geqq 2$ that $u(z)$ has perfectly regular growth, even if $\alpha_p < \infty$. Quite recently Kennedy has shown,[3] in two as yet unpublished papers, that the best possible result in this connection is

$$\log B(r) = \frac{p}{2} \log r + o\{\log r\}^{\frac{1}{2}}, \text{ as } r \to \infty,$$

even for entire functions. There is thus a striking contrast to the case $p = 1$.

If $f(z) \to 0$ as $z \to \infty$ along a curve γ, then $u(z) = \log | f(z) | \to -\infty$ as $z \to \infty$ along γ, and since all sufficiently large circles $| z | = r$ meet γ, we have

$$A(r) \to -\infty. \tag{7}$$

We have seen from the Wiman-Heins theorem that if $p = 1$, this latter, weaker hypothesis is sufficient to imply (6). Beurling [3] has suggested that if $f(z)$ is entire and (7) holds for each of the functions $u_w(z) = \log | f(z) - w |$, for the p distinct values of $w_1, w_2, \cdots, w_p$ of w, then (6) holds. A much stronger hypothesis than (7) is that the corresponding value w is defective, i.e., that

$$\delta = \delta(w) = \liminf_{r\to\infty} \frac{m(r)}{T(r)} = 1 - \limsup_{r\to\infty} \frac{N(r)}{T(r)} > 0, \text{ for } u_w(z). \tag{8}$$

The second fundamental theorem of Nevanlinna [16] tells us that the number of defective values is at most countable and that $\sum_w \delta(w) \leqq 1$. For functions of finite order k, Pfluger [17] has shown that equality is possible here only if k is a positive integer and all the defects $\delta(w)$ are integral multiples of $1/k$. In particular, if k is not an integer, $\delta(w) < 1$ for every w, as was first shown by Nevanlinna [16]. Collingwood [5] conjectured that a defective value is necessarily asymptotic. An example by Mme Laurent Schwartz [14] showed this to be false for meromorphic functions. If it were true for integral functions, a function with p distinct defective values would necessarily satisfy (6). However, I shall give an example

[3] The positive result has just appeared: P. B. Kennedy, "On a conjecture of Heins," *Proc. London Math. Soc.* (3) 5 (1955), 22–47.

which disproves Collingwood's conjecture even for integral functions. For all we know, a function of finite order may even have an infinite number of defective values. Here is a rich field for further research.

It is natural to ask if any hypothesis stronger than (8)—for instance $\delta(w) = 1$, i.e., $N(r) = o\{T(r)\}$—is sufficient to ensure that w is asymptotic. For entire functions of infinite order we have only the theorem of Iversen [12] that $n(r) = O(1)$ or $N(r) = O\{\log r\}$ has this implication. However, for functions of finite order Shah [21] has shown that if $u_w(z)$ satisfies

$$N(r) = O\left\{\frac{T(r)}{\phi(r)}\right\} \text{ as } r \to \infty,$$

where $\phi(r)$ is an increasing function such that $\int^\infty [r\phi(r)]^{-1}\, dr$ diverges, e.g., $\phi(r) = [\log r]^{1+\epsilon}$, then w is an asymptotic value. In fact, $f(z)$ behaves substantially like $w + e^{P(z)}$ in this case, where $P(z)$ is a polynomial. Both these theorems extend to subharmonic functions.

5. An example. I wish now to discuss an example [9] that will throw a little light on some of the problems considered above. Let

$$f(z) = \prod_{n=1}^{\infty}\left[1 + \left(\frac{z}{n}\right)^{3n}\right]^{2n}.$$

It is not difficult to show that $f(z)$ has the following two basic properties:

(i) *$f(z)$ has infinite order and when $|z| = n + \frac{1}{2}$, where n is a large positive integer,*

$$8.01 \cdot 2^n < \log |f(z)| < 9.99 \cdot 2^n.$$

(ii) *$f(z)$ has a zero of multiplicity 2^n at each of the points given by $z_0 = ne^{i\theta}$ with*

$$\theta = (2k + 1)\pi/3n.$$

Take now $0 < \delta < \frac{1}{2}$. Then if z_0 is such a zero and $|z - z_0| < \delta$, we have by Schwarz's lemma and (i), (ii) the inequalities:

$$|f(z)| < [\exp (10 \cdot 2^n)](2\delta)^{2^n},$$

$$\log |f(z)| < 2^n[10 + \log (2\delta)] < -(1 - \epsilon)2^n \log \frac{1}{\delta},$$

if δ is so small that $\delta^\epsilon < \frac{1}{2}e^{-10}$.

Thus, qualitatively speaking, we see that in circles of radius δ around the zeros, which we may look on as "pits," the order of magnitude of $u(z) = \log|f(z)|$ is $-B(r)\log(1/\delta)$, provided δ is less than a small but positive absolute constant.

However, all these pits have their centers on the circles $|z| = n$. In order to make sure that every large circle $|z| = r$ meets a reasonable number of the pits, we consider

$$g(z) = f(\tfrac{1}{2} + z),\ v(z) = u(z + \tfrac{1}{2}) = \log|g(z)|.$$

The zeros of $g(z)$ of multiplicity 2^n now lie on the circles $|z + \frac{1}{2}| = n$. Given any $r \geqq \frac{1}{2}$, we choose n so that $n - \frac{1}{2} \leqq r \leqq n + \frac{1}{2}$. Then the circles $|z| = r$, $|z + \frac{1}{2}| = n$ intersect. Also,

$$B[r, v(z)] \leqq B[r + \tfrac{1}{2}, u(z)] \leqq 9.99 \cdot 2^{n+1} = 19.98 \cdot 2^n.$$

Again the zeros of $g(z)$ are equally spaced on $|z + \frac{1}{2}| = n$, and

$$\left|\frac{d}{d\theta}\left|-\frac{1}{2} + ne^{i\theta}\right|\right| = \frac{n\,|\sin\theta|}{2\,|ne^{i\theta} - \frac{1}{2}|} \leqq 1.$$

Hence if $|-\frac{1}{2} + ne^{i\phi}| = r$ for some ϕ, we shall have

$$||-\tfrac{1}{2} + ne^{i\theta}| - r| < \delta$$

on the arc $|\theta - \phi| < \delta$. If we choose $\delta = \pi/3n$, there will be a zero $z_0 = -\frac{1}{2} + ne^{i\theta}$ of $g(z)$ for which $|\theta - \phi| \leqq \delta$, and so if z is the point on $|z| = r$ nearest to this zero z_0, z will lie in a δ pit surrounding z_0, and so if r is large,

$$\begin{aligned}\log|g(z)| &< -(1-\epsilon)2^n \log\frac{1}{\delta}\\ &= -(1-\epsilon)2^n\log(3n/\pi) < -(1-2\epsilon)2^n\log n.\end{aligned}$$

Thus for all large r, $g(z)$ will satisfy:

$$A(r) < -(1-2\epsilon)2^n\log n, \qquad B(r) < 19.98\ 2^n,$$

and so $A(r) < -.05B(r)\log\log B(r)$. Again, if δ is a sufficiently small positive constant, we have $\log|g(z)| < -B(r)$ at all points of $|z| = r$ in a δ pit. The zeros $-\frac{1}{2} + ne^{i\theta}$ for which $\theta = 2k\pi/3n$ and $|\theta - \phi| < \frac{1}{2}\delta$ will lie within $\frac{1}{2}\delta$ of some point on $|z| = r$, and so arcs of length $\frac{1}{2}\delta$ of $|z| = r$ with center at such a point will lie in the δ pits. The number of such arcs is at least Cn or Cr, where C is a suitable constant, for all large r, and they are mutually exclusive if δ is small. Thus a finite proportion of $|z| = r$ lies in the δ pits for any fixed positive δ. Hence

$$m(r, g) = \frac{1}{2\pi}\int_0^{2\pi} \log^+ \left|\frac{1}{g(re^{i\theta})}\right| d\theta > \text{constant} \cdot B(r), \; r > r_0.$$

Thus 0 is a defective value for $g(z)$. On the other hand, it follows from the property (i) that $f(z) = g(z - \frac{1}{2})$ possesses no asymptotic or defective value; accordingly, $g(z)$ has no asymptotic value, though it has the defective value zero. An example of a meromorphic function whose defect changes under translation was first given by Dugué [7]. But the example above is the first one of an entire function having this property. However, I do not know whether the defect of an entire function of finite order can be altered by translation.

Examples similar to that above can be constructed of large finite order or of arbitrarily rapid growth having zero as a defective but not asymptotic value and $-A(r)$ large compared with $B(r)$. The zeros are arranged to have high multiplicity and to lie on a certain sequence of circles such that every circle $|z| = r$ meets a circle of zeros somewhere. On circles intermediate to the circles of zeros the function becomes uniformly large. For functions of large finite order k we can ensure in this way that

$$A(r) < -C \log k \, B(r)$$

for all large r, where C is a positive absolute constant.

It is naturally more difficult to prove the positive results. However, the example above illustrates the extremal situation fairly well. For a subharmonic function $u(z)$ it is possible on a set of r of positive lower density to choose an $h = h(r)$ such that when $|z_0| = r$ both the mass in the circle $|z - z_0| < h$ and the average

$$\left|\frac{1}{2\pi}\int_0^{2\pi} u(z_0 + he^{i\theta})\, d\theta\right|$$

are $O\{B(r)\}$. From this result the positive theorems can be deduced.

BIBLIOGRAPHY

1. Ahlfors, L. V. *Untersuchungen zur Theorie der konformen Abbildung und der ganzen Funktionen,* Acta Soc. Sci. Fennicae, Nova Ser. A 1, No. 9 (1930), 1–40.

2. Besicovitch, A. S. *On integral functions of order* <1, Math. Ann. 97 (1927), 675–695.

3. Beurling, A. *Études sur un problème de majoration*. Thèse. Uppsala, 1933.

4. —— *Some theorems on boundedness of analytic functions*, Duke Math. J. 16 (1949), 355–359.

5. Collingwood, E. F. *Sur les valeurs exceptionelles des fonctions entières d'ordre fini*, C. R. Acad. Sci. Paris 179 (1924), 1125–1127.

6. Denjoy, A. *Sur les fonctions entières de genre fini*, C. R. Acad. Sci. Paris 145 (1907), 106–108.

7. Dugué, D. *Le défaut au sens de M. Nevanlinna dépend de l'origine choisie*, C. R. Acad. Sci. Paris 225 (1947), 555–556.

8. Hayman, W. K. *The minimum modulus of large integral functions*, Proc. London Math. Soc. (3) 2 (1952), 469–512.

9. —— *An integral function with a defective value that is neither asymptotic nor invariant under change of origin*, J. London Math. Soc. 28 (1953), 369–376.

10. Heins, M. H. *Entire functions with bounded minimum modulus; subharmonic function analogues*, Ann. of Math. 49 (1948), 200–213.

11. —— *On the Denjoy-Carleman-Ahlfors theorem*, Ann. of Math. 49 (1948), 533–537.

12. Iversen, F. *Recherches sur les fonctions inverses des fonctions méromorphes*. Thèse. Helsingfors, 1914.

13. Kjellberg, B. *On certain integral and harmonic functions*. Thesis. Uppsala, 1948.

14. Laurent Schwartz, Mme H. *Exemple d'une fonction méromorphe ayant des valeurs déficientes non asymptotiques*, C. R. Acad. Sci. Paris 212 (1941), 382–384.

15. Littlewood, J. E. *A general theorem on integral functions of finite order*, Proc. London Math. Soc. (2) 6 (1908), 189–204.

16. Nevanlinna, R. *Le théorème de Picard-Borel et la théorie des fonctions méromorphes*. Paris, 1929.

17. Pfluger, A. *Zur Defektrelation ganzer Funktionen endlicher Ordnung*, Comment. Math. Helv. 19 (1946), 91–104.

18. Pólya, G. Aufgabe 105, Jahresber. d. Deutsch. Math. Ver. 40 (1931), Heft 9–12, Abteilung 2, p. 80.

19. Radò, T. *Subharmonic functions*. Ergebnisse der Mathematik, Bd. 5, Heft 1. Berlin 1937.

20. Riesz, F. *Sur les fonctions subharmoniques et leur rapport à la théorie du potentiel. II*, Acta Math. 54 (1930), 321–360.

21. SHAH, S. M. *On exceptional values of entire functions*, Compositio Math. 9 (1951), 227–238.

22. VALIRON, G. *Sur les fonctions entières d'ordre nul et d'ordre fini et en particulier les fonctions à correspondance régulière*, Ann. Fac. Sci. Univ. Toulouse (3) 5 (1913), 117–257.

23. WHITTAKER, J. M. *The lower order of integral functions*, J. London Math. Soc. 8 (1933), 20–27.

24. WIMAN, A. *Über eine Eigenschaft der ganzen Funktionen von der Höhe Null*, Math. Ann. 76 (1915), 197–211.

25. —— *Über den Zusammenhang zwischen dem Maximalbetrage einer analytischen Funktion und dem grössten Betrage bei gegebenem Argumente der Funktion*, Acta Math. 41 (1918), 1–28.

UNIVERSITY COLLEGE
EXETER, ENGLAND

UNIFORMLY NORMAL FAMILIES

W. K. HAYMAN

1. Introduction. A family $\mathfrak{F}$ of functions regular in $|z| < 1$ is called *normal* [11] if, given any sequence $f_n(z) \in \mathfrak{F}$, either $f_n \to \infty$ at each point z in $|z| < 1$ or else there exists a subsequence $f_{n_p}(z)$ which converges uniformly in $|z| \leqq \rho$ for every ρ, $0 < \rho < 1$.

It is an immediate consequence of this definition that, if $\mathfrak{F}$ is normal, then there exists a constant $B = B(\mathfrak{F}) \geqq 0$ such that

$$\text{(i)} \qquad f(z) \in \mathfrak{F} \quad \textit{and} \quad |f(0)| \leqq 1 \to |f(z)| < e^B, \quad \textit{if} \quad |z| < \tfrac{1}{2}.$$

For otherwise we could find a sequence $f_n \in \mathfrak{F}$ such that $|f_n(0)| \leqq 1$, but

$$M_n = \sup_{|z|<\frac{1}{2}} |f_n(z)| \to \infty.$$

Thus no subsequence $f_{n_p}(z)$ is uniformly bounded, nor, a fortiori, uniformly convergent in $|z| \leqq \frac{1}{2}$.

Among examples of normal families we may cite the following. First, let D_1, D_2, D_3 be three bounded Jordan domains whose closures have no common points. Let $\mathcal{S}\{D_1, D_2, D_3\}$ be the family of all functions regular in $|z| < 1$, but mapping no subdomain Δ of $|z| < 1$ one-to-one and conformally onto a D_j, $j = 1$ to 3. Secondly, let $\mathcal{S}\{D_1, D_2\}$ be the family of all $f(z)$ regular in $|z| < 1$ which do not map any Δ conformally and one-to-one onto D_1 or D_2 or two-to-one onto D_1. The families $\mathcal{S}\{D_1, D_2, D_3\}$ and $\mathcal{S}\{D_1, D_2\}$ were shown to be normal by Ahlfors (see [3], [13]).

Clearly, if $a \in D$ and all the roots of the equation $f(z) = a$ have multiplicity at least k, every map of Δ onto D by $f(z)$ has multiplicity at least k. In the corresponding special cases $k = 2$ for three points a_1, a_2, a_3, or $k = 2$, $k = 3$ for two points a_1, a_2, the proof of normality is due to Nevanlinna [12]. Specializing still further, we have the case $f(z) \neq 0, 1$, considered by Schottky [15]. The conditions given above cannot, however, be further relaxed, since the family of functions $\sin nz$ clearly does not satisfy (i), whereas the equations $\sin nz = \pm 1$ have only double roots.

The families discussed above have one common characteristic. They consist of all maps of $|z| < 1$ onto certain types of Riemann surfaces. Analytically these families satisfy the condition

$$\text{(ii)} \quad f(z) \in \mathfrak{F}, \quad |z_0| < 1, \quad \textit{and } \lambda \textit{ real}, \quad \rightarrow f\left[e^{i\lambda}\frac{(z - z_0)}{1 - \bar{z}_0 z}\right] \in \mathfrak{F}.$$

A family $\mathfrak{F}$ which satisfies (ii) may be called *invariant*.

The conditions (i) and (ii) together give

$$\text{(iii)} \quad \begin{array}{l} f(z) \in \mathfrak{F} \textit{ and } |z_1| < 1, |z_2| < 1, \\ \qquad |f(z_1)| \leqq 1, |f(z_2)| \geqq e^B \rightarrow \left|\dfrac{z_2 - z_1}{1 - \bar{z}_1 z_2}\right| \geqq \dfrac{1}{2}. \end{array}$$

For if $f(z) \in \mathfrak{F}$, so does $f([z_1 - z]/[1 - \bar{z}_1 z])$ by (ii); hence if $|f(z_1)| \leq 1$, we have $|f([z_1 - z]/[1 - \bar{z}_1 z])| < e^B$ for $|z| < \frac{1}{2}$ by (i).

A family of functions $f(z)$ satisfying (iii) may be called *uniformly normal*, since the condition is uniform on the hyperbolic metric in $|z| < 1$. We study the family $\mathfrak{N}(B)$ of all functions satisfying (iii) for a particular $B \geqq 0$. Clearly, if $B = 0$, the condition reduces to $|f| < 1$ or $|f| > 1$ throughout the disk $|z| < 1$. A normal invariant family belongs to $\mathfrak{N}(B)$ for some $B \geqq 0$. On the other hand, the family $\mathfrak{N}(B)$ clearly satisfies both (i) and (ii). We shall show not only that $\mathfrak{N}(B)$ is in fact normal, as we had anticipated in the phrase "uniformly normal" but that the growth of $f(z) \in \mathfrak{N}(B)$ in terms of the maximum modulus, characteristic, and so on, is in every instance restricted in much the same way as is known to be the case when $f(z) \neq 0, 1$; see [7], [5], [9], [15]. This will lead to a number of new results regarding, for instance, the classes $\mathcal{S}\{D_1, D_2\}$ and $\mathcal{S}\{D_1, D_2, D_3\}$ of Ahlfors.

An example of a family which is normal but not uniformly normal is the family of $f(z)$ regular in $|z| < 1$ such that $f(z) \neq 0, f'(z) \neq 1$. The normality was proved by Milloux [10]. By a modification of our method, all the results that we shall prove can be extended to this family also.

2. Notation and examples. We shall write, if $f(z)$ is continuous in $|z| < 1$ and $0 \leqq r < 1, \lambda \geqq 1$,

$$M(r, f) = \max_{|z|=r} |f(z)|,$$

$$I_\lambda(r, f) = \frac{1}{2\pi}\int_0^{2\pi} |f(re^{i\theta})|^\lambda \, d\theta,$$

$$T_\lambda(r, f) = \frac{1}{2\pi} \int_0^{2\pi} \{\log \sqrt{(1 + |f(re^{i\theta})|^2)}\}^\lambda \, d\theta.$$

We shall be interested in the growth of the quantities $M(r)$ and $T_\lambda(r)$ for $f(z) \in \mathfrak{N}(B)$; in that of $I_\lambda(r, u)$, $I_\lambda(r, v)$, where $g(z) = u + iv = \sum_{n=0}^{\infty} g_n z^n$, $|z| < 1$, and $e^{g(z)} \in \mathfrak{N}(B)$; also in that of the coefficients g_n of $g(z)$. Note that $T_1(r, f)$ is the Ahlfors-Shimizu form of the characteristic function of $f(z)$ [1], [16]. As examples of the type of results we can hope for, we give the following:

(a)
$$f(z) = e^{(1+z)/(1-z)}.$$

Here $|f(z)| > 1$ in $|z| < 1$, so that $f(z) \in \mathfrak{N}(0)$. Also

$$\log M(r) = \frac{1+r}{1-r}; \qquad T_\lambda(r) \sim C(\lambda)(1-r)^{1-\lambda} \quad \text{as } r \to 1;$$

$$g(z) = \log f(z) = 1 + 2z + 2z^2 + \cdots, g_n = 2, n \geqq 2;$$

$$h(z) = [g(z)]^2 = 1 + 4z + \cdots + 4nz^n + \cdots.$$

(b) Let $f(z)$ be an elliptic modular function mapping $|z| < 1$ onto the covering surface of the plane punctured at 0, 1. It was first shown by Littlewood [8], [9] that

$$T_1(r, f) \sim C_1 \log \frac{1}{1-r}, \qquad \text{as } r \to 1,$$

$$I_1(r, \log f) \sim C_2 \left\{\log \frac{1}{1-r}\right\}^2, \qquad \text{as } r \to 1.$$

Thus the real and imaginary parts of $\log f(z)$ behave differently.

(c) Littlewood also gave the example of

$$\chi(z) = -16 \sum_0^{\infty} \frac{1}{2m+1} \frac{z^{2m+1}}{1 + z^{2(2m+1)}} = \sum_0^{\infty} g_n z^n.$$

Here $\chi(z) = 2k\pi i$ only at the origin and so, as was pointed out by Flett [5], $\frac{1}{2}[\chi(z) - 1] \neq 2k\pi i$ for any integer k, so that

$$e^{\frac{1}{2}[\chi(z)-1]} \neq 0 \text{ or } 1 \text{ in } |z| < 1,$$

but $\chi(z)$ does not have bounded coefficients. In point of fact, $g_n \neq o\{\log \log n\}$.

We shall denote by $B_1, B_2, \cdots$ constants depending on B only, and by $B(a_0)$, $B(a_0, \lambda)$, $\cdots$, constants depending on B, a_0; B, a_0 and λ; and so on.

3. Basic result. THEOREM 1. *Suppose*

$$f(z) = a_0 + a_1 z + \cdots \in \mathfrak{N}(B).$$

Then

$$|a_1| \leqq 2\mu(\log \mu + B_1),$$

where $\mu = \max(1, |a_0|)$.

Suppose first $|a_0| \leqq e^B$. Then either $|f(z)| < e^B$ or $|f(z)| > 1$ for $|z| < \frac{1}{8}$. For if $|f(z_1)| \leqq 1$, $|f(z_2)| \geqq e^B$ with $|z_1| < \frac{1}{8}$, $|z_2| < \frac{1}{8}$, we should have

$$\left|\frac{z_2 - z_1}{1 - \bar{z}_1 z_2}\right| < \frac{(1/8) + (1/8)}{63/64} < \frac{1}{2},$$

which contradicts (iii).

If $|f(z)| < e^B$ in $|z| < \frac{1}{8}$, we have $|a_1| \leqq 8e^B$ by Cauchy's inequality. If $|f(z)| > 1$, we have $|1/f| < 1$, and so Cauchy's inequality gives $|f'(0)|/|f(0)|^2 < 8$; we therefore conclude that $|f'(0)| \leqq 8|f(0)|^2 \leqq 8e^{2B}$. Thus the result follows again.

Suppose next $|a_0| > e^B$. We need a result from the theory of subordination.

LEMMA 1. *Suppose* $\phi(z) = b_0 + b_1 z + \cdots$ *is regular and satisfies* $|\phi(z)| > 1$ *in* $|z| < 1$. *Then we have* $|b_1| \leqq 2|b_0| \log |b_0|$ *and, if* $|z_i| < 1$, $i = 1, 2$, *we have*

$$|\phi(z_1)| \geqq |\phi(z_2)|^{(1-t)/(1+t)},$$

where

$$t = \left|\frac{z_1 - z_2}{1 - \bar{z}_1 z_2}\right|.$$

We may without loss in generality suppose that $z_1 = 0$ and that b_0 is real and positive, since the family of $\phi(z)$ with $|\phi| > 1$ is invariant and contains $e^{-i\lambda}\phi(z)$ whenever it contains $\phi(z)$, when λ is real. Put

$$g(z) = \log \phi(z) = g_0 + g_1 z + g_2 z^2 + \cdots, \qquad g_0 > 0.$$

Then $g(z)$ has positive real part and so $\mu(z) = [g(z) - g_0]/[g(z) + g_0]$ satisfies the conditions of Schwarz's lemma. Thus

$$|\mu'(0)| = \left|\frac{g'(0)}{2g_0}\right| = \frac{|b_1|}{2|b_0||\log|b_0||} \leqq 1,$$

and $|\mu(z_2)| \leqq |z_2| = t$, so that $|g(z_2)| \leqq g_0(1+t)/(1-t)$ and

$$|\phi(z_2)| \leqq e^{g_0(1+t)/(1-t)} = |b_0|^{(1+t)/(1-t)}.$$

This proves the lemma.

Suppose now that in Theorem 1 $|a_0| > e^B$. Let ρ be the largest positive number such that $|f(z)| > 1$, $|z| < \rho$. If $\rho \geqq 1$, Theorem 1 follows from the lemma with $B_1 = 0$. If $\rho < 1$, let $r < \rho$ be the largest number such that $|f(z)| > e^B$, $|z| < r$.

There exists as θ such that $|f(re^{i\theta})| = e^B$. Consider the function $\phi(z) = f(\rho z)$. This satisfies the conditions of the lemma and, taking $z_2 = 0$, $z_1 = (r/\rho)e^{i\theta}$, we have

$$e^B = |\phi(z_1)| \geqq |a_0|^{(\rho-r)/(\rho+r)},$$

$$\frac{\rho - r}{\rho + r}\log|a_0| \leqq B. \tag{1}$$

On the other hand, for a suitable θ_1 we have $|f(\rho e^{i\theta_1})| = 1$, whereas by hypothesis $|f(re^{i\theta_1})| \geqq e^B$. Since $f \in \mathfrak{N}(B)$, this implies by (iii)

$$\frac{\rho - r}{1 - \rho r} \geqq \frac{1}{2}. \tag{2}$$

Combining (1) and (2) we obtain

$$B \geqq \frac{\rho - r}{\rho + r}\log|a_0| \geqq \frac{1}{4}(1 - \rho r)\log|a_0|,$$

$$1 - \rho \leqq \frac{4B}{\log|a_0|}. \tag{3}$$

Also, we have from the lemma,

$$|\phi'(0)| = \rho|f'(0)| = \rho|a_1| \leq 2|a_0|\log|a_0|.$$

Hence we find

$$|a_1| \leqq \frac{2}{\rho}|a_0|\log|a_0| = 2|a_0|\log|a_0| + \frac{2(1-\rho)}{\rho}|a_0|\log|a_0|$$
$$\leqq 2|a_0|\log|a_0| + 16B|a_0|,$$

using (3) and noting that, since $|a_0| > e^B$, $\rho > \frac{1}{2}$. Theorem 1 is thus proved in all cases.

As an immediate consequence we have [7] the following theorem:

THEOREM 2. *If* $|z_0| = r < 1$ *and* $f(z) \in \mathfrak{N}(B)$, *then*

$$|f'(z_0)| < \frac{2}{1-r^2}\mu_0(\log \mu_0 + B_1),$$

where $\mu_0 = \max[1, |f(z_0)|]$, *and*

$$M(r, f) \leqq \mu^{(1+r)/(1-r)} e^{2B_1 r/(1-r)}.$$

Thus for $f(z) \in \mathfrak{N}(B)$ we have $\log M(r) = O(1)/(1-r)$. For the classes of Ahlfors, only

$$\log M(r) = \frac{O(1)}{1-r}\log\frac{1}{1-r}$$

was known previously [2].

To prove the first inequality of Theorem 2 we apply Theorem 1 to

$$f\left(\frac{z_0+z}{1+\bar{z}_0 z}\right) = f(z_0) + (1-r^2)f'(z_0)\,z + \cdots,$$

which also belongs to $\mathfrak{N}(B)$, since $\mathfrak{N}(B)$ is an invariant class. The second inequality then follows by integrating along a radius.

4. The logarithmic means. We can also demonstrate that the growth of the means $T_\lambda(r)$ shown by our examples (a), foı $\lambda > 1$, and (b), for $\lambda = 1$, is the strongest possible:

THEOREM 3. *Suppose* $f(z) \in \mathfrak{N}(B)$. *Then*

$$T_\lambda(r) \leqq \begin{cases} T_1(0) + B_2 \log[1/(1-r)], \ 0 \leqq r < 1, & \text{if } \lambda = 1; \\ B(a_0, \lambda)(1-r)^{1-\lambda}, \quad 0 \leqq r < 1, & \text{if } \lambda > 1. \end{cases}$$

To prove Theorem 3 we need the following special case of a general identity due to Spencer [17]. The present proof is due to Flett [6].

LEMMA 2. *Suppose that* $G(R) = [\log(1+R^2)]^\lambda$, $1 \leqq \lambda \leqq 2$, *and*

$$g(R) = \frac{4\lambda(\lambda-1)R^2}{(1+R^2)^2}[\log(1+R^2)]^{\lambda-2} + \frac{4\lambda}{(1+R^2)^2}[\log(1+R^2)]^{\lambda-1}.$$

Then for $0 < r < 1$

$$r \frac{d}{dr} \int_0^{2\pi} G(|f(re^{i\theta})|)\, d\theta = \int_0^r t\, dt \int_0^{2\pi} g(|f(te^{i\theta})|)\, |f'(te^{i\theta})|^2\, d\theta.$$

The function $G(|f(re^{i\theta})|)$ is twice continuously differentiable. Thus we have by Green's formula

$$r \frac{d}{dr} \int_0^{2\pi} G(|f(re^{i\theta})|)\, d\theta = \int_0^{2\pi} \frac{\partial G(|f(re^{i\theta})|)}{\partial r}\, r\, d\theta$$

$$= \int_0^r t\, dt \int_0^{2\pi} \nabla^2 G(|f(te^{i\theta})|)\, d\theta.$$

To evaluate $\nabla^2 G(|f(te^{i\theta})|)$ we may suppose $f(te^{i\theta}) \neq 0$. In this case $|f(te^{i\theta})| = e^u$, where u is harmonic near $te^{i\theta}$. Now

$$\left(\frac{\partial}{\partial x}\right)^2 G(e^u) = [e^{2u} G''(e^u) + e^u G'(e^u)] \left(\frac{\partial u}{\partial x}\right)^2 + e^u G'(e^u) \frac{\partial^2 u}{\partial x^2},$$

$$\left(\frac{\partial}{\partial y}\right)^2 G(e^u) = [e^{2u} G''(e^u) + e^u G'(e^u)] \left(\frac{\partial u}{\partial y}\right)^2 + e^u G'(e^u) \frac{\partial^2 u}{\partial y^2}.$$

Adding, we have, since u is harmonic,

$$\nabla^2 G(e^u) = \{|f|^2 G''(|f|) + |f| G'(|f|)\} |f'|^2 / |f|^2.$$

Upon substitution of $G(R) = [\log(1 + R^2)]^\lambda$, the lemma follows.

We now prove Theorem 3. We put $|f(te^{i\theta})| = R$ and note that Theorem 2 gives

$$|f'(te^{i\theta})|^2 \leqq \frac{1}{(1 - t^2)^2} (R^2 + 1) [\log(1 + R^2) + 2B_1]^2.$$

Thus the lemma gives

$$\frac{d}{dr} r \frac{d}{dr} \int_0^{2\pi} G(|f(re^{i\theta})|)\, d\theta \leqq \frac{r}{(1 - r^2)^2} \int_0^{2\pi} \gamma(|f(re^{i\theta})|)\, d\theta,$$

where

$$\gamma(R) = \frac{4\lambda(\lambda - 1)R^2}{(1 + R^2)} [\log(1 + R^2) + 2B_1]^2 [\log(1 + R^2)]^{\lambda - 2}$$

$$+ \frac{4\lambda}{(1 + R^2)} [\log(1 + R^2) + 2B_1]^2 [\log(1 + R^2)]^{\lambda - 1}.$$

We may confine ourselves to the case where $1 \leqq \lambda \leqq 2$, since for $\lambda > 2$

$$T_\lambda(r) \leqq \{\log \sqrt{1 + [M(r)]^2}\}^{\lambda-2} T_2(r) \leqq B(a_0, \lambda)(1 - r)^{2-\lambda} T_2(r)$$

by Theorem 2. We have, clearly,

$$\gamma(R) \leqq 4\lambda(\lambda - 1)[\log (1 + R^2)]^\lambda + B(\lambda)[1 + \log (1 + R^2)]^{\lambda-1},$$
$$1 \leqq \lambda \leqq 2.$$

Hence if $\lambda = 1$, we deduce immediately

$$\frac{d}{dr} r \frac{d}{dr} 2T_1(r) \leqq \frac{r}{(1 - r^2)^2} B(1), \qquad 0 \leqq r < 1;$$

whence we obtain on integration

$$T_1(r) \leqq \frac{1}{8} B(1) \log \frac{1}{1 - r^2} + T_1(0), \qquad 0 \leqq r < 1.$$

This proves the result when $\lambda = 1$.

If $1 < \lambda \leqq 2$, Theorem 3 evidently holds for $r \leqq 1/e$ by Theorem 2. Also, we have now for $1/e \leqq r < 1$

$$r \frac{d}{dr} r \frac{d}{dr} 2^\lambda T_\lambda(r) \leqq \frac{r^2}{(1 - r^2)^2} \{4\lambda(\lambda - 1) 2^\lambda T_\lambda(r) + B(\lambda)[1 + 2T_1(r)]\}.$$

Putting $x = \log r$, $y = T_\lambda(r)$, and using the bound for $T_1(r)$, we deduce

$$\frac{d^2 y}{dx^2} \leqq \frac{\lambda(\lambda - 1)y}{x^2} + \frac{B(a_0, \lambda)}{x^2}\left(1 + \log \frac{1}{|x|}\right).$$

We put $y = |x|^{1-\lambda} z$ and obtain

$$\frac{d}{dx}\left(|x|^{2-2\lambda} \frac{dz}{dx}\right) \leqq B(a_0, \lambda) |x|^{-1-\lambda}\left(1 + \log \frac{1}{|x|}\right).$$

We integrate twice from $x = -1$, where z, dz/dx are bounded by $B(a_0, \lambda)$ and deduce:

$$z \leqq B(a_0, \lambda), \qquad -1 < x < 0,$$

so that

$$T_\lambda(r) \leqq B(a_0, \lambda)[\log (1/r)]^{1-\lambda}, \qquad 1/e < r < 1.$$

This completes the proof of Theorem 3.

5. Certain classes of uniformly normal families. It is natural to ask for conditions under which the maps of the unit circle onto a class of Riemann surfaces form a normal and hence uniformly normal family. Though necessary and sufficient conditions in this general case seem hard to find, we can find them in the case where the surfaces contain no points lying over the origin. The solution is a consequence of the theorem that follows:

THEOREM 4. *Let* $\{\mathfrak{R}\}$ *be a class of Riemann surfaces spread over the* w *plane and let* $\mathfrak{F}$ *be the family of functions* $e^{g(z)}$, *where* $w = g(z)$ *maps* $|z| < 1$ *one-to-one conformally onto one of the surfaces* $\{\mathfrak{R}\}$. *Then* $\mathfrak{F}$ *is uniformly normal if and only if the radii of schlicht circles in* $\{\mathfrak{R}\}$, *whose centers lie over the imaginary* w *axis, are uniformly bounded.*

Suppose in fact that the condition is satisfied. Then the surfaces of the functions $g(z)$ do not contain any schlicht circles of radius A, with center on the imaginary axis, where A is some constant. Hence the surfaces of the functions

$$g_0(z) = \frac{g(z) - iv}{A}, \qquad v \text{ real},$$

contain no such circle of radius greater than 1, and in particular the functions $g_0(z)$ do not give a schlicht map of any subdomain Δ of $|z| < 1$ onto any of the three circles $|w - 3i| < 1$, $|w| < 1$, $|w + 3i| < 1$. Thus by the theorem of Ahlfors [3], the family of functions $g_0(z)$ is normal and it follows that $g_0(0) = 0$ implies $\operatorname{Re} g_0(z) < A_1$, $|z| < \frac{1}{2}$, where A_1 is an absolute constant. Consequently, since v is an arbitrary real number, $\operatorname{Re} g(0) = 0$ implies $\operatorname{Re} g(z) < AA_1$; i.e.,

$$|f(0)| = 1 \rightarrow |f(z)| < e^{AA_1}, \qquad |z| < \tfrac{1}{2},$$

where $f(z) = e^{g(z)}$ is an arbitrary function of $\mathfrak{F}$. Thus $\mathfrak{F} \subset \mathfrak{N}(AA_1)$ and so $\mathfrak{F}$ is uniformly normal, since $\mathfrak{F}$ is evidently invariant.

Suppose, conversely, that a Riemann surface $\mathfrak{R}$ contains a schlicht circle $|w - iv| < d$. Let

$$w = g(z) = iv + g_1 z + \cdots$$

map $|z| < 1$ onto $\mathfrak{R}$. The inverse function maps $|w - iv| < d$ onto a subdomain Δ of $|z| < 1$ containing $z = 0$, corresponding to $w = iv$, and hence, if the point $z = z_1$ corresponds to $w = iv + \frac{1}{2}d$

in this mapping, we have by Schwarz's lemma $|z_1| \leqq \frac{1}{2}$. In other words, we have $g(z_1) = iv + \frac{1}{2}d$, and so, if $f(z) = e^{g(z)}$,

$$f(0) = e^{iv}, \qquad |f(z_1)| = e^{d/2}, \qquad |z_1| \leqq \tfrac{1}{2}.$$

If d can be as large as we please, the functions $f(z)$ cannot satisfy (i) for any positive B and so do not form a normal family. This completes the proof of Theorem 4.

The restrictions on the growth of the functions $g(z)$ can be deduced from those for $f(z) = e^{g(z)}$, when $f(z) \in \mathfrak{N}(B)$. We have the following theorem:

THEOREM 5. *Suppose that* $g(z) = u + iv = \alpha + i\beta + \sum_{n=1}^{\infty} g_n z^n$ *is regular in* $|z| < 1$ *and that* $e^{g(z)} \in \mathfrak{N}(B)$. *Then we have*

(i) $$|g_1| \leqq 2(|\alpha| + B_3),$$

(ii) $$|g_n| < B_4(|\alpha| + \log n), \qquad n > 1.$$

Further, we have for $0 \leqq r < 1$,

(iii) $$M(r, g) \leqq |g(0)| \frac{1+r}{1-r} + \frac{2B_3 r}{1-r};$$

(iv) $$I_1(r, u) < |\alpha| + B_5\left(1 + \log\frac{1}{1-r}\right),$$
$$I_1(r, g) < |g(0)| + |\alpha| \log\frac{1+r}{1-r} + rB_6\left[1 + \left(\log\frac{1}{1-r}\right)^2\right];$$

(v) $$I_\lambda(r, g) < B(g(0), \lambda)\,(1-r)^{1-\lambda}, \qquad \lambda > 1.$$

We note first that the family of functions e^{-g} is also uniformly normal in $|z| < 1$, and so $e^{-g} \in \mathfrak{N}(B')$ for some B' depending only on B. Writing $f = e^g$, we have from Theorem 2, if $u(z) \geqq 0$ so that $|f(z)| \geqq 1$,

$$|g'(z)| = \left|\frac{f'(z)}{f(z)}\right| \leqq \frac{2}{1-r^2}(u(z) + B_1), \qquad |z| = r.$$

If $u(z) < 0$, we have similarly, by considering e^{-g},

$$|g'(z)| \leqq \frac{2}{1-r^2}(-u(z) + B_1'), \qquad |z| = r,$$

where B_1' depends on B' and so on B. Thus in all cases

$$(4) \qquad | g'(z) | \leqq \frac{2}{1 - r^2} (| u(z) | + B_3), \qquad | z | = r.$$

On putting $z = 0$, we have (i). Further, we deduce

$$\frac{\partial}{\partial r} \log (| g(\rho e^{i\theta}) | + B_3) \leqq \frac{| g'(\rho e^{i\theta}) |}{| g(\rho e^{i\theta}) | + B_3} \leqq \frac{2}{1 - \rho^2},$$

and on integrating this from $\rho = 0$ to r, we deduce (iii).

Next we have

$$| u |^\lambda < \{\log \sqrt{(1 + | e^{2g} |)}\}^\lambda + \{\log \sqrt{(1 + | e^{-2g} |)}\}^\lambda,$$

and hence

$$(5) \qquad I_\lambda(r, u) < T_\lambda(r, e^g) + T_\lambda(r, e^{-g}).$$

The bound for $I_1(r, u)$ in Theorem 5 (iv) follows at once from this and Theorem 3. We have also

$$| g_n | = \left| \frac{1}{\pi r^n} \int_0^{2\pi} u(re^{i\theta}) e^{-in\theta} \, d\theta \right| \leqq \frac{2}{r^n} I_1(r, u),$$

and, on taking $r = 1 - 1/n$, (ii) follows, also.

Further, (4) gives

$$\frac{d}{dr} I_1(r, g) \leqq \frac{1}{2\pi} \int_0^{2\pi} | g'(re^{i\theta}) | \, d\theta \leqq \frac{2}{1 - r^2} (I_1(r, u) + B_3).$$

Now the second inequality of (iv) follows from the first by integration.

It remains to prove (v). We may confine ourselves to the case $1 < \lambda \leqq 2$, since if $\lambda > 2$ we have

$$I_\lambda(r, g) \leqq [M(r, g)]^{\lambda - 2} I_2(r, g),$$

so that (v) for $\lambda > 2$ follows from (v) for $\lambda = 2$ and (iii). By (5) and Theorem 3 we have

$$I_\lambda(r, u) < B(g(0), \lambda)(1 - r)^{1-\lambda}, \qquad 0 \leqq r < 1, \qquad \lambda > 1.$$

Thus (v) will be an immediate consequence of this and the following lemma:

LEMMA 3. *Suppose $g(z) = u + iv$ is regular in $|z| < 1$. Then*

$$I_\lambda(r, g) - |g(0)|^\lambda \leqq \frac{\lambda}{\lambda - 1}\{I_\lambda(r, u) - |u(0)|^\lambda\},$$

$$0 < r < 1, \qquad 1 < \lambda \leqq 2.$$

The lemma is a weak form of a well-known theorem of M. Riesz [14]. The following proof, similar to that of Lemma 2, is again due to Flett [6]. We have for any positive ϵ

$$\nabla^2\{(\epsilon + |g|^2)^{\lambda/2}\}$$
$$= \lambda |g'|^2[\lambda(\epsilon + |g|^2)^{(\lambda/2)-1} + \epsilon(2 - \lambda)(\epsilon + |g|^2)^{(\lambda/2)-2}],$$
$$\nabla^2\{(\epsilon + u^2)^{\lambda/2}\}$$
$$= \lambda |g'|^2[(\lambda - 1)(\epsilon + u^2)^{(\lambda/2)-1} + \epsilon(2 - \lambda)(\epsilon + |u|^2)^{(\lambda/2)-2}].$$

Thus we have for $\epsilon > 0$ and $1 < \lambda \leqq 2$

$$\nabla^2\{(\epsilon + |g|^2)^{\lambda/2}\} \leqq \frac{\lambda}{\lambda - 1}\nabla^2\{(\epsilon + u^2)^{\lambda/2}\}.$$

Hence Green's formula gives

$$r\frac{d}{dr}\frac{1}{2\pi}\int_0^{2\pi}(\epsilon + |g(re^{i\theta})|^2)^{\lambda/2}\,d\theta \leqq \frac{\lambda}{\lambda - 1}\,r\frac{d}{dr}\int_0^{2\pi}[\epsilon + u(re^{i\theta})^2]^{\lambda/2}\,d\theta.$$

Letting $\epsilon \to 0$ in this, we deduce

$$\frac{d}{dr}I_\lambda(r, g) \leqq \frac{\lambda}{\lambda - 1}\frac{d}{dr}I_\lambda(r, u).$$

Now Lemma 3 follows by integration, and the proof of Theorem 5 is complete.

Our examples show that all the results except the bounds for g_n are best possible. As to the g_n, example (c) shows that they need not be bounded, as might have been expected, but in all probability $g_n = O\{\log n\}$ is far from the truth.

The results of Theorem 5 were obtained by Littlewood [8], [9] in the case where $g(z) \neq 2k\pi i$ or, equivalently, $e^{g(z)} \neq 0$ or 1. His proof was based on an analytical expression for the superordinate function, which in this case is related to elliptic modular functions. However, this method could not be extended to more general cases, such as those considered here, where one can hardly hope to obtain a simple analytical expression for the functions in question. As a contribution to the problem of the coefficients, it should be mentioned that Flett [5] has obtained $|g_n| = O\{[\log n]^{\frac{3}{4}+\epsilon}\}$ for the superordinate function $g(z)$ which maps the unit circle onto the covering surface of the plane punctured at the points $2k\pi i$. This result, however, does not immediately extend to the subordinate case in which $g(z) \neq 2k\pi i$, and here $g_n = O\{\log n\}$ remains the best that is known.

Littlewood also considered the functions $h(z) = [g(z)]^2$. If $f(z) = e^{g(z)} \neq 0$ or 1, $g(z) \neq 2k\pi i$ and $h(z) \neq -4\pi^2 k^2$, where k is any integer. If we merely assume that $f(z) \in \mathfrak{N}(B)$ for a suitable $B \geqq 0$, we can obtain a characterization of the Riemann surfaces of $h(z)$ from Theorem 4. They must have branch points of an even order over the origin, and the schlicht circles contained in them, whose centers lie over $-d$, must have radii $O(d^{\frac{1}{2}})$ as $d \to +\infty$. The bounds for the growth of $h(z)$ follow from those for $g(z)$. However, for $h(z)$ we can obtain the correct order of magnitude for the coefficients h_n. We have, in fact, putting $r = n/(n+1)$,

$$|h_n| \leqq \frac{1}{r^n} I_1(r, h) \leqq eI_2(r, g) = \frac{O(1)}{1-r} = O(n).$$

Our example (a) shows that this is best possible.

The results for $g(z)$ prompt the question as to whether there is any nontrivial restriction on the Riemann surface of a function which results in bounded coefficients. The hypothesis of Bloch, that the surface contains no schlicht circle of radius greater than R, is sufficient for this. In fact, let $b(z) = \sum_{n=0}^{\infty} b_n z^n$ be such a function. Using the lower bound of $\frac{1}{4}\sqrt{3}$ obtained by Ahlfors [4] for Bloch's constant, we deduce: $|b_1| \leqq 4R/\sqrt{3}$. Using the invariance of our class, we deduce:

$$|b'(re^{i\theta})| \leqq \frac{4R}{\sqrt{3}(1-r^2)}.$$

Hence, applying the Cauchy inequality to $b'(z) = \sum_{n=1}^{\infty} nb_n z^{n-1}$ with $r^2 = (n-1)/(n+1)$, we find

$$n\,|b_n| \leqq \frac{1}{r^{n-1}} M[r, b'(z)] \leqq \frac{4R}{\sqrt{3}\, r^{n-1}(1-r^2)} = \frac{2R}{\sqrt{3}} \left[\frac{(n+1)^{n+1}}{n^2(n-1)^{n-1}}\right]^{\frac{1}{2}}.$$

Thus we have

$$|b_n| < \frac{2e}{\sqrt{3}} R, \qquad n \geqq 2.$$

Here $2e/\sqrt{3} = 3.14 \cdots$ cannot be replaced by 2, for $n \geqq 2$, as the example $b(z) = 2Rz^n$ shows.

BIBLIOGRAPHY

1. AHLFORS, L. V. *Beiträge zur Theorie der meromorphen Funktionen*, C. R. 7. Cong. Math. Scand. Oslo (1929), pp. 84–88.
2. —— *Sur les domaines dans lesquels une fonction méromorphe prend des valeurs appartenant à une région donnée*, Acta Soc. Sci. Fennicae, Nova Ser. A, 2 No. 2 (1933), 1–17.
3. —— *Zur Theorie der Überlagerungsflächen*, Acta Math. 65 (1935), 157–194.
4. —— *An extension of Schwarz's lemma*, Trans. Amer. Math. Soc. 43 (1938), 359–364.
5. FLETT, T. M. *On a coefficient problem of Littlewood and some trigonometrical sums*, Quart. J. Math. Oxford Ser. (2) 2 (1951), 26–52.
6. —— *Note on a function-theoretic identity*, J. London Math. Soc. 29 (1954), 115–118.
7. HAYMAN, W. K. *Some remarks on Schottky's theorem*, Proc. Cambridge Philos. Soc. 43 (1947), 442–454.
8. LITTLEWOOD, J. E. *On inequalities in the theory of functions*, Proc. London Math. Soc. (2) 23 (1924), 481–519.
9. —— *Lectures on the theory of functions.* Oxford, 1944.
10. MILLOUX, H. *Les fonctions méromorphes et leur dérivées.* Paris, 1940.
11. MONTEL, P. *Leçons sur les familles normales de fonctions analytiques et leurs applications.* Paris, 1927.
12. NEVANLINNA, R. *Le théorème de Picard-Borel et la théorie des fonctions méromorphes.* Paris, 1929.
13. —— *Eindeutige analytische Funktionen.* Berlin, 1936.
14. RIESZ, M. *Sur les fonctions conjugées*, Math. Zeit. 27 (1928), 218–244.
15. SCHOTTKY, F. *Über den Picardschen Satz und die Borelschen Ungleichungen*, Preuss. Akad. Wiss. Sitzungsber. 1904 (1904), 1244–1262.
16. SHIMIZU, T. *On the theory of meromorphic functions*, Jap. J. Math. 6 (1929), 119–171.
17. SPENCER, D. C. *A function-theoretic identity*, Amer. J. Math. 65 (1943), 147–160.
18. ZYGMUND, A. *Sur les fonctions conjugées*, Fund. Math. 13 (1929), 284–303.

UNIVERSITY COLLEGE
EXETER, ENGLAND

LOCAL THEORY OF PSEUDOANALYTIC FUNCTIONS*

LIPMAN BERS

PART I. INTRODUCTION

1. The theory of pseudoanalytic functions is a generalization of the theory of analytic functions in which the Cauchy-Riemann equations

$$\phi_x = \psi_y , \qquad \phi_y = -\psi_x$$

are replaced by a general linear elliptic system

$$\begin{aligned} \phi_x &= \sigma_{11}(x, y)\psi_x + \sigma_{12}(x, y)\psi_y , \\ \phi_y &= \sigma_{21}(x, y)\psi_x + \sigma_{22}(x, y)\psi_y . \end{aligned} \tag{1.1}$$

In this generalization the group property of analytic functions and their property of forming an algebra are, of course, lost. Nevertheless, a surprising number of function-theoretical results and concepts can be carried over.

The theory was originally formulated under the assumption that the coefficients σ_{ik} have Hölder-continuous partial derivatives.[1] In this paper we consider the more general case in which only the coefficients themselves have to be Hölder-continuous. (This generality is useful for application to the theory of nonlinear equations.) With a single exception we shall be concerned only with the local aspects of the theory.

---

* Work sponsored by the Office of Ordnance Research, U. S. Army (Contract DA-30-069-ORD-335).

[1] In papers of Bers [7], [8]. The theory contains and unifies previous generalizations of complex-function theory by Picard [31], [32], Beltrami [3], [4], Bers and Gelbart [12], [13], [14], Bers [5], Markuševič, as reported by Petrovskii [30], Lukomskaya [26], and Položiĭ [33], [34]. See also papers of Agmon and Bers [1], Bers [7], [9], [11], Lukomskaya [27], Vekua [37], and Hartman and Wintner [20]. For extensions to 2n independent variables, see the papers of Diaz [16] and Douglis [18].

2. It is well known that, if the coefficients in (1.1) are Hölder-continuous and satisfy the ellipticity condition

$$4\sigma_{12}\sigma_{21} - (\sigma_{11} - \sigma_{22})^2 < 0, \qquad \sigma_{12} > 0,$$

then system (1.1) can be reduced, by introducing new independent variables, to the canonical form

$$\begin{aligned} \phi_x &= \tau(x, y)\psi_x + \sigma(x, y)\psi_y, \\ \phi_y &= -\sigma(x, y)\psi_x + \tau(x, y)\psi_y, \end{aligned} \tag{2.1}$$

with $\sigma > 0$. We may therefore limit ourselves to systems (2.1). It turns out that it is convenient to consider together the function

$$\omega = \phi + i\psi \tag{2.2}$$

and the function

$$w = \phi + (-\tau + i\sigma)\psi, \tag{2.3}$$

where ϕ and ψ satisfy (2.1). Setting

$$w = u + iv$$

and assuming for the moment that τ and σ are continuously differentiable, we may write system (2.1) in the form

$$\begin{aligned} u_x - v_y &= a_{11}(x, y)u + a_{12}(x, y)v, \\ u_y + v_x &= a_{21}(x, y)u + a_{22}(x, y)v, \end{aligned} \tag{2.4}$$

the a_{ik} being fixed rational functions of σ, τ, and their partial derivatives.

Continuously differentiable solutions, $w(z) = u + iv$, of (2.4) obviously possess two properties: (i) a linear combination, with real constant coefficients, of two solutions is again a solution; (ii) if a solution $w(z)$ vanishes at a point z_0 the complex derivative $w'(z_0)$ exists.

It should be observed that the class of *analytic* functions is characterized by properties (i), (ii), and the requirement that it contain the two functions $w \equiv 1$, $w \equiv i$. In what follows we shall characterize the class of functions (2.3), with ϕ and ψ satisfying (2.1), by conditions (i), (ii) and the requirement that the class contain the two functions $w \equiv 1$ and $w \equiv -\tau + i\sigma$. In fact, it will be more convenient to consider instead of the pair $(1, -\tau + i\sigma)$ an arbitrary pair of functions (F, G) subject to the conditions: $F \neq 0$, $G \neq 0$, $\operatorname{Im}(G/F) > 0$.

PART II. GENERATORS; DIFFERENTIATION

3. Two continuous functions[2] $F(z)$, $G(z)$ defined in a domain D_0 are said to form a *generating pair* if

$$\operatorname{Im}\{\overline{F(z)}G(z)\} > 0. \tag{3.1}$$

With every generating pair (F, G) we associate the complex-valued function $\alpha(z)$ and the real-valued functions $\sigma(z)$, $\tau(z)$, $e(z)$ defined by the relations

$$\alpha = \frac{F + iG}{F - iG}, \tag{3.2}$$

$$-\tau + i\sigma = \frac{G}{F}, \tag{3.3}$$

$$e = \frac{1 + \tau^2 + \sigma^2}{2\sigma} = \frac{1 + |\alpha|^2}{1 - |\alpha|^2}. \tag{3.4}$$

We call e the *eccentricity* of (F, G). It is to be noted that

$$\sigma > 0, \qquad |\alpha| < 1, \qquad e \geqq 1. \tag{3.5}$$

If F and G have derivatives (with respect to x and y), the characteristic coefficients

$$a, b, A, B$$

of (F, G) are defined by the equations[3]

$$\begin{aligned} F_{\bar z} &= aF + b\bar F, \qquad & F_z &= AF + B\bar F \\ G_{\bar z} &= aG + b\bar G, \qquad & G_z &= AG + B\bar G. \end{aligned} \tag{3.6}$$

The dependence of all these quantities on (F, G) will be denoted, whenever desirable, by subscripts:

$$\alpha = \alpha_{(F,G)}, \qquad \tau = \tau_{(F,G)}, \quad \text{and so on.}$$

---

[2] We write functions of x, y as functions of $z = x + iy$ without implying analyticity. A bar over a complex number denotes the conjugate ($\bar z = x - iy$).

[3] We use the formal differential operators $\partial/\partial z$, $\partial/\partial \bar z$, and denote partial derivatives by subscripts. Thus $2w_z = w_x - iw_y$, $2w_{\bar z} = w_x + iw_y$.

Two generating pairs (F, G) and $(\hat{F}, \hat{G})$ will be called *equivalent* if there exist real constants λ_{ij} such that

$$\hat{F} = \lambda_{11}F + \lambda_{12}G, \qquad \hat{G} = \lambda_{21}F + \lambda_{22}G$$

(clearly $\lambda_{11}\lambda_{22} - \lambda_{12}\lambda_{21} > 0$). Equivalent differentiable generating pairs have the same characteristic coefficients.

$(\hat{F}, \hat{G})$ and (F, G) will be called *similar* if there exists a function $H(z)$ such that

$$\hat{F} \equiv HF, \qquad \hat{G} \equiv HG.$$

Clearly, (F, G) is similar to $(1, -\tau_{(F,G)} + i\sigma_{(F,G)})$, and

$$a_{(HF,HG)} \equiv a_{(F,G)}, \qquad e_{(HF,HG)} = e_{(F,G)}.$$

The *dual* generating pair

$$(F, G)^* = (F^*, G^*)$$

is defined by the relations

$$F^* = \frac{2\bar{G}}{F\bar{G} - \bar{F}G}, \qquad G^* = \frac{2\bar{F}}{F\bar{G} - \bar{F}G}, \tag{3.7}$$

so that

$$(F, G)^{**} = (F, G). \tag{3.8}$$

If $(\hat{F}, \hat{G})$ is equivalent to (F, G), $(\hat{F}, \hat{G})^*$ is equivalent to $(F, G)^*$. Note also that

$$(HF, HG)^* = (F^*/H, G^*/H),$$

$$a_{(F,G)^*} = \overline{-a_{(F,G)}}, \tag{3.9}$$

$$e_{(F,G)^*} = e_{(F,G)}.$$

The computation of the characteristic coefficients of $(F, G)^*$ is left to the reader.

4. From now on, let (F, G) denote, unless stated otherwise, a fixed generating pair in D_0. Every function $w(z)$ defined in a domain $D \subset D_0$ admits the unique representation

$$w(z) = \phi(z)F(z) + \psi(z)G(z) \tag{4.1}$$

with *real* ϕ, ψ. We write

$$w = {}^*\omega, \qquad \omega = {}_*w \qquad (\text{mod } F, G)$$

and note that

$$*1 = F, \qquad *G = i,$$

$$*(\lambda\omega) = \lambda(*\omega), \quad \lambda \text{ a real constant},$$

$$*(\omega_1 + \omega_2) = (*\omega_1) + (*\omega_2).$$

If

$$\omega = {}_*w \ (\text{mod } F, G), \qquad \hat{\omega} = {}_*w \ (\text{mod } \hat{F}, \hat{G}),$$

then

$$\hat{\omega}(z) = k_1(z)\omega(z) + k_2(z)\overline{\omega(z)}, \qquad |k_1| > |k_2|,$$

where k_1 and k_2 depend only on the pairs (F, G), $(\hat{F}, \hat{G})$. If $(\hat{F}, \hat{G})$ is equivalent to (F, G), k_1 and k_2 are constants.

If

$$\omega = {}_*w \qquad (\text{mod } F, G)$$

then

$$\omega = {}_*(Hw) \qquad (\text{mod } HF, HG).$$

Note also that the ratio $| w/{}_*w |$ has upper and lower bounds depending only on (F, G).

The function (4.1) is said to possess at the point $z_0 \in D$ the (F, G)-*derivative*

$$\dot{w}(z_0) = \left.\frac{d_{(F,G)}w(z)}{dz}\right|_{z=z_0},$$

if the limit

$$\dot{w}(z_0) = \lim_{z \to z_0} \frac{w(z) - \phi(z_0)F(z) - \psi(z_0)G(z)}{z - z_0} \tag{4.2}$$

exists and is finite.

5. Lemma 5.1. *If $\dot{w}(z_0)$ exists, then $\omega = {}_*w$ is differentiable at z_0, and the equations*

$$\phi_{\bar{z}}F + \psi_{\bar{z}}G = 0, \tag{5.1}$$

$$\phi_z F + \psi_z G = \dot{w} \tag{5.2}$$

hold at this point. Conversely, if ω is continuously differentiable at z_0 and (5.1) *holds at this point,* $\dot{w}(z_0)$ *exists.*

Proof. Set

$$W(z) = [\phi(z) - \phi(z_0)]F(z) + [\psi(z) - \psi(z_0)]G(z),$$

$$W_0(z) = [\phi(z) - \phi(z_0)]F(z_0) + [\psi(z) - \psi(z_0)]G(z_0).$$

Assume that $\dot{w}(z_0) = W'(z_0)$ exists. Then $_*w(z) - {}_*w(z_0) = O(|z - z_0|)$, as $z \to z_0$, so that

$$\lim_{z \to z_0} \frac{W(z) - W_0(z)}{z - z_0} = 0.$$

Hence $W_0'(z_0) = W'(z_0)$, so that $W_0(z_0)$ is differentiable at z_0 (which implies the existence of $\omega_x(z_0)$, $\omega_y(z_0)$), $W_{0,\bar{z}}(z_0) = 0$ (which implies (5.1)), and $\dot{w}(z_0) = W_0'(z_0) = W_{0,z}(z_0)$ (which implies (5.2)). The second assertion is proved by reversing the argument.

Equations (5.1) and (5.2) imply that

$$(5.3) \qquad 2\phi_z = F^*\dot{w}, \qquad 2\psi_z = -G^*\dot{w}.$$

We note that equation (5.1) is equivalent to the system (2.1), σ and τ being defined by (3.3). Also it can be written in the form

$$(5.4) \qquad \omega_{\bar{z}} = \alpha\bar{\omega}_{\bar{z}},$$

α being given by (3.2).

COROLLARY 5.2. *If F, G are differentiable at z_0 and $\dot{w}(z_0)$ exists, then w is differentiable at this point and*

$$(5.5) \qquad w_{\bar{z}} = aw + b\bar{w},$$

$$(5.6) \qquad \dot{w} = w_z - Aw - B\bar{w}.$$

Conversely, if F, G and w are continuously differentiable at z_0, and (5.5) *holds at this point,* $\dot{w}(z_0)$ *exists.*

Proof. If F and G are differentiable (continuously differentiable) at z_0, differentiability (continuous differentiability) of w is equivalent to that of ω. Hence the corollary follows from the lemma by a direct computation.

If we set

$$2(a + b) = a_{11} + ia_{21}, \qquad 2(\bar{a} - \bar{b}) = a_{22} + ia_{12},$$

then equation (5.5) becomes equivalent to the system (2.4).

6. A function $w(z)$ possessing an (F, G)-derivative at all points of a domain D is called regular (F, G)-*pseudoanalytic of the first kind* in D, or simply pseudoanalytic if there is no danger of confusion.

Pseudoanalytic functions are continuous. If w_1 and w_2 are pseudoanalytic, the function $w = \lambda_1 w_1 + \lambda_2 w_2$, λ_1 and λ_2 being real constants, is pseudoanalytic and

$$\dot{w} = \lambda_1 \dot{w}_1 + \lambda_2 \dot{w}_2 .$$

The generators F and G are pseudoanalytic and $\dot{F} \equiv \dot{G} \equiv 0$. Conversely, it follows from (5.3) that every function w with $\dot{w} \equiv 0$ is a linear combination of the generators with real constant coefficients.

7. If $(\hat{F}, G)$ is equivalent to (F, G), $(\hat{F}, \dot{G})$-pseudoanalyticity is equivalent to (F, G)-pseudoanalyticity, and

$$\frac{d_{(F,G)}w}{dz} = \frac{d_{(\hat{F},\hat{G})}w}{dz}.$$

More generally, two generative pairs, (F, G) and $(\hat{F}, \hat{G})$, are called *equipotent* if every (F, G)-pseudoanalytic function is $(\hat{F}, \hat{G})$-pseudoanalytic and vice versa. It is not difficult to verify that a necessary and sufficient condition for equipotency is that the functions $\hat{F}(z)$ and $\hat{G}(z)$ be (F, G)-pseudoanalytic. If this condition is satisfied, the existence of one of the derivatives

$$\frac{d_{(F,G)}w}{dz}, \qquad \frac{d_{(\hat{F},\hat{G})}w}{dz}$$

implies that of the other, but the values of these derivatives are, in general, different. If the equipotent pairs (F, G), $(\hat{F}, \hat{G})$ are differentiable, then

$$a_{(F,G)} = a_{(\hat{F},\hat{G})} , \qquad b_{(F,G)} = b_{(\hat{F},\hat{G})} ,$$

but, in general, $A_{(F,G)} \neq A_{(\hat{F},\hat{G})}$, $B_{(F,G)} \neq B_{(\hat{F},\hat{G})}$.

Let $H(z)$, $z \in D_0$, be a continuous nonvanishing function. The function w is (F, G)-pseudoanalytic if and only if Hw is (HF, HG)-pseudoanalytic and

$$\frac{d_{(HF,HG)}Hw}{dz} = H\,\frac{d_{(F,G)}w}{dz},$$

if these derivatives exist.

8. Pseudoanalyticity is a conformally invariant property.

LEMMA 8.1. *Let* $z = \chi(\zeta)$ *be a one-to-one conformal mapping of* Δ_0 *onto* D_0, *and set* $F[\chi(\zeta)] = \hat{F}(\zeta)$, $G[\chi(\zeta)] = \hat{G}(\zeta)$. *A function* $\hat{w}(\zeta) = w[\chi(\zeta)]$, $\zeta \in \Delta \subset \Delta_0$, *is* $(\hat{F}, \hat{G})$*-pseudoanalytic if and only if* $w(z)$ *is* (F, G)*-pseudoanalytic in* $D = \chi(\Delta)$. *If this condition is satisfied,*

$$\frac{d_{(\hat{F},\hat{G})}w[\chi(\zeta)]}{d\zeta} = \left.\frac{d_{(F,G)}w(\zeta)}{d\zeta}\right|_{z=\chi(\zeta)} \chi'(\zeta).$$

The proof is clear.

This lemma leads to a natural definition of pseudoanalyticity on Riemann surfaces.[4] In particular, $w(z)$ is called (F, G)-pseudoanalytic at $z = \infty$, if $\hat{w}(\zeta) = w(1/\zeta)$ is $(\hat{F}, \hat{G})$-pseudoanalytic at $\zeta = 0$, where $\hat{F}(\zeta) = F(1/\zeta)$, $\hat{G}(\zeta) = G(1/\zeta)$. This definition assumes, of course, the existence of the limits $F(\infty)$, $G(\infty)$, $w(\infty)$ and the inequality $\operatorname{Im}\{\overline{F(\infty)}G(\infty)\} > 0$.

9. If $w = \phi F + \psi G$ is (F, G)-pseudoanalytic of the first kind, the function $\omega = {}_*w = \phi + i\psi$ is called (F, G)*-pseudoanalytic of the second kind.* In particular, every complex constant is pseudoanalytic of the second kind.

Pseudoanalytic functions of the second kind remain unchanged if (F, G) is replaced by a similar generating pair. They undergo a homogeneous linear transformation with fixed constant (variable) coefficients if (F, G) is replaced by an equivalent (equipotent) generating pair.

10. From now on we make the essential hypothesis that *the generators* $F(z)$, $G(z)$ *are Hölder-continuous in* D_0 : that is, that they satisfy a uniform Hölder condition on every compact subset of D_0.

Let S be such a subset. A number $\beta > 0$ is called an *essential bound* of (F, G) in S if for z, z' in S the following inequalities hold:

$$\max\left\{|F(z)|, \frac{1}{|F(z)|}, |G(z)|, \frac{1}{|G(z)|}, \frac{1}{\operatorname{Im}\{\overline{F(z)}G(z)\}}\right\} \leqq \beta,$$

$$|F(z) - F(z')|, \qquad |G(z) - G(z')| \leqq \beta\,|z - z'|^{1/\beta}.$$

Note that in S the eccentricity $e_{(F,G)}$ can be estimated in terms of β.

[4] See my paper [7] for a sketch of the theory of pseudoanalytic functions on Riemann surfaces.

A family of generating pairs (F^ν, G^ν) in D_0 will be called *equibounded* if the pairs (F^ν, G^ν) possess a common essential bound on every compact $S \subset D_0$.

We shall give special attention to generators $F(z)$, $G(z)$ which in D_0 possess Hölder-continuous partial derivatives with respect to x and y (and hence Hölder-continuous characteristic coefficients). Such generating pairs (F, G) will be called *smooth.*[5]

PART III. CONTINUITY OF THE DERIVATIVE; INTEGRATION

11. In Part III our aim is to prove the basic theorem:

THEOREM 11.1. *The (F, G)-derivative of an (F, G)-pseudoanalytic function is Hölder-continuous.*

We note this corollary:

COROLLARY 11.2. *The real and imaginary parts of a pseudoanalytic function of the second kind satisfy the maximum principle.*

In fact, the maximum principle is known to hold for continuously differentiable functions satisfying equations (2.1) or (5.1).[6]

12. Another consequence of Theorem 11.1 is the possibility of defining an (F, G)-integration process. In fact, this theorem, together with equations (5.3), implies the following lemma:

LEMMA 12.1. *Let $w(z)$ be (F, G)-pseudoanalytic in D and set $\omega(z) = {}_*w(z)$. Then*

$$(12.1) \qquad \omega(z) - \omega(z_0) = \operatorname{Re} \int_{z_0}^{z} F^* \dot{w}\, dz - i \operatorname{Re} \int_{z_0}^{z} G^* \dot{w}\, dz,$$

the integration being performed along any path in D.

The converse assertion is independent of Theorem 11.1.

LEMMA 12.2. *Let $W(z)$ be continuous in a domain $D \subset D_0$. If*

$$\operatorname{Re} \oint_\Gamma F^* W\, dz = \operatorname{Re} \oint_\Gamma G^* W\, dz = 0 \qquad \textit{when } \Gamma \sim 0 \textit{ in } D,$$

[5] Most results on smooth generating pairs can be extended to the case where F and G possess derivatives in the weak sense, provided that these derivatives are of class L_p, $p > 2$. These results will not be discussed here. See Vekua [37], [38].

[6] Several proofs of this fact are known. See, for instance, Douglis [17].

then there exists an (F, G)-pseudoanalytic (not necessarily single-valued) function $w(z)$ in D such that $\dot{w} \equiv W$.

(Here and hereafter $\Gamma \sim 0$ in D means that Γ is homotopic to 0 in D.)

Proof. We may assume that D is a disk, with center z_0. The functions

$$\phi(z) = \operatorname{Re} \int_{z_0}^{z} F^*W\, dz, \qquad \psi(z) = -\int_{z_0}^{z} G^*W\, dz$$

are well-defined and continuously differentiable in D. We have that $\phi_z = F^*W/2$, $\phi_{\bar{z}} = \overline{F^*W}/2$, $\psi_z = -G^*W/2$, $\psi_{\bar{z}} = -\overline{G^*W}/2$. Hence by (3.7)

$$F\phi_{\bar{z}} + G\psi_{\bar{z}} = 0, \qquad F\phi_z + G\psi_z = W,$$

so that the assertion follows from Lemma 5.1.

13. As the first step in proving Theorem 11.1 we establish another lemma:

LEMMA 13.1. *Let z_0 be a given point in D_0, γ_0 and $\gamma_1 \neq 0$ given complex numbers. If $r > 0$ is sufficiently small, there exists in $|z - z_0| < r$ an (F, G)-pseudoanalytic function $w(z)$ such that $\dot{w}(z)$ is Hölder-continuous, $w(z_0) = \gamma_0$, $\dot{w}(z_0) = \gamma_1$.*

Proof. We may assume that $F(z_0) = 1$, $G(z_0) = i$, since this can be achieved by replacing (F, G) by an equivalent generative pair. Then

$$\alpha(z_0) = 0, \tag{13.1}$$

and if we set $\omega = {}_*w$, our task is to find in $|z - z_0| < r$ a Hölder-continuously differentiable solution of equation (5.4) satisfying the conditions

$$\omega(z_0) = \gamma_0, \qquad \omega_z(z_0) = \gamma_1. \tag{13.2}$$

This can be achieved by repeating the main steps in the successive-approximations argument used by Lichtenstein [24], [25] for solving the Beltrami equations. It will suffice to sketch this argument.

Assume that a solution $\omega(z)$ is given, ω and ω_z satisfying a Hölder condition in $|z - z_0| \leqq r$. Set

$$\omega(z) = -\frac{1}{\pi} \iint_{|z-z_0|<r} \frac{\alpha(\zeta)\overline{\omega_\zeta(\zeta)}}{\zeta - z}\, d\xi\, d\eta + f(z). \tag{13.3}$$

Then $f(z)$ is analytic for $|z - z_0| < r$ and

$$(13.4) \quad \omega_z(z) = -\frac{1}{\pi}\iint_{|\zeta - z_0| < r} \frac{\alpha(\zeta)\overline{\omega_\zeta(\zeta)} - \alpha(z)\overline{\omega_z(z)}}{(\zeta - z)^2}\, d\xi\, d\eta + f'(z).$$

This follows from Hölder's formulas for the derivatives of a logarithmic potential.

Write (13.4) in the symbolic form

$$\omega_z = T\omega_z + f'.$$

If f is analytic and $\chi(z)$ is a uniformly Hölder-continuous solution of the equation

$$\chi = T\chi + f',$$

then the function

$$(13.5) \quad \omega(z) = -\frac{1}{\pi}\iint_{|\zeta - z| < r} \frac{\alpha(\zeta)\overline{\chi(\zeta)}}{\zeta - z}\, d\xi\, d\eta + f(z)$$

is a Hölder-continuous solution of (5.4), and $\omega_z(z_0) = \chi(z_0)$.

Let B denote the real Banach space of complex-valued functions $\chi(z)$ defined for $|z - z_0| < r$ and satisfying a Hölder condition with exponent δ, the norm of χ being

$$\|\chi\| = \max|\chi(z)| + \text{l.u.b.}\frac{|\chi(z_1) - \chi(z_2)|}{|z_1 - z_2|^\delta}.$$

If δ is chosen smaller than the Hölder exponent of $\alpha(z)$, T becomes a bounded linear operator in B. Also it can be shown that, in view of (13.1),

$$\lim_{r \to 0} \|T\| = 0,$$

where

$$\|T\| = \text{l.u.b.}_{\|\chi\|=1} \|T(\chi)\|.$$

Hence, for r sufficiently small $(1 - T)^{-1}$ exists, and $\|(1 - T)^{-1}\| \leqq (1 - \|T\|)^{-1}$. In particular, we define $\chi_1(z)$ and $\chi_2(z)$ by the relations

$$\chi_1 - T\chi_1 = 1, \qquad \chi_2 - T\chi_2 = i.$$

Since

$$|\chi_1(z_0) - 1| \leqq \|\chi_1 - 1\| \leqq \|T\|\,\|\chi_1\| \leqq \frac{\|T\|}{1 - \|T\|}$$

and similarly for $|\chi_2(z_0) - i|$, we may achieve, by choosing r small, that Im $\{\overline{\chi_1(z_0)}\chi_2(z_0)\} \neq 0$. Hence there exist real constants λ_1, λ_2 such that $\lambda_1\chi_1(z_0) + \lambda_2\chi_2(z_0) = \gamma_1$. Setting $\chi(z) = \lambda_1\chi_1(z) + \lambda_2\chi_2(z)$ and defining $\omega(z)$ by (13.5), where $f(z) = (\lambda_1 + i\lambda_2)z + \mu$, μ being a suitably chosen complex constant, we obtain the desired solution.

14. Now we give the proof of Theorem 11.1. Let z_0 be a point of D, the domain of definition of the (F, G)-pseudoanalytic function $w(z)$, S a sufficiently small disk with center at z_0. According to Lemma 13.1, there exists in S a Hölder-continuously differentiable (F^*, G^*)-pseudoanalytic function of the second kind $\zeta(z) = \xi + i\eta$ with $\zeta_z(z_0) \neq 0$. We may assume that $\zeta(z)$ is a homeomorphism of S, since this can be achieved by diminishing S. A straightforward computation (based on relation (3.9)) shows that the mapping $z \to \zeta(z)$ transforms system (2.1) into the system

$$\phi_\xi = 2\tau\psi_\xi + (\sigma^2 + \tau^2)\psi_\eta, \qquad \phi_\eta = -\psi_\xi. \tag{14.1}$$

We show next that

$$\text{Re} \oint_\Gamma \omega\, d\zeta = 0 \qquad \text{if } \Gamma \sim 0 \text{ in } S, \tag{14.2}$$

where $\omega = {}_*w$. The statement would be obvious, in view of the second equation (14.1), if we knew that $\omega(z)$ is continuously differentiable.

Let z_1 be a fixed but arbitrary point in S, T a triangle of diameter δ containing z_1 or containing z_1 in its interior. If we knew that

$$\text{Re} \oint_T \omega\, d\zeta = o(\delta^2), \qquad \delta \to 0, \tag{14.3}$$

equation (14.2) would follow by the familiar argument used in Goursat's proof of Cauchy's theorem. By the previous remark, the value of the integral in (14.3) is not changed if ω is replaced by $\omega - \tilde{\omega}$, where $\tilde{\omega} = {}_*\tilde{w}$, $\tilde{w}(z)$ being an (F, G)-pseudoanalytic function with a continuous (F, G)-derivative. Therefore, noting Lemma 13.1, we may prove (14.3) under the assumption that

$$w(z_0) = \dot{w}(z_0) = 0. \tag{14.4}$$

Recalling the definition of $\dot{w}$, we conclude from (14.4) that $w(z) =$

$o(|z - z_1|)$, $z \to z_0$. Hence the integrand in (14.3) is $o(\delta)$ on T, which implies (14.3).

Next, (14.2) implies the existence of a real-valued function $\Phi(\zeta)$ in $\Sigma = \zeta(S)$ such that

$$\phi = \Phi_\xi, \qquad \psi = -\Phi_\eta .$$

In view of the first equation (14.1),

$$\Phi_{\xi\xi} + 2\tau\Phi_{\xi\eta} + (\sigma^2 + \tau^2)\Phi_{\eta\eta} = 0. \tag{14.5}$$

It is known that all solutions of a linear elliptic equation

$$A_{11}(\xi, \eta)\Phi_{\xi\xi} + 2A_{12}(\xi, \eta)\Phi_{\xi\eta} + A_{22}(\xi, \eta)\Phi_{\eta\eta} = 0$$

with Hölder-continuous A_{ij} have Hölder-continuous second derivatives.[7] Since σ and τ are Hölder-continuous functions of $\zeta = \zeta(z)$, ϕ and ψ have Hölder-continuous partial derivatives with respect to ξ and η, and hence also with respect to x and y. In view of equation (5.2) this implies Theorem 11.1.

15. THEOREM 15.1. *If the generating pair (F, G) is smooth, an (F, G)-pseudoanalytic function of the first kind is Hölder-continuously differentiable.*

Though the statement follows at once from Theorem 11.1, a direct proof will be more instructive.

LEMMA 15.2. *Let (F, G) be smooth, and let $w(z)$ be a bounded continuous function defined in a domain D with compact closure $\bar{D} \subset D_0$. Set*

$$w(z) = -\frac{1}{\pi}\iint_D \frac{a(\zeta)w(\zeta) + b(\zeta)\overline{w(\zeta)}}{\zeta - z}\, d\xi\, d\eta + f(z). \tag{15.1}$$

Then $w(z)$ is (F, G)-pseudoanalytic if and only if $f(z)$ is analytic.

Proof.[8] Assume that $f(z)$ is analytic, hence Hölder-continuous.

---

[7] The statement follows from these remarks: (i) one can solve the first boundary-value problem for equation (14.4) and obtain a solution having Hölder-continuous second derivatives in a disk S and assuming prescribed continuously differentiable boundary values on the circumference; (ii) the maximum principle for solutions of (14.4) can be proved without assuming the continuity of the second derivatives. See E. Hopf [21], [22], and Schauder [35], [36].

[8] See the references in the preceding footnote.

Then equation (15.1) shows that w is Hölder-continuous. So also is $aw + b\bar{w}$, so that the double integral in (15.1) is Hölder-continuously differentiable and has the $\bar{z}$-derivative $aw + b\bar{w}$. It follows that w is Hölder-continuously differentiable and, since $f_{\bar{z}} \equiv 0$, that equation (5.5) holds. In view of Corollary 5.2, w is pseudoanalytic.

This argument shows that Theorem 15.1 will be proved once the second part of Lemma 15.2 is established.

Assume now that $w(z)$ is pseudoanalytic. Set $R(z) = \phi(z_0)F(z) + \psi(z_0)G(z)$, where $\phi + i\psi = {}_*w$ and z_0 is an arbitrary but fixed point in D. Since $R(z)$ is Hölder-continuously differentiable and $R_{\bar{z}} = aR + b\bar{R}$, the function $h(z)$ defined by the relation

$$R(z) = -\frac{1}{\pi}\iint_D \frac{a(\zeta)R(\zeta) + b(\zeta)\overline{R(\zeta)}}{\zeta - z}\, d\xi\, d\eta + h(z)$$

is analytic. Set $W(z) = w(z) - R(z)$. Then

$$W(z) = -\frac{1}{\pi}\iint_D \frac{a(\zeta)W(\zeta) + b(\zeta)\overline{W(\zeta)}}{\zeta - z}\, d\xi\, d\eta + f(z) - h(z),$$

and

$$0 = -\frac{1}{\pi}\iint_D \frac{a(\zeta)W(\zeta) + b(\zeta)\overline{W(\zeta)}}{\zeta - z_0}\, d\xi\, d\eta + f(z_0) - h(z_0),$$

so that

$$\frac{f(z) - f(z_0)}{z - z_0} = \frac{W(z)}{z - z_0} + \frac{h(z) - h(z_0)}{z - z_0} + \iint_D \frac{\rho(\zeta)\, d\xi\, d\eta}{\zeta - z}, \tag{15.2}$$

where

$$\rho(z) = \frac{a(z)}{\pi}\,\frac{W(z)}{z - z_0} + \frac{b(\zeta)}{\pi}\,\frac{\overline{W(z)}}{z - z_0}.$$

The first term on the right-hand side of (15.2) approaches the value $\dot{w}(z_0)$ as $z \to z_0$. The second term has the limit $h'(z_0)$. Since the existence of $\dot{w}(z_0)$ implies the boundedness of $\rho(z)$, the double integral also approaches a finite limit as $z \to z_0$. Therefore $f'(z_0)$ exists, and since z_0 was arbitrary, $f(z)$ is analytic.

16. THEOREM 16.1. *If (F, G) is smooth, every (F, G)-pseudoanalytic function of the second kind is twice Hölder-continuously differentiable.*

Proof. By hypothesis, the coefficients σ, τ of system (2.1) are Hölder-continuously differentiable. Formal elimination of ψ from the system yields the equation

$$\psi_{xx} + \psi_{yy} + \gamma\psi_x + \delta\psi_y = 0, \tag{16.1}$$

where the coefficients

$$\gamma = (\sigma_x + \tau_y)/\sigma, \qquad \delta = (\sigma_y - \tau_x)/\sigma \tag{16.2}$$

are Hölder-continuous. Every continuously differentiable solution of (16.1) is, of course, the imaginary part of a pseudoanalytic function of the second kind. On the other hand, the Dirichlet problem (say in a disk) for equation (16.1) always has a twice Hölder-continuously differentiable solution. This remark, together with the maximum principle (Corollary 11.2), implies the assertion.

THEOREM 16.2. *If (F, G) is smooth, the (F, G)-derivative of an (F, G)-pseudoanalytic function w is Hölder-continuously differentiable and*

$$(\dot{w})_{\bar{z}} = a\dot{w} - B\overline{\dot{w}}. \tag{16.3}$$

Proof. The first assertion follows from Theorem 16.1 and equation (5.2). Next,

$$(\dot{w})_{\bar{z}} = (F\phi_z + G\psi_z)_{\bar{z}} = F_{\bar{z}}\phi_z + G_{\bar{z}}\psi_z + F\phi_{z\bar{z}} + G\psi_{z\bar{z}}\,. \tag{16.4}$$

But, in view of (5.1),

$$F\phi_{z\bar{z}} + G\psi_{z\bar{z}} = -F_z\phi_{\bar{z}} - G_z\psi_{\bar{z}}\,. \tag{16.5}$$

Substituting (16.5) into (16.4), expressing the functions ϕ_z, $\phi_{\bar{z}}$, ψ_z, $\psi_{\bar{z}}$ in terms of $\dot{w}$, $\overline{\dot{w}}$ by means of equations (5.6), and noting the definition (3.6) of the characteristic coefficients, one obtains (16.3).

17. Having identified pseudoanalytic functions $\omega = \phi + i\psi$ of the second kind with continuously differentiable solutions of system (2.1), we can apply known results and methods for estimating derivatives of such solutions [21], [22], [35], [36]. In this way we obtain the following lemma:

LEMMA 17.1. *Let $w(z)$ be a bounded (F, G)-pseudoanalytic function defined in the domain $|z - z_0| < r$, and let M be an upper bound for $|w(z)|$. Then*

$$|\dot{w}(z_0)| \leqq MCr^{-\lambda},$$

$$|\dot{w}(z_0 + h) - \dot{w}(z_0)| \leqq MC_1r^{-\lambda_1}|h|^{\mu} \quad \textit{for} \quad |h| \leqq r/2,$$

where C, λ, C_1, λ_1, μ *are positive constants depending only on an essential bound for* (F, G) *in* $|z - z_0| \leqq r$.

The following convergence theorems are an immediate consequence.

THEOREM 17.2. *Let* $\{(F^{\nu}, G^{\nu})\}$ *be an equibounded sequence of generating pairs defined in* D_0, (F, G) *a generating pair such that* $F^{\nu}(z) \to F(z)$, $G^{\nu}(z) \to G(z)$, $z \in D_0$. *Let* $\{w_{\nu}(z)\}$ *be a uniformly bounded sequence of functions defined in a domain* $D \subset D_0$. *If* w_{ν} *is* (F^{ν}, G^{ν})*-pseudoanalytic,* $\nu = 1, 2, \cdots$, *then the sequence* $\{w_{\nu}\}$ *contains a convergent subsequence.*

THEOREM 17.3. *Under the hypotheses of Theorem* 17.2, *assume that* $w_{\nu}(z) \to w(z)$, $z \in D$. *Then this convergence is uniform on every compact subset of* D, w *is* (F, G)*-pseudoanalytic, and* $\dot{w}_{\nu}(z) \to \dot{w}(z)$, *uniformly on every compact subset of* D.

(Here $\dot{w}_{\nu} = d_{(F^{\nu},G^{\nu})}w_{\nu}/dz, \qquad \dot{w} = d_{(F,G)}w/dz.$)

PART IV. INTERIORITY AND QUASICONFORMALITY

18. THEOREM 18.1. *A pseudoanalytic function of the second kind is an interior transformation.*[9]

This means that for every pseudoanalytic function of the second kind $\omega(z)$ defined in a domain D there exists a homeomorphism

$$\zeta = \xi + i\eta = \chi(z), \qquad z = \chi^{-1}(\zeta) \tag{18.1}$$

of D such that the function $f(\zeta) = w[\chi^{-1}(\zeta)]$ is analytic in $\Delta = \chi(D)$.

Theorem 18.1 asserts that pseudoanalytic functions of the second kind have all topological properties of analytic functions, as well as the *unique continuation property.*[10] In particular, it implies the following lemma:

LEMMA 18.2. *Let* $\omega(z) = \phi + i\psi$ *be a nonconstant pseudoanalytic function of the second kind. Then* $\omega(z)$ *is a local homeomorphism, except at isolated points.*

---

[9] In the sense of Stoïlow.

[10] This means that a pseudoanalytic function regular in the neighborhood of a point z_0 is uniquely determined by its values on a sequence of points converging to z_0.

On the other hand, Theorem 18.1 follows from this lemma via the general uniformization theorem.[11]

The points at which $\dot{w} = 0$ (where $w = {}^*\omega$), that is, $\phi_x^2 + \phi_y^2 = \psi_x^2 + \psi_y^2 = 0$, are called critical points of ω. Since equations (2.1) imply that

$$\phi_x^2 + \phi_y^2 + \psi_x^2 + \psi_y^2 = 2e\cdot(\phi_x\psi_y - \phi_y\psi_x), \tag{18.2}$$

where e is the eccentricity of (F, G) (see equation (3.4)), the Jacobian of ω is positive (zero) at a noncritical (critical) point. Hence Lemma 18.2 would be established if we could prove Lemma 18.3:

LEMMA 18.3. *Under the hypothesis of Lemma* 18.2 *the critical points of* ω *are isolated.*

This lemma would also imply the following theorem:

THEOREM 18.4. *A homeomorphism* (18.1) *which takes a nonconstant pseudoanalytic function of the second kind into an analytic function is Hölder-continuously differentiable and satisfies the relation*

$$\xi_x^2 + \xi_y^2 + \eta_x^2 + \eta_y^2 = 2e\cdot(\xi_x\eta_y - \xi_y\eta_x) > 0 \tag{18.3}$$

except at isolated points.

In fact, ζ must be an analytic function of ω at every point at which $\omega(z)$ is a local homeomorphism, so that the assertion follows at once from Lemma 18.3 and (18.2).

The theorem implies that the homeomorphism χ is of *bounded eccentricity* if e is bounded in D, hence, in particular, whenever the closure $\bar{D}$ of D is compact.

After proving Theorems 18.1 and 18.4, we shall establish a further theorem:

THEOREM 18.5. *The critical points of a pseudoanalytic function of the second kind* $\omega(z)$ *are precisely the points in the neighborhood of which the mapping* $z = \omega(z)$ *is not one-to-one.*

For a pseudoanalytic function of the first kind, $w(z)$, Theorem 18.1 asserts that if $w \not\equiv 0$, the zeros of $w(z)$ are isolated. If (F, G) is smooth, this also follows directly from Theorem 16.1 and equation (5.5), since Carleman [15][12] proved that the zeros of a solution of

---

[11] See, for instance, the proof of Lemma 2.7 in Bers [10].

[12] Another proof of Carleman's theorem will be found in Bers [11].

(5.5) are isolated except if $w \equiv 0$. Noting Theorem 16.2, we conclude from Carleman's theorem that the zeros of $\dot{w}(z)$ are also isolated, unless $\dot{w} \equiv 0$, that is, unless $\omega = {}_*w \equiv$ const. Hence Lemma 18.3 is proved for the case of smooth generators, and so are Lemma 18.2 and Theorems 18.1 and 18.4.

19. Now let $\omega(z)$ be an (F, G)-pseudoanalytic function of the second kind, $S : |z - z_0| < r$ a disk whose closure $\bar{S}$ belongs to the domain of definition $D \subset D_0$ of ω. It is easy to construct in D_0 an equibounded sequence of smooth generating pairs (F^ν, G^ν) converging to (F, G). For every ν we can find an (F^ν, G^ν)-pseudoanalytic function of the second kind

$$\omega_\nu(z) = {}_*w_\nu(z) \qquad (\mathrm{mod}\ F^\nu, G^\nu)$$

such that

$$\begin{aligned} \mathrm{Im}\ \omega_\nu(z) &= \mathrm{Im}\ \omega(z), \qquad |z - z_0| = r, \\ \mathrm{Re}\ \omega_\nu(z_0) &= \mathrm{Re}\ \omega(z_0). \end{aligned} \tag{19.1}$$

Indeed, this requires only the possibility of solving the Dirichlet problem for equations of the form (16.1) in a disk.

Since (F^ν, G^ν) is smooth, we can apply Theorem 18.1 and find for every ν a homeomorphism $\zeta = \chi_\nu(z)$ of S which takes $\omega_\nu(z)$ into an analytic function. This homeomorphism is determined up to a conformal mapping; we may assume that χ takes S onto the disk $|\zeta - z_0| < r$ and that $\chi(z_0) = z_0$. In view of the equiboundedness assumption and Theorem 18.4 already established for smooth generators, all homeomorphisms χ_ν have their eccentricities bounded by the same constant, say E. By the fundamental inequality (due to Morrey, Ahlfors, and Lavrentieff) for quasiconformal homeomorphisms (see [2], [23], [28], [29]), there exists a constant $K = K(E)$ such that for z_1 and z_2 in S

$$\begin{aligned} |\chi_\nu(z_1) - \chi_\nu(z_2)| &\leqq K |z_1 - z_2|^\delta, \\ |z_1 - z_2| &\leqq K |\chi_\nu(z_1) - \chi_\nu(z_2)|^\delta, \end{aligned} \tag{19.2}$$

with

$$\delta = E + \sqrt{E^2 - 1}. \tag{19.3}$$

The mappings $\chi_\nu(z)$ are therefore homeomorphisms of $\bar{S}: |z - z_0| \leqq r$.

20. Consider now the analytic functions $f_\nu(\zeta) = \omega_\nu[\chi_\nu^{-1}(\zeta)]$. If ζ_1, ζ_2 are two points on $|\zeta - z_0| = r$, we have that

$$(20.1)\quad \begin{aligned} |\operatorname{Im} f_\nu(\zeta_1) - \operatorname{Im} f_\nu(\zeta_2)| &= |\operatorname{Im} \omega[\chi_\nu^{-1}(\zeta_1)] - \operatorname{Im} [\chi_\nu^{-1}(\zeta_2)]| \\ &\leqq m\,|\chi_\nu^{-1}(\zeta_1) - \chi_\nu^{-1}(\zeta_2)| \leqq mK\,|\zeta_1 - \zeta_2|^\delta \end{aligned}$$

where m is the maximum of the modulus of grad ψ = grad Im ω on $|z - z_0| = r$. By Privaloff's theorem on conjugate functions it follows that $f_\nu(\zeta)$ is continuous for $|\zeta - z_0| \leqq r$ and that

$$(20.2)\qquad |f_\nu(\zeta_1) - f_\nu(\zeta_2)| \leqq mK_1K\,|\zeta_1 - \zeta_2|^\delta$$

for $|\zeta_1 - z_0| \leqq r$, $|\zeta_2 - z_0| \leqq r$, with some $K_1 = K_1(\delta, r)$. Also $f_\nu(z_0) = \operatorname{Re} \omega(z_0)$ and $|\operatorname{Im} f_\nu(z_0)| \leqq M = \max|\psi|$, so that there exists a constant M_1 such that

$$(20.3)\qquad |f_\nu(\zeta)| \leqq M_1, \qquad |\zeta - z_0| \leqq r.$$

Noting (19.2), (20.2), and (20.3), we conclude that there exist an increasing sequence of integers $\{\nu_j\}$, a homeomorphism $\zeta = \chi(z)$ of $|\zeta - z_0| \leqq r$ onto $|\zeta - z_0| \leqq r$, and an analytic function $f(\zeta)$, $|\zeta - z| < r$, continuous for $|\zeta - z_0| \leqq r$, such that

$$\chi_{\nu_j}(z) \to \chi(z), \qquad \chi_{\nu_j}^{-1}(z) \to \chi^{-1}(z), \qquad f_{\nu_j}(\zeta) \to f(\zeta)$$

uniformly. It follows that

$$\lim_{j\to\infty} \omega_{\nu_j}(z) = \lim_{j\to\infty} f_{\nu_j}[\chi_{\nu_j}(z)] = f[\chi(z)],$$

so that the function $\tilde{\omega}(z) = f[\chi(z)]$ is (F, G)-pseudoanalytic, by Theorem 17.3. Since $\operatorname{Im} \tilde{\omega}(z) = \operatorname{Im} \omega(z)$ for $|z - z_0| = r$, and $\operatorname{Re} \tilde{\omega}(z_0) = \operatorname{Re} \omega(z_0)$, we have that $\tilde{\omega}(z) \equiv \omega(z)$, so that

$$(20.4)\qquad \omega(z) = f[\chi(z)].$$

This formula shows that $\omega(z)$ satisfies (in the neighborhood of the fixed but arbitrary point z_0) Lemma 18.2. Hence this lemma, as well as Theorem 18.1, are proved also for nonsmooth generators.

We note for further reference that

$$(20.5)\qquad \frac{\chi(z) - z_0}{|z - z_0|^\delta} = O(1), \qquad \frac{|z - z_0|}{|\chi(z) - z_0|^\delta} = O(1), \qquad z \to z_0,$$

where δ is given by (19.3).

21. Keeping the previous notations, we assume that

$$(21.1)\qquad F(z_0) = 1, \qquad G(z_0) = i.$$

Let $\eta > 0$ be a given positive number. In view of (21.1) $e_{(F,G)}(z_0) = 0$, and hence we can choose r so small that $| e_{(F,G)}(z) | < \eta/2$ for $| z - z_0 | < r$. Since by hypothesis $e_{(F_\nu,G_\nu)}(z) \to e_{(F,G)}(z)$ uniformly on every compact subset of D_0, $| e_{(F_\nu,G_\nu)}(z) | < \eta$ for $| z - z_0 | < r$ and ν sufficiently large. That means that we may set $E = \eta$. Noting (19.3), (20.4), and (20.5), we conclude that for *every* $\epsilon > 0$ our function $\omega(z)$ admits in a neighborhood of z_0 a representation (20.4), $\chi(z)$ being a homeomorphism such that

$$(21.2) \qquad \frac{\chi(z) - z_0}{| z - z_0 |^{1-\epsilon}} = O(1), \qquad \frac{z - z_0}{| \chi(z) - z_0 |^{1-\epsilon}} = O(1), \qquad z \to z_0,$$

and $f(\chi)$ being analytic at $\chi = z_0$.

Assume next that $\omega(z)$ is one-to-one in the neighborhood of z_0. Then $f'(z_0) \neq 0$, so that by (21.2)

$$(21.3) \qquad \frac{\omega(z) - \omega(z_0)}{| z - z_0 |^{1-\epsilon}} = O(1), \qquad \frac{z - z_0}{| \omega(z) - \omega(z_0) |^{1-\epsilon}} = O(1), \quad z \to z_0,$$

for every $\epsilon > 0$.

Next, in the neighborhood of z_0, $\dot{w}(z)$ satisfies a Hölder condition with some exponent λ. The relation $\dot{w}(z_0) = 0$ would imply that $\dot{w}(z) = O(| z - z_0 |^{\lambda})$, $z \to z_0$, so that, by (12.1),

$$(21.4) \qquad \omega(z) - \omega(z_0) = O(| z - z_0 |^{1+\lambda}), \qquad z \to z_0,$$

which would contradict (21.3).

Hence the one-to-one character of $\omega(z)$ at z_0 implies that $\dot{w}(z_0) \neq 0$. The converse implication being trivial, and condition (21.1) being irrelevant (since it can be achieved by replacing (F, G) by an equivalent pair), Theorem 18.5 is proved. This theorem, in conjunction with Lemma 18.2, implies Lemma 18.3 for nonsmooth generators, also.

Part V. Successors; Pseudoanalyticity of the Derivative

22. We want to show next that the (F, G)-derivative of a pseudoanalytic function is itself a pseudoanalytic function, though with respect to another pair of generators. We shall need the following definitions.

A generating pair (F_1, G_1) in D_0 is called a *successor* of the generating pair (F, G) if there exist in D_0 two (F, G)-pseudoanalytic functions $W_1(z)$, $W_2(z)$ such that

$$\frac{d_{(F,G)} W_1}{dz} = F_1, \qquad \frac{d_{(F,G)} W_2}{dz} = G_1.$$

If this condition is satisfied, we call (F, G) the *predecessor* of (F_1, G_1). A sequence of generating pairs $\{(F_\nu, G_\nu)\}$, $\nu = 0, \pm 1, \pm 2, \cdots$, is called a *generating sequence* if $(F_{\nu+1}, G_{\nu+1})$ is a successor of (F_ν, G_ν), for all ν. In this case (F_0, G_0) is said to be *imbedded* in the sequence $\{(F_\nu, G_\nu)\}$.

THEOREM 22.1. *Every generating pair (F, G) in D_0 has a successor.*

The proof is based on the following lemma:

LEMMA 22.2. *Let (F, G) be a generating pair in D_0. There exist in D_0 two (F, G) pseudoanalytic functions of the second kind, $\Omega_1(z)$, and $\Omega_2(z)$, such that any function*

$$\Omega(z) = \lambda_1 \Omega_1(z) + \lambda_2 \Omega_2(z),$$

where λ_1, λ_2 are any real constants, $\lambda_1^2 + \lambda_2^2 \neq 0$, is a homeomorphism of D_0.

This lemma was proved by me in a previous paper [9] under the assumption that the generating pair (F, G) is smooth. A slight modification of the argument in [9] gives the present result.

In order to prove Theorem 22.1, set

$$W_1 = {}^*\Omega_1, \qquad W_2 = {}^*\Omega_2 \qquad (\text{mod } F, G).$$

In view of Theorem 18.5, we have that $\lambda_1 \dot{W}_1(z) + \lambda_2 \dot{W}_2(z) \neq 0$, for all real $\lambda_1, \lambda_2, \lambda_1^2 + \lambda_2^2 \neq 0$. Hence either $\operatorname{Im}(\overline{\dot{W}_1} \dot{W}_2) > 0$ and we may set $F_1 = \dot{W}_1$, $G_1 = \dot{W}_2$, or $\operatorname{Im}(\overline{\dot{W}_1} \dot{W}_2) < 0$ and we may set $F_1 = \dot{W}_2$, $G_1 = \dot{W}_1$.

23. LEMMA 23.1. *Let (F, G) and (F_1, G_1) be two generating pairs in D_0. The pair (F_1, G_1) is a successor of (F, G) if and only if*

$$\begin{aligned}(23.1)\qquad \oint_\Gamma \operatorname{Re}(F^* F_1\, dz) &= \oint_\Gamma \operatorname{Re}(G^* F_1\, dz) = \oint_\Gamma \operatorname{Re}(F^* G_1\, dz) \\ &= \oint_\Gamma \operatorname{Re}(G^* G_1\, dz) = 0 \quad \textit{for } \Gamma \sim 0 \textit{ in } D_0.\end{aligned}$$

This follows from the definition and from Lemmas 12.1, 12.2.

COROLLARY 23.2. *If (F_1, G_1) is a successor of (F, G), then $(F, G)^*$ is a successor of $(F_1, G_1)^*$.*

Proof. The differentials in (23.1) are the real parts of

$$(F_1)^{**}F^*\,dz,\ (F_1)^{**}G^*\,dz, \qquad (G_1)^{**}F^*\,dz,\ (G_1)^{**}G^*\,dz,$$

respectively.

Noting Theorem 22.1, we have the following corollary:

COROLLARY 23.3. *Every generating pair in D_0 has a predecessor.*

More generally, we have this theorem:

THEOREM 23.4. *Every generating pair can be imbedded in a generating sequence.*

24. THEOREM 24.1. *Let (F_1, G_1) be a successor of the generating pair (F, G). (i) Every (F_1, G_1)-pseudoanalytic function is the (F, G)-derivative of a (perhaps multiple-valued) (F, G)-pseudoanalytic function. (ii) The (F, G)-derivative of every (F, G)-pseudoanalytic function is (F_1, G_1)-pseudoanalytic.*

We prove (i) first. Let $W(z)$ be (F_1, G_1)-pseudoanalytic in a domain D. According to Lemma 12.2, we must prove that

$$\text{(24.1)} \qquad \operatorname{Re} \oint_\Gamma F^*W\,dz = 0, \qquad \operatorname{Re} \oint_\Gamma G^*W\,dz = 0 \quad \text{if } \Gamma \sim 0 \text{ in } D.$$

It will suffice to consider the first integral and to show that, for every fixed z_0 in D and every triangle T of diameter δ in D which either contains z_0 or contains it in its interior,

$$\text{(24.2)} \qquad \operatorname{Re} \oint_T F^*W\,dz = o(\delta^2).$$

Set $W(z) = \Phi F_1 + \Psi G_1$. By hypothesis,

$$W(z) = \Phi(z_0)F_1(z) + \Psi(z_0)G_1(z) + \dot{W}(z_0)(z - z_0) + o(|z - z_0|),\ z \to z_0.$$

In view of (23.1), the integral (24.2) equals

$$\operatorname{Re} \oint_T F^*(z)\{\dot{W}(z_0)(z - z_0) + o(\delta)\}\,dz$$

$$= \operatorname{Re} \oint_T \{F^*(z_0) + [F^*(z) - F^*(z_0)]\}\dot{W}(z_0)(z - z_0)\,dz + o(\delta^2) = o(\delta^2),$$

which proves the assertion.

We prove (ii) first for smooth generating pairs. It follows from

Theorem 15.1 that every successor (F_1, G_1) of a smooth generating pair (F, G) is smooth, and that

$$a_{(F_1, G_1)} = a_{(F, G)}, \; b_{(F_1, G_1)} = -B_{(F, G)} .$$

If we now apply Corollary 5.2 and Theorem 16.2, assertion (ii) follows.

Now let $w(z)$ be any (F, G)-pseudoanalytic function, (F, G) not being smooth. Let S be a disk whose closure $\bar{S}$ lies in the domain of definition of w_1. If (F_1, G_1) is a successor of (F, G) then there exist, in a disk S_1 containing S, two single-valued (F, G)-pseudoanalytic functions, w_1 and w_2, such that $F_1 = \dot{w}_1$, $G_1 = \dot{w}_2$. As in § 20 we can find an equibounded sequence of smooth generating pairs $\{(F^\nu, G^\nu)\}$ converging to (F, G), and sequences of functions $\{w_\sigma^\nu\}$, $\sigma = 0, 1, 2$, defined and continuous on $\bar{S}$ such that w_σ^ν is (F^ν, G^ν)-pseudoanalytic in S and $w_\sigma^\nu \to w_\sigma$ uniformly in $\bar{S}$. Set

$$\dot{w}_\sigma^\nu = \frac{d_{(F_\nu, G_\nu)} w_\sigma^\nu}{dz} .$$

By Theorem 17.3,

$$\text{(24.3)} \qquad \dot{w}_1^\nu \to F_1, \qquad \dot{w}_2^\nu \to G_1, \qquad \dot{w}_0^\nu \to \dot{w}_0 ,$$

uniformly on every compact subset of S.

Let S_0 be a disk whose closure is contained in S. We have that in S_0

$$\operatorname{Im} (\overline{\dot{w}_1^\nu} \dot{w}_2^\nu) > 0$$

for sufficiently large ν, so that $(\dot{w}_1^\nu, \dot{w}_2^\nu)$ may be regarded as a generating pair in S_0. Since (F^ν, G^ν) is smooth, the functions $\dot{w}_\sigma^\nu(z)$, $\sigma = 0, 1, 2$, are (F_1^ν, G_1^ν)-pseudoanalytic, (F_1^ν, G_1^ν) being some successor of (F^ν, G^ν). Hence $(\dot{w}_1^\nu, \dot{w}_2^\nu)$ is equipotent to (F_1^ν, G_1^ν), so that $\dot{w}_0^\nu$ is $(\dot{w}_1^\nu, \dot{w}_2^\nu)$-pseudoanalytic. Since it is easy to verify that the sequence $(\dot{w}_1^\nu, \dot{w}_1^\nu)$ is equibounded, it follows from (24.3) and Theorem 17.2 that $\dot{w}_0$ is (F_1, G_1)-pseudoanalytic.

The preceding considerations also show that all successors of a generating pair are equipotent. The same is true for predecessors in view of Corollary 23.2.

25. A generating sequence $\{(F_\nu, G_\nu)\}$ is said to have *period* n if $(F_{\nu+n}, G_{\nu+n}) = (F_\nu, G_\nu)$. A generating pair is said to have *minimum period* n if it can be imbedded in a generating sequence of period n but not in a generating sequence of period $m < n$. A generating sequence has minimum period $+\infty$ if it can be imbedded in no periodic sequence.

The important (and open) *periodicity problem*[13] consists in deciding whether or not there exist generating pairs for a given minimum period n (including $n = \infty$) and in characterizing such pairs.

A smooth generating pair (F, G) *is its own successor (has minimum period* 1) *if and only if* $F(z)/G(z)$ *is a function of* x *only.* In fact, such a pair must satisfy the relation $b_{(F,G)} + B_{(F,G)} = 0$, which is equivalent to $\partial(F/G)/\partial y = 0$.

Let $X(x)$, $Y(y)$ be real-valued Hölder-continuously differentiable functions, and set

$$(F, G) = (e^{X+Y}, ie^{-X-Y}).$$

Then $(F_1, G_1) = (e^{-X+Y}, ie^{X-Y})$ is a successor and a predecessor of (F, G). Thus *there exist generating pairs of minimum period* 2. Finally, Protter[14] proved that *there exist generating pairs with minimum period exceeding* 2.

Beyond this nothing is known.

26. Let $w(z)$ be an (F, G)-pseudoanalytic function and $\{(F_\nu, G_\nu)\}$ a generating sequence in which (F, G) is imbedded, so that $(F, G) = (F_0, G_0)$. In view of Theorem 24.1 we can form the higher derivatives of w, defined by the recursion formulas

$$w^{[0]}(z) = w(z),$$

$$w^{[n+1]}(z) = \frac{d_{(F_n,G_n)} w^{[n]}(z)}{dz}, \quad n = 1, 2, \cdots .$$

THEOREM 26.1. *The sequence* $\{w^{[n]}(z_0)\}$, $n = 0, 1, \cdots$, *determines the pseudoanalytic function* $w(z)$ *uniquely.*

The proof will be given in Part VI.

27. We conclude this section by an analogue of Morera's theorem.

THEOREM 27.1. *Let* (F_{-1}, G_{-1}) *be a predecessor of* (F, G) *and set*

---

[13] The problem was first stated, within the framework of a different formalism, by Markuševič; see Petrovskii [30], Lukomskaya [26].

[14] Oral communication.

$(F_{-1}, G_{-1})^* = (F_{-1}^*, G_{-1}^*)$. *A continuous function* $w(z)$ *defined in a domain* D *is* (F, G) *pseudoanalytic if and only if*

$$\operatorname{Re} \oint_\Gamma (F_{-1}^*)w\,dz = \operatorname{Re} \oint_\Gamma (G_{-1}^*)w\,dz = 0, \text{ if } \Gamma \sim 0 \text{ in } D.$$

This follows at once from Theorem 24.1 and Lemma 12.2.

Part VI. Zeros and Singularities

28. We want next to describe the behavior of a pseudoanalytic function in the neighborhood of a (regular or isolated singular) point. For the sake of orientation we consider first the case of smooth generators.

Two functions defined in a domain D will be called *similar* if their ratio is continuous on the closure of D.

Theorem 28.1. (Similarity principle.) *Let* (F, G) *be a smooth generating pair in* D_0, *and* D *a domain with compact closure* $\bar{D} \subset D_0$. (i) *Every* (F, G)*-pseudoanalytic function of the first kind* $w(z)$, $z \in D$, *is similar in* D *to an analytic function* $f(z)$. (ii) *Every (single-valued) analytic function* $f(z)$, $z \in D$, *is similar in* D *to an* (F, G)*-pseudoanalytic function.*

The proof of this statement (somewhat strengthened) will be found in my papers [8] and [11]. I mention only that (i) is proved simply by exhibiting f:

$$f(z) = e^{s(z)}w(z),\ s(z) = \frac{1}{\pi}\iint_D \frac{a(\zeta) + b(\zeta)[\overline{w(\zeta)}/w(\zeta)]}{\zeta - z}\,d\xi\,d\eta,$$

a and b being the first two characteristic coefficients of (F, G).

Applying Theorem 28.1(i) to a function $w(z)$ defined in D: $0 < |z - z_0| < r$, we obtain the familiar trichotomy: either $w(z)$ approximates every complex number as $z \to z_0$, or $w(z) \sim \text{const}\,(z - z_0)^{-n}$ for some positive integer n, or the finite limit $w(z_0)$ exists. In the last case it follows easily from Lemma 15.2 that w is regular at z_0. If $w(z_0) = 0$, $w \neq 0$, then it follows, again by Theorem 28.1(i), that $w(z) \sim \text{const}\,(z - z_0)^n$.

In the sequel we shall reëstablish these results without using the similarity principle and without assuming (F, G) to be smooth.

29. We say that a pseudoanalytic function $w(z)$ possesses at z_0 an isolated *essential singularity* if it is defined and single-valued for $0 < |z - z_0| < r$, and if

$$\overline{\lim}_{z \to z_0} |(z - z_0)^N w(z)| = +\infty \quad \text{for every} \quad N > 0. \tag{29.1}$$

THEOREM 29.1. *Let z_0 be an isolated essential singularity of an (F, G)-pseudoanalytic function (of the first kind) $w(z)$. Then* (i) *$\omega(z) = {}_*w(z)$ takes on every value, save perhaps one, in every neighborhood of z_0;* (ii) *$w(z)$ comes arbitrarily close to every value in every neighborhood of z_0; and* (iii) *$\dot{w}(z)$ has at z_0 an essential singularity.*

We shall need the following lemma:

LEMMA 29.2. *Let $w(z)$ be (F, G)-pseudoanalytic for $0 < |z - z_0| < r$.* (i) *There exists a homeomorphism $\zeta = \chi(z)$ of $|z - z_0| < r$ onto $|\zeta - z_0| < r$ and an analytic function $f(\zeta)$, $0 < |\zeta - z_0| < r$, such that χ and the inverse mapping χ^{-1} are Hölder-continuous, $\chi(z_0) = z_0$, and*

$$\omega(z) = {}_*w(z) = f[\chi(z)]. \tag{29.2}$$

(ii) *The function $f(\zeta)$ has an essential singularity at $\zeta = z_0$ if and only if $z = z_0$ is an essential singularity of $w(z)$.*

Proof. (i) According to Theorem 18.1, there exists a homeomorphism $\zeta = \chi(z)$ of $D_1 : 0 < |z - z_0| < r$ which takes ω into an analytic function. It is of bounded eccentricity (except in the trivial case $\omega \equiv$ const) by Theorem 18.4. Hence the boundary continuum of $\chi(D_1)$ corresponding to z_0 is a point, so that χ may be treated as a homeomorphism of the disk $|z - z_0| < r$. From here on the argument goes as in § 5. The proof of (ii) is obvious.

Statement (i) of Theorem 29.1 follows from the lemma and implies statement (ii). To prove (iii), assume that $\dot{w}(z)$ does not have an essential singularity at z_0. Then there is an $N > 1$ such that for $z \to z_0$ we have $\dot{w}(z) = O(|z - z_0|^{-N})$, so that by (12.1) $w(z) = O(|z - z_0|^{-N+1})$, which contradicts the hypothesis.

30. A pseudoanalytic function $w(z)$, defined and single-valued in a deleted neighborhood of z_0, is said to possess a *pole* at z_0 if

$$\begin{aligned} &\overline{\lim}_{z \to z_0} |w(z)| = +\infty, \\ &\lim_{z \to z_0} |(z - z_0)^N w(z)| = 0 \quad \text{for some} \quad N > 0. \end{aligned} \tag{30.1}$$

THEOREM 30.1. *Let the pseudoanalytic function of the first kind,*

$w(z)$, have a pole at $z = z_0$. There exist an integer $n > 0$ (order of the pole) and a complex number $a \neq 0$ such that

$$w(z) \sim a(z - z_0)^{-n}, \qquad z \to z_0, \tag{30.2}$$

$$\dot{w}(z) \sim -na(z - z_0)^{-n-1}, \qquad z \to z_0, \tag{30.3}$$

and $\omega(z) = {}_*w(z)$ maps a neighborhood of z_0 onto an n-times-covered neighborhood of $\omega = \infty$.

The proof will be based on the following lemma:

LEMMA 30.2. *Under the hypotheses of Lemma 29.2, assume that $\dot{w} \not\equiv 0$, that z_0 is not an essential singularity of $w(z)$, and that*

$$F(z_0) = 1, \qquad G(z_0) = i. \tag{30.4}$$

Then the homeomorphism $\chi(z)$ is continuously differentiable in a neighborhood of z_0, and

$$\chi_z(z_0) \neq 0, \qquad \chi_{\bar{z}}(z_0) = 0. \tag{30.5}$$

The proof will be given later (in § 32).

Proof of Theorem 30.1. We may assume that (30.4) holds, since this can be achieved by considering an equivalent generating pair. It is clear that the function f in (29.2) has a pole at $\zeta = z_0$, so that $\omega[\chi(\zeta)] = f(\zeta) \sim a_0(\zeta - \zeta_0)^{-n}$ as $\zeta \to \zeta_0$, $a_0 \neq 0$. This implies the assertion concerning ω. Next, by (30.5), $\chi(z) \sim a_1(z - z_0)$ as $z \to z_0$, $a_1 \neq 0$, and by (30.4) $w(z) \sim \omega(z)$ as $z \to z_0$, so that (30.2) follows.

In order to prove (30.3), we note that by (30.2) and Lemma 17.1, $\dot{w}(z) = O(|z - z_0|^{-N})$, $z \to z_0$, for some $N > 0$. Also $\dot{w}(z)$ is not bounded, for otherwise $w(z)$ would be bounded in view of (12.1). But $\dot{w}(z)$ is (F_1, G_1)-pseudoanalytic, (F_1, G_1) being some successor of (F, G). Hence, by the assertion already proved, $\dot{w}(z) \sim b(z - z_0)^{-m}$ as $z \to z_0$ for some $b \neq 0$, $m > 0$. Equation (12.1) shows that either of the assumptions $b \neq -na$, $m \neq n + 1$ leads to a contradiction of (30.2). Hence (30.3) is proved.

31. THEOREM 31.1. *Let $w(z)$ be single-valued and pseudoanalytic for $0 < |z - z_0| < r$. If z_0 is neither a pole nor an essential singularity of w (that is, if w is bounded), then w is regular at z_0.*

The proof follows at once from Lemma 30.2. Indeed, the analytic function $f(\zeta)$ is bounded and hence regular at $\zeta = z_0$, so that the derivatives of $\omega(z) = {}_*w(z)$ remain continuous at z_0.

THEOREM 31.2. *Let z_0 be a zero of a pseudoanalytic function $w(z) \not\equiv 0$. Then there exist an integer $n > 0$ (order of the zero) and a number $a \neq 0$ such that*

$$w(z) \sim a(z - z_0)^n \quad as \quad z \to z_0, \tag{31.1}$$

$$\dot{w}(z) \sim na(z - z_0)^{n-1} \quad as \quad z \to z_0, \tag{31.2}$$

and $\omega(z) = {}_*w(z)$ maps a neighborhood of z_0 onto an n-times-covered neighborhood of $\omega = 0$.

The proof is so similar to that of Theorem 30.1 that it may be omitted.

32. We now prove Lemma 30.2. First we establish the following lemma:

LEMMA 32.1. *Under the hypotheses of Lemma 30.2 set*

$$\beta(z) = \alpha(z)[\bar{\omega}_{\bar{z}}(z)/\omega_z(z)], \tag{32.1}$$

α being the function defined by (3.2). The function $\beta(z)$ is Hölder-continuous in a neighborhood of z_0.

Proof. Let (F_1, G_1) be a successor of (F, G) chosen so that

$$F_1(z_0) = 1, \qquad G_1(z_0) = i, \tag{32.2}$$

and set

$$\Omega(z) = {}_*\dot{w}(z) \qquad (\text{mod } F_1, G_1). \tag{32.3}$$

By (5.3), (30.4), and (32.2), we have that

$$\omega_z(z) = \Omega(z) + \lambda(z)\Omega(z) + \mu(z)\overline{\Omega(z)},$$

where λ, μ are Hölder-continuous functions, and

$$\lambda(z_0) = \mu(z_0) = 0. \tag{32.4}$$

Also by (30.4),

$$\alpha(z_0) = 0. \tag{32.5}$$

Now, setting

$$\beta_0 = \alpha\bar{\Omega}/\Omega, \qquad \beta_1 = \mu\bar{\Omega}/\Omega,$$

we have that

$$\beta(z) = \beta_0(z)\,\frac{1 + \overline{\lambda(z)} + \beta_1(z)}{1 + \lambda(z) + \overline{\beta_1(z)}}. \tag{32.6}$$

Next, by the argument used in the proof of Theorem 30.1, $\dot{w}(z)$ does not have an essential singularity at z_0. Applying Lemma 29.2 to the (F_1, G_1)-pseudoanalytic function $\dot{w}(z)$, we obtain a Hölder-continuous homeomorphism $t = T(z)$ of a neighborhood of z_0 onto a neighborhood of $t = z_0$, and an analytic function of the form

$$g(t) = (t - z_0)^k[A_0 + A_1(t - z_0) + \cdots], \; A_0 \neq 0, \quad k \text{ integer},$$

such that $T(z_0) = z_0$ and $\Omega(z) = g(T(z))$. It is immediately clear that the functions $\beta_0[T^{-1}(t)]$ and $\beta_1[T^{-1}(t)]$ are Hölder-continuous, since the homeomorphism $T^{-1}(t)$ is Hölder-continuous by Lemma 29.2, and, for instance,

$$\beta_0[T^{-1}(t)] = \alpha[T^{-1}(t)] \left(\frac{\bar{t} - \bar{z}_0}{t - z_0}\right)^k \frac{\bar{A}_0 + \bar{A}_1(\bar{t} - \bar{z}_0) + \cdots}{A_0 + A_1(t - z_0) + \cdots}.$$

This implies the Hölder-continuity of $\beta_0(z)$ and $\beta_1(z)$, and, by (32.4) and (32.6), that of $\beta(z)$.

In order to prove Lemma 30.2, consider the differential equation for the function $Z(z) = X + iY$,

$$Z_{\bar{z}}(z) = \beta(z)Z_z(z), \tag{32.7}$$

which is equivalent to a Beltrami system for the functions X, Y. If $Z = Z_1$ and $Z = Z_2$ are two solutions of (32.7), and Z_1 is a homeomorphism, then, as is well known, Z_2 is an analytic function of Z_1. There exists (see § 13 above and [24]) a solution $Z(z)$ of (32.7) which is defined in the neighborhood of z_0 and satisfies the conditions

$$Z(z_0) = z_0, \qquad Z_z(z_0) = 1. \tag{32.8}$$

It is a homeomorphism of a neighborhood of z_0. Since our function $\omega(z) = {}_*w(z)$ satisfies equation (5.4), it also satisfies the equation $\omega_{\bar{z}} = \beta\omega_z$. Hence the function $f_1(Z)$ defined by the relation

$$\omega(z) = f_1[Z(z)]$$

is analytic. Set $h(\zeta) = Z[\chi^{-1}(\zeta)]$, χ being the homeomorphism of Lemma 29.2. Since $\omega[\chi^{-1}(\zeta)]$ is analytic for small positive values of $|\zeta - z_0|$, the same is true of h. Also, by the theorem on removable singularities, $h(\zeta)$ is analytic at $\zeta = z_0$. Let k be the function inverse to h. We have that $\chi(z) = k[Z(z)]$, and since k is analytic in the neighborhood of z_0, $\chi(z)$ is continuously differentiable. Since $k'(z_0) \neq 0$, and $Z_{\bar{z}}(z_0) = 0$ by (32.5) and (32.7), we have that $\chi_z(z_0) =$

$k'(z_0)Z_z(z_0) \neq 0$, $\chi_{\bar{z}}(z_0) = k'(z_0)Z_{\bar{z}}(z_0) = 0$. Thus Lemma 30.2 is proved.

33. Now we can prove Theorem 26.1. We must show that a pseudoanalytic function $w(z)$ regular at z_0 and satisfying the relations

$$w^{[n]}(z_0) = 0, \qquad n = 0, 1, \cdots \tag{33.1}$$

vanishes identically. Assume that $w \not\equiv 0$. Since $w(z_0) = w^{[0]}(z_0) = 0$, we have by Theorem 31.2 that for some $n > 0$ and some $a \neq 0$ one has $w(z) \sim a(z - z_0)^n$ as $z \to z_0$. By the same theorem we have then that $w^{[n]}(z_0) = n!a \neq 0$.

It is natural to ask how the function $w(z)$ can be computed if the values of $w^{[n]}(z_0)$ are given. But this problem leads into the *global* theory of pseudoanalytic functions, which deals with "formal powers" and the analogues of Cauchy's integral and of Taylor and Laurent expansions.[15] It lies, therefore, beyond the scope of the present paper.

BIBLIOGRAPHY

1. Agmon, S., and Bers, L. *The expansion theorem for pseudo-analytic functions*, Proc. Amer. Math. Soc. 3 (1952), 757–764.

2. Ahlfors, L. *On quasi-conformal mappings.* J. Analyse Math. 3 (1953–54), 1–58 (correction on pp. 207–208).

3. Beltrami, E. *Sulle funzioni potenziali di sistemi simmetrici intorno ad un asse.* Opere mat., III, 115–128. Milan, 1911.

4. —— *Sulla teoria delle funzioni potenziali simmetriche.* Opere mat., III, 349–377. Milan, 1911.

5. Bers, L. *The expansion theorem for sigma-monogenic functions*, Amer. J. Math. 72 (1950), 705–712.

6. —— *Partial differential equations and generalized analytic functions*, Proc. Nat. Acad. Sci. U.S.A. 36 (1950), 130–136, and 37 (1951), 42–47.

7. —— *Partial differential equations and pseudo-analytic functions on Riemann surfaces*, Annals of Mathematics Studies, No. 30, pp. 157–165. Princeton, 1953.

8. —— *Theory of pseudo-analytic functions.* New York University, 1953. (Mimeographed lecture notes.)

[15] For the case of smooth generating pairs, these results will be found in Bers [6] and [8] and in Agmon and Bers [1]. Nonsmooth generators will be considered elsewhere.

9. —— *Univalent solutions of linear elliptic systems*, Comm. Pure Appl. Math. 6 (1953), 513–526.

10. —— *Existence and uniqueness of a flow past a given profile*, Comm. Pure Appl. Math. 7 (1954), 441–504.

11. —— *Function-theoretical properties of solutions of partial differential equations of elliptic type*, Annals of Mathematics Studies, No. 33, pp. 69–94. Princeton, 1954.

12. —— AND GELBART, A. *On a class of differential equations in mechanics of continua*, Quart. Appl. Math. 1 (1943), 168–188.

13. —— —— *On a class of functions defined by partial differential equations*, Trans. Amer. Math. Soc. 56 (1944), 67–93.

14. —— —— *On generalized Laplace transformations*, Ann. of Math. 48 (1947), 342–357.

15. CARLEMAN, T. *Sur les systèmes linéaires aux derivées partielles du premier ordre à deux variables*, C. R. Acad. Sci. Paris 197 (1933), 471–474.

16. DIAZ, J. B. *On a class of partial differential equations of even order*, Amer. J. Math. 68 (1946), 611–659.

17. DOUGLIS, A. *An extremum principle for solutions of a class of elliptic systems of differential equations with continuous coefficients.* Proceedings of the International Congress of Mathematicians, 1950, vol. 1, pp. 431–432. Providence, 1952.

18. —— *A function-theoretic approach to elliptic systems of equations in two variables*, Comm. Pure Appl. Math. 6 (1953), 259–289.

19. —— *Function-theoretic properties of certain elliptic systems of first-order linear equations.* (In the present volume, pp. 335–340.)

20. HARTMAN, P., AND WINTNER, A. *On the local behavior of solutions of non-parabolic partial differential equations*, Amer. J. Math. 75 (1953), 449–476.

21. HOPF, E. *Elementare Bemerkungen über die Lösungen partieller Differentialgleichungen zweiter Ordnung vom elliptischen Typus*, Preuss. Akad. Wiss. Sitzungsber. 19 (1927), 147–152.

22. —— *Über den funktionalen insbesondeie den analytischen Charakter der Lösungen elliptischer Differentialgleichungen zweiter Ordnung*, Math. Zeit. 34 (1931), 194–233.

23. LAVRENTIEFF, M. A. *A fundamental theorem of the theory of quasi-conformal mapping of plane regions*, Izvestiya Akad. Nauk URSS Ser. Mat. 12 (1948), 513–554. Amer. Math. Soc. Translation, No. 29. New York, 1950.

24. LICHTENSTEIN, L. *Zur Theorie der konformen Abbildung, Konforme Abbildung nichtanalytischer singularitätenfreier Flächenstücke auf ein Gebiet*, Bull. Intern. Acad. Sci. Cracovie Ser. A (1916), 192–217.

25. Lichtenstein, L. *Neuere Entwicklung der Theorie partieller Differentialgleichungen zweiter Ordnung vom elliptischen Typus.* Enzykl. Math. Wiss., vol. II C, no. 12, pp. 1277–1334. Berlin, 1924.

26. Lukomskaya, M. A. *On a generalization of the class of analytic functions,* C. R. (Doklady) Acad. Sci. URSS 73 (1950), 885–888.

27. —— *On cycles of systems of linear homogeneous differential equations,* Mat. Sbornik 29 (71) (1951), 551–558.

28. Morrey, C. B. *On the solutions of quasi-linear elliptic partial differential equations,* Trans. Amer. Math. Soc. 43 (1938), 126–166.

29. Nirenberg, L. *On nonlinear elliptic partial differential equations and Hölder continuity,* Comm. Pure Appl. Math. 6 (1953), 103–156.

30. Petrovskii, I. G. *On some problems of the theory of partial differential equations,* Uspehi Mat. Nauk (N.S.) 1 (1946), 44–70.

31. Picard, É. *Sur un système d'équations aux derivées partielles,* C. R. Acad. Sci. Paris 112 (1891), 685–688.

32. —— *Sur une généralisation des équations de la théorie des fonctions d'une variable complexe,* C. R. Acad. Sci. Paris 112 (1891), 1399–1403.

33. Položiĭ, G. N. *On p-analytic functions of a complex variable,* C. R. (Doklady) Acad. Sci. URSS 58 (1947), 1275–1278.

34. —— *Singular points and residues of p-analytic functions of a complex variable,* C. R. (Doklady) Acad. Sci. URSS 60 (1948), 769–772.

35. Schauder, J. *Über das Dirichletsche Problem im Grossen für nichtlineare elliptische Differentialgleichungen,* Math. Zeit. 37 (1933), 623–634.

36. —— *Über lineare elliptische Differentialgleichungen zweiter Ordnung,* Math. Zeit. 38 (1934), 257–282.

37. Vekua, I. N. *Systems of differential equations of the first order of elliptic type and boundary value problems, with an application to the theory of shells,* Mat. Sbornik 31 (73) (1952), 217–314.

38. —— *The general representation of functions of two independent variables admitting a derivative in the sense of S. L. Sobolev and the problem of primitives,* C. R. (Doklady) Acad. Sci. URSS 89 (1953), 773–775.

New York University

FUNCTIONALS ON RIEMANN SURFACES*

LEO SARIO

1. Introduction

1.1. Let W be an open Riemann surface and C a class of functions p on W. Consider an exhaustion $\{W_n\}$ of W, the boundary β_n of W_n consisting of a finite number of analytic Jordan curves. On each W_n, a class C_n of functions is given with the property that every function $p \in C_{n+1}$ on W_{n+1} belongs to C_n on W_n. It is understood that this holds, correspondingly, for C, W and C_n, W_n.

On W_n and for $p \in C_n$ a functional $m(W_n, p)$ is given such that, for $p_1 \in C_n$ tending uniformly to $p_2 \in C_n$ on W_n, $m(W_n, p_1)$ tends to $m(W_n, p_2)$. The functional $m(W, p)$ for $p \in C$ is defined by $m(W, p) = \lim_{W_n \to W} m(W_n, p)$, the existence of the limit being postulated.

The following reduction theorem is known [4]:

THEOREM A. *Suppose that:*

(i) *There exists a function p_n in C_n with*

$$\min_{p \epsilon C_n} m(W_n, p) = m(W_n, p_n);$$

(ii) *The inequality*

$$m(W_n, p) \leqq m(W_{n+1}, p)$$

holds for all $p \in C_{n+1}$;

(iii) *The family $\{p_n\}$ is normal, the limiting functions belonging to C. Then every limiting function $p_0 = \lim_{n \to \infty} p_n$, say, gives the minimum*

$$m(W, p_0) = \min_{p \epsilon C} m(W, p) = \lim_{n \to \infty} m(W_n, p_n).$$

Briefly, if the functional increases with the region and the family

* This investigation was carried out under the sponsorship of the Office of Ordnance Research, U. S. Army, under Contract DA 19-020-ORD-1903, Harvard University.

of minimizing functions for subregions is normal, then the solvability of the minimum problem for W_n implies that for W.

1.2. Consider, in particular, the class C of all single-valued harmonic functions p on W with a finite number of prescribed singularities. It imposes no restriction to assume that these singularities z_i are centers of disjoint parameter disks K_i $(i = 1, \cdots, n)$. The functions p have the following expansions in K_i:

$$(1) \qquad p = \operatorname{Re}\left\{\sum_0^\infty a_\nu z^\nu + \lambda \cdot \sum_1^m b_\nu z^{-\nu}\right\} + \lambda \cdot c \log \frac{1}{|z|}.$$

Here a_ν, b_ν are complex, c is real, and λ is a real parameter; additional indices i for the a_ν, b_ν, c, z referring to the K_i are omitted. We assume that $\sum_i c = 0$, and normalize the p by the condition $\operatorname{Re} a_0 = 0$ at z_1. The class $\{p\}$ for fixed b_ν, c and subsequently fixed λ shall be denoted by C_λ. In particular, C_0 is the class of regular single-valued harmonic functions on W.

For the functional $m(W, p)$ on C, we choose

$$(2) \qquad m(W, p) = \int_\beta p\, dp* + 2\pi(h - k) \sum_i \operatorname{Re}\left[ca_0 + \sum_{\nu=1}^m \nu b_\nu a_\nu\right].$$

Here h, k are real parameters with $h + k = \lambda$, and the integral along the ideal boundary β is defined as the limit of integrals taken along boundaries of the W_n. Conjugate harmonic functions, here p^*, shall be indicated by stars.

The reduction theorem has the following consequence [4]:

THEOREM B. *There exists a uniquely determined function p_{hk} in C_λ such that*

$$(3) \qquad \min_{p \in C_\lambda} m(W, p) = m(W, p_{hk}).$$

The p_{hk} are interrelated by the identity

$$(4) \qquad p_{hk} = hp_1 + kp_2,$$

where p_1, p_2 stand for p_{10}, p_{01} respectively.

The minimum value of $m(W, p)$ depends solely on the a_ν-coefficients $a_{\nu 1}$, $a_{\nu 2}$ of p_1, p_2:

$$(5) \qquad \begin{aligned} m(W, p_{hk}) = 2\pi \textstyle\sum_i \operatorname{Re}\,[c(h^2 a_{01} - k^2 a_{02}) \\ + \textstyle\sum_{\nu=1}^m \nu b_\nu (h^2 a_{\nu 1} - k^2 a_{\nu 2})]. \end{aligned}$$

The deviation from this minimum is given by the Dirichlet integral:

(6) $$m(W, p) - m(W, p_{hk}) = D(p - p_{hk}).$$

1.3. Theorems A and B were established in [4] to solve interpolation problems on Riemann surfaces. Here we shall deduce new consequences in a variety of other extremal problems. For planar surfaces, in particular, some sharpenings of classical extremal properties of canonical mappings will follow. Our reasoning is based on the extremal method introduced in [2].

2. Functionals on arbitrary Riemann surfaces

2.1. Theorem B has the following immediate consequences:

THEOREM 1. *The functional*

(7) $$\int_\beta p\, dp^* + 2\pi \sum_i \operatorname{Re}\,[ca_0 + \sum_\nu \nu b_\nu a_\nu]$$

in C_1 is minimized by p_1, the minimum being

(8) $$2\pi \sum_i \operatorname{Re}\,[ca_{01} + \sum_\nu \nu b_\nu a_{\nu 1}].$$

THEOREM 2. *The function p_2 minimizes the functional*

(9) $$\int_\beta p\, dp^* - 2\pi \sum_i \operatorname{Re}\,[ca_0 + \sum_\nu \nu b_\nu a_\nu]$$

in C_1. The value of the minimum is

(10) $$-2\pi \sum_i \operatorname{Re}\,[ca_{02} + \sum_\nu \nu b_\nu a_{\nu 2}].$$

THEOREM 3. *The inequalities*

(11) $$\begin{aligned}\sum_i \operatorname{Re}\,[ca_{01} + \sum_\nu \nu b_\nu a_{\nu 1}] &\leqq \sum_i \operatorname{Re}\,[ca_0 + \sum_\nu \nu b_\nu a_\nu] \\ &\leqq \sum_i \operatorname{Re}\,[ca_{02} + \sum_\nu \nu b_\nu a_{\nu 2}]\end{aligned}$$

hold for the functions p in C_1 with $\int_\beta p\, dp^* \leqq 0$.

THEOREM 4. *The boundary integral*

(12) $$\int_\beta p\, dp^*$$

in C_1 is minimized by $\frac{1}{2}(p_1 + p_2)$, the minimum being

$$\frac{1}{2}\pi \sum_i \operatorname{Re}\,[c(a_{01} - a_{02}) + \sum_\nu \nu b_\nu (a_{\nu 1} - a_{\nu 2})]. \tag{13}$$

THEOREM 5. *The function $\frac{1}{2}(p_1 - p_2)$ gives the minimum* (13) *to the functional*

$$D(p) + 2\pi \sum_i \operatorname{Re}\,[ca_0 + \sum_\nu \nu b_\nu a_\nu] \tag{14}$$

in the class C_0 of single-valued harmonic functions, D signifying the Dirichlet integral.

THEOREM 6. *The function $\frac{1}{2}(p_1 - p_2)$ gives the minimum*

$$\min D(p) = \frac{1}{2}\pi \sum_i \operatorname{Re}\,[c(a_{02} - a_{01}) + \sum_\nu \nu b_\nu (a_{\nu 2} - a_{\nu 1})] \tag{15}$$

among all harmonic functions p on W with the fixed values

$$\begin{aligned}\sum_i \operatorname{Re}\,[ca_0 + \sum_\nu \nu b_\nu a_\nu] = \tfrac{1}{2} \sum_i \operatorname{Re}\,[c(a_{01} - a_{02}) \\ + \sum_\nu \nu b_\nu (a_{\nu 1} - a_{\nu 2})].\end{aligned} \tag{16}$$

If the b_ν are taken real, (16) is satisfied, in particular, by the p that have the fixed values

$$\operatorname{Re} a_\nu = \tfrac{1}{2} \operatorname{Re}\,(a_{\nu 1} - a_{\nu 2}) \tag{16'}$$

for $\nu = 0, \cdots, m$. Here the right-hand sides can be prescribed at will [4], by properly choosing the b_ν, c. Hence Theorem 6 gives the solution of the interpolation problem for harmonic functions with given values of $u(z_i)$ and $\partial^\nu u(z_i)/\partial x^\nu$ ($\nu = 1, \cdots, m$).

In the theorems of the present number, the minimizing function is unique and the deviation formula holds.

2.2. It is useful to consider the subclass F_λ of C_λ defined by the following modification. Let $\{W_n\}$ be an exhaustion of W with the additional property that each of the Jordan curves β_{ni} constituting the boundary β_n of W_n divides W into disjoint parts. The existence of such an exhaustion is assured [2]. The subclass F_λ of C_λ consists, by definition, of all those functions $q \in C_\lambda$ which satisfy the additional condition

$$\int_{\beta_{ni}} dq^* = 0 \tag{17}$$

for all β_{ni}. It is understood that the $z_i \in W_1$.

One finds the following extension:

THEOREM 7. *Theorems* 1–6 *remain valid for arbitrary Riemann surfaces if the class* C_λ *is replaced by the subclass* F_λ *defined by the restriction* (17).

For the proof, we recall [4] that p_1 and p_2 were defined as limits on W of functions p_{1n}, p_{2n} on W_n characterized by the conditions:

$$p_{1n} = c_n \text{ (const) on } \beta_n,$$
$$\frac{\partial p_{2n}}{\partial n} = 0 \text{ on } \beta_n .$$

These functions are now replaced by q_{1n}, q_{2n}, determined by the corresponding conditions in F_λ:

$$q_{1n} = c_{ni} \text{ (const) on } \beta_{ni},$$
$$\frac{\partial q_{2n}}{\partial n} = 0 \text{ on } \beta_n . \tag{18}$$

Here the c_{ni} are so chosen that (17) is satisfied. The proof [4] of Theorem B will then hold *mutatis mutandis* and Theorem 7 follows for the limiting functions q_1, q_2.

3. Functionals on planar Riemann surfaces

3.1. The main significance of the class F_λ appears in the case of a planar W. If the $c = 0$ in the expansion (1), then Theorems 1–6 hold for the real parts of single-valued analytic functions $Q = q + iq^*$ with ordinary poles. If, also, logarithmic poles are present (some $c \neq 0$), then the functions $S = e^Q$ are single-valued and analytic, and the theorems hold for $\log S$.

3.2. Expression (15) will be simplified in the present case as follows:

THEOREM 8. *On a planar Riemann surface, the function* $\frac{1}{2}(q_1 - q_2)$ *gives the minimum*

$$\min D(q) = \tfrac{1}{2}\pi \textstyle\sum_i [c(a_{02} - a_{01}) + \sum_\nu \nu b_\nu (a_{\nu 2} - a_{\nu 1})] \tag{19}$$

among those $q \in F_0$ *which satisfy the condition*

$$\textstyle\sum_i \operatorname{Re}\,[ca_0 + \sum_\nu \nu b_\nu a_\nu] = \tfrac{1}{2}\sum_i [c(a_{01} - a_{02}) + \sum_\nu \nu b_\nu (a_{\nu 1} - a_{\nu 2})]. \tag{20}$$

Proof. Suppose the constant

$$\delta = \sum_i [c(a_{01} - a_{02}) + \sum_\nu \nu b_\nu(a_{\nu 1} - a_{\nu 2})] \tag{21}$$

were not real. Then the function

$$Q_0 = \frac{\operatorname{Re} \delta}{\delta} (Q_1 - Q_2) \tag{22}$$

would have the Dirichlet integral

$$D(Q_0) = \left| \frac{\operatorname{Re} \delta}{\delta} \right|^2 D(Q_1 - Q_2) < D(Q_1 - Q_2). \tag{23}$$

On the other hand, when $Q_1 - Q_2$ is multiplied by $(\operatorname{Re} \delta)/\delta$, so are $a_{01} - a_{02}$, $a_{\nu 1} - a_{\nu 2}$, and consequently δ, the coefficients c, b_ν being fixed. The value of δ is hereby changed into $\delta_0 = \operatorname{Re} \delta$, and we find that the value of the left-hand side in (20) for Q_0 is $\operatorname{Re} \delta_0 = \operatorname{Re} \delta$, the latter being the value of the same functional for $Q_1 - Q_2$. Hence $\frac{1}{2} Q_0$ belongs to the class determined by (20), with the minimum value $\frac{1}{4} D(Q_1 - Q_2)$ of $D(q)$. This contradicts (23), and the theorem follows.

3.3. Suppose now, in particular, that the $c = 0$ and all the $b_\nu = e^{i\phi}$, ϕ being a fixed constant, $0 \leqq \phi < 2\pi$. Denote the corresponding functions Q by Q^ϕ, and their class by F^ϕ. In particular, Q_1^0, Q_2^0 are the functions Q_1^ϕ, Q_2^ϕ for the $b_\nu = 1$.

THEOREM 9. *On a planar Riemann surface, the functions Q_1^ϕ, Q_2^ϕ can be expressed in terms of Q_1^0, Q_2^0 as follows:*

$$\begin{aligned} Q_1^\phi &= Q_1^0 \cos \phi + i Q_2^0 \sin \phi, \\ Q_2^\phi &= i Q_1^0 \sin \phi + Q_2^0 \cos \phi. \end{aligned} \tag{24}$$

Proof. First replace W by an approximating W_n. Then in the first equation the real part of the right-hand side is constant on each of the boundary curves; in the second equation it has a vanishing normal derivative. Moreover, the combinations on the right have residues $e^{i\phi}$, and consequently coincide with Q_1^ϕ, Q_2^ϕ. The theorem then follows by letting W_n tend to W.

One notes two immediate consequences of Theorem 9:

$$Q_1^\phi + Q_2^\phi = e^{i\phi}(Q_1^0 + Q_2^0), \tag{25}$$

$$Q_1^\phi - Q_2^\phi = e^{-i\phi}(Q_1^0 - Q_2^0). \tag{26}$$

4. Functionals of univalent functions

4.1. Suppose now that all the $c = 0$, $b_1 = e^{i\phi}$ at z_1, all the other $b_\nu = 0$. We are then dealing with the class F^ϕ of single-valued analytic functions Q^ϕ on a planar W with no other singularities than a single pole with residue $e^{i\phi}$. The $Q^0 \in F^0$ and the $Q^\phi \in F^\phi$ are in one-to-one correspondence by $Q^\phi = e^{i\phi}Q^0$ or, equivalently, by $a_\nu^\phi = e^{i\phi}a_\nu^0$.

Let $Q_{(\psi)}^0$, with a_1-coefficients $a_{1(\psi)}^0$, be the function in F^0 which maps W onto the parallel-slit region with the direction ψ $(0 \leqq \psi < \pi)$ of the slits. Extremal properties of $Q_{(\psi)}^0$ can be found by suitably interpreting properties of the function

$$Q_1^{(\pi/2)-\psi} = e^{i[(\pi/2)-\psi]}Q_{(\psi)}^0 .$$

Since the residue b_1 of $Q_1^{(\pi/2)-\psi}$ is $e^{i[(\pi/2)-\psi]}$, and its a_1-coefficient is $e^{i[(\pi/2)-\psi]}a_{1(\psi)}^0$, we have the following result:

THEOREM 10. *The parallel-slit mapping $Q_{(\psi)}^0$ with direction ψ of the slits minimizes the functional*

$$\int_\beta q\, dq^* + 2\pi \operatorname{Re}\,[e^{i(\pi-2\psi)}a_1^0] \tag{27}$$

among all $Q^0 \in F^0$.

For univalent functions, $\int_{-\beta} q\, dq^*$ is the complementary area A of the image of W, and we find, in particular, that $Q_{(\psi)}^0$ minimizes $2\pi\cdot$ $\operatorname{Re}\,(e^{i(\pi-2\psi)}a_1^0) - A$ among all univalent Q^0. The vertical-slit mapping minimizes $2\pi \operatorname{Re} a_1^0 - A$, and the horizontal-slit mapping maximizes $2\pi \operatorname{Re} a_1^0 + A$. Less sharply, we have the well-known results that $Q_{(\psi)}^0$ minimizes $\operatorname{Re}\,[e^{i(\pi-2\psi)}a_1^0]$, Q_1^0 minimizes $\operatorname{Re} a_1^0$, and Q_2^0 maximizes $\operatorname{Re} a_1^0$ among univalent Q^0.

4.2. As a special case of Theorem 9, we deduce the well-known fact that every parallel-slit mapping $Q_{(\psi)}^0$ with the direction ψ of the slits is a linear combination of the horizontal- and vertical-slit mappings:

$$Q_{(\psi)}^0 = e^{i\psi}(-iQ_1^0 \sin\psi + Q_2^0 \cos\psi). \tag{28}$$

This follows by evaluating $Q_2^{-\psi}$ by (24) and substituting in the equation $Q_{(\psi)}^0 = e^{i\psi}Q_2^{-\psi}$.

5. Functionals of exponential functions

5.1. We now turn to the application of Theorem B when some $c \neq 0$. The simplest case, under our assumption $\sum c = 0$, is that $c = -1$ at z_1, $c = 1$ at z_2, the other $c = 0$, and all the $b_\nu = 0$. We are then faced with the class F of functions Q on a planar Riemann surface with no other singularities than two logarithmic poles, $\log z$ at z_1, $-\log z$ at z_2, and no other periods than those of q^* around these poles.

The functions $T = e^Q$ are single-valued and analytic and have the expansions

$$T(z) = z \cdot \exp \sum_0^\infty a_\nu z^\nu \tag{29}$$

at z_1, with the normalization $\operatorname{Re} a_0 = 0$, and the expansions

$$T(z) = \frac{1}{z} \exp \sum_0^\infty a_\nu z^\nu \tag{29'}$$

at z_2. Here we again omit the additional indices 1, 2 referring to z_1, z_2. We have

$$T(z_1) = 0, \qquad |T'(z_1)| = 1, \qquad T(z_2) = \infty. \tag{30}$$

The class $\{T\}$ will be denoted by E; $T \in E$ if and only if $\log T \in F$.

It is well known that $T_1 = e^{Q_1}$ and $T_2 = e^{Q_2}$ map W onto the circular- and radial-slit regions. The integral

$$K = \int_{-\beta} \log |T| \, d \arg T \tag{31}$$

is the logarithmic area of the complement of $T(W)$ for univalent T.

THEOREM 11. *The circular-slit mapping T_1 gives to the functional*

$$2\pi \log |\operatorname{Res} T(z_2)| - K \tag{32}$$

its minimum, $2\pi \log |\operatorname{Res} T_1(z_2)|$, in E; the radial-slit mapping T_2 gives to the functional

$$2\pi \log |\operatorname{Res} T(z_2)| + K \tag{33}$$

its maximum, $2\pi \log |\operatorname{Res} T_2(z_2)|$, in E.

Less accurately, T_1 minimizes, T_2 maximizes $|\operatorname{Res} T(z_2)|$ among all univalent T, as is well known.

5.2. Furthermore, we find easily:

THEOREM 12. *The function*

(34) $$T_3 = \sqrt{T_1 T_2}$$

gives the extremum

(35) $$\max_{T \in E} K = \tfrac{1}{2}\pi \log \left| \frac{\operatorname{Res} T_2(z_2)}{\operatorname{Res} T_1(z_2)} \right| .$$

In particular, we have the well-known result (Ahlfors and Beurling [1]) that T_3 maximizes the logarithmic complementary area among all univalent T.

5.3. Consider the class F_0 of regular Q on a planar W with Re $a_0 = 0$ at z_1. Let E_0 be the class of corresponding functions $T = e^Q$, $| T(z_1) | = 1$.

THEOREM 13. *The functional*

(36) $$D(\log T) + 2\pi \log | T(z_2) |$$

is minimized by $T_0 = \sqrt{T_1/T_2}$ *in* E_0, *the minimum being the negative of* (35).

5.4. Applied to the interpolation problem, Theorem 13 leads to

THEOREM 14. *The function*

(37) $$T_0 = \sqrt{T_1/T_2}$$

gives to the logarithmic area of the image of W *the minimum*

(38) $$\min D(\log T) = \tfrac{1}{2}\pi \log \left| \frac{\operatorname{Res} T_2(z_2)}{\operatorname{Res} T_1(z_2)} \right|$$

among all regular analytic functions $T \in E_0$ *on* W *with the fixed values*

(39) $$| T(z_1) | = 1, \qquad | T(z_2) | = \sqrt{| \operatorname{Res} T_1(z_2)/\operatorname{Res} T_2(z_2) |}.$$

Here the right-hand side of the second condition can be arbitrarily prescribed in a manner analogous to the prescription of Re $(a_{\nu 1} - a_{\nu 2})$ in (16′).

6. Functionals of logarithmic functions

6.1. We now turn to the case where $\sum c$ in (1) does not vanish. More precisely, consider an open Riemann surface W, and a class L

of single-valued harmonic functions s on W with the singularities

$$s = \text{Re}\,\{\textstyle\sum_0^\infty a_\nu z^\nu + \sum_1^m b_\nu z^{-\nu}\} + c \log |z| \tag{40}$$

at given points z_i $(i = 1, \cdots, n)$. Note that we are now taking the c with opposite signs to those in (1). As before, the a_ν, b_ν are complex, c is real, and the normalization is chosen: Re $a_0 = 0$ at z_1.

Let $W_n \subset W$ be bounded by a finite set β_n of analytic Jordan curves. In L, defined on W_n, there exists a unique function s_n with

$$s_n = k_n \text{ (const)} \quad \text{on} \quad \beta_n. \tag{41}$$

We set

$$k_\beta = \lim_{n\to\infty} k_n, \tag{42}$$

where the existence of the limit will soon be verified.

Theorem B has here the following counterpart:

THEOREM 15. *There exists a function s_β which minimizes the functional*

$$m(W, s) = \int_\beta s\, ds^* + 2\pi \sum_i \text{Re}\,[-ca_0 + \textstyle\sum_\nu \nu b_\nu a_\nu] \tag{43}$$

in L. The value of the minimum is

$$m(W, s_\beta) = 2\pi \textstyle\sum_i \text{Re}\,[-c(a_{0\beta} - k_\beta) + \sum_\nu \nu b_\nu a_{\nu\beta}], \tag{44}$$

where $a_{0\beta}$, $a_{\nu\beta}$ are coefficients of s_β.

If $k_\beta < \infty$, then the deviation of $m(W, s)$ from this minimum is

$$m(W, s) - m(W, s_\beta) = D(s - s_\beta), \tag{45}$$

and the minimizing function is unique.

Proof. The theorem is based on the reduction theorem A. We must first show that condition (i) is fulfilled, i.e., s_n minimizes $m(W_n, s)$ in L defined for W_n.

We have

$$D(s - s_n) = \int_{\beta_n} s\, ds^* + \int_{\beta_n} s_n\, ds_n^* - \int_{\beta_n} s\, ds_n^* - \int_{\beta_n} s_n\, ds^*, \tag{46}$$

where clearly

$$\int_{\beta_n} s_n\, ds_n^* = \int_{\beta_n} s_n\, ds^* = k_n \cdot 2\pi \textstyle\sum_i c, \tag{47}$$

and the second and the last integral in (46) cancel. For the third integral we have

$$\int_{\beta_n} s\, ds_n^* = k_n \cdot 2\pi \textstyle\sum_i c + \displaystyle\int_{\beta_n} (s\, ds_n^* - s_n\, ds^*).$$

By means of the Stokes formula, the integral on the right is first transferred from β_n to the circumferences of the parameter disks with centers z_i. Then the expansions (40) can be substituted for s and s_n, and we find that

$$\begin{aligned}(48) \qquad & \int_{\beta_n} (s\, ds_n^* - s_n\, ds^*) \\ & \qquad = 2\pi \sum_i \operatorname{Re}\,[-c(a_{0n} - a_0) + \sum_\nu \nu b_\nu (a_{\nu n} - a_\nu)].\end{aligned}$$

Combination of (46)–(48) gives the desired result (45), with notations (43), (44).

Condition (ii) of the reduction theorem is easily established:

$$(49) \qquad m(W_{n+1}, s) - m(W_n, s) = \int_{\beta_{n+1} - \beta_n} s\, ds^* \geqq 0$$

for $s \in L$ on W_{n+1}.

It also follows that

$$\begin{aligned} k_n \cdot 2\pi \sum_i c = \int_{\beta_n} s_n\, ds_n^* \leqq \int_{\beta_n} s_{n+1}\, ds_{n+1}^* \leqq \int_{\beta_{n+1}} s_{n+1}\, ds_{n+1}^* \\ = k_{n+1} 2\pi \sum_i c.\end{aligned}$$

Consequently, $k_n \leqq k_{n+1}$, and the existence of (42) is assured.

For preparation of the proof of condition (iii), i.e., the normality of the family $\{s_n\}$, we decompose s_n as follows. Suppose p_n is the function s_n in L for which all the $c = 0$. Similarly, let $c^{(i)}$ signify c at z_i, and let $s_n^{(i)}$ be the function s_n in L with $c^{(i)} = 1$, $c^{(j)} = 0$ for $j \neq i$, all the $b = 0$, and $\operatorname{Re} a_0 = 0$ at z_1. Then

$$\begin{aligned} s_n = p_n + \textstyle\sum_{i=1}^n c^{(i)} s_n^{(i)} = p_n + \sum_{i=2}^n c^{(i)} (s_n^{(i)} - s_n^{(1)}) \\ + \textstyle\sum_{i=1}^n c^{(i)} s_n^{(1)}.\end{aligned}$$

From the proof of Theorem B [4] it is known that the family $\{p_n + \sum_{i=2}^n c^i (s_n^{(i)} - s_n^{(1)})\}$ is normal, for the corresponding $\sum c = 0$.

Therefore, it suffices to show that $\{s_n^{(1)}\}$ is normal. But here we are dealing with the class of functions s with one logarithmic pole only, with $c = 1$, Re $a_0 = 0$; and in this case the normality of the family is known [3]. Condition (iii) of the reduction theorem follows.

By the reduction theorem, we conclude that there is, in the general class L, a function s_β on W with the property

$$\min_{s \in L} m(W, s) = m(W, s_\beta), \tag{50}$$

where

$$m(W, s_\beta) = \lim_{n\to\infty} m(W_n, s_n). \tag{51}$$

The equality (44) also follows.

Suppose now that $k_\beta < \infty$. For $s - s_\beta = h$ and $s_\epsilon = s_\beta + \epsilon h$ (ϵ real), we have

$$m(W, s_\epsilon) = m(W, s_\beta) + \epsilon[\cdots] + \epsilon^2 D(h),$$

where the expression in brackets vanishes by the minimum property $dm/d\epsilon = 0$ of s_β for $\epsilon = 0$. It follows, for $\epsilon = 1$, that the deviation formula (45) holds. This completes the proof of Theorem 15.

6.2. Suppose, in particular, that all the $b = 0$ and the $c = 1$. Then s_β minimizes the functional $\int_\beta s\, ds^* - 2\pi \sum_i \text{Re}\, a_0$, and the minimum is $-2\pi\sum_i \text{Re}\,(a_{0\beta} - k_\beta)$. If, more specially, there is one logarithmic pole only, at z_1, we have the minimum of $\int_\beta s\, ds^*$. We recall [3] that the capacity c_β of β is defined by $c = e^{-k_\beta}$, where $k_\beta = (1/2\pi) \min \int_\beta s\, ds^*$.

BIBLIOGRAPHY

1. Ahlfors, L., and Beurling, A. *Conformal invariants and function-theoretic null-sets*, Acta Math. 83 (1950), 101–129.

2. Sario, L. *An extremal method on arbitrary Riemann surfaces*, Trans. Amer. Math. Soc. 73 (1952), 459–470.

3. —— *Capacity of the boundary and of a boundary component*, Ann. of Math. 59 (1954), 135–144.

4. —— *Extremal problems and harmonic interpolation on open Riemann surfaces*, Trans. Amer. Math. Soc. (1955).

Harvard University

POSITIVE HARMONIC FUNCTIONS*

LEO SARIO

Introduction

Let O_F signify the class of Riemann surfaces with F-removable boundary [5]. By definition, there exists no nonconstant function f belonging to a given class F on $W \in O_F$. We are interested in the classes G, HB, HP, HD of Green's functions, and single-valued harmonic functions which are bounded, positive, or possess a finite Dirichlet integral, respectively.

It is well known that the inclusions

$$O_G \subset O_{HP} \subset O_{HB} \tag{1}$$

hold at least in the nonstrict sense. The purpose of the present study is to show that the inclusions are strict. Our reasoning is suggested by a recent example by Tôki [6], who established the strictness of the inclusions $O_G \subset O_{HB} \subset O_{HD}$.

In § 1 we shall construct a Riemann surface W to serve as a counterexample; § 2 is devoted to the proof that every $u \in HP$ on W has an axis of symmetry. By induction we then show in § 3 that there are infinitely many such axes of symmetry and that, consequently, u reduces to a constant. The existence of a Green's function, immediately verifiable, then gives the strictness of the inclusion $O_G \subset O_{HP}$, while the surface obtained from W by removing the pole of the Green's function serves to establish the strictness of $O_{HP} \subset O_{HB}$. For the sake of completeness we also give, in § 4, a somewhat simplified version of Tôki's proof for $O_{HB} \subset O_{HD}$.

1. Construction of W

1.1. We first construct a hyperbolic Riemann surface W which does not admit harmonic positive functions.

* This investigation was carried out under the sponsorship of the Office of Ordnance Research, U. S. Army, under Contract DA 19-020-ORD-1903, Harvard University.

Let q_m be the sequence of odd primes; then the quantities $\mu = q_m 2^n$ are mutually different for all $m, n = 1, 2, \cdots$. Set $r_i = 1 - 2^{-i}$, and consider the disk $|z| < 1$, $z = re^{i\phi}$, with the radial slits R_{mn}^{ν}:

$$(2) \qquad \begin{aligned} r_{2\mu} &\leqq r \leqq r_{2\mu+1}, \\ \phi &= \nu \cdot 2\pi/2^{m+\lambda}, \end{aligned}$$

where $\nu = 1, \cdots, 2^{m+\lambda}$ and the $\lambda = \lambda(\mu)$ are positive integers to be specified later. For each $m = 1, 2, \cdots$ we have an infinite sequence $n = 1, 2, \cdots$ of collections of slits $\nu = 1, \cdots, 2^{m+\lambda}$.

For each (fixed) m, let S_{mk} denote the sector

$$(3) \qquad (k - 1)2\pi/2^{m-1} \leqq \phi \leqq k \cdot 2\pi/2^{m-1},$$

$k = 1, \cdots, 2^{m-1}$. Identify, by pairs, those edges of the R_{mn}^{ν} that lie in the same sector S_{mk}, symmetrically located with respect to the bisecting half-ray d_{mk} of S_{mk}. The edges facing d_{mk} are here identified, and similarly the edges away from d_{mk}. In particular, the edges of a slit on d_{mk} are mutually identified, and the left edge of a slit on $\phi = (k - 1)2\pi/2^{m-1}$ is identified with the right edge of the slit on $\phi = k \cdot 2\pi/2^{m-1}$.

The points thus identified on the slits shall be denoted by p and $p_m = p_m(p)$. For an end point p of a slit on the boundary of S_{mk}, there are 2^{m-1} identical points $p_m^{i}(p)$, where $i = 1, \cdots, 2^{m-1}$.

When this identification is performed for each $m = 1, 2, \cdots$ a surface W is obtained.

1.2. W becomes a Riemann surface when a conformal structure is imposed by a covering $\mathcal{V}$ of W by open sets V and their homeomorphic mappings $t = h(p)$ onto parametric disks $|t| < \rho$ as follows.

Let $z = z(p)$ signify the projection on $|z| < 1$ of $p \in W$. For a point p not on a slit, let V be a disk about p not touching any slit, and let $t = h(p) \equiv z(p)$. If p is on the edge of a slit but different from its end points, V is to consist of two half-disks on W with their (equal) diameters, one centered at p, the other at $p_m(p)$, neither reaching the end points or touching other slits. The half-disks are then transferred, by proper rigid rotations $\tilde{p}(p)$ around $z = 0$, so as to form a connected full disk; the mapping h is taken as $t = z[\tilde{p}(p)]$.

Then let p be an end point of a slit R_{mn}^{ν} that does not lie on the boundary of S_{mk}. The neighborhood V of p shall consist of two slit disks of equal radius, one centered at p, the other at $p_m(p)$, neither disk reaching the other end points or touching other slits. By proper rigid rotations $\tilde{p}(p)$ about $z = 0$, the two slit disks are transferred so as to form a connected doubly covered disk. The mapping $t = [z(\tilde{p}(p))]^{\frac{1}{2}}$ now serves as h.

Finally, if p is an end point of a slit on the boundary of S_{mk}, V shall consist of 2^{m-1} slit disks centered at the points $p_m^{\ i}(p)$, $i = 1, \cdots, 2^{m-1}$. By suitable rigid rotations $\tilde{p}(p)$ around $z = 0$, the slit disks are again transferred so as to form a connected 2^{m-1}-fold disk. The mapping h of V is now $t = [z(\tilde{p}(p))]^{2^{-m+1}}$.

The collection of the V thus chosen is an open covering $\mathcal{V}$ of W, and the h form a family $\mathcal{H}$ of homeomorphic mappings of V onto disks $|t| < \rho$. For any $V_1, V_2 \in \mathcal{V}$ and corresponding $h_1, h_2 \in \mathcal{H}$, the change of parameter $t_2 = h_2(h_1^{-1}(t_1))$ is directly conformal in $h_1(V_1 \cap V_2)$. Thus $(\mathcal{V}, \mathcal{H})$ is a conformal structure on W, and $(W, \mathcal{V}, \mathcal{H})$ is a Riemann surface. In the sequel, we shall speak of the Riemann surface W without explicit reference to its structure.

2. Symmetry of $u \in HP$ about the real axis

2.1. For $m = 1$, the sectors S_{mk} reduce to the single sector $S_{1,1}$: $0 \leqq \phi \leqq 2\pi$, and the bisecting half-ray $d_{1,1}$ is the (negative) real axis. For every p on W, we define $p_1 = p_1(p)$ to be the symmetric point with respect to the real axis. The uniqueness of $p_1(p)$ is established as follows.

If p lies on a slit, so does p_1, the edges corresponding in an obvious manner. In particular, for $p \in R_{1n}^{\ \nu}$, p_1 coincides with p_1 defined in § 1.1. If $p \in R_{mn}^{\ \nu}$ with $m > 1$, we first exclude the case where p is an end point of an $R_{mn}^{\ \nu}$ on the boundary of S_{mk}. Then p is identical with $p_m(p)$, and the operation p_1 leads to two points, $p_1(p)$ and $p_1(p_m(p))$. Since the S_{mk} are, by pairs, symmetrically placed about the real axis, these two points are identified by $p_m(p)$, and the operation p_1 becomes unique.

Finally, if p is an end point of an $R_{mn}^{\ \nu}$ that lies on the boundary of S_{mk}, then p is one of the 2^{m-1} identical points $p_m^{\ i}(p)$, $i = 1, \cdots, 2^{m-1}$. The points $p_1(p_m^{\ i}(p))$ are, in a different order, identical with the $p_m^{\ i}(p)$, and the operation p_1 reduces to $p = p_1(p)$.

Thus $p_1(p)$ is uniquely defined on all of W. In terms of the local parameters $t = h(p)$, $t_1 = h_1(p_1)$, the corresponding transformation $t_1 = h_1\{p_1[h^{-1}(t)]\}$ is a sense-reversing conformal mapping of W onto itself.

2.2. Let $u(t)$ be a positive harmonic function on W. In order to prove that u reduces to a constant, we shall first show that u is symmetric with respect to the real axis.

We may normalize $u(t)$ so as to have $u(t_0) = 1$, where t_0 corresponds to the point on W that covers $z = 0$. By virtue of the indirect conformality of $t_1(t)$, the function $u[t_1(t)]$ is harmonic on W. The same is true of the difference

$$u_1(t) = u(t) - u[t_1(t)], \tag{4}$$

with $u_1(t) = 0$ on the R_{1n}'', and we infer that

$$\int_{K_r} |u_1[t(z)]|\, d\phi \leqq \int_{K_r} u[t(z)]\, d\phi + \int_{K_r} u[t_1\{t(z)\}]\, d\phi = 4\pi \tag{5}$$

for K_r chosen as $r = \text{const} < 1$.[1] In fact, the value of each integral on the right is equal to $2\pi u(t_0) = 2\pi$.

2.3. Consider the annulus

$$A_\mu : r_{2\mu-1} \leqq r \leqq r_{2\mu+2}, \tag{6}$$

for $m = 1$ ($\mu = 3 \cdot 2^n$). The function $u_1[t(z)]$ vanishes on the slits in A_μ but is not harmonic on them. Let $v_\mu(z)$ be a harmonic function in A_μ, defined by $v_\mu(z) = |u_1[t(z)]|$ on the boundary β_μ of A_μ. Then

$$|u_1[t(z)]| \leqq v_\mu(z) \tag{7}$$

in A_μ. We denote by $g(\zeta, z)$ the Green's function in A_μ, with pole at z, and consider the annulus

$$B_\mu : r_{2\mu} \leqq r \leqq r_{2\mu+1}. \tag{8}$$

If C_i is the circle $r = r_i$, we have, by (5), $\int v_\mu(z)\, d\phi \leqq 4\pi$ along $C_{2\mu-1}$ and $C_{2\mu+2}$. It follows that, for $z \in B_\mu$,

$$v_\mu(z) = \frac{1}{2\pi} \int_{\beta_\mu} v_\mu(\zeta) \frac{\partial g(\zeta, z)}{\partial n}\, ds \leqq 4 \max \frac{\partial g(\zeta, z)}{\partial n} = M_\mu, \tag{9}$$

where the maximum is taken for $\zeta \in \beta_\mu$ and $z \in B_\mu$. In view of (7), we conclude that $|u_1| \leqq M_\mu$ in B_μ, the bound M_μ being independent of u and of λ.

---

[1] This evaluation was suggested by L. Ahlfors, to whom I am grateful for stimulating discussions on the subject.

2.4. If we let the number $2^{1+\lambda}$ of the slits in B_μ tend to infinity, the width of the sectors T_{1n}^{ν}, bounded by R_{1n}^{ν}, $R_{1n}^{\nu+1}$, $C_{2\mu}$, $C_{2\mu+1}$, goes to zero. Consider the harmonic function $h(z)$ in T_{1n}^{ν} with $h = 0$ on R_{1n}^{ν}, $R_{1n}^{\nu+1}$ and $h = M_\mu$ on $C_{2\mu}$, $C_{2\mu+1}$. We choose $\lambda = \lambda(\mu)$ to be the smallest positive integer for which $h(z) \leqq 2^{-\mu}$, say, on the circle D_μ: $r = \frac{1}{2}(r_{2\mu} + r_{2\mu+1})$. Since $u_1 = 0$ on R_{1n}^{ν}, $R_{1n}^{\nu+1}$, and $| u_1 | \leqq M_\mu$ on $C_{2\mu}$, $C_{2\mu+1}$, we have $| u_1 | \leqq h$ on B_μ, and, consequently, $| u_1 | \leqq 2^{-\mu}$ on D_μ. On letting $\mu \to \infty$, we conclude that $u_1 \equiv 0$ on W.

Thus $u(t)$ is symmetric about the real axis, and $\partial u/\partial \phi = 0$ on the slits R_{1n} and at the points on the real axis that are not located on any slit.

3. The inclusions $O_G \subset O_{HP} \subset O_{HB}$

3.1. We are now in a position to prove, by induction, the symmetry of $u(t)$ on S_{mk} about d_{mk} for any m. Suppose, indeed, that the symmetry has been established for d_{ik} with $i = 1, \cdots, m-1$ and $k = 1, \cdots, 2^{i-1}$; furthermore, $\partial u/\partial \phi = 0$ on the R_{in} and at the points on d_{ik} that do not lie on any slit.

For p on S_{mk}, let $p_m = p_m(p)$ be the symmetric point about d_{mk}. If p is interior to S_{mk}, p_m is on a slit R_{hn}^{ν} if and only if p is. In the affirmative case, the uniqueness of the operation p_m is established as in § 2.1, by $p_h\{p_m[p_h(p)]\} = p_m(p)$. The corresponding transformation $t_m(t)$ is sense-reversing and conformal, and the function $u[t_m(t)]$ is harmonic in the interior of S_{mk}. The same remains true if p is on (an edge of) R_{jn}^{ν}, $j \geqq m$, on the boundary of S_{mk}.

The (radial) boundary of S_{mk} consists of some d_{in} with $i < m$. If p is on this boundary but not placed on an R_{jn}^{ν} with $j \geqq m$, then a sufficiently small neighborhood U of p is transformed by $p_m(p)$ onto two half-disks. The diameters of the latter lie again on some d_{in} with $i < m$, and are placed either on some slits R_{in} with $i < m$ or not on any slit. But at such points $\partial u/\partial \phi = 0$, and we conclude, by the symmetry of $u(t)$ about any d_{in} with $i < m$, that $u[t_m(t)]$ is harmonic on U. Thus the function

$$u_m(t) = u(t) - u[t_m(t)] \tag{10}$$

is harmonic on all of W.

In the same fashion as for $m = 1$ (§ 2.4) we conclude that, with the $\lambda = \lambda(\mu)$ properly chosen, $u_m(t) \equiv 0$ on W. and $u(t)$ on S_{mk} is symmetric about d_{mk}. Furthermore, $\partial u/\partial\phi = 0$ on the R_{mn}^{ν} and at the points on d_{mk} that do not lie on any slit.

3.2. Let $C_\rho: |z| = \rho$ be a fixed circle without common points with any R_{mn}^{ν}. Since $\partial u/\partial\phi = 0$ at $C_\rho \cap d_{mk}$, we find, on letting $m \to \infty$, that $\partial u/\partial\phi = 0$ on all of C_ρ. Consequently, $u(t) \equiv$ const and $W \in O_{HP}$.

On the other hand, $\log|z|$ is a Green's function on W, and we have established the strictness of the inclusion $O_G \subset O_{HP}$.

3.3. Let W_0 be the Riemann surface that is obtained by removing $z = 0$ from W. Since any $u \in HB$ on W_0 becomes positive on adding a proper constant c, and $z = 0$ is a removable singularity, $u(t) + c$ is positive and harmonic on all of W. Hence $u =$ const, whereas $\log|z| \in HP$ on W_0, and the strictness of the inclusion $O_{HP} \subset O_{HB}$ is established.[2]

4. The inclusion $O_{HB} \subset O_{HD}$

4.1. It is well known that $O_{HD} = O_{HBD}$ where HBD is the class of single-valued bounded harmonic functions with a finite Dirichlet integral. For this reason it suffices to construct a Riemann surface W which admits a $u \in HB$ but does not admit any $u \in HBD$.

Consider the annulus $1 < |z| < 3$ with the slits Q_{mn}^{ν}:

$$\begin{aligned} &2 + r_{2\mu} \leqq r \leqq 2 + r_{2\mu+1}, \\ &2 - r_{2\mu+1} \leqq r \leqq 2 - r_{2\mu}, \\ &\phi = \nu \cdot 2\pi/2^{m+\lambda}, \end{aligned} \tag{11}$$

with $\mu = q_m \cdot 2^n$, $m, n = 1, 2, \cdots$, and $\nu = 1, \cdots, 2^{m+\lambda}$ (cf. § 1.1). Take an infinite collection $\{F(k)\}$, $k = 1, 2, \cdots$, of copies of these slit annuli F and, successively for each fixed $m = 1, 2, \cdots$ and subsequently fixed $j = 0, 1, \cdots$, join $F(i + 2^m j)$ with $F(i + 2^{m-1} + 2^m j)$, $i = 1, \cdots, 2^{m-1}$, along the edges of $E_m = \bigcup_{n,\nu} Q_{mn}^{\nu}$, with a folding at each edge. Upon the surface thus obtained a conformal structure is imposed in a manner analogous to that of § 1.2, so as to form a Riemann surface W.

4.2. With each point $p \in W$, we associate a point $p_m = p_m(p)$ as follows. Let p on the copy $F(k)$ be denoted by $p(k)$. The operation

[2] During the printing of these lectures, Y. Tôki [7] independently submitted another proof for the strictness of the inclusions $O_G \subset O_{HP} \subset O_{HB}$. Our reasoning may, nevertheless, have some interest.

$p_m(p)$ shall assign the point $p_m = p(k \pm 2^{m-1})$ to $p(k)$. Here p_m lies, in the identical position, on the copy $F(k \pm 2^{m-1})$, which was joined with $F(k)$ along E_m; the choice of minus or plus sign depends on the sheet on which p lies.

An ambiguity in the operation p_m seems to arise if $p \in F(k)$ belongs to some E_h with $h \neq m$. In fact, then $p(k)$ is identical with $p(k \pm 2^{h-1})$, and p_m carries the former into $p(k \pm 2^{m-1})$, the latter into $p(k \pm 2^{h-1} \pm 2^{m-1})$; here the signs of 2^{m-1}, 2^{h-1} are, individually, the same as above. But $p(k \pm 2^{h-1} \pm 2^{m-1})$, lying on an E_h, is identical with $p(k \pm 2^{h-1} \pm 2^{m-1} \mp 2^{h-1}) = p(k \pm 2^{m-1})$, and the two positions of $p_m(p)$ coincide. Thus the operation $p_m(p)$ is uniquely determined.

The corresponding transformation of the local parameter will be denoted by $t_m = t_m(t)$.

4.3. If $u(t) \in HBD$ on W, the function $u_m(t) = u(t) - u[t_m(t)]$ vanishes on E_m, and we conclude again that, for properly chosen λ, $u_m \equiv 0$. For $m \to \infty$ it follows that $u(t)$ takes identical values on all copies of F. This gives, the Dirichlet integral being finite, the HD-removability relation $u(t) = \text{const}$. The proof is completed by the fact that $\log |z| \in HB$ on W.

BIBLIOGRAPHY

1. Ahlfors, L. *Remarks on the classification of open Riemann surfaces*, Ann. Acad. Sci. Fennicae. A. I, No. 87 (1951), 1–8.

2. —— and Royden, H. L. *A counterexample in the classification of open Riemann surfaces*, Ann. Acad. Sci. Fennicae A. I, No. 120 (1952), 1–5.

3. Royden, H. L. *Some counterexamples in the classification of open Riemann surfaces*, Proc. Amer. Math. Soc. 4 (1953), 363–370.

4. Sario, L. *Über Riemannsche Flächen mit hebbarem Rand*, Ann. Acad. Sci. Fennicae A. I, No. 50 (1948), 1–79.

5. —— *Sur la classification des surfaces de Riemann*, C. R. 11. Cong. Math. Scand. Trondheim (1949), pp. 229–238.

6. Tôki, Y. *On the classification of open Riemann surfaces*, Osaka Math. J. 4 (1952), 191–201.

7. —— *On examples in the classification of Riemann surfaces, I*, Osaka Math. J. 5 (1953), 267–280.

Harvard University

DISTRIBUTION OF ZEROS OF POLYNOMIALS*

P. C. ROSENBLOOM

PART I. GENERAL POTENTIAL-THEORETIC CONSIDERATIONS[1]

The properties of the simplest of all analytic functions, the polynomials, often serve as a guide to the general theory, and therefore have been studied very intensively from various points of view. In this paper we shall discuss the distribution of the zeros of polynomials, especially regarding the determination of domains containing very many or very few zeros in comparison to the degree of the polynomial. In contrast with the work of Walsh [50] and Marden [25], in which algebraic and geometric methods are used to determine domains containing no zeros or at least one zero, or sometimes all zeros, of a given polynomial, the tools most appropriate for the present type of problem are potential- and function-theoretic.

If $P(z) = \sum_{n=0}^{k} a_n z^n$ is a polynomial of degree k, then $u = \log (1/|P|)$ is a potential of a mass distribution with discrete positive masses placed at the zeros of P, the amount being equal to the corresponding multiplicity. Now a mass distribution is uniquely determined by its potential; more precisely, if the potential is known throughout a domain, then the distribution of masses in that domain can be completely determined. By Bloch's principle that a theorem on the infinite must be a limiting case of theorems on the finite, this must be a limiting case of theorems to the effect that certain finite amounts of information about the potential imply finite amounts of information about the mass distribution.

---

* This paper is based in part on my thesis [38] presented for the Ph.D. degree at Stanford University in 1944. The inspiring influence of that wonderful team Pólya and Szegö is evident in every phase of this work. I have also profited greatly from stimulating conversation with Erdös over a long period. I wish here to express my deep gratitude to these kind friends and teachers.

[1] The work of Delange [7] suggested many of the ideas in this section.

Most results of this type can be obtained from the *reciprocity law:* If

$$u_\phi(z) = \int \log \frac{1}{|z - \zeta|} d\phi(\zeta) \quad \text{and} \quad u_\mu(z) = \int \log \frac{1}{|z - \zeta|} d\mu(\zeta)$$

are potentials of charge distributions ϕ and μ, then

$$\int u_\phi \, d\mu = \int u_\mu \, d\phi. \tag{1}$$

Under appropriate hypotheses ϕ and μ may be distributions in the sense of L. Schwartz [42]. If D is a domain and U is an open set such that $\partial D \subset U$ (where ∂D is the boundary of D) and $\phi \equiv 0$ in U, then we may choose for μ a suitable dipole distribution on ∂D and obtain

$$\phi(D) = -\frac{1}{2\pi} \int_{\partial D} \frac{\partial u_\phi}{\partial n} \, ds. \tag{2}$$

More generally, let D be a domain, let F_0 be a closed subset of D, and let $F_1 = \partial D$. Let η_{F_0,F_1} be the equilibrium distribution of a total charge $+1$ on F_0 and -1 on F_1; that is, $u_{\eta_{F_0,F_1}}$ is constant on F_0 and zero on F_1, if we neglect sets of capacity zero. Then

$$\int u_\phi \, d\eta_{F_0,F_1} = \int u_{\eta_{F_0,F_1}} \, d\phi. \tag{3}$$

This is a generalization of Jensen's formula and of Nevanlinna's first fundamental theorem and can be used in the same way as the latter to obtain relations between the growth of a potential and the mass distribution (see [39] and Arsove [2]). The special case where F_0 is a point z_0 and D is the circle $C(z_0, r): |z - z_0| < r$, yields Jensen's formula:

$$\begin{aligned} u_\phi(z_0) - L(u_\phi, z_0, r) &= \int \log^+ \frac{r}{|z - z_0|} \, d\phi(z) \\ &= \int_{C(z_0,r)} \log^+ \frac{r}{|z - z_0|} \, d\phi(z), \end{aligned} \tag{4}$$

where

$$L(u, z_0, r) = \frac{1}{2\pi r} \int_{\partial C(z_0,r)} u(z) \, ds$$

is the arithmetic mean of u on $\partial C(z_0, r)$.

Clearly the application of (2) is limited to special situations where it is known that there are no masses in a neighborhood of ∂D, but when (2) does apply it is often very useful, since it gives information about $\phi(D)$ in terms of the values of u_ϕ on a small set, namely a curve. From (3), when $\phi \geqq 0$ (which is equivalent to u_ϕ being superharmonic), we obtain the inequalities

$$(5) \qquad \phi(F_0) \leqq C(F_0, F_1)\int u_\phi d\eta_{F_0,F_1} \leqq \phi(D),$$

where $C(F_0, F_1)$ is the capacity of the condensor formed by F_0 and F_1. Thus we can estimate from above or below the amount of mass in certain sets in terms of the integrals of u_ϕ with respect to certain charge distributions. We note that from (5) we could determine $\phi(D)$ to within an arbitrarily small error if we could evaluate all integrals of the form given above, since $\phi(F_0)$ can be made arbitrarily close to $\phi(D)$. Unfortunately, there are only a few pairs of closed sets F_0, F_1 for which η_{F_0,F_1} is known very accurately, and so it is usually very difficult to apply (5) in concrete cases.

We can obtain a somewhat cruder, and more elementary, formula by averaging (4). Let

$$f_r(z) = \frac{2}{\pi r^2}[u_\phi(z) - L(u_\phi, z, r)].$$

We note that if $u_\phi \in C^2$ at z_0, then $\lim_{r\to 0} f_r(z_0) = -\Delta u_\phi(z_0)/2\pi$, and, in fact, this limiting process yields the Blaschke-Privalov generalized Laplacian. This suggests the introduction of a new mass distribution (see [39])

$$\phi_r(E) = \int_E f_r(z)\, dA(z),$$

where A is the ordinary area (Lebesgue measure) in the plane. Applying Fubini's theorem, we obtain the following identity relating ϕ to u_ϕ:

$$(6) \quad \phi_r(E) = \frac{2}{\pi r^2}\int [c_E(z) - m_E(z, r)]u_\phi(z)\, dA(z) = \int \lambda_E(z, r)\, d\phi(z),$$

where c_E is the characteristic function of the set E,

$$m_E(z, r) = \frac{|E \cap \partial C(z, r)|}{|\partial C(z, r)|}, \qquad \chi_E(z, r) = \frac{A(E \cap C(z, r))}{A(C(z, r))},$$

and

$$\lambda_E(z, r) = 2 \int_0^1 t\chi_E(z, tr)\, dt.$$

Here $|E|$ is the length (or one-dimensional measure) of E, and all integrations, unless otherwise specified, are over the whole plane. We note that

$$\lim_{r\to 0} \chi_E(z, r) = c_E(z)$$

for almost all z, by the Lebesgue density theorem, and

$$\lim_{r\to 0} \lambda_E(z, r) = \lim_{r\to 0} \chi_E(z, r)$$

whenever the latter limit exists. Equation (6) can be applied in many cases when u_ϕ is approximately equal, in a large set, to the potential of a known mass distribution.

Let us illustrate these general remarks with some applications.

THEOREM 1. *Let* $P(z) = \sum_0^k a_n z^n$ *be a polynomial of degree* k, *and let* $\lambda = k^{-1} \log (M(1, P)^2/|a_0|\cdot|a_k|)$, *where* $M(r, P) = \max_{|z|=r} |P(z)|$. *Let* $\phi(E)$ *be the number of zeros of* P *in* E, *divided by* k. *Then*

$$\phi\{C(0, \exp[-\lambda^{\frac{1}{2}}])\} + (1 - \phi\{C(0, \exp[\lambda^{\frac{1}{2}}])\}) \leqq \lambda^{\frac{1}{2}} \tag{7}$$

and, if E *is the set:* $\frac{1}{2} \leqq |z| \leqq 2$, $|\arg z - \alpha| \leqq \tau/2$, *then*

$$|\phi(E) - \tau/2\pi| \leqq 36\lambda^{\frac{1}{3}} \log (2 + \lambda^{-1}). \tag{8}$$

If we formulate Theorem 1 in terms of the potential u_ϕ, then we see that it is a special case of the following theorem.

THEOREM 1a. *Let* ϕ *be a nonnegative mass distribution on the plane* E_2 *with compact support not containing the point* 0, *and such that* $\phi(E_2) = 1$, *and let*

$$\lambda = u_\phi(0) - 2 \min_{|z|=1} u_\phi(z).$$

Then (7) *and* (8) *hold.*

We note that since u_ϕ is superharmonic, $u_\phi(0) - L(u_\phi, 0, 1) \geqq 0$. Also,

$$v(z) = u_\phi(z^{-1}) - \log|z| = -\int \log|1 - z\zeta|\, d\phi(\zeta)$$

$$= -\int \log|\zeta|\, d\phi(\zeta) - \int \log|\zeta^{-1} - z|\, d\phi(\zeta)$$

is superharmonic, so that $0 \leqq v(0) - L(v, 0, 1) = -L(u_\phi, 0, 1)$, and therefore

$$0 \leqq \lambda_1 = u_\phi(0) - 2L(u_\phi, 0, 1) \leqq \lambda.$$

Proof. Inequality (7) is an immediate consequence of Jensen's formula (4), which yields

$$\{\phi(C(0, r)) + 1 - \phi(C(0, r^{-1}))\} \log r^{-1} \leqq \lambda_1 \leqq \lambda.$$

In order to prove (8), we first note a remark of Schur [41]: If $\zeta = re^{i\theta}$ and $|z| = 1$, then $|z - \zeta|^2 \geqq |\zeta| |z - e^{i\theta}|^2$, so that if ψ is the projection of ϕ on the unit circle, then

$$u_\phi(z) \leqq \tfrac{1}{2}\int \log |1/\zeta| \, d\phi(\zeta) + u_\psi(z) = (u_\phi(0)/2) + u_\psi(z)$$

for $|z| = 1$, and therefore

$$\begin{aligned} \lambda = u_\phi(0) - 2 \min_{|z|=1} u_\phi(z) &\geqq -2 \min_{|z|=1} u_\psi(z) \\ &= u_\psi(0) - 2 \min_{|z|=1} u_\psi(z). \end{aligned}$$

Thus it is sufficient to prove (8) for ψ. Let

$$c = -2 \min_{|z|=1} u_\psi(z).$$

Then $2u_\psi + c$ is a nonnegative harmonic function in the unit circle, so that, by Harnack's inequality,

$$-c/2 \leqq u_\psi(z) \leqq cr/(1 - r) \quad \text{for} \quad |z| \leqq r < 1.$$

A similar argument shows that

$$-c/2 \leqq u_\psi(z) - \log(1/|z|) \leqq c/(r - 1) \quad \text{for} \quad |z| \geqq r > 1.$$

Let μ be the uniform distribution of a unit mass on the unit circle, so that $u_\mu(z) = -\log^+ |z|$. The last two inequalities state that

$$-c/2 \leqq u_\psi(z) - u_\mu(z) \leqq cr/(1 - r)$$

for $|z| \leqq r < 1$ or $|z| \geqq r^{-1} > 1$.

We now apply (6):

$$\begin{aligned} \psi_\epsilon(E) - \mu_\epsilon(E) &= \frac{2}{\pi\epsilon^2} \int (c_E(z) - m_E(z, \epsilon))(u_\psi(z) - u_\mu(z)) \, dA(z) \\ &= \frac{2}{\pi\epsilon^2} \int (c_E(z) - m_E(z, \epsilon))(u_\psi(z) - u_\mu(z) + c/2) \, dA(z). \end{aligned}$$

Here we have used the fact that if E is a bounded set and ϕ is the uniform distribution of a unit mass on a large circle, then $\phi_\epsilon(E) = 0$, and u_ϕ is constant in that large circle, which implies that

$$\int (c_E(z) - m_E(z, \epsilon))\, dA(z) = 0.$$

Let $E(\epsilon)$ be the set of points z at a distance $\leqq \epsilon$ from E. Then $| c_E(z) - m_E(z, \epsilon) | \leqq 1$ on $E(\epsilon)$ and is zero otherwise. Hence

$$| \psi_\epsilon(E) - \mu_\epsilon(E) | \leqq \frac{2}{\pi\epsilon^2} \int_{E(\epsilon)} (u_\psi(z) - u_\mu(z) + c/2)\, dA(z).$$

We now choose E to be the set: $\frac{1}{2} \leqq |z| \leqq 2$, $|\arg z| \leqq \tau/2$, where $0 < \tau \leqq \pi$. Then $A(E(\epsilon)) \leqq 6\epsilon + 5\tau\epsilon < 7\pi\epsilon$, so that

$$\frac{2}{\pi\epsilon^2} \int_{E(\epsilon)} (c/2)\, dA(z) \leqq \frac{7c}{\epsilon}.$$

Let $E(\epsilon, r) = E(\epsilon) \cap C(0, r)$, $F = E(\epsilon, r^{-1}) - E(\epsilon, r)$. Then for $\frac{1}{2} < r < 1$, we have

$$\int_{E(\epsilon,r)} (u_\psi(z) - u_\mu(z))\, dA(z) \leqq A[E(\epsilon, r)]\, cr/(1 - r)$$

and, similarly,

$$\int_{E(\epsilon)-E(\epsilon,r^{-1})} (u_\psi(z) - u_\mu(z))\, dA(z) \leqq A[E(\epsilon) - E(\epsilon, r^{-1})]\, cr/(1 - r).$$

It is also easy to make the estimation:

$$\begin{aligned}\int_F [-u_\mu(z)]\, dA(z) &\leqq \log (r^{-1}) A[E(\epsilon, r^{-1}) - E(\epsilon, 1)] \\ &\leqq 4\epsilon(r^{-1} - 1) \log (r^{-1}) \\ &\leqq 16\epsilon(1 - r)^2.\end{aligned}$$

There remains only to estimate

$$\int_F u_\psi(z)\, dA(z) = \int_{|\zeta|=1} \int_F \log \frac{1}{|z - \zeta|}\, dA(z)\, d\psi(\zeta).$$

But by a known lemma (see Kellogg [21, pp. 148–150]), we have

$$\int_F \log \frac{1}{|z - \zeta|}\, dA(z) \leqq \int_{C(0,a)} \log \frac{1}{|z|}\, dA(z),$$

where $A[C(0, a)] = A(F)$. Hence

$$\int_F \log \frac{1}{|z - \zeta|}\, dA(z) \leqq \frac{A(F)}{2} \log \frac{e\pi}{A(F)} = 2\epsilon(r^{-1} - r) \log \frac{e\pi}{4\epsilon(r^{-1} - r)},$$

which yields

$$\int_F u_\psi(z)\, dA(z) \leqq 3\epsilon(1 - r) \log \frac{e\pi}{12\epsilon(1 - r)}.$$

Putting all this together, we obtain

$$| \psi_\epsilon(E) - \mu_\epsilon(E) | \leqq \frac{7c}{\epsilon} + \frac{14c}{\epsilon(1 - r)} + \frac{32(1 - r)^2}{\epsilon} + \frac{3(1 - r)}{2\epsilon} \log \frac{e\pi}{12\epsilon(1 - r)}.$$

Set $\epsilon = c^{1/4}$, $1 - r = c^{1/2}$, assuming $c \leqq \frac{1}{4}$. Then

(9) $$| \psi_\epsilon(E) - \mu_\epsilon(E) | \leqq 35c^{1/4} \log (1/c) < 35c^{1/4} \log (2 + c^{-1}).$$

If $c \geqq \frac{1}{4}$, then

$$| \psi_\epsilon(E) - \mu_\epsilon(E) | \leqq 1 \leqq 35c^{1/4} \log (2 + c^{-1}),$$

so that (9) holds for all c.

Let us now denote the set E above by $S(\tau)$. Then

$$\psi[S(\tau - 2\delta)] \leqq \psi_\epsilon[S(\tau)] \leqq \psi[S(\tau + 2\delta)], \qquad \sin \delta = \epsilon,$$

and similarly for μ. It is now trivial to deduce

$$\psi_\epsilon[S(\tau - 2\delta)] - \mu_\epsilon[S(\tau - 2\delta)] - \epsilon \leqq \psi[S(\tau)] - \mu[S(\tau)] \leqq \psi_\epsilon[S(\tau + 2\delta)] - \mu_\epsilon[S(\tau + 2\delta)] + \epsilon,$$

from which the theorem follows.

Erdös and Turán have obtained for (8) in Theorem 1 the bound $8\sqrt{2}\, \lambda^{1/2}$, which is best possible except perhaps for the numerical factor. It would be interesting to know whether this sharper result also holds in Theorem 1a. By making the estimates somewhat more carefully, we have been able to obtain only $O(\lambda^{2/5})$.

As Erdös and Turán pointed out, Theorem 1 contains the theorem of Jentzsch [20], in the sharpened form due to Szegö [45], as a simple corollary. The inequalities

(10) $$4 \sum_1^N | b_n |^2/n^2 \leqq ((2N + 1)e\lambda)^2,$$

(11) $$\lambda \leqq \textstyle\sum_1^N | b_n |/n + 2(N+1)^{-\frac{1}{3}},$$

where

$$b_n = \int z^n \, d\phi(z)$$

and ϕ is a nonnegative distribution of a unit mass on the boundary of the unit circle, show that for a sequence of such potentials $\lambda \to 0$ if and only if $b_n \to 0$ for all n, and therefore Theorem 1a is equivalent to a finite form of Weyl's equidistribution theorem (see [52] and Erdös-Turán [12]).

We remark that $\lambda = 0$ if and only if $\phi = \mu$, the equilibrium distribution on the unit circle. Thus Theorem 1a shows how one can measure the deviation of a given distribution from this particular equilibrium distribution. Clearly the result and the method can be generalized to other geometric configurations and to higher dimensions. The theorem of Arsove [1, pp. 345–347], can also be profitably applied to such problems.

Theorem 1 can also be generalized in another direction:

THEOREM 2. *If* $P_k(z) = \sum_{n=0}^{k} a_{nk} z^k$ *is a sequence of polynomials such that*

(12) $$M(1, P_k)^{1/k} \to 1, \; | a_{0k} |^{1/k} \to 1, \; \liminf_{k\to\infty} \max_{tk \leqq n \leqq k} | a_{nk} |^{1/n} \geqq c^{-1} > 0,$$

where $0 < t \leqq 1$, *and if* $n_k(r)$ *is the number of zeros of* P_k *in* $| z | \leqq r$, *then*

$$\liminf_{k\to\infty} \frac{n_k(r)}{k} \geqq \omega(h, t, c) > 0, \qquad r = c + h > c,$$

where ω *depends only on the indicated parameters. In fact,*

$$\omega(h, t, c) \geqq \left(C_1^{-1} t \log\left(1 + \frac{h}{2c}\right)\right)^{\beta},$$

where C_1 *is as given below and*

$$\beta = \frac{\log (8c + 6h)}{\log [(4c + 3h)/(4c + 2h)]}.$$

This estimate for ω is rather crude and can probably be improved. Theorem 2 is a consequence of the following theorem.

THEOREM 2a. *Let* $P(z) = \sum_{n=0}^{k} a_n z^n$ *be a polynomial of degree* k *with* $a_0 = 1$, *and let* $0 < t \leqq 1$,

$$\lambda = k^{-1} \log (M(1, P)), \qquad \rho_n = | a_n |^{-1/n},$$

$$C_1(c) = \log (3c + h) + \left[8\left(1 + \frac{c}{h}\right)\right]^{\log 2} 2^{-1+2/\beta}(\log 2)^{1/\beta},$$

$$C_2(c) = (5/3) + \log (8c + 4h)/\log 2,$$

where $\beta = \beta(c)$ *is as above. Then for* $n \geqq tk$, $h > 0$, *we have*

$$t \log\left(1 + \frac{h}{2\rho_n}\right) \leqq C_1(\rho_n)\omega^{1/\beta(\rho_n)} + C_2(\rho_n)\lambda + \left[8\left(1 + \frac{\rho_n}{h}\right)\right]^{\log 2} 2^{-1+2/\beta(\rho_n)}\lambda^{1/\beta(\rho_n)},$$

and $\omega = n_k(c + h)/k = \omega(c + h)$.

The proof of Theorem 2a is straightforward in principle but involved in its details, and will only be sketched here. Let

$$P(z) = \prod_{n=1}^{k} (1 - z_n z), \ | z_n | = r_n ,$$

where the z_n's are the reciprocals of the roots of P. Choose a fixed number $\rho > \frac{1}{2}$, and let

$$Q(z) = \prod_{1 \leqq r_n\rho \leqq 2\rho}(1 - z_n z), \qquad R(z) = \prod_{r_n\rho < 1} (1 - z_n z),$$

$$T(z) = Q(z)R(z), \quad \text{and} \quad S(z) = P(z)/T(z),$$

$$q = \deg Q, \qquad s = \deg S, \qquad M = M(1, P).$$

Then $| S(z) | \geqq (2| z | - 1)^s$ for $| z | > \frac{1}{2}$, and in particular $| S(z) | \geqq 1$ for $| z | = 1$, so that $| T(z) | \leqq M$ for $| z | = 1$, and therefore for $| z | \leqq 1$. But $T(z) \neq 0$ for $| z | < \frac{1}{2}$, $T(0) = 1$. A well-known inequality of Borel and Hadamard (see Ostrowski [29] and Pólya-Szegö [37, vol. I, problems 285, 287, p. 140]) yields

$$| T(z) | \geqq M^{-4r/(1-2r)} \quad \text{for} \quad | z | \leqq r < \tfrac{1}{2},$$

and in particular $| T(z) | \geqq M^{-2/3}$ for $| z | = \frac{1}{8}$. From this we obtain the bound $| S(z) | \leqq M^{5/3}$ for $| z | = \frac{1}{8}$, and therefore (see Pólya-Szegö [37, vol. I, problem 269, p. 137])

$$| S(z) | \leqq (8r)^s M^{5/3} \quad \text{for} \quad | z | = r \geqq \tfrac{1}{8}.$$

Now $|Q(z)| \geqq (1-2r)^q$ for $|z| \leqq r < \frac{1}{2}$, and $|R(z)| \leqq 2^k$ for $|z| \leqq \rho$. Hence

$$|R(z)| = |T(z)|/|Q(z)| \leqq M2^q \quad \text{for} \quad |z| = \tfrac{1}{4}.$$

Since $R(z) \neq 0$ for $|z| \leqq \rho$, the function $g(z) = k^{-1} \log R(z)$, taking the determination which vanishes at the origin, is analytic in that circle and satisfies Re $g(z) \leqq \log 2$ for $|z| \leqq \rho$, Re $g(z) \leqq \lambda + \omega(\rho) \log 2$. (Note that $n_k(\rho) = q + s$.) We now apply the Borel-Carathéodory inequality (see Pólya-Szegö [37, vol. I, problem 284, p. 139]) to obtain

$$|g(z)| \leqq 2[\lambda + \omega(\rho) \log 2] \quad \text{for} \quad |z| \leqq \tfrac{1}{8},$$

$$|g(z)| \leqq 2r \log 2/(\rho - r) \quad \text{for} \quad |z| \leqq r < \rho.$$

If $\frac{1}{8} < \sigma < r < \rho$, we obtain a bound for $|g(z)|$ on $|z| = \sigma$ by the Hadamard three-circle theorem, and then a bound for

$$|P(z)| = |Q(z)|\,|R(z)|\,|S(z)|;$$

$|P(z)| \leqq (1 + 2\sigma)^q (8\sigma)^s M^{5/3} \exp \{k \text{ Re } [g(z)]\}$ on $|z| = \sigma$. But this bound is equal to or greater than $|a_n|\sigma^n = (\sigma/\rho_n)^n$. If we choose $\sigma = \rho_n + (h/2)$, $\rho = \rho_n + h$, then we obtain Theorem 2a by elementary computation.

Theorem 2 is a slight generalization of a theorem of Erdös and Fried [10], and its original proof was based on various verbal remarks of Erdös. Theorem 2a is the corresponding finite theorem suggested by Bloch's principles.

In some problems, as we shall see below, a result as precise as Weyl's equidistribution theorem is not true, but it is still true that there is a positive percentage of zeros in any direction. The simplest general result of this sort is the theorem that follows.

THEOREM 3. *If* $P(z) = \sum_{n=0}^{k} a_n z^n$, $|a_0| \geqq a > 0$, $|a_k| \geqq b^k > 0$, $M(r, P) \leqq M$, $r > 0$, *and* $\tau > 0$, *and the parameters* a, b, r, M *and* τ *are given, then there exist* $\omega > 0$ *and* A *depending only upon these parameters such that the number of zeros of* P *in the sector:* $|z| \leqq 5b^{-1}$, $|\arg z - \alpha| \leqq \tau$, *is at least* $k\omega - A$.

There is a generalization analogous to Theorem 2:

THEOREM 3a. *If, in the notation of Theorem* 3, $|a_0| \geqq a > 0$, $|a_n| \geqq b^n > 0$, *for some* $n \geqq k/c$, *where* $1 \leqq c < +\infty$, $M(r, P) \leqq$

M, $r > 0$, $\tau > 0$, then there exist $\omega_1 = \omega_1(a, b, r, M, \tau, c)$ and $A_1 = A_1(a, b, r, M, \tau, c)$ such that the number of zeros of P in the sector: $|z| \leqq 2^{c+2}c^c/b(c-1)^{c-1}$, $|\arg z - \alpha| \leqq \tau$ is at least $k\omega_1 - A_1$.

These theorems can be obtained from a general potential-theoretic principle which is valid in any number of dimensions (see [39]).

THEOREM 3b. *Let D be a domain bounded by the closed set F_5, and let F_1, F_2, F_3, F_4 be closed subsets of D such that F_1 is contained in the interior of F_2 and F_4 is the closure of a domain which intersects F_3 and the interior of F_2. Let m_i be the minimum of the potential u_ϕ on the set F_i, where ϕ is a mass distribution in the plane such that $\phi \geqq 0$ on D. We suppose, without loss of generality, that $m_5 = 0$. Then there is a function $\omega = \omega(m_1, m_2, m_3)$, depending only on the geometrical configuration, such that $\phi(F_4) \geqq \omega$. The function ω is positive if m_3/m_1 and $(m_1 - m_2)/m_1$ are smaller than certain constants depending on the geometrical configuration.*

An explicit lower bound for ω in Theorem 3b was given in [39], and a detailed proof of a special case was given in [40], where it was applied to a four-circle analogue of the Hadamard three-circle theorem:

THEOREM 3c. *Let $0 < r_1 < r_2 < r_3 < 1$, and $0 < \tau < \pi$, and let α_0 be the maximum on $|z| = r_3$ of the function $v(z)$ which is harmonic in the annular sector S: $r_2 < |z| < 1$, $|\arg z| < \pi - \tau$, and which is 1 on $|z| = 1$ and 0 on the rest of the boundary of S. Let f be analytic in $|z| \leqq 1$ and suppose that*

$$(13)\quad 0 < a \leqq M(r_1, f), \qquad M(r_2, f) \leqq b, \qquad M(r_3, f) \geqq M(1, f)^\alpha,$$

where $\alpha > \alpha_0$. Then there are constants K and Ω, depending only on a, b, r_1, r_2, r_3, α, and τ, such that if $M(1, f) \geqq K$, then f has at least $\Omega \log M(1, f)$ zeros in every sector $\gamma \leqq \arg z \leqq \gamma + 2\tau$ with aperture 2τ and vertex at the origin.

In this paper we shall show how Theorem 3 can be deduced from Theorem 3c quite easily. A direct proof of Theorem 3 would be shorter than the demonstration of Theorem 3c together with the present argument, although it is considerably longer than the latter alone. The present argument does not give quite so sharp an estimate for the radius of the sector; the direct argument shows that if $d(\rho)$ is the transfinite diameter (see Fekete [13]) of the keyhole-shaped region formed by the circle $|z| \leqq r$ and the sector $|z| \leqq \rho$, $|\arg z| \leqq \tau$, then $5b^{-1}$ can be replaced by any ρ such that $bd(\rho) > 1$.

Proof of Theorem 3. By trivial transformations we find that we can assume $a_0 = 1$, $r = 1$. Then

$$(b\rho)^k \leqq M(\rho, P) \leqq M\rho^k$$

for all $\rho \geqq 1$. We choose ρ_1, ρ_2 such that $1 < \rho_1 < \rho_2$ and try to determine values of these numbers so that $f(z) = P(\rho_2 z)$ satisfies the hypotheses of Theorem 3c with $r_1 = 1/(2\rho_2)$, $r_2 = 1/\rho_2$, $r_3 = \rho_1/\rho_2$. We find that

$$\alpha = \frac{\log M(r_3, f)}{\log M(1, f)} = \frac{\log M(\rho_1, P)}{\log M(\rho_2, P)} \geqq \frac{k \log (b\rho_1)}{\log M + k \log \rho_2},$$

which approaches $\log (b\rho_1)/\log \rho_2$ as $k \to \infty$. In order to complete the proof we need an estimate of α_0.

LEMMA 1. *Let $v(z, r, \tau)$ be the function harmonic in the annular sector $r < |z| < 1$, $|\arg z| < \pi - \tau$, which is 1 on $|z| = 1$ and zero on the rest of the boundary. Let $\gamma = 2 - 2\tau/\pi$. Then for $r \leqq 2^{-\gamma}$, $\rho = (\frac{3}{4})^\gamma$, we have*

$$\max_{|z|=\rho} v(z, r, \tau) \leqq \frac{\log (\rho/r)}{\log (1/r)} - c, \qquad c = \min_{|z|=3/4, x \leqq 0} w(x + iy),$$

where $w(z)$ is the function harmonic in the annulus $\frac{1}{2} < |z| < 1$, and equal to 1 on $|z| = 1$, $\operatorname{Re}(z) > 0$, and zero on the rest of the boundary.

Proof. An elementary conformal mapping shows that

$$v(z^\gamma, r, \tau) = v(z, r^{1/\gamma}, \pi/2) = v_1(z, r^{1/\gamma}).$$

By the reflection principle, $v_1(z, r)$ is the harmonic function in the annulus $r < |z| < 1$ which is equal to 1 on $|z| = 1$, $\operatorname{Re}(z) > 0$, to -1 on $|z| = 1$, $\operatorname{Re}(z) < 0$, and to zero on $|z| = r$. Let $w(z, r)$ be the harmonic function in this annulus which is 1 on $|z| = 1$, $\operatorname{Re}(z) > 0$, and vanishes on the rest of the boundary. Then

$$v_1(z, r) = w(z, r) - w(-\bar{z}, r),$$

so that for $r < \sigma < 1$

$$\max_{|z|=\sigma, x>0} v_1(z, r) \leqq \max_{|z|=\sigma, x>0} w(z, r) - \min_{|z|=\sigma, x<0} w(z, r).$$

But the maximum principle shows that

$$w(z, r) \leqq \frac{\log (|z|/r)}{\log (1/r)}.$$

On the other hand, the maximum principle also shows that $w(z, r)$ is a decreasing function of r for any fixed z such that $|z| > r$. Hence for $r \leqq \frac{1}{2}$, $\sigma = \frac{3}{4}$, $|z| = \sigma$, $x < 0$, we have $w(z, r) \geqq c$. The lemma follows by trivial computation.

We now obtain the theorem by choosing ρ_2 to be any fixed number greater than max $(2^\gamma, b^{-1/c})$, and $\rho_1 = (\frac{3}{4})^\gamma \rho_2$.

Part II. Sequences of Polynomials, Especially Sections of Power Series

It is convenient to preface the applications which will be given now by some general remarks. If $\{f_n\}$ is a sequence of analytic functions, then a point z is said to belong to the *domain of boundedness* of the sequence if the sequence is analytic and uniformly bounded in some neighborhood. The *radius of boundedness* $R(z)$, is the radius of the largest circle with center at z contained in the domain of boundedness. These concepts were suggested by the work of Ostrowski [28].

The following theorem is a generalization of the Cauchy-Hadamard formula for the radius of convergence of a power series. The proof is trivial.

Theorem 4. *If* $f_n(z) = \sum a_{nm} z^m$ *is analytic at* $z = 0$ *for all* n, *then for* $R(0) = R > 0$ *it is necessary and sufficient that*

$$A_m = \sup_n |a_{nm}| < +\infty \quad \textit{for all } m, \tag{1}$$

and

$$\limsup_{m\to\infty} A_m^{1/m} = 1/R. \tag{2}$$

There is an intimate relation between the distribution of the zeros of a polynomial and its gaplike structure. This is already foreshadowed by some of the results above. In order to formulate a general principle, we need a measure for this gaplike structure. We define the *gap-index* $\lambda(z)$ of a sequence of polynomials $P_n(z) = \sum_{m=0}^{n} a_{nm} z^m$ by the following formula, stated for $z = 0$: $\lambda(0)$ is the least upper bound of the numbers λ such that

$$\limsup_{n\to\infty} \max_{m \geqq (1-\lambda)n} |a_{nm}|^{1/m} < R(0)^{-1}.$$

We remark that $\lambda(z)$ is lower semicontinuous; this remark contains, essentially as a special case, a result of Bourion [4].

THEOREM 5. *If* $P_n(z) = \sum_{m=0}^{n} a_{nm}z^m$, *and* $n(r, P)$ *is the number of zeros of* P *in* $|z| \leqq r$, *and* L *is the least upper bound of the numbers* r *such that* $n(r, P_k) = o(k)$, *then*

$$L[1 - \lambda(0)]^{\lambda(0)/(1-\lambda(0))} \leqq R(0),$$

if $\limsup_{n\to\infty} |P_n(0)|^{1/n} < +\infty$. (The left-hand side is to be interpreted as 0 if $\lambda(0) = 1$.)

We note that if the set E of points z for which the sequence $\{|P_n(z)|^{1/n}\}$ is unbounded is not empty, then its complement is of first category. By an argument of Lelong [23], one can probably prove that the exceptional set is even of capacity zero. Hence the origin in the theorem above is either a very exceptional point or can be replaced by any other point. As immediate consequences of Theorem 5, we see that if $L > R(0)$, then $\lambda(0) > 0$, and if $R(0) = 0$, $\lambda(0) < 1$, then $L = 0$.

We shall now focus our attention on the sections $s_n(z) = \sum_0^n a_k z^k$ of a power series $f(z) = \sum_0^\infty a_k z^k$. Without loss of generality, we may assume that $a_0 = 1$. It turns out that in general most of the zeros of s_n are of the order of $\rho_n = |a_n|^{-1/n}$. In many respects the polynomials

$$\psi_n(z) = z^n s_n(\rho_n/z) = a_n\rho_n^n + \cdots + z^n$$

have a simpler behavior than $\{s_n(z)\}$. Let

$$c = \liminf_{n\to\infty} \frac{\log \rho_n}{\log n}.$$

If f is an entire function of order ρ, then $c = 1/\rho$; if f is an entire function of infinite order or has a finite or zero radius of convergence, then $c \leqq 0$.

Our main result is as follows:

THEOREM 6. *If* $c < +\infty$, *then there is a subsequence of* $\{\psi_n\}$ *for which* $R(0) \geqq \min(1, e^{-c})$. *For the whole sequence* $\{\psi_n\}$, $R(0) > 0$ *if and only if* $A_1 = \sup_n |a_{n-1}|/|a_n|^{(n-1)/n} < +\infty$, *and then* $R(0) \geqq 1/A_1$.

The first part is proved with the aid of certain lemmas of Pólya (see [34] or Pólya-Szegö [37, vol. I, p. 18, problems 101, 108]) on the structure of real sequences. The second part is an easy consequence of Theorem 4. We remark that $c \leqq \log A_1$.

If $c \leqq 0$, then Theorem 1 applies, while if $c < +\infty$, then Theorem 3 applies. This contains the classical theorem of Jentzsch in the sharp form due to Szegö (see Jentzsch [20] and Szegö [45]). The results on entire functions of nonzero order were first stated by Carlson [5] in 1924, but his proofs were first published in 1948 (see [6]). In the meantime, these results were obtained by me in my thesis (see [38]) and were communicated to Carlson in 1947. Korevaar [22] and Turán (private communication) independently obtained many of these results. There are some classes of entire functions of order zero for which $R(0) > 0$ for some subsequence of $\{\psi_n\}$, but such a function cannot grow too slowly. Hardy [16] and Petrovich [31] gave examples of entire functions of zero order for which the zeros of the sections are all real. We call attention to the following corollary.

Corollary 6a. *If $f(z)$ is a formal power series and if there is some angle with vertex at the origin containing $o(n)$ zeros of $s_n(z)$, then $f(z)$ is an entire function of order zero.*

This contains results of Pólya [33], Weisner [51], and Szász [43] (see also Benz [3]).

The preceding results are quite complete for $c \leqq 0$ since in this case as $n \to \infty$ through a certain sequence all but $o(n)$ zeros of ψ_n accumulate around the unit circle and the arguments are equidistributed. For $0 < c < +\infty$, that is, when f is an entire function of finite positive order ρ, the theorems above tell us that for a certain subsequence of $\{\psi_n\}$ there is a positive density of zeros in any angle with vertex at the origin. Let $\{N\}$ denote the sequence of indices for such a subsequence. The methods given above also yield the following result.

Corollary 6b. *If $0 \leqq r < 1$ and $\epsilon > 0$, then*

$$\liminf_{N\to\infty} \{n(\rho_N(e^{1/\rho} + \epsilon), s_N) - n(\rho_N r, s_N)\}/N \geqq 1 - r^\rho > 0.$$

The method of Carlson yields an arbitrarily narrow annulus containing a positive proportion of zeros of s_N.

The case when $f(z)$ is an entire function of finite positive order reveals many interesting phenomena which have no analogues for the other cases. For example, when we know the asymptotic behavior of f as $|z| \to +\infty$, then we can determine the asymptotic distribution of the zeros of s_n quite precisely. The following theorem applies to all the functions ordinarily occurring in analysis.

THEOREM 7. *Suppose that the following conditions hold:*

(i) *For some sequence of determinations,* $f(\rho_N z)^{1/N}$ *converges uniformly to a single-valued analytic function* $g(z)$ *in some subdomain* D *of the circle* $C(0, e^{1/\rho})$;

(ii) $w = g(z)/z$ *maps* D *univalently onto a domain* D_1;

(iii) *No limit function of the sequence*

$$F_N(z) = [f(\rho_N z) - s_N(\rho_N z)]/z^N$$

is identically zero in D;

(iv) $F_N(z) \neq 0$ *in* D *for* $N > N_0$.

Then the only limit points of the zeros of $s_N(\rho_N z)$ *in* D *are the points on the curve* $|g(z)/z| = 1$, *and their images in* D_1 *under the mapping* $w = g(z)/z$ *are equidistributed about the unit circle* $|w| = 1$; *i.e., the number which accumulate about any arc of length* α *contained in* D_1 *is asymptotically* $N\alpha/2\pi$.

If $N_1 < N_2 < \cdots$ is the sequence of indices under consideration, then (iii) is satisfied if $N_{k+1} - N_k$ is bounded. For example, this is true for the whole sequence $\{F_n\}$ if $|a_{n-1}|/|a_n|^{(n-1)/n}$ is bounded.

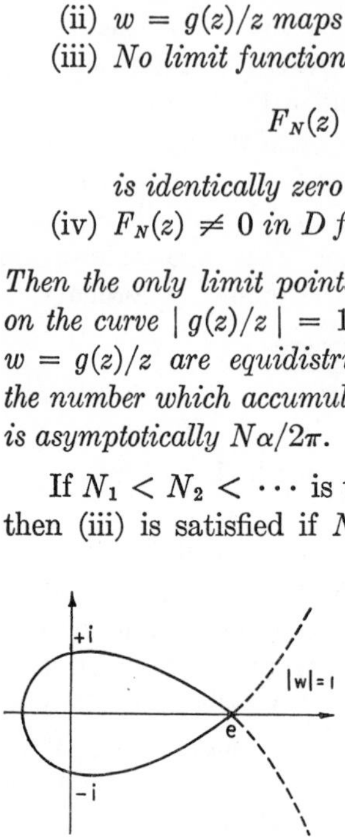

FIG. 1

Thus, if $f(z) = e^z = \sum z^n/n!$, then $\rho = 1$, $\rho_n = (n!)^{1/n} \sim n/e$, $\psi_n(z) \to (1 - ez)^{-1}$ for $|z| < e^{-1}$, $F_n(z) \to z/(e - z)$ for $|z| < e$, and the mapping in (ii) is $w = z^{-1} \exp(z/e)$. The limit points of the zeros of $s_n(\rho_n z)$ form the portion of the curve $|z \exp(-z/e)| = 1$ contained in the circle $|z| \leqq e$ (see Fig. 1), and the number which accumulate around any arc of this curve is asymptotically proportional to the change in arg w on this arc.

If $f(z) = e^z - a$, $a \neq 0$, then w is as above in the right half-plane, but $w = 1/z$ for Re $(z) < 0$. The distribution of the zeros of $s_n(\rho_n z)$ in this case is asymptotically the same as before in the right half-plane, but in the left half-plane their limit points form the unit semicircle, and the arguments are equidistributed in the sense of Weyl. In addition, every point of the segment $z = iy$, $|y| \leqq 1$, of the imaginary axis is a limit point of the zeros of $s_n(\rho_n z)$, and the proportion which accumulate about any segment of length l is asymptotically $l/2\pi e$. These conclusions also hold for $f(z) = e^z - P(z)$, where $P(z)$ is any polynomial $\neq 0$. The results described were first obtained by Szegö [46] and were later rediscovered by Dieudonné [8].

If $f(z) = \int_0^z \exp(-t^2)\,dt = z/1 - z^3/3\cdot 1! + z^5/5\cdot 3! - \cdots$, then $\rho = 2$, $\rho_n \sim (n/2e)^{\frac{1}{2}}$ for n odd, $(-1)^{(n-1)/2}\psi_n(z) \to (1 + ez^2)^{-1}$ for $|z| < e^{-\frac{1}{2}}$, $(-1)^{(n-1)/2}F_n(z) \to -z^2/(e + z^2)$ for $|z| < e^{-1/2}$, and the mapping (ii) is $w = g(z)/z = z^{-1}\exp(-z^2/2e)$ for $\pi/4 < |\arg z| < 3\pi/4$ and $w = z^{-1}$ for $|\arg(\pm z)| < \pi/4$. The limit points of the zeros of $s_n(\rho_n z)$ in $|\arg(\pm z)| < \pi/4$ form the arcs of the unit circles in these two sectors and their arguments are equidistributed, while in the other two sectors they form the portion of the curve, $|z \exp(z^2/2e)| = 1$ contained in $|z| \leqq e^{\frac{1}{2}}$, and the proportion which accumulate about any arc of this curve is asymptotically proportional to the corresponding change in $\arg w$. In addition, the points of the rays $\arg z = \pi/4 + k\pi/2$, $k = 0, 1, 2, 3$, contained in $|z| \leqq 1$ are also limit points of the zeros of $s_n(\rho_n z)$, and the proportion which accumulate about any segment $z = re^{i\theta}$, $0 < r_1 \leqq r \leqq r_2$, of any of these rays is asymptotically $(r_2^2 - r_1^2)/4\pi e$. This result is proved with the aid of a method due to Hille [17].

The limit points on the imaginary axis when $f(z) = e^z - P(z)$ and on the range $\arg z = \pi/4 + k\pi/2$ when $f(z)$ is the error function are instances of a general phenomenon. This is explained, in part, by the following theorem:

THEOREM 8. *There is a certain function $\alpha = \alpha(\rho) > 0$ for $0 < \rho < +\infty$ such that if f is an entire function of order ρ and z_0 is a Julia point of the sequence $\{f(\rho_n z)\}$ contained in the circle $|z| < \alpha(\rho)$, then z_0 is a limit point of the zeros of $s_n(\rho_n z) - a$ for all a with at most one exception.*

If $\{f_n\}$ is a sequence of functions analytic in a domain D, then a point z_0 is said to be a *Julia point* of the sequence if the sequence is not normal in any neighborhood of z_0. This general concept was introduced by Ostrowski (see [30]); the combination of Ostrowski's beautiful results with Theorem 8 leads to many very detailed results on the distribution of the zeros of $s_n(\rho_n z)$. The principal tool in the proof of Theorem 8 is a slight sharpening of an inequality of Nevanlinna [26]:

LEMMA 2. *If $f(z)$ is meromorphic in $|z| \leqq kr$, $k > 1$, $r > 0$, and $M(t, f) = \max |f(z)|$ on $|z| = t$, while $T(t, f)$ is the Nevanlinna characteristic function, then*

$$r^{-1} \int_0^r \log^+ M(t, f)\, dt \leqq C(k) T(kr),$$

where $C(k) = 1 + 8/\log k$.

Nevanlinna has a $C(k)$ which approaches $+\infty$ as $k \to +\infty$, while it is essential for our purpose to have a bound which approaches 1. Both approach $+\infty$ as $k \to 1$. The proof consists only in making Nevanlinna's intermediate estimates more carefully.

Unfortunately there is no room in this paper to give an exposition of the beautiful and very refined results of Dvoretzky [9] on Jentzsch's theorem.

At present there are practically no positive results on the zeros of the sections of power series of entire functions of zero order. Though many of the results of the present chapter could be extended to Dirichlet series and other representations of analytic functions as limits of special types (see, for example, Hirschman [18]), some problems of this type are extremely deep. For instance, Turán [48] has shown that the Riemann hypothesis is equivalent to a problem on the zeros of the partial sums of a Dirichlet series.[2]

BIBLIOGRAPHY

1. ARSOVE, M. J. *Functions representable as differences of subharmonic functions*, Trans. Amer. Math. Soc. 75 (1953), 327–365.

2. —— *Functions of potential type*, Trans. Amer. Math. Soc. 75 (1953), 526–551.

3. BENZ, E. *Über lineare, verschiebungstreue Funktionaloperationen und die Nullstellen ganzer Funktionen*, Comment. Math. Helv. 7 (1935), 243–289.

[2] Since this paper was written, there has appeared a fine dissertation by a young Swedish mathematician, T. Ganelius, "Sequences of analytic functions and their zeros" (*Ark. Mat.* 3 (1954), 1–50), which has many results overlapping mine. He has, also, some pretty extensions to exponential polynomials.

4. Bourion, G. *L'ultraconvergence dans les séries de Taylor*. Actualités Scientifiques et Industrielles, No. 472. Paris, 1937.

5. Carlson, F. *Sur les fonctions entières*, C. R. Acad. Sci. Paris 179 (1924), 1583–1585.

6. —— *Sur les fonctions entières*, Ark. Mat. Astr. Fys., vol. 35A, No. 14 (1948), 1–18.

7. Delange, H. *Sur la convergence des séries de polynomes de la forme* $\Sigma\, a_n P_n(z)$ *et sur certaines suites de polynomes*, Ann. École Norm. 56 (1939), 173–275.

8. Dieudonné, J. *Sur les zéros des polynomes-sections de* e^x, Bull. Sci. Math. 70 (1935), 333–351.

9. Dvoretzky, A. *On sections of power series*, Ann. of Math. 51 (1950), 643–696.

10. Erdös, P., and Fried, H. *On the connection between gaps in power series and the roots of their partial sums*, Trans. Amer. Math. Soc. 62 (1947), 53–61.

11. —— and Turán, P. *On the uniformly-dense distribution of certain sequences of points*, Ann. of Math. 41 (1940), 162–173.

12. —— —— *On a problem in the theory of uniform distribution, I, II*, Indagationes Math. 10 (1948), 370–378 and 406–413.

13. Fekete, M. *Über die Verteilung der Wurzeln bei gewissen algebraischen Gleichungen mit ganzzahligen Koeffizienten*, Math. Zeit. 17 (1923), 228–249.

14. Frostman, O. *Potentiel d'équilibre et capacité des ensembles avec quelques applications à la théorie des fonctions*, Meddel. Lunds Univ. Mat. Sem. 3 (1935), 1–115.

15. Hardy, G. H. *On the zeroes of certain integral functions*, Messenger of Math. New Ser. 32 (1902), 36–45.

16. —— *On the zeroes of a class of integral functions*, Messenger of Math. New Ser. 35 (1904), 97–101.

17. Hille, E. *Zero-point problems for linear differential equations of the second order*, Mat. Tidsskrift B (1927), 25–44.

18. Hirschman, I. I., Jr. *Two power series theorems extended to the Laplace transform*, Duke Math. J. 11 (1944), 793–797.

19. Izumi, S. *On the distribution of the zero points of sections of a power series*, Jap. J. Math. 4 (1927), 29–32.

20. Jentzsch, R. *Untersuchungen zur Theorie der Folgen analytischer Funktionen*. Dissertation. Univ. of Berlin, 1914. Also Acta Math. 41 (1918), 219–251.

21. Kellogg, O. D. *Foundations of potential theory*. Berlin, 1929.

22. Korevaar, J. *The zeros of approximating polynomials and the canonical representation of an entire function*, Duke Math. J. 18 (1951), 573–592.

23. Lelong, P. *On a problem of M. A. Zorn*, Proc. Amer. Math. Soc. 2 (1951), 12–19.

24. Maillet, E. *Sur les fonctions entières et quasi-entières*, J. Math. Pures Appl. (5) 8 (1902), 329–386.

25. Marden, M. *The geometry of the zeros of a polynomial in a complex variable*. Mathematical Surveys, No. 3. New York, 1949.

26. Nevanlinna, R. *Le théorème de Picard-Borel et la théorie des fonctions méromorphes*. Paris, 1929.

27. Okada, M. *Note on power series*, Tôhoku Science Reports 11 (1922), 43–50.

28. Ostrowski, A. *Über vollständige Gebiete gleichmässiger Konvergenz von Folgen analytischer Funktionen*, Abh. Math. Sem. Hansischen Univ. 1 (1922), 327–350.

29. —— *Über den Schottkyschen Satz und die Borelschen Ungleichungen*, Preuss. Akad. Wiss. Sitzungsber. (1925), pp. 471–484.

30. —— *Studien über den Schottkyschen Satz*. Basel, 1931.

31. Petrovich, M. *Une classe remarquable de séries entières*. Quatrième Congrès International des Mathematiciens, 1908, vol. 2, pp. 36–43. Rome, 1909.

32. Pólya, G. *Über Annäherung durch Polynome mit lauter reellen Wurzeln*, Rend. Circ. Mat. Palermo 36 (1913), 279–295.

33. —— *Über Annäherung durch Polynome, deren sämtliche Wurzeln in einem Winkelraum fallen*, Nachr. Ges. Wiss. Göttingen (1913), pp. 326–330.

34. —— *Bemerkungen über unendliche Folgen und ganze Funktionen*, Math. Ann. 88 (1923), 169–183.

35. —— *Untersuchungen über Lücken und Singularitäten von Potenzreihen, II*, Ann. of Math. 34 (1933), 731–777.

36. —— and Lindwart, E. *Über einen Zusammenhang zwischen Konvergenz von Polynomfolgen und der Verteilung ihrer Wurzeln*, Rend. Circ. Mat. Palermo 37 (1914), 297–304.

37. —— and Szegö, G. *Aufgaben und Lehrsätze aus der Analysis*, vols. I, II. Berlin, 1925.

38. Rosenbloom, P. C. *On sequences of polynomials, especially sections of power series*. Thesis. Stanford Univ., 1944. Abstracts in Bull. Amer. Math. Soc. 48 (1942), 830; 49 (1943), 689.

39. —— *Mass distributions and their potentials*, C. R. 11. Cong. Math. Scand. Trondheim (1949), pp. 130–138.

40. —— *Quelques classes de problèmes extrémaux, II*, Bull. Soc. Math. France 80 (1952), 183–215.

41. SCHUR, I. *Untersuchungun über algebraische Gleichungen. I. Bemerkungen zu einem Satz von E. Schmidt*, Preuss. Akad. Wiss. Sitzungsber. (1933), 403–428.

42. SCHWARTZ, L. *Théorie des distributions*, vols. I, II. Actualités Scientifiques et Industrielles, Nos. 1091, 1122. Paris, 1950–1951.

43. SZÁSZ, O. *On sequences of polynomials and the distribution of their zeros*, Bull. Amer. Math. Soc. 49 (1943), 377–383.

44. SZEGÖ, G. *Über die Nullstellen der Polynome einer Folge, die in einem einfach zusammenhängenden Gebiet gleichmässig konvergiert*, Nachr. Ges. Wiss. Göttingen (1922), pp. 137–143.

45. —— *Über die Nullstellen von Polynomen, die in einem Kreise gleichmässig konvergieren*, Berlin Math. Ges. Sitzungsber. 21 (1922), 59–64.

46. —— *Über eine Eigenschaft der Exponentialreihe*, Berlin Math. Ges. Sitzungsber. 23 (1924), 50–64.

47. TSUJI, M. *On the distribution of the zero points of the sections of a power series, I, II, III*, Jap. J. Math. 1 (1924), 109–140; 2 (1926), 147–154; 3 (1926), 49–52.

48. TURÁN, P. *On some approximative Dirichlet-polynomials in the theory of the zeta-function of Riemann*, Danske Vid. Selsk. Mat.-Fys. Medd., vol. 24, No. 17 (1948), 1–36.

49. VALIRON, G. *Sur les zéros des polynomes sections d'une fonction entière*, Tôhoku Math. J. 32 (1930), 144–151.

50. WALSH, J. L. *The location of critical points of analytic and harmonic functions*. Amer. Math. Soc. Colloquium Publications, No. 34. New York, 1950.

51. WEISNER, L. *Power series the roots of whose partial sums lie in a sector*, Bull. Amer. Math. Soc. 47 (1941), 160–163.

52. WEYL, H. *Über die Gleichverteilung von Zahlen mod Eins*, Math. Ann., 77 (1916), 313–352.

53. YOSIDA, Y. *Sur les zéros des sommes partielles d'une série entière*, Proc. Imp. Acad. Tokyo 3 (1927), 45–49.

UNIVERSITY OF MINNESOTA

APPROXIMATION BY POLYNOMIALS

P. C. ROSENBLOOM AND S. E. WARSCHAWSKI

1. Introduction. For a certain large class of variational problems, the study of the rate of convergence of the Rayleigh-Ritz method can be reduced to the study of the approximation of a particular function by linear combinations of certain known functions. The function to be approximated is in general unknown, but by methods such as those of Morrey [13] and Shiffman [18] a priori estimates for measures of smoothness—moduli of continuity of the function and its derivatives—may be obtained. Hence when one attempts a solution of variational problems in the complex domain by restricting the competing functions to be polynomials of prescribed degree, it is important to know how well an analytic function in a given domain may be approximated by polynomials. Usually such problems have been studied under the assumption that either the boundary of the domain is analytic or the function to be approximated is analytic in the closure of the domain (see, for example, Walsh [21], Sewell [17], and Walsh and Elliott [22]). On the other hand, there are some studies of the possibility of approximation by polynomials under quite general conditions (see Smirnov [19] and Mergelyan [12]).

In this paper we are interested in quantitative results on the degree of approximation when the function to be approximated and the boundary of the domain of analyticity are sufficiently smooth. Usually we shall impose somewhat heavier restrictions than are necessary to insure the possibility of approximation. Indeed, in the present exposition we shall make no attempt to attain the greatest possible generality, but shall leave the more refined questions for another paper. The applications to variational problems will also be treated in a later paper. Here we shall only sketch the results with some indication of the methods of proof. Many of these results are due to our students, C. Y. Wang [23] and E. R. Johnston [9]. This report is necessarily incomplete, since it represents work in progress.

We shall be especially concerned with the expansion of a given function in terms of the Szegö polynomials, obtained by orthogonalization over the boundary, and the Carleman polynomials, obtained by orthogonalization over the area. In such problems the Szegö and the Bergman kernels play, of course, an important role (see Szegö [20] and Bergman [1].) We shall obtain a number of equiconvergence theorems which show how results from the classical theory of Fourier series can be carried over to these more general orthogonal expansions.

2. Szegö polynomials. Let C be a rectifiable Jordan curve of length L, let D be its interior, and let D_1 be its exterior. Let

$$\psi(w) = aw + a_0 + \sum_1^\infty \frac{a_n}{w^n}$$

map $|w| > 1$ onto D_1, $a > 0$, and let $\phi(z) = a^{-1}z + \cdots$ be its inverse function. We introduce the Faber polynomials associated with $\phi^n \cdot (\phi')^{\frac{1}{2}}$ by

$$\phi^n \cdot (\phi')^{\frac{1}{2}} = \mathfrak{F}_n(z) - \mathfrak{H}_n(z),$$

where $\mathfrak{F}_n(z)$ is the polynomial part of the expansion of $\phi^n \cdot (\phi')^{\frac{1}{2}}$ about $z = \infty$, and $\mathfrak{H}_n$ is analytic in D_1, $\mathfrak{H}_n(\infty) = 0$. Then

$$\mathfrak{F}_n(z) = a^{-n-\frac{1}{2}}z^n + \cdots$$

is a polynomial of degree n. We shall throughout this paper denote by Γ_r the circle $|w| = r$, and by C_r the image of Γ_r under the mapping ψ. An easy application of Cauchy's theorem shows that if $1 < \rho < r$, $z \in C_r$, $w = \phi(z)$, then

$$[\psi'(w)]^{\frac{1}{2}}\mathfrak{H}_n(z) = \frac{1}{2\pi i}\int_{\Gamma_\rho} W^n g(W, w)\, dW,$$

where

$$g(W, w) = \frac{[\psi'(W)\psi'(w)]^{\frac{1}{2}}(W - w) - [\psi(W) - \psi(w)]}{[\psi(W) - \psi(w)](W - w)}$$

$$= [\psi'(w)]^{\frac{1}{2}} \sum_{\nu=0}^{\infty} \frac{\mathfrak{H}_\nu(\psi(w))}{W^{\nu+1}}.$$

Now g is analytic for $|W| > 1$, $|w| > 1$. If the nontangential limit of $\psi'(\omega)$ exists as $\omega \to w$, $|w| = 1$, and if this limit, which we shall denote simply by $\psi'(w)$, is different from zero, then $g(W, w)$ is analytic in $|W| > 1$. If g, as a function of W for fixed w on Γ_1, is in the Hardy class $H(1, E(\Gamma_1))$ ($E(\Gamma)$ means the exterior of Γ), then $\mathcal{H}_\nu(\psi(w))$ are the Fourier coefficients of a function of L_1, and hence $\mathcal{H}_n(\psi(w)) \to 0$ as $n \to \infty$. More precisely (see Zygmund [24]),

$$|[\psi'(w)]^{\frac{1}{2}}\mathcal{H}_n(\psi(w))|$$
$$\leqq \frac{1}{4\pi}\int_{|W|=1} |g(We^{i\pi/(n+1)}, w) - g(We^{-i\pi/(n+1)}, w)|\,|dW|,$$

which shows how the rate of approach of $\mathcal{H}_n(\psi(w))$ to zero depends on the smoothness of the boundary in the neighborhood of w. Incidentally, g as a function of W is clearly of class L_2 over any closed arc on Γ_1 not containing w.

We introduce a convenient class of curves, which we call of type $\mathfrak{W}_M$, namely those for which

$$\frac{1}{(2\pi)^2}\int_{\Gamma_r}\int_{\Gamma_\rho} |g(W, w)|^2\,|dW|\,|dw| \leqq M^2$$

for $r > 1$, $\rho > 1$. (This integral is a decreasing function of r and ρ, so that it suffices to assume that the limit as $r, \rho \to 1$ is at most M^2.) For a curve of type $\mathfrak{W}_M$, $g(W, w)$ is of class $H(2, E(\Gamma_1))$ as a function of W for almost all $w \in \Gamma_1$. A curve with continuously turning tangent for which the tangent angle satisfies a Hölder condition with exponent $> \frac{1}{2}$ is always of type $\mathfrak{W}_M$.

A function f is said to be of type $H(p, D)$ if f is analytic in D and there is a sequence of rectifiable curves C_n in D such that every closed subset of D is in the interior of C_n for all sufficiently large n, and such that

$$\int_{C_n} |f(z)|^p\,|dz|$$

is bounded independently of n. It has been demonstrated (see Brock [4]) that if $p \geqq 1$, then f has nontangential boundary values of class L_p almost everywhere on C and is representable as a Cauchy integral in terms of these boundary values. (See also Smirnov [19].) If $f \in H(2, D)$, then $f(\psi(w))[\psi'(w)]^{\frac{1}{2}}$ is of class L_2 on Γ_1. We can then define the *Faber coefficients* of f as

$$a_n = \frac{1}{2\pi i}\int_{\Gamma_1} \frac{f(\psi(w))[\psi'(w)]^{\frac{1}{2}}}{w^{n+1}}\, dw, \qquad n = 0, \pm 1, \cdots,$$
$$= \frac{1}{2\pi i}\int_C f(z)\phi(z)^{-n-1}[\phi'(z)]^{\frac{1}{2}}\, dz.$$

Let $A(C)$ be the set of points $z = \psi(w)$, $|w| = 1$, such that $\psi'(w) \neq 0$ and $g(W, w) \in H(2, E(\Gamma_1))$ as a function of W. Then the measure of $C - A(C)$ is zero if C is of type $\mathfrak{W}_M$.

By Parseval's formula we have

$$[\psi'(w)]^{\frac{1}{2}} \sum_{n=0}^{\infty} a_n \mathcal{H}_n(z) = \frac{1}{2\pi i}\int_{|W|=1} f(\psi(W))\, [\psi'(W)]^{\frac{1}{2}}\, g(W, w)\, dW$$

for $z \in A(C)$, and hence

$$\lim_{n\to\infty}\left(\sum_{\nu=0}^{n} a_\nu\, \mathfrak{F}_\nu(z) - [\phi'(z)]^{\frac{1}{2}} \sum_{\nu=0}^{n} a_\nu\, w^\nu\right)$$

exists for all $z \in A(C)$, all $f \in H(2, D)$. In other words, the Faber expansion of f and a certain Fourier series are equiconvergent on the set $A(C)$, independent of the function $f \in H(2, D)$. Let $A_N(C)$ be the set of $z \in A(C)$ such that

$$\frac{1}{2\pi}\int_{\Gamma_1} |g(W, w)|^2\, |dW| \leqq N^2, \qquad |\psi'(w)| \geqq 1/N.$$

The measure of $C - A_N(C)$ approaches zero as $N \to \infty$, and can be readily estimated. On the set $A_N(C)$ the equiconvergence is uniform, not only with respect to z but also with respect to f in the class of functions for which $f(\psi(w))\sqrt{\psi'(w)}$ has a given mean square modulus of continuity on Γ_1.

In proving this and related results, the following simple inequalities, which must be known, are used. Let

$$I(h, F) = \frac{1}{2\pi h}\int_0^h \int_0^{2\pi} |F(\theta + t) - F(\theta - t)|^2\, d\theta\, dt,$$

$$R_n = \sum_{|\nu| \geqq n} |a_\nu|^2, \qquad a_\nu = \frac{1}{2\pi}\int_0^{2\pi} F(\theta)e^{-i\nu\theta}\, d\theta.$$

Then $R_n \leqq I\left(\frac{1}{n}\right)$, $I(h) \leqq 2\|F\|^2 h + 4R_N$, $N = [h^{-\frac{1}{2}}]$, $\|F\|^2 = \frac{1}{2\pi}\int_0^{2\pi} |F(\theta)|^2\, d\theta$.

In obtaining more refined results the Hermitian matrix

$$\epsilon_{mn} = \frac{1}{2\pi} \int_C \mathcal{H}_m(z)\overline{\mathcal{H}_n(z)}\, |dz|$$

is important. The generating function is

$$\Upsilon(w_1, \bar{w}_2) = \frac{1}{2\pi} \int_{\Gamma_1} g(w_1, W)\overline{g(w_2, W)}\, |dW|$$

$$= \sum_{m,n=0}^{\infty} \frac{\epsilon_{mn}}{w_1^{m+1}\bar{w}_2^{n+1}}.$$

We have

$$\sum_{m,n=0}^{\infty} |\epsilon_{mn}|^2 = \frac{1}{(2\pi)^2} \int_{\Gamma_1} \int_{\Gamma_1} |\Upsilon(w_1, w_2)|^2\, |dw_1|\, |dw_2|,$$

$$\sum_{n=0}^{\infty} \epsilon_{nn} = \frac{1}{(2\pi)^2} \int_{\Gamma_1} \int_{\Gamma_1} |g(w, W)|^2\, |dw|\, |dW| \leqq M^2,$$

and $|\epsilon_{mn}|^2 \leqq \epsilon_{mm}\epsilon_{nn}$. Thus $C \in \mathfrak{W}_M$ if and only if $\sum \epsilon_{nn} \leqq M^2$. This is equivalent to the condition that $\Upsilon(w_1, \bar{w}_2)$ on $\Gamma_1 \times \Gamma_1$ be a kernel of the trace class (see Schatten [16], Ruston [15], and Graves [8]). It would be interesting to know the significance of the integral equation with this kernel. Many of the results we shall state hold under the more general condition that $\sum |\epsilon_{mn}|^2$ converge. We shall not, however, discuss the consequences of this condition here.

If $C \in \mathfrak{W}_M$ and $f \in H(2, D)$, and its Faber coefficients are defined as above, then

$$\sum_{n+1}^{\infty} |a_\nu|^2 \leqq \frac{1}{2\pi} \int_C \left| f(z) - \sum_{0}^{n} a_\nu \mathfrak{F}_\nu(z) \right|^2 |dz|$$

$$\leqq \left(1 + \sum_{n+1}^{\infty} |\epsilon_{\mu\nu}|^2\right) \sum_{n+1}^{\infty} |a_\nu|^2 = (1 + o(1)) \sum_{n+1}^{\infty} |a_\nu|^2$$

$$\leqq (1 + M^4) \sum_{n+1}^{\infty} |a_\nu|^2.$$

Now

$$\sum_{n+1}^{\infty} |a_\nu|^2 = \frac{1}{2\pi} \int_{\Gamma_1} |f(\psi(w))[\psi'(w)]^{\frac{1}{2}} - \sum_{-\infty}^{n} a_\nu w^\nu |^2\, |dw|$$

is the L_2 error in the Fourier expansion of $f(\psi(w))[\psi'(w)]^{\frac{1}{2}}$. Hence the series $\sum_0^\infty a_\nu \mathfrak{F}_\nu$ converges to f in the L_2 sense on C, and uniformly in any closed subset of D; the error is asymptotically the same as that for the corresponding Fourier expansion.

This quantitative result should be contrasted with the important qualitative result of Smirnov [19], established under much weaker hypotheses. He proved that a necessary and sufficient condition that every function of class $H(2, D)$ be approximable arbitrarily closely, in the L_2 norm on C, by polynomials, is that $\log |\Psi'(w)|$, where Ψ maps $|w| < 1$ onto D conformally, be representable by the Poisson-Lebesgue integral in terms of its boundary values. For a general rectifiable boundary it is of course true that this function has a Poisson-Stieltjes representation. Lavrentiev and Keldysh [11] have given an example of a domain with rectifiable boundary which does not satisfy Smirnov's condition. So far we have not succeeded in obtaining quantitative results for a general Smirnov domain.

We now turn to the consideration of the Szegö polynomials. It is convenient to introduce the L_2 norm on C:

$$||f||^2 = \frac{1}{L}\int_C |f|^2 \, |dz|.$$

Let $p_0, p_1, \cdots$ be the polynomials obtained by orthogonalizing $1, z, z^2, \cdots$ on C, normalized so that the coefficient of z^n in p_n is positive. These polynomials are also characterized by the extremal problem: to find the polynomial P of degree n of the form $P(z) = z^n + \cdots$ with minimum norm. The extremal polynomial is $m_n p_n$, where m_n is the value of the minimum. The function $a^{n+\frac{1}{2}}\phi^n(\phi')^{\frac{1}{2}}$ is the solution of the extremal problem: to find the function F analytic in D_1 with a pole of order n at $z = \infty$, of the form $F(z) = z^n + \cdots$, such that $\| F \|$ is a minimum. By taking $a^{n+\frac{1}{2}}\mathfrak{F}_n$ as a competing function in the first problem and $m_n p_n$ as a competing function in the other, we obtain the inequality

$$1 \leqq \frac{L}{2\pi}\frac{m_n^2}{a^{2n+1}} \leqq 1 + \epsilon_{nn}.$$

This yields the usual asymptotic relation between m_n and a in a particularly strong form for curves of type $\mathfrak{W}_M$.

As a consequence we easily obtain

$$\left\| p_n - \frac{a^{n+\frac{1}{2}}}{m_n}\mathfrak{F}_n \right\|^2 \leqq \epsilon_{nn},$$

$$\left\| p_n - \frac{a^{n+\frac{1}{2}}}{m_n} \phi^n (\phi')^{\frac{1}{2}} \right\|^2 \leqq \frac{\epsilon_{nn}}{1 + \epsilon_{nn}} \leqq \epsilon_{nn} ,$$

which yields the asymptotic relation between p_n and $\mathfrak{F}_n$ in D, and the relation between p_n and $\phi^n(\phi')^{\frac{1}{2}}$ in D_1 for curves of type $\mathfrak{W}_M$.

Let $f \in H(2, C)$,

$$c_n = \frac{1}{L} \int_C f\overline{p_n} \, | dz |, \qquad \sigma_N = \sum_0^N c_n p_n , \qquad s_N = \sum_0^N a_n \mathfrak{F}_n .$$

Then on $A_K(C)$ we have

$$| \sigma_N(z) - s_N(z) |^2 \leqq 4LK \, || f ||^2 \sum_{N+1}^{\infty} \epsilon_{nn} ,$$

so that the expansions in Szegö and Faber polynomials are uniformly equiconvergent on $A_K(C)$. We also have

$$\sum_{\nu=n+1}^{\infty} | a_\nu |^2 \leqq || f - \sigma_n ||^2 \leqq || f - s_n ||^2 \leqq (1 + o(1)) \sum_{n+1}^{\infty} | a_\nu |^2,$$

which show that the degree of approximation to f by σ_n in the L_2 norm is asymptotically the same as that for $f(\psi(w))[\psi'(w)]^{\frac{1}{2}}$ by its Fourier expansion.

As in the classical theory of approximation by polynomials, there are also converse theorems which enable us to derive smoothness properties of a function from the degree of approximation by polynomials. We shall give two simple examples of this type of result. Let

$$K(z, \bar{z}_0) = \sum_0^{\infty} p_n(z)\overline{p_n(z_0)} = \frac{L}{2\pi} \{\Phi'(z)\overline{\Phi'(z_0)}\}^{\frac{1}{2}},$$

where Φ maps D onto $| w | < 1$, $\Phi(z_0) = 0$, $\Phi'(z_0) > 0$, be the Szegö kernel of D, and let

$$R_n(z) = \textstyle\sum_{n+1}^{\infty} | p_n(z) |^2$$

be the remainder in the series for $K(z, \bar{z})$ after n terms. The trivial formula

$$R_n(z_0) = \frac{1}{L} \int_C \left| K(z, \bar{z}_0) - \sum_0^n p_\nu(z)\overline{p_\nu(z_0)} \right|^2 | dz |,$$

true for all Smirnov domains, shows the connection between $R_n(z_0)$ and the L_2 approximation of $[\Phi'(z)]^{\frac{1}{2}}$ by polynomials on C. We thus find that if $R_n(z_0) = O(c^{2n})$ for some $c < 1$, then Φ is analytic in C_R for $R < 1/c$. Similarly, if $R_n(z_0) = O(n^{-k})$ for some $k > 6$, then $\Phi'(z)$ is continuous in $\bar{D}$. In proving the last result we use the inequality

$$| P(z) | \leqq \frac{2Lae^2}{\rho^2} (n+1)^2 \, || P ||,$$

for any polynomial of degree n, and any $z \in C$. Here ρ is the radius of a circle contained in D. If one already has information regarding the smoothness of the boundary, then these estimates can be improved.

The case of analytic boundaries and its applications to variational problems has been studied by our student, C. Y. Wang [23].

3. Carleman polynomials. We now turn to problems associated with the polynomials obtained by orthogonalization over the area. Though the corresponding kernel had been introduced and studied earlier by Bergmann [2] (see also Bochner [3]), the first detailed investigation of the orthogonal polynomials was made by Carleman [5]. The theorem on the possibility of approximation in the sense of the area norm is due to Farrell [6].

We consider the class $\mathfrak{L}^2(D)$ of functions f analytic in D and such that

$$||f||^2 = \int_D |f(z)|^2 \, dA_z < +\infty.$$

Here dA is the area element and "z" indicates the variable of integration. This is a Hilbert space with the scalar product

$$(f, g) = \int_D f(z)\overline{g(z)} \, dA_z .$$

The polynomials obtained by orthogonalization of $1, z, z^2, \cdots$ with respect to this scalar product are called the *Carleman polynomials* and denoted by $q_0, q_1, \cdots$. Here $q_n(z)$ is normalized so that the coefficient of z^n is positive. Farrell found that the Carleman polynomials are complete in $\mathfrak{L}^2(D)$ if and only if D is the interior of its closure. Such a domain we call a *Carleman domain*. We shall, for the most part, restrict ourselves to a narrower class of domains for which we can put Farrell's results in quantitative form.

The results of this section are mostly due to our student, E. R. Johnston.

As before, q_n can be characterized by an extremal property. Let m_n be the minimum of $\| P \|$ as P ranges through the polynomials of degree n such that $P(z) = z^n + \cdots$. Then the extremal polynomial is $m_n q_n$.

It is easy to show that $m_n^{1/n} \to a$ and that the zeros of q_n are in the convex hull H of $\bar{D}$. (See Féjer [7].) It is somewhat more difficult to show that $q_n^{1/n} \to \phi$ uniformly inside the exterior of H. If $\mathfrak{N}_n(R)$ is the number of zeros of q_n in $E(C_R)$, then $\mathfrak{N}_n(R) = o(n)$ for all $R > 1$. It follows that $q_n^{1/n} \to \phi$ in $E(D)$ except possibly on a set of capacity zero. If C, the boundary of D, is either piecewise analytic with no exterior angles equal to 2π, or if at each point z_0 of C there is a circle of fixed radius δ contained in D with z_0 on its boundary, then $\mathfrak{N}_n(R) = O(\log n)$ for $R > 1$, and

$$\frac{a}{m_n^{1/n}} - 1 = O\left(\frac{\log n}{n}\right),$$

and

$$\frac{q_n^{1/n}}{\phi} - 1 = O\left(\frac{\log n}{n}\right)$$

in $E(H)$.

The case of an analytic boundary, studied by Carleman, suggests the results for more general domains. In this case, if $\psi(w)$ is analytic and univalent for $| w | > r$, $r < 1$, then

$$\frac{\pi a^{2(n+1)}}{n+1}(1 - r^{2(n+1)}) \leqq m_n^2 \leqq \frac{\pi a^{2(n+1)}}{n+1}.$$

(The right-hand side is valid for general Carleman domains.) Also,

$$q_n(z) = \left(\frac{n+1}{\pi}\right)^{\frac{1}{2}} \phi^n(z)\phi'(z)(1 + O(r^n n^{\frac{1}{2}}))$$

in $|\phi(z)| \geqq \rho$, $r < \rho < 1$. The zeros of $q_n - A$, $A \neq 0$, are equidistributed on C, while $q_n \neq 0$ for $| \phi(z) | \geqq \rho > r$ for $n > n_0(\rho)$.

These results lead us to introduce the corresponding Faber polynomials in the following way:

$$\left(\frac{n+1}{\pi}\right)^{\frac{1}{2}} \phi(z)^n \phi'(z) = f_n(z) - h_n(z),$$

$$\frac{1}{[\pi(n+1)]^{\frac{1}{2}}}\,\phi^{n+1} = F_{n+1}(z) - H_{n+1}(z),$$

where f_n and F_n are polynomials of degree n, and h_n and H_n are analytic in $E(D)$ and vanish at ∞. It follows easily that h_n and H_n are $o(\phi^n)$ uniformly in $E(C_R)$, $R > 1$. More precisely, if $z = \psi(w)$, $|w| > 1$, then

$$(\pi n)^{\frac{1}{2}} H_n(z) = \frac{1}{2\pi i}\int_{|W|=1} W^n G(W, w)\, dW,$$

where

$$G(W, w) = \frac{\psi'(W)}{\psi(W) - \psi(w)} - \frac{1}{W - w} = \frac{\partial}{\partial W}\log\frac{\psi(W) - \psi(w)}{W - w}$$
$$= \sqrt{\pi}\sum_{n=1}^{\infty}\frac{\sqrt{n}H_n(\psi(w))}{W^{n+1}}$$

for $|W|, |w| > 1$. Similarly,

$$\left(\frac{\pi}{n+1}\right)^{\frac{1}{2}} h_n(z) = \frac{1}{2\pi i}\int_{|W|=1} W^n g(W, w)\, dW,$$

where

$$g(W, w) = \frac{1}{\psi(W) - \psi(w)} - \frac{1}{\psi'(w)(W - w)}$$
$$= \frac{1}{\psi'(w)}\frac{\partial}{\partial w}\log\frac{W - w}{\psi(W) - \psi(w)}$$
$$= \pi^{\frac{1}{2}}\sum_{n=0}^{\infty}\frac{h_n(\psi(w))}{(n+1)^{\frac{1}{2}}W^{n+1}}$$

for $|W| > 1$, $|w| > 1$.

It is sometimes useful to consider the "Faber" kernel

$$F_D(z, \bar{\zeta}) = \sum_{0}^{\infty} f_n(z)\overline{f_n(\zeta)}, \qquad z, \zeta \in D,$$

which has the elementary expression

$$F_D(z, \bar{\zeta}) = \frac{1}{\pi^2}\int_{E(D)}\frac{dA_\sigma}{(\sigma - z)^2\overline{(\sigma - \zeta)^2}},$$

and in particular

$$F_D(z) = F_D(z, \bar{z}) = \sum_0^\infty |f_n(z)|^2 = \frac{1}{\pi^2}\int_{E(D)} \frac{dA_\zeta}{|\zeta - z|^4}.$$

It easily follows that

$$F_D(z) \leqq \frac{1}{\pi\delta^2}, \qquad \delta = \text{dist}(z, C).$$

If[1] $\liminf_{\delta\to 0} |C(\sigma, \delta) \cap D|/|C(\sigma, \delta)| > 0$, then $F_D(z)|z - \sigma|^2 \geqq$ const > 0. It can be compared with the less elementary Bergmann kernel,

$$K_D(z, \bar{\zeta}) = \sum_0^\infty q_n(z)\overline{q_n(\zeta)}.$$

We have

$$\frac{F_D(z, \bar{z})}{K_D(z, \bar{z})} \leqq 1 \qquad \text{for } z \in D.$$

For a wide class of domains this ratio is bounded on the other side by the constant λ_0 which we introduce below. The rate of convergence of the series for F_D can be estimated in terms of the smoothness of C by means of the inequality

$$\sum_N^\infty |f_n(z)|^2 \leqq \frac{1}{\pi^2 h}\int_0^h \int_{|w|>1} |\mathfrak{F}(we^{it}, z) - \mathfrak{F}(we^{-it}, z)|^2 \, dA_w \, dt,$$

where

$$\mathfrak{F}(w, z) = \frac{\psi'(w)}{(\psi(w) - z)^2}$$

and $h = 1/(N + 2)$.

It follows easily that if $\sum |b_n|^2 < \infty$, then $\rho(z) = \sum b_n f_n(z)$ is analytic in D, and is in fact in $\mathfrak{L}^2(D)$, if the area of C is zero.

Let

$$\epsilon_{mn} = \int_{E(D)} h_m(z)\overline{h_n(z)}\, dA_z = \delta_{mn} - (f_m, f_n).$$

---

[1] The circle with center at σ and radius δ is denoted by $C(\sigma, \delta)$. If E is a subset of the plane, then $|E|$ is its measure.

Then $0 \leqq \epsilon_{nn} < 1$, $\epsilon_{mn} = \overline{\epsilon_{nm}}$, $|\epsilon_{mn}| \leqq \sqrt{\epsilon_{nn}\epsilon_{mm}}$. If $\rho = \sum_0^\infty b_n f_n$, then

$$\|\rho\|^2 = \sum (\delta_{mn} - \epsilon_{mn}) b_m \overline{b_n} \leqq \sum_0^\infty |b_n|^2$$

if the area of C is zero. It follows easily that

$$\sum_{\substack{m \neq n \\ m=0}}^{\infty} |\epsilon_{mn}|^2 \leqq 2 \text{ for all } n.$$

The matrix (ϵ_{mn}) is basic for a detailed study of the Carleman polynomials. By consideration of the generating functions, we see that $\sum \epsilon_{nn} < +\infty$ if and only if

$$\text{(1)} \qquad \int_{E(\Gamma_1)} \int_{E(\Gamma_1)} |G(W, w)|^2 \, dA_W \, dA_w < +\infty.$$

Let

$$\Omega(w_1, \overline{w}_2) = \int_{E(D)} \frac{\partial}{\partial w_1} g(w_1, \phi(z)) \overline{\frac{\partial}{\partial w_2} g(w_2, \phi(z))} \, dA_z .$$

Then $\sum |\epsilon_{mn}|^2 < \infty$ if and only if

$$\text{(2)} \qquad \int_{E(\Gamma_1)} \int_{E(\Gamma_1)} |\Omega(w_1, \overline{w}_2)|^2 \, dA_{w_1} \, dA_{w_2} < +\infty.$$

These conditions are certainly satisfied if the boundary is sufficiently smooth. Domains which satisfy condition (1) will be said to be of type J_1, and those which satisfy (2) will be said to be of type J_2. Clearly, $J_1 \subset J_2$.

The following generalization of theorems of von Koch and Ostrowski are useful in this connection:

THEOREM 1. *If* $\sum_0^\infty |c_{mn}|^2 = s^2 < \infty$, $c_{mn} = \overline{c_{nm}}$, *and if there are constants* $\Lambda_k > 0$ *independent of* N *such that*

$$\Lambda_k |z_k|^2 \leqq \sum_{m,n \leqq N} (\delta_{mn} - c_{mn}) z_m \overline{z_n}, \qquad k \leqq N,$$

and if $\lambda_0^{(N)}$ *is the smallest eigenvalue of the truncated matrix* $(\delta_{mn} - c_{mn})$ $(m, n \leqq N)$, *then*

$$\lim_{N \to \infty} \lambda_0^{(N)} = \lambda_0 > 0$$

exists. Let $K = K(\epsilon)$ *be such that*

$$\sum_{m,n \leqq K(\epsilon)} |c_{mn}|^2 \geqq s^2 - \epsilon^2, \qquad 0 < \epsilon < s, \qquad \epsilon < \tfrac{1}{10}, \qquad C_K = \sum_{k=0}^{K} \frac{1}{\Lambda_k}.$$

Then

$$\lambda_0 \geqq \min\left(1, \frac{1}{C_K}, \frac{(1-\epsilon)^2}{\{1-(1-\epsilon)C_K + 2\epsilon C_K{}^2\}^2}\right).$$

Let $D_N = \det(\delta_{mn} - c_{mn})$, $m, n \leqq N$. *Then*

$$\left|\frac{D_N}{D_{N-1}} - (1 - c_{NN})\right| \leqq \frac{1}{\lambda_0} \sum_{m=0}^{\infty} | c_{mN} |^2,$$

and

$$\lim_{N\to\infty} D_N \exp\left(\textstyle\sum_0^N c_{nn}\right)$$

exists and $\neq 0$. *If* $(c_{mn})_{m,n\leq N}$ *is nonnegative and* $\sum_0^\infty c_{nn} = T < +\infty$, *then*

$$D_N \geqq \lambda_0{}^{1 + T/(1-\lambda_0)}.$$

Suppose $D \in J_1$, $\sum \epsilon_{nn} = T$, and suppose that

$$\Psi' \in H(1 + \epsilon, I(\Gamma_1)),$$

where $\Psi(w)$ maps $| w | < 1$ onto D, and that $\phi' \in H(1 + \delta, E(D))$. Then for the matrix (ϵ_{mn}) the constants Λ_k and λ_0 can be estimated explicitly and we obtain quite precise results. We shall denote this class of domains by $J_1(T, \epsilon, \delta)$.

If $D \in J_1(T, \epsilon, \delta)$, then

$$m_n{}^2 = \frac{a^{2(n+1)}}{n+1}(1 - \delta_n), \text{ where } 0 \leqq \delta_n \leqq \frac{\epsilon_{nn}(\lambda_0 + T)}{\lambda_0},$$

$$a = \lim_{n\to\infty} \frac{m_{n+1}}{m_n},$$

$$\| f_n - q_n \|^2 \leqq \left(\frac{\lambda_0 + 2T}{\lambda_0}\right) \epsilon_{nn},$$

$$q_n(z) = \left(\frac{n+1}{\pi}\right)^{\frac{1}{2}} \phi(z^n)\phi'(z)[1 + O(\epsilon_{nn}^{\frac{1}{2}})]$$

for $z \in \overline{E(D)}$, and $F_D(z, \bar{z}) \geqq \lambda_0 K_D(z, \bar{z})$ for $z \in D$.

If $f \in \mathfrak{L}^2(D)$, then $F(z) = \int_\zeta^z f(t)\, dt \in H(p, D)$ and $F(\psi(w)) \in$

$L^p(\Gamma_1)$ for all $p > 1$; furthermore,

$$\left\{\frac{1}{2\pi}\int_{|w|=r} | F(\Psi(w)) |^p \, | dw |\right\}^{1/p} \leqq A(p, \epsilon, \delta) \, ||f||$$

for $r \leqq 1$, and

$$\left\{\frac{1}{2\pi}\int_{|w|=1} | F(\psi(w)) |^p \, | dw |\right\}^{1/p} \leqq B(p, \epsilon, \delta) \, ||f||.$$

As a matter of fact, $F(\psi(w))$ has a fractional derivative on $| w | = 1$ of order $\frac{1}{2}$ in L_2.

If $f \in \mathfrak{L}^2(D)$, $D \in J_1(T, \epsilon, \delta)$, then

$$b_n = [(n + 1)\pi]^{\frac{1}{2}} \frac{1}{2\pi i}\int_{\Gamma_1} \frac{F(\psi(w))}{w^{n+2}} \, dw$$

is defined, and $| b_n | \leqq A(p, \epsilon, \delta, C)(n + 1)^{\frac{1}{2}} || f ||$. Furthermore,

$$\lambda_0 \sum_{n=0}^{\infty} | b_n |^2 \leqq || f ||^2 \leqq \sum_0^{\infty} | b_n |^2,$$

and $f(z) = \sum_0^\infty b_n f_n(z)$ in D. We have

$$|| f - \sum_{\nu=0}^{n} b_\nu f_\nu ||^2 \leqq A \cdot$$

$$\int_0^{\pi}\int_{\Gamma_1} \left| F(\psi(we^{it})) - F(\psi(we^{-it})) - 2i \sum_{-\infty}^{n+1} a_\nu w^\nu \sin(\nu t) \right|^2 t^{-2} \, | dw | \, dt,$$

where

$$a_n = [(n + 1)/\pi]^{\frac{1}{2}} b_n .$$

If C is rectifiable and $f \in H(2, D)$, then we can go much further. We have (L = length of C)

$$|| f ||^2 \leqq \frac{L}{2}\int_C | f |^2 \, | dz |.$$

It easily follows that the rate of convergence of the series for f in Carleman polynomials is dominated by that of the Szegö expansion of f:

$$\left\| f - \sum_0^n c_k q_k \right\|^2 \leqq \frac{L}{2}\int_C \left| f - \sum_0^n \gamma_k p_k \right|^2 | dz |$$

where $c_k = (f, q_k)$, and the γ_k are the Szegö coefficients of f. If C

is of type $\mathfrak{W}_M$, then the estimates of the first part yield quantitative results.

More generally, we can estimate the error in the Faber expansion of f, which of course dominates the Carleman expansion, if C is rectifiable and $g(\theta) = f(\psi(e^{i\theta}))\psi'(e^{i\theta}) \in L_p[0, 2\pi]$, $p > 1$. Let $\| g \|_p$ be its L_p norm on $[0, 2\pi]$. Then

$$\| f - \textstyle\sum_0^n b_k f_k \| \leqq A(p)B(n) \| g \|_p,$$

where

$$B(n) = \frac{1}{\sqrt{n}}, \frac{\log n}{\sqrt{n}}, \text{and} \left(\frac{1}{n}\right)^{1-(1/p)},$$

for $p > 2$, $p = 2$, and $1 < p < 2$, respectively.

It may be mentioned that the work of Johnston suggested many of the results of § 2.

BIBLIOGRAPHY

1. BERGMAN[N], S. *Über die Entwicklung der harmonischen Funktionen der Ebene und des Raumes nach Orthogonalfunktionen*, Math. Ann. 86 (1922), 238–271.

2. —— *The kernel function and conformal mapping.* Mathematical Surveys, No. 5. New York, 1950.

3. BOCHNER, S. *Über orthogonale Systeme analytischer Funktionen*, Math. Zeit. 14 (1922), 180–207.

4. BROCK, JOHN E. *Generalized Blaschke products.* Dissertation. Univ. Minnesota, 1950.

5. CARLEMAN, T. *Über die Approximation analytischer Funktionen durch lineare Aggregate von vorgegebenen Potenzreihen*, Ark. Mat. Astr. Fys., vol. 17, No. 9 (1923), 1–30.

6. FARRELL, O. *On approximation to a function analytic in a simply connected region*, Bull. Amer. Math. Soc. 41 (1935), 707–711.

7. FÉJER, L. *Über die Lage der Nullstellen von Polynomen, die aus Minimumforderungen gewisser Art entspringen*, Math. Ann. 85 (1922), 41–48.

8. GRAVES, R. L. *The Fredholm theory in Banach spaces.* Dissertation. Harvard Univ., 1951.

9. JOHNSTON, E. R. *A study in polynomial approximation in the complex domain.* Dissertation. Univ. Minnesota, 1954.

10. VON KOCH, H. *Über das Nichtverschwinden einer Determinante nebst Bemerkungen über Systeme unendlich vieler linearer Gleichungen*, Jber. Deutschen Math. Verein 22 (1913), 285–291.

11. LAVRENTIEV, M. A., AND KELDYSH, M. V. *Sur la réprésentation conforme des domaines limités par des courbes rectifiables*, Ann. École Norm. 54 (1937), 1–38.

12. MERGELYAN, S. N. *Certain questions of the constructive theory of functions.* Trudy Mat. Inst. Steklov, vol. 37. Moscow, 1951.

13. MORREY, C. B., JR. *Multiple integral problems in the calculus of variations and related topics*, Univ. California Publ. Math. 1 (1943), 1–130.

14. OSTROWSKI, A. *Sur la détermination des bornes inférieures pour une classe des déterminantes*, Bull. Sci. Math. 61 (1937), 19–32.

15. RUSTON, A. F. *On the Fredholm theory of integral equations for operators belonging to the trace class of a general Banach space*, Proc. London Math. Soc. (3) 53 (1951), 109–124.

16. SCHATTEN, R. *A theory of cross-spaces.* Annals of Mathematics Studies, No. 26. Princeton, 1950.

17. SEWELL, W. E. *Degree of approximation by polynomials in the complex domain.* Annals of Mathematics Studies, No. 9. Princeton, 1942.

18. SHIFFMAN, M. *Differentiability and analyticity of solutions of double integral variational problems*, Ann. of Math. 48 (1947), 274–284.

19. SMIRNOV, V. I. *Sur les formules de Cauchy et de Green et quelques problèmes qui s'y rattachent*, Izvestiya Akad. Nauk. URSS (7) (1932), 337–372.

20. SZEGÖ, G. *Orthogonal polynomials.* Amer. Math. Soc. Colloquium Publications, No. 23. New York, 1939.

21. WALSH, J. L. *Degree of approximation to functions on a Jordan curve*, Trans. Amer. Math. Soc. 73 (1952), 447–458.

22. —— AND ELLIOTT, H. M. *Degree of approximation on a Jordan curve*, Proc. Nat. Acad. Sci. U.S.A. 38 (1952), 1058–1066.

23. WANG, C. Y. *I. Polynomial approximation to solutions of variational problems in the complex domain. II. On the mean convergence of the mapping functions in conformal mapping of regions bounded by "nearly smooth" curves.* Dissertation. Univ. Minnesota, 1953.

24. ZYGMUND, A. *Trigonometrical series.* Warsaw, 1935.

UNIVERSITY OF MINNESOTA

BOUNDARY COMPONENTS OF ABSTRACT RIEMANN SURFACES*

MAKOTO OHTSUKA

1. Introduction. We shall consider an open abstract Riemann surface R with connectivity at least 3. Its universal covering surface R^∞ will be of hyperbolic type.

We are first concerned with definitions of *ideal boundary points* of R; we are not concerned with either ordinary or accessible or geodesic boundary points, whose definitions depend upon the basic surface in which R is imbedded or which R covers. The first type of ideal boundary point which we shall mention is that of *boundary component*, which has been defined—and investigated—by Kerékjártó [3] and Stoïlow [7]. A boundary component is defined by means of a nested sequence of domains with compact relative boundaries and with no intersection in R. The set of all boundary components P_c will be denoted by C_R. A neighborhood of P_c on $R + C_R$ is defined as a set consisting of one domain D of the determining sequence of P_c, and of boundary components which are determined by sequences of domains contained in D. The topological space $R + C_R$ thus defined is compact and metrizable, and C_R is its null-dimensional closed subset. As a second type of ideal boundary point, we mention the *boundary points of R. S. Martin* for the case when R has a positive boundary. (See [6] and the lectures of Professor Brelot in the present volume.) The topology of this boundary is finer than that of C_R, a boundary component being actually defined as a connected component of Martin's boundary and suitable for representing positive harmonic functions on R by integrals.

Once we have fixed the definition of ideal boundary points of R, we have the following program of problems in regard to them:

(I) To define images of the ideal boundary points on $\Gamma: |z| = 1$

* The details of this note have been published in *Nagoya Mathematical Journal* 7 (1954) 65–83, under the title "Boundary components of Riemann surfaces."

under the conformal mapping of R onto $U: |z| < 1$ and to determine the correspondence between the ideal boundary points and their images.

(II) To solve the Dirichlet problem for a boundary function ϕ distributed on the ideal boundary points of R by Perron-Brelot's method.

(III) Assuming that ϕ is transformed into a function ψ defined almost everywhere on Γ by the mapping $R^\infty \to U$, to find relations between the solutions of the Dirichlet problems on R for ϕ and in U for ψ.

In this lecture we adopt C_R as ideal boundary and shall treat these problems for C_R.

2. Problem (I). (See [3].) We shall classify points of C_R. The point $P_c \in C_R$ is said to be of first class if there is a domain of planar character in the determining sequence of P_c; otherwise, it is of second class. Map such a domain of planar character conformally onto a plane domain. If P_c corresponds to an isolated boundary point of this plane domain, it is called *parabolic;* otherwise, it is called *hyperbolic,* regardless of its class. This is illustrated in Graph 1.

$$C_R \begin{cases} \text{first class} \\ \text{second class} \end{cases} \quad \begin{cases} \text{parabolic (isolated)} \\ \text{hyperbolic (isolated or not)} \end{cases}$$

GRAPH 1

Map R^∞ onto U, and denote by $f(z)$ the corresponding function: $U \to R$ (through R^∞), and by $\mathfrak{G}$ the Fuchsian or Fuchsoid group under which $f(z)$ is automorphic. $\mathfrak{G}$ contains no elliptic transformations but does contain hyperbolic, and possibly parabolic, transformations. Their fixed points (called hyperbolic or parabolic) lie on Γ. The points of Γ are classified under $\mathfrak{G}$ as shown in Graph 2.

We define an image on Γ of $P_c \in C_R$ with a determining sequence $\{D^{(n)}\}$ by $\bigcap_n \bar{G}_n$ ($\bar{G}_n$ denotes the closure of G_n), where $f(G_n) = D^{(n)}$ and $G_n \supset G_{n+1}$. An image is a point or a closed arc. A point of Γ is an image (or contained in an arc image) of some P_c if and only if there is a curve terminating in U such that its image on R converges to P_c.

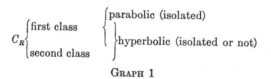

- Γ
  - regular points (properly discontinuous with respect to $\mathfrak{G}$; form an open set)
    - completely regular arcs (end points are fixed points of one hyperbolic transformation)
    - others (end points are nonfixed singular points)
  - singular points (the set coincides with the closure of all fixed points)
    - fixed points
      - parabolic
      - hyperbolic
        - end points of completely regular arcs
        - others
    - others

GRAPH 2

The following theorems show the correspondence between points of C_R and their images on Γ:

THEOREM 1. *Different images have no common points.*

THEOREM 2. *Each parabolic point P_c of C_R corresponds to a class of parabolic fixed points, equivalent under $\mathfrak{G}$; the correspondence is one-to-one and onto the set of all equivalence classes. Each isolated hyperbolic point P_c of the first class corresponds to a class of completely regular closed arcs, equivalent under $\mathfrak{G}$; the correspondence is one-to-one and onto the set of all equivalence classes. Every other P_c has as image*[1] *some nonfixed singular points of the power of the continuum and, possibly, a finite or infinite number of equivalence classes of noncompletely regular closed arcs. The set of points of Γ which are not contained in the image of points of C_R consists of other (see Graph 2) hyperbolic fixed points and of some nonfixed singular points of the power of the continuum.*

THEOREM 3. (See [8].) *If R has a null (positive) boundary, the set of images on Γ of C_R has linear measure zero* (2π).

We shall not prove any of these theorems. But if we know the following theorem, the correspondence between parabolic P_c and parabolic fixed points can be proved in a classical way (see, for example, [2]).

THEOREM 4. (See [5] and [1].) (Extension of Picard's theorem.) *Designate by U_n the region* $0 < |z| < 1/n$ $(n = 1, 2, \cdots)$ *and let* $T(z)$

[1] It is an open question whether there is a difference between the images on nonisolated P_c of the first class and the images of any P_c of the second class.

be a transformation of U_1 into an abstract Riemann surface F. Then either

(i) $\{T(U_n)\}$ *converges to an inner point of F, or*

(i′) $\{T(U_n)\}$ $(n \geqq 2)$ *determines a parabolic boundary component of F, or*

(ii) $\bigcap_n T(U_n)$ *is conformally equivalent to a Riemann sphere with the possible exception of two points, or*

(ii′) $\bigcap_n T(U_n)$ *is conformally equivalent to a torus.*

There are other ways to prove the correspondence of parabolic P_c and fixed points (see [4], [6]), but this theorem is mentioned for its possible independent interest.

3. Problem (II). (See the lectures by Professor Brelot in the present volume.) Here, as in § 4 below, we assume R to have a positive boundary. Let ϕ be any real function (which may take on the values $\pm\infty$) defined on C_R. The class $\mathfrak{U}_\phi^{C_R}$ ($\mathfrak{B}_\phi^{C_R}$) consists of all subharmonic (superharmonic) functions bounded from above (below) with upper (lower) limit not greater (less) than the value of ϕ at every point of C_R and of the function $-\infty$ $(+\infty)$; $\underline{H}_\phi^{C_R}(P)$ $(\bar{H}_\phi^{C_R}(P))$ designates the supremum (infimum) of this class at the point P of R. If $\underline{H}_\phi^{C_R}(P) \equiv \bar{H}_\phi^{C_R}(P)$ and both are finite, the common value will be denoted by $H_\phi^{C_R}(P)$, and ϕ is then called *resolutive*. We can solve the Dirichlet problem in the sense of Perron-Brelot in the following way:

THEOREM 5. *The characteristic function χ_G of every open set G in C_R is resolutive. A σ-algebra $\mathfrak{E}$ in C_R, containing the Borel class, and a regular (approachable by the values for open sets from above), complete (for which every null set is in $\mathfrak{E}$) measure $\mu^P(E)$ defined on $\mathfrak{E}$ are uniquely determined at every P of R by the requirement: $\mu^P(G) \equiv H_{\chi_G}^{C_R}(P)$. Furthermore, for every ϕ*

$$\underline{H}_\phi^{C_R}(P) \equiv \underline{\int}_{C_R} \phi(Q)\, d\mu^P(Q) \text{ and } \bar{H} \equiv \overline{\int} \cdots .$$

(The integral $\underline{\int}$ $\left(\overline{\int}\right)$ is defined by the sup (inf) of $\int \phi'\, d\mu^P$ with ϕ $\mathfrak{E}$-measurable and bounded from above (below).)

COROLLARY. *A function ϕ is resolutive if and only if it is $\mathfrak{E}$-measurable and has a finite μ^P-integral.*

4. Problem (III). By Theorems 1 and 3, ϕ is transformed into a function ψ defined almost everywhere on Γ. We can define $\underline{H}_{\psi}{}^{U}(z)$ and $\bar{H}_{\psi}{}^{U}(z)$ for this ψ and prove the following theorem:

THEOREM 6. *$\underline{H}_{\phi}{}^{C_R}(f(z)) \equiv \underline{H}_{\psi}{}^{U}(z)$ and $\bar{H}^{C_R} \equiv \bar{H}^{U}$.*

COROLLARY. *A subset X of C_R belongs to $\mathfrak{C}$ if and only if its image on Γ is linearly measurable.*

We make the following concluding remark: the topology of C_R is at times "too rough." For instance, if R is a domain bounded by three circles, each of them is a point of C_R and has a constant as the assigned boundary value. We feel, therefore, that we should try to resolve problems (I), (II), and (III) for boundary points in the sense of Martin; in the example given above the ordinary topology coincides with that of Martin's boundary.

BIBLIOGRAPHY

1. HUBER, H. *Über analytische Abbildungen Riemannscher Flächen in sich*, Comment. Math. Helv. 27 (1953), 1–73.
2. JULIA, G. *Leçons sur la représentation conforme des aires multiplement connexes*. Paris, 1934.
3. v. KERÉKJÁRTÓ, B. *Topologie*. Berlin, 1923.
4. OHTSUKA, M. *Dirichlet problems on Riemann surfaces and conformal mappings*, Nagoya Math. J. 3 (1951), 91–137.
5. —— *On the behavior of an analytic function about an isolated boundary point*, Nagoya Math. J. 4 (1952), 103–108.
6. PARREAU, M. *Sur les moyennes des fonctions harmoniques et analytiques et la classification des surfaces de Riemann*, Ann. Inst. Fourier Grenoble 3 (1952), 103–197.
7. STOÏLOW, S. *Leçons sur les principes topologiques de la théorie des fonctions analytiques*. Paris, 1938.
8. TSUJI, M. *Some metrical theorems on Fuchsian groups*, Kōdai Math. Sem. Rep., Nos. 4–5 (1950), 89–93.

HARVARD UNIVERSITY *and*
NAGOYA UNIVERSITY

CONFORMAL DEFORMATION

H. L. ROYDEN

1. Introduction. Let Z and W be two plane domains of finite connectivity, some of whose boundary components may be single points. Writing I for the unit interval $0 \leqq t \leqq 1$, we say that two conformal[1] mappings $f_0(z)$ and $f_1(z)$ of Z into W are conformally isotopic or that they belong to the same conformal deformation class if there is a continuous mapping $g(z, t)$ of $Z \times I$ into W which has the properties that for each fixed $t \in I$ the function $g(z, t)$ is a conformal mapping of Z into W and $g(z, 0) = f_0(z)$ while $g(z, 1) = f_1(z)$.

In the application of variational techniques to the theory of univalent functions, a natural restriction to put on a family of functions competing for an extremum is that they should all belong to the same conformal deformation class. In fact, the variational methods give necessary conditions on the extrema in each conformal deformation class. Thus it is natural to ask for criteria for determining whether or not two mappings are conformally isotopic or not. The most desirable sort of criterion would be one which assigned to each mapping a set of numerical invariants with the property that two mappings belong to the same conformal deformation class if and only if their corresponding numerical invariants are equal. Let me say at once that I have not succeeded in establishing such a criterion, but only in reducing the problem to the old topological one of determining homotopy classes. Moreover, I must also specialize to the case in which a pair of corresponding boundary components are points. More precisely, we have the following theorem:

THEOREM 1. *Let Z and W be two multiply connected plane domains such that the origin is a boundary component of each. Then two conformal mappings f_0 and f_1 of Z into W for which $f_0(0) = f_1(0) = 0$ are conformally isotopic if and only if they are homotopic, i.e., if there is*

---

[1] By a conformal mapping we shall always mean a one-to-one mapping by an analytic function.

a continuous mapping $\phi(z, t)$ *of* $Z \times I$ *into* W *such that* $\phi(z, 0) = f_0(z)$ *and* $\phi(z, 1) = f_1(z)$.

Note that for a fixed t we do not require $\phi(z, t)$ to be either analytic or *one-to-one*. Since a conformal mapping which is defined in a complete neighborhood of a point is also a conformal mapping at the point, we may think of Z as being bounded only by proper continua, but we allow only conformal mappings having specified values w_i at the points z_i which would otherwise be boundary components of Z. Then the mapping $g(z, t)$ is called a conformal deformation if for each fixed t it is conformal and $g(z_i, t) = w_i$; and a necessary and sufficient condition for the conformal isotopy in this sense of two conformal mappings is that they be homotopic as mappings of Z, punctured at the points z_i, into W, punctured at the points w_i.

The restriction in the theorem about the corresponding pair of boundary points is probably superfluous; it could be removed if we knew the proper generalization of the theorem on conformal rigidity to the non-fixed-point case. Another direction for generalizing the theorem is suggested by the following question: Given the continuous deformation $\phi(z, t)$ of f_0 to f_1, is it possible to construct the conformal deformation $g(z, t)$ such that ϕ and g are homotopic as mappings of $Z \times I$ into W? In contrast to the earlier generalization, this question seems to lie entirely beyond the scope of the methods used here. However, the method used here should be capable of extension to the case in which Z and W are finite Riemann surfaces.

As a historical remark, I should like to point out that deformations through a family of analytic functions have been considered by Morse and Heins [3], who deal with the case of Z, a multiply punctured disk, and W, the doubly punctured sphere. They determine a complete set of numerical invariants for the deformation of one analytic function into another through a family of analytic functions which have fixed the points (in Z) at which the functions have vanishing derivatives, i.e., which keep fixed the "branch-point antecedents." Their method, however, seems to depend greatly on the fact that W is the doubly punctured sphere, whereas the variational methods used in the present paper do not lend themselves to fixing the branch-point antecedents unless the branch points are also fixed.

Recently, Huber [2] has considered the analytic deformation classes of mappings of a Riemann surface into itself.

2. Extremal mappings. Having performed preliminary conformal transformations on Z and W, we may suppose that all boundary components are either circles or points. Let $W^{\blacktriangle}$ be the domain consisting of W together with those boundary components of W which are single points. Then we shall say that a domain W_1 contained in W is properly contained in W if the closure of W_1 is contained in $W^{\blacktriangle}$. A conformal mapping of Z into W is called an extremal mapping if it is not conformally isotopic (in W) to a mapping of Z into a domain properly contained in W. We shall characterize the extremal mappings with the aid of the variational methods of Garabedian and Schiffer [1].

Let us vary W by changing its boundaries by a mapping of the form

$$w^* = w + \sum_{t=1}^{N} \frac{\epsilon\, a_t}{w - w_t} + O(\epsilon^2), \qquad w_t \in W. \tag{1}$$

Then from formulas (182), (183), and (184) of [1] we see that the conformal moduli of W are changed by

$$\pi_j^* = \pi_j + \epsilon \operatorname{Re} a_t p_j(w_t) + O(\epsilon^2), \tag{2}$$

where the p_j are analytic functions which have simple poles at the boundary points of W and for which $p_j(w)\,dw^2$ is nonpositive along the boundary continua of W. If, moreover, the points w_t also lie in $f(Z)$, then application of the variation (1) on the boundary of $f(Z)$ transforms $f(Z)$ into a new domain whose conformal moduli are

$$\omega_j^* = \omega_j + \epsilon \operatorname{Re} a_t q_j(w_t) + O(\epsilon^2), \tag{3}$$

where the q_j are analytic functions in $f(Z)$ which have simple poles at the boundary points of $f(Z)$ and for which $q_j(w)\,dw^2$ is nonpositive along the boundary continua of $f(Z)$, i.e., for which $q_j[f(z)][f'(z)]^2\,dz^2$ is nonpositive on the boundary continua of Z.

Now if it is possible to make a variation of the form (1) which preserves the conformal type of W and which for each ϵ, $0 < \epsilon \leqq t_0$, takes $f(Z)$ into a domain conformally equivalent to a domain Z_ϵ which properly contains Z, then f is not an extremal mapping, since the mappings g_ϵ which map Z_ϵ into the variations of $f(Z)$ map Z into a proper subdomain of W and can be made to depend continuously on ϵ and hence to be conformally equivalent.

But use of the implicit function theorem guarantees such a variation unless there are real constants $\{\lambda_j\}$ and $\{\mu_j\}$ not all zero such that

$$\sum_{j=1}^{m} \lambda_j p_j(w_t) = \sum_{j=1}^{m'} \mu_j q_j(w_t) \tag{4}$$

for all $w_t \in f(Z)$. Hence an extremal function $w = f(z)$ must satisfy

$$P(w)\, dw^2 = Q(z)\, dz^2, \tag{5}$$

where we have set

$$P(w) = -\sum_{j=1}^{m} \lambda_j p_j(w) \tag{6}$$

and

$$Q(z) = -\sum_{j=1}^{m'} \lambda_j q_j[f(z)] \left(\frac{dw}{dz}\right)^2. \tag{7}$$

Hence $P(w)\, dw^2$ is a quadıatic differential of W, and from the fact that $Q(z)\, dz^2$ is nonnegative on the boundary of Z it follows that $f(Z)$ is bounded by trajectories of the quadratic differential $P(w)\, dw^2$. Standard variational techniques show also that $f(Z)$ is dense in W. Thus by a theorem on conformal rigidity [4] we may conclude that the identity is the only conformal mapping of $f(Z)$ into W which is homotopic to the identity. Consequently $f(z)$ is the only conformal mapping in its homotopy class.

3. Proof of Theorem 1. It follows from the preceding section that if either of the two homotopic conformal mappings f_1 and f_2 is extremal then they are identical and the theorem is true. We shall complete the proof by reducing the general case to this.

If we exclude the relatively trivial case in which f_0 and f_1 are homotopic to the function $f \equiv 0$, then one can construct by elementary means a deformation $h(w, t)$ which is continuous in $W^{\blacktriangle} \times I$ and has the following properties:

(i) $h(w, 0) = w$;

(ii) $h(p, t) = p$, if p is a point which is a boundary component of W;

(iii) For each t, $h(w, t)$ is an isomorphism of W onto a domain W_t;

(iv) If $t' > t''$, then $W_{t'}$ is properly contained in $W_{t''}$;

(v) There is no conformal mapping of Z into W_1 which is homotopic (in W) to $f_1(z)$.

Let τ be the least upper bound of those t such that there are functions f_{0t} and f_{1t} which are conformally isotopic (in W) to f_0 and f_1, respectively, and which map Z into W_t. Then $\tau < 1$, and it can be shown by a lengthy argument using normal families (see [6]) that there are functions g_0 and g_1 which are conformally isotopic to f_0 and f_1, respectively, and which map Z into W_τ.

Now g_0 is homotopic to g_1 not only in W but also in W_τ, and by the definition of τ one of the functions g_0 and g_1 is extremal with respect to W_τ. Hence, by the preceding section they are identical, whence f_0 and f_1 are conformally isotopic and the theorem is proved.

BIBLIOGRAPHY

1. GARABEDIAN, P. R., AND SCHIFFER, M. *Identities in the theory of conformal mapping*, Trans. Amer. Math. Soc. 65 (1949), 187–238.

2. HUBER, H. *Über analytische Abbildungen Riemannscher Flächen in sich*, Comment. Math. Helv. 27 (1953), 1–72.

3. MORSE, M., AND HEINS, M. H. *Deformation classes of meromorphic functions and their extensions to interior transformations*, Acta Math. 79 (1947), 51–103.

4. ROYDEN, H. L. *The conformal rigidity of certain subdomains on a Riemann surface*, Trans. Amer. Math. Soc. 76 (1954), 14–25.

5. —— *The interpolation problem for schlicht functions*, Ann. of Math. 60 (1954), 326–344.

6. SCHMITTROTH, L. *The conformal mapping of annuli*. Thesis. Stanford Univ., 1954.

STANFORD UNIVERSITY

FUNCTIONS IN ONE COMPLEX VARIABLE AS VIEWED FROM THE THEORY OF FUNCTIONS IN SEVERAL VARIABLES

SALOMON BOCHNER

The theory of functions in several variables, holomorphic or harmonic or the like, is of course guided by the facts, proofs, and viewpoints of the classical theory of holomorphic (and also harmonic) functions in one complex variable, but it may be said that the ever-growing theory of functions in several variables bids fair to exercise certain retroactions on the classical theory itself; of these I shall present several instances in this article.

1. The theorem of Cauchy-Goursat. If we put $f(z) = u(x, y) + iv(x, y)$, $A_1 = iu - v$, $A_2 = -u - iv$, then the Cauchy-Riemann equations,

$$u_x = v_y, \qquad u_y = -v_x, \tag{1}$$

imply $\partial A_1/\partial x + \partial A_2/\partial y = 0$. Therefore the Cauchy-Goursat theorem

$$\int_B f(z)\, dz = 0 \tag{2}$$

is contained in Green's theorem

$$\int_B A_1\, dy - A_2\, dx = \int_S \left(\frac{\partial A_1}{\partial x} + \frac{\partial A_2}{\partial y} \right) dx\, dy, \tag{3}$$

which is nonholomorphic and comprehensive. However, it is commonly felt that in proving (2) by way of (3) more continuity properties would have to be imposed upon the partial derivatives u_x, u_y, v_x, v_y than are implied in Goursat's requirement that $f(z)$ shall have a limit

$$\lim_{h \to 0} \frac{f(z + h - f(z)}{h} \qquad (= f'(z)) \tag{4}$$

at every point z of a domain (and nothing else); it is also vaguely felt that Goursat's own proof for (2), which requires only this property of $f(z)$, has a peculiar affinity to complex variables.

Now we find that this is not so, and by use of Goursat's method we shall establish a comprehensive version of the general (nonharmonic) formula (3) of which (2) will be a direct special case. In order to underline the nonaffinity of the method to holomorphy, we shall do this for any number of real variables as well. However, we shall deal only with domains having "rectilinear" boundaries, because the subsequent transition from such boundaries to general ones is no longer part of Goursat's own distinctive reasoning.

In a domain D of the real Euclidean $E_k : (x_1, \cdots, x_k)$, $k \geqq 2$, we take a real- or complex-valued function $A(x_j)$—or in fact a Banach-valued function—and we say that it has a total derivative at a point $x^0 = (x_j^0)$ if we can put

$$A(x_j) = A(x_j^0) + \textstyle\sum_{j=1}^{k} a_j \cdot (x_j - x_j^0) + \epsilon(x^0; x), \tag{5}$$

where the quantities $a_j = a_j(x^0)$ are independent of x, and

$$\epsilon(x^0; x) = o(|\, x - x^0 \,|), \qquad \text{as } x \to x^0, \tag{6}$$

in the sense that for any $\eta > 0$ there is a $\delta = \delta(x^0, \eta) > 0$ such that we have

$$|\, \epsilon(x^0; x)| \leqq \eta \tag{7}$$

whenever

$$|\, x - x^0 \,| \equiv [\textstyle\sum_j (x_j - x_j^0)^2]^{\frac{1}{2}} \leqq \delta.$$

If $A(x)$ has a total derivative at x^0, then the partial derivatives

$$\frac{\partial A}{\partial x_j}, \qquad j = 1, \cdots, k, \tag{8}$$

exist at x^0, and their values are the coefficients a_j, so that the latter are uniquely determined; but the mere existence of the partial derivatives at a point does not secure the existence of a total derivative as we have defined it. If the partial derivatives (8) exist in D and are themselves continuous functions in D, then the total derivative exists everywhere in D, but we emphasize that the converse is not true, and that the continuity of the derivatives (8) will not be required in our discussion.

If in $E_2 : (x, y)$ we introduce the symbol $z = x + iy$ and, following the usual custom (of which we disapprove), denote the general function $A(x, y)$ by $f(z)$, then $f(z)$ has a Goursat derivative $f'(z)$ at a point z^0, as defined by (4), if and only if

$$f(z) = f(z^0) + f'(z^0)(z - z^0) + o(|z - z^0|). \tag{9}$$

For the function $A(x, y)$ this means that it has a total derivative at (x^0, y^0). If we put

$$A(x, y) = A(x^0, y^0) + a(x^0, y^0)(x - x^0) + b(y^0, y^0)(y - y^0) + \epsilon(x^0, y^0; x, y),$$

then

$$a \cdot (x - x^0) + b \cdot (y - y^0) = f'(z^0)[(x - x^0) + i(y - y^0)],$$

and because of the uniqueness of a, b we have the following lemma:

LEMMA 1. *A function $f(z) = u(x, y) + i\,v(x, y)$ has a Goursat derivative $f'(z^0)$ at a point (x^0, y^0) if and only if the real and imaginary parts u, v have each a total derivative there, and the equations* (1) *hold.*

We return to the general case.

THEOREM 1. *If in a domain D of $E_k : (x_j)$ there are given k functions*

$$A_1(x_j), \cdots, A_k(x_j), \tag{10}$$

if each of them has a total derivative at every point, and if the "divergence"

$$\operatorname{div} A \equiv \frac{\partial A_1}{\partial x_1} + \cdots + \frac{\partial A_k}{\partial x_k} \tag{11}$$

is continuous in D, then the Green-Stokes relation

$$\int_B \sum_{j=1}^{k} A_j(x)(-1)^{j-1}\, dx_1 \cdots dx_{j-1}\, dx_{j+1} \cdots dx_k = \int_S \operatorname{div} A\, dx_1 \cdots dx_k \tag{12}$$

holds for every nonsingular rectilinear simplex S which together with its (oriented) boundary B is contained in D.

COROLLARIES. (i) *In particular if $A_1, \cdots, A_k$ have total derivatives everywhere, and*

$$\frac{\partial A_1}{\partial x_1} + \cdots + \frac{\partial A_k}{\partial x_k} = 0, \tag{13}$$

then we have

$$\int_B \sum_{j=1}^{k} A_j(x)(-1)^{j-1}\, dx_1 \cdots dx_{j-1}\, dx_{j+1} \cdots dx_k = 0.$$

(ii) *By Lemma* 1, *Cauchy's theorem* (2) *holds if* $f(z)$ *has a Goursat derivative at every point.*

(iii) *If a function* $u(x, y)$ *in* D *has continuous partial derivatives* u_x, u_y *in* D, *if each of these has a total derivative everywhere in* D, *so that* u_{xx}, u_{yy} *are defined, and if* $u_{xx} + u_{yy} = 0$, *then*

$$\int_B (u_x\, dy - u_y\, dx) = 0$$

for the boundary B *of any triangle* S *in* D.

Proof. As in a previous paper [2], the abbreviations

$$\sigma^j = (-1)^{j-1}\, dx_1 \cdots dx_{j-1}\, dx_{j+1} \cdots dx_k$$

and $dv_x = dx_1 \cdots dx_k$ are introduced. If the theorem were false, then for a certain pair (S_1, B_1) we would have

$$\left| \int_{B_1} A_j \cdot \sigma^j - \int_{S_1} \operatorname{div} A \cdot dv_x \right| = \alpha > 0. \tag{14}$$

Following Goursat, we subdivide S_1 into 2^k congruent rectilinear simplices $\{S_2^{(\nu)}\}$ so that their one-dimensional edges are half as long as the corresponding edges of S_1 itself. Because of the "additivity" of the relation (12), assumption (14) implies that we have

$$\left| \int_{B_2} A_j \cdot \sigma^j - \int_{S_2} \operatorname{div} A \cdot dv_x \right| \geqq \frac{\alpha}{2^k}$$

for at least one of the simplices $S_2^{(\nu)}$, which we have chosen fixed and denoted by S_2, with boundary B_2. Now, continuing in this manner, we obtain a sequence of simplices $S_1 \supset S_2 \supset S_3 \supset \cdots$ with the following properties: First, we have

$$\left| \int_{B_n} A_j \cdot \sigma^j - \int_{S_n} \operatorname{div} A \cdot dv_x \right| \geqq \frac{\alpha}{2^{kn}}. \tag{15}$$

Secondly, we have

$$\delta(S_n) = O\left(\frac{1}{2^n}\right), \qquad n \to \infty,$$

where $\delta(S_n)$ is the point-set diameter of S_n; if we denote the volume of S_n by V_n and the $(k-1)$-dimensional volume of B_n by Ω_n, we have, by congruence,

$$\Omega_n = \frac{\Omega_1}{2^{n(k-1)}}, \qquad V_n = \frac{V_1}{2^{nk}}.$$

Thirdly, the point-set closures of the sets S_n have a point in common, which we denote by (x_j^0).

If now we put $A_j(x) = A_j'(x) + A_j''(x)$, where

$$A_j'(x) = A_j(x^0) + \sum_{l=1}^{k} \frac{\partial A_j}{\partial x_l}\bigg|_{x=x^0} \cdot (x_l - x_l^0),$$

and where A_j'' is the remainder, then the functions A_j' are linear functions in the variables x_l; for such functions we take our theorem as known (as Goursat does also in his case). However, for the remainder function A_j'' we have

$$A_j'' = o(|x - x^0|) = o\left(\frac{1}{2^n}\right), \quad \text{for} \quad x \text{ on } B_n, \quad n \to \infty,$$

$$\sum_{j=1}^{k} \frac{\partial A_j''}{\partial x_j} = o(1), \quad \text{for} \quad x \text{ in } S_n, \qquad n \to \infty,$$

the latter by continuity of $\operatorname{div} A'' = \operatorname{div} A - \operatorname{div} A'$. Therefore we have

$$\left| \int_{B_n} A_j'' \cdot \sigma^j \right| = O(\max_{x \in B_n} |A_j''| \cdot \Omega_n) = o\,(1/2^{nk}),$$

$$\int_{S_n} \frac{\partial A_j''}{\partial x_j}\, dv_x = O(\max_{x \in S_n} |\operatorname{div} A''| \cdot V_n) = o(1/2^{nk}),$$

and this would not be compatible with relation (15) for $A_j = A_j''$ and $\alpha > 0$.

2. The theorem of Morera. This is a (local) converse to Cauchy's theorem. It states that if a continuous function $A(x, y)$ is such that

$$\int_B A(x, y)(dx + i\,dy) = 0 \tag{16}$$

for every triangle B, say, then $A(x, y) = f(z)$ has a Goursat derivative everywhere. A natural line of proof would be to utilize Green's theorem:

$$(17)\qquad \int_B A(x, y)(dx + i\,dy) = \int_S \left(-\frac{\partial A}{\partial x} + i\frac{\partial A}{\partial y}\right) dx\,dy,$$

in the following manner. By assumption (16), the left side in (17) is zero; therefore, so is the right side, also. But if the right side vanishes for every triangle S, then we must have $-A_x + iA_y = 0$, which means that the Goursat derivative $f'(z)$ exists as claimed. However, on the face of it, this proof has the difficulty of requiring that $A(x, y)$ shall be known to have partial derivatives A_x, A_y in D, whereas the underlying requirement (16) itself can be stated if $A(x, y)$ is merely known to be continuous; the emphasis of the theorem lies in the fact that only continuity of $A(x, y)$, say, shall be presupposed given. In keeping with this desideratum, the traditional proof of the theorem proceeds in another manner, more or less as follows. From (16), the integral

$$g(z) \equiv G(x, y) = \int_{x^0, y^0}^{x, y} A(x, y)(dx + i\,dy)$$

is independent of the path, thus defining, for fixed x^0, y^0, a function of the point x, y, and this function $g(z)$ has a Goursat derivative $g'(z)$ whose value is $A(x, y)$. But at this state various consequences from Cauchy's theorem are already presupposed known, one of them being that such a derivative $g'(z)$ itself has a derivative, which means that $A(x, y)$ has a Goursat derivative, as claimed.

If we turn to several variables, various generalizations and modifications of Morera's theorem suggest themselves rather convincingly. But the last-named traditional proof is all but useless for carrying the syllogistic burden of such generalizations, whereas the natural line of proof, namely the one by way of Stokes's theorem, far from being abortive, turns out to be as pliable and adaptable as one could wish. We shall give a brief outline of its adaptation [7].

In Euclidean $E_k : (t_1, \cdots, t_k)$ it is possible to construct a sequence of functions $\phi^n(t_1, \cdots, t_k)$ having the following properties.

Each $\phi^n(t)$ is defined in all of E_k and is of class C^∞ in E_k; that is, it has continuous partial derivatives of every mixed order, but vanishes outside a sphere $K_n : (t_1^2 + \cdots + t_k^2) \leqq \delta_n^2$ where $\lim_{n\to\infty} \delta_n = 0$. Furthermore, we have $\phi^n(t) \geqq 0$ and

$$\int_{E_k} \phi^n(t)\, dv_t \equiv \int_{K_n} \phi^n(t)\, dv_t = 1.$$

Now let $F(x_1, \cdots, x_k)$ be defined and continuous, and also bounded, in a domain D; we supplement it by values 0 outside D. If we set up the expressions

$$F^n(x_1, \cdots, x_k) = \int_{E_k} F(x_1 + t_1, \cdots, x_k + t_n)\phi^n(t_1, \cdots, t_n)\, dv_t$$

$$\equiv \int_{K_n} F(x_1 + t_1, \cdots, x_n + t_k)\phi^n(t_1, \cdots, t_k)\, dv_t,$$

$n = 1, 2, \cdots$, then they approximate to $F(x_j)$ in D in the following sense:

LEMMA 2. *Each $F^n(x_j) \in C^\infty$ in E_k, and if $D' \subset D$ is a subdomain whose closure is likewise contained in D, $\bar{D}' \subset D$, then*

$$\lim_{n\to\infty} F^n(x_j) = F(x_j) \tag{18}$$

uniformly in every D'.

If, moreover, $F \in C^r$, $r \geqq 1$, then we also have

$$\lim_{n\to\infty} \frac{\partial^{q_1+\cdots+q_k} F^n(x_j)}{\partial x_1^{q_1} \cdots \partial x_k^{q_k}} = \frac{\partial^{q_1+\cdots+q_k} F(x_j)}{\partial x_1^{q_1} \cdots \partial x_k^{q_k}} \tag{19}$$

for $0 \leqq q_1 + \cdots + q_r \leqq r$, again uniformly in D'.

Now take a continuous vector field $A_1(x_1), \cdots, A_k(x_k)$, and assume that we have

$$\int_B A_j(x) \cdot \sigma^j = 0, \tag{20}$$

for every B, as before. For a *given* B, since this also holds for "every other" B, it holds in particular for translated B's; thus

$$\int_{B-(t)} A_j(x) \cdot \sigma^j = 0, \tag{21}$$

at least for (t) sufficiently small. After a change of variables we thus obtain

$$\int_B A_j^n(x) \cdot \sigma^j = 0, \tag{22}$$

where

$$A_j^n(x) = \int_{E_k} A_j(x + t)\phi^n(t)\, dv_t, \tag{23}$$

and $A_j(x) = 0$ outside D, by convention.

However, A_j^n has continuous derivatives, by Lemma 2, and (12) applies to it. If (22) holds for every B, then we obtain div $A^n = 0$. Hence we have the following theorem:

THEOREM 2. *If, in a domain D in E_k, for a continuous vector field $\{A_j(x)\}$ we have the Morera assumption* (20) *for all B as before, then the vector field is a continuous limit in D of a sequence of vector fields $\{A_j^n(x)\}$ each of which is of class C^∞ and satisfies*

$$\sum_{j=1}^{k} \frac{\partial A_j^n(x)}{\partial x_j} = 0. \tag{24}$$

Further, the approximating vector fields can be chosen to be weighted averages, as in (23).

If we apply this to Morera's own original situation, then the function $A(x, y) = f(z)$ is a continuous limit of functions $f^n(z)$, each of which is holomorphic. If we apply the Weierstrass limit theorem, which is another consequence of the Cauchy-Goursat theorem already assumed known, then $f(z)$ itself must be holomorphic, which is the Morera conclusion, differently arrived at.

Now the Weierstrass limit theorem is not restricted to holomorphy, but is more or less coextensive with "ellipticity," and it is at any rate present for the solutions of the Laplacean

$$\frac{\partial^2 \phi}{\partial x_1^2} + \cdots + \frac{\partial^2 \phi}{\partial x_k^2} = 0 \tag{25}$$

for any $k \geqq 2$; hence the following corollary:

THEOREM 3. *If, in a domain D in E_k, a function $\phi(x_j)$ has continuous partial derivatives ϕ_{x_j}, $j = 1, \cdots, k$, and if we have*

$$\int_B \sum_{j=1}^{k} \frac{\partial \phi}{\partial x_j} \cdot \sigma^j = 0 \tag{26}$$

for all B, as before, then $\phi(x_j)$ is analytic in the real variables x_j and is a solution of (25).

If we seek an actual generalization of Morera's own theorem to several complex variables, then the first version provable by our method is as follows:

THEOREM 4. *In the space* E_{2k} *of the* k *complex variables* $z_\alpha = x_\alpha + iy_\alpha$, $\alpha = 1, \cdots, k$, *if a function*

$$f = f(z_1, \cdots, z_k; \bar{z}_1, \cdots, \bar{z}_k)$$

is continuous in a domain D, *and if we have*

$$\int_{B_{p+q}} f\, dz_{\alpha_1} \cdots dz_{\alpha_p}\, d\bar{z}_{\beta_1} \cdots d\bar{z}_{\beta_q} = 0 \tag{27}$$

over every $(p + q)$*-dimensional cycle* B_{p+q}, *where*

$$1 \leqq \alpha_1 < \alpha_2 < \cdots < \alpha_p \leqq k, \qquad 1 \leqq \beta_1 < \beta_2 < \cdots < \beta_q \leqq k$$

are fixed indices with $0 \leqq p$, $0 \leqq q$, $1 < p + q \leqq 2k - 1$, *then we have*

$$\frac{\partial f}{\partial z_\alpha} = 0, \qquad \alpha \neq \alpha_1, \cdots, \alpha_p \quad \text{and} \quad \frac{\partial f}{\partial \bar{z}_\beta} = 0, \qquad \beta \neq \beta_1, \cdots, \beta_q,$$

these Goursat derivatives existing.

Another version, more or less due to Severi, which is harder to obtain, is as follows:

THEOREM 5. *In the same space* E_{2k}, *if* f *is continuous and if we have*

$$\int_{B_k} f\, dz_1 \cdots dz_k = 0$$

for all holomorphically placed cycles B_k *in* D, *then* f *is holomorphic in* $z_1, \cdots, z_k$; *a cycle is called holomorphically placed in* D *if a suitable one-to-one holomorphic transformation*

$$w_j = \phi_j(z_1, \cdots, z_k), \qquad j = 1, \cdots, k,$$

of D *into a domain* D' *in* E_{2k}: $(w_1, \cdots, w_k)$ *will carry* B_k *into a direct product* $B^1 \times \cdots \times B^k$, *where* B^j *is a one-cycle in the* w^j*-plane,* $j = 1, \cdots, k$.

3. Removable singularities. The classical theorem is that if $f(z)$ is defined and holomorphic in the "punctured" neighborhood

$0 < |z| \leqq \rho$, and if we have $f(z) = O(1)$ as $|z| \to 0$ or, more generally,

$$\int_{C_\epsilon} |f(\zeta)| \cdot |d\zeta| = o(1) \qquad \text{as } \epsilon \to 0, \tag{28}$$

where C_ϵ is the circumference $|\zeta| = \epsilon$, then $f(z)$ has an analytic continuation into the entire neighborhood $|z| \leqq \rho$. The usual proof (even when disguised by the use of the Laurent expansion) amounts to setting up for $\epsilon < |z| < \rho$ the Cauchy formula

$$f(z) = \frac{1}{2\pi i} \int_{C_\rho} \frac{f(\zeta)\, d\zeta}{\zeta - z} + \frac{1}{2\pi i} \int_{C_\epsilon} \frac{f(\zeta)\, d\zeta}{\zeta - z}$$

and then letting $\epsilon \to 0$. The second integral "disappears" as a consequence of (28) and the remaining integral

$$f(z) = \frac{1}{2\pi i} \int_{C_\rho} \frac{f(\zeta)\, d\zeta}{\zeta - z}$$

has the continuation property claimed. The method is obviously quite universal. It applies, for instance, if we replace the single point $z = 0$ by any compact "exceptional" set A in D, and C_ϵ by any curve or system of curves encircling A and "constricting" on A as $\epsilon \to 0$, and if we leave assumption (28) literally as before.

The reasoning applies likewise to harmonic and similar functions in k variables, whenever the functions can be represented by an "associated" Green's formula over $(k - 1)$-dimensional hypersurfaces. The formula may involve not only the function $f(z)$ itself but also certain of its partial derivatives, provided we extend the analogue of assumption (28) to include such derivatives as needed. Furthermore, the Cauchy integral over a single variable, with other variables being parameters, has been used extensively in the theory of functions in several complex variables for related theorems, some of which may not yet have been re-proved differently.

Nevertheless, when studying the problem afresh ([3], [8, Chap. VIII]) we have found that it is possible and rather profitable to replace integrals over hypersurfaces, which encircle and thus avoid the singularities, by certain k-dimensional volume integrals which are taken directly across the singularities themselves. The results ensuing have turned out to be in certain respects more general than those previously known. When proceeding in this manner we may start in E_k, $k \geqq 2$, with a system of linear equations in several functions $f_1(x_j), \cdots, f_r(x_j)$:

$$(29) \qquad \sum_{\rho=1}^{r} \sum_{0 \leqq n_1+\cdots+n_k \leqq N} a^{\sigma\rho}{}_{n_1\cdots n_k} \frac{\partial^{n_1+\cdots+n_k} f_\rho(x)}{\partial x_1^{n_1} \cdots \partial x_k^{n_k}} = 0,$$

$$\sigma = 1, \cdots, s,$$

having the following properties: (i) the coefficients $a^{\sigma\rho}{}_{(n)}$ are constants (this probably could be weakened), (ii) any solution $\{f_\rho(x)\}$ of class C^N in a domain D is, say, automatically analytic there, and (what is decisive) (iii) if we are given a sequence of solutions $\{f_\rho{}^n\}$, $n = 1, 2, 3, \cdots$, and if they have (locally) a limit $\{f_\rho\}$ in the L_1-norm,

$$\lim_{n\to\infty} \int (|f_1 - f_1{}^n| + \cdots + |f_r - f_r{}^n|)\, dv_x = 0,$$

then $\{f_\rho\}$ equals an (analytic) solution almost everywhere.

The last property is, of course, the Weierstrass limit theorem, but stated in a stronger form than in the elementary part of the classical theory, although it is well known to so hold. The reason for our requiring the theorem in this stronger form is that it then more cogently expresses the "ellipticity" of the system (29) without a Green's formula being needed to supplement it.

We now take in a domain D an "exceptional" set A which is bounded and relatively closed, but not necessarily compact, so that it may extend to the boundary of D, and which may also decompose D into various connected parts. We shall, however, assume that the k-dimensional Lebesgue measure of A is zero, $v(A) = 0$, although even this could be weakened to an extent. We next denote by A_ϵ the points in $D - A$ having a distance $< \epsilon$ from A, and our general theorem is as follows:

THEOREM 6. *If $\{f_\rho(x)\}$ is a solution of* (29) *in $D - A$ and if we have*

$$(30) \qquad \int_{A_\epsilon} (|f_1| + \cdots + |f_r|)\, dv_x = o(\epsilon^N), \qquad \epsilon \to 0,$$

where N is the integer occurring in (29), *then $\{f_\rho(x)\}$ has an analytic continuation into all of D.*

Note that assumption (30) is more restrictive the larger N is, but our assumption does not involve the partial derivatives of order $\leqq N - 1$, as a direct use of Green's integral might be expected to do.

For $k = 2$, holomorphy of $f(z)$ amounts to $f_x - if_y = 0$, so that $N = 1$, and for $f(z)$ in $0 < |z| < \rho$ our condition (30) is

$$\int_{0<|z|<\epsilon} |f(z)| \, dx \, dy = o(\epsilon),$$

which at any rate includes (28). But now take for $z = x + iy$ a holomorphic function $\phi(z)$ in the upper half-plane $y > 0$, and assume that on the segment $0 < x < 1$ of $y = 0$ it has boundary values 0, approached uniformly in x, say. It is known that such a function $\phi(z)$ is $\equiv 0$; the usual interpretation of this statement is that it is a uniqueness theorem, by which a holomorphic function is $\equiv 0$ if it is 0 on a segment only, even if this segment is on the boundary. However, from our approach, this is a theorem on removable singularities; it is deducible from Theorem 6 in the following manner. Denote by D the domain in the z-plane which arises by removing the segment $0 < x < 1, y = 0$. But now we consider this segment as an exceptional set A, so that $D - A$ decomposes into the two half-planes $y > 0$, $y < 0$, and in $D - A$ we define a holomorphic function $f(z)$ to be $= \phi(z)$ for $y > 0$ and $= 0$ for $y < 0$. Now A_ϵ is the point set $0 < x < 1$, $0 < |y| < \epsilon$, and if we assume $\phi(z) \to 0$ as $y \downarrow 0$ for $0 < x < 1$, uniformly in x, say, then we obtain $\int_{A_\epsilon} |\phi(z)| \, dx \, dy = o(\epsilon^1)$. By Theorem 6, $\phi(z)$ has an analytic continuation into the (connected) domain D, but since it is $= 0$ for $y < 0$, it is $\equiv 0$, and thus $\phi(z) \equiv 0$, as claimed.

4. Inversion of holomorphic transformations. In real variables, if a function $y = \phi(x)$ is C^1 and if $\phi'(x^0) \neq 0$, then locally there exists an inverse function $x = \psi(y)$ and it is likewise C^1. Now this statement has a converse, but only of the following kind. If a mapping $y = \phi(x)$ is C^1, and if the mapping has an inverse $x = \psi(y)$ which is likewise known to be C^1, then we must have $\phi'(x) \neq 0$ and also $\psi'(y) \neq 0$; this follows from the fact that the identity $\psi(\phi(x)) = x$ may be differentiated thus:

$$\frac{d\psi}{dy} \cdot \frac{d\phi}{dx} = 1.$$

If, however, we know only that the mapping $y = \phi(x)$ is C^1 and that it has an inverse mapping $x = \psi(y)$ which is one-to-one (and thus automatically C^0), then we may well have $\phi'(x^0) = 0$ at a point, say; this is exemplified by the mapping $y = x^3$, which is one-to-one on $(-\infty, \infty)$ and for which $dy/dx = 0$ at $x = 0$.

For a holomorphic transformation $w = \phi(z)$, however, the situation is much more precise. Not only does $\phi'(z^0) \neq 0$ imply that the mapping is locally one-to-one and that the inverse function is likewise holomorphic, but, conversely, if the mapping is one-to-one, then the inverse must be holomorphic, and thus we must have $\phi'(z) \neq 0$. Strangely enough, this converse is usually not derived by itself, as just stated, but is obtained as part of a fuller analysis, as follows. If we have $\phi'(z^0) = 0$, then, since $\phi'(z)$ is itself holomorphic, it must have at z^0 a zero of a specific order $n \geqq 2$; it is then shown—for example, by means of residues (that is, fundamentally, by means of Kronecker's integral)—that the mapping is strictly n to 1 except at the origin, and this in particular is incompatible with the assumption that it be one-to-one.

We turn now to several complex variables. If for a holomorphic transformation

$$w_j = \phi_j(z_1, \cdots, z_k), \qquad j = 1, \cdots, k, \tag{31}$$

the Jacobian

$$\frac{\partial(w_1, \cdots, w_k)}{\partial(z_1, \cdots, z_k)} \tag{32}$$

is $\neq 0$ at the origin, for example, then locally the transformation is one-to-one and its inverse is holomorphic. However, the following remarkable fact is likewise true.

THEOREM 7. *If a holomorphic transformation* (31) *is one-to-one, then, locally, its inverse must be holomorphic, too, so that the Jacobian must be* $\neq 0$.

This proposition is of considerable importance, and it is of special interest, because it is one of the extremely few theorems occurring in the theory of functions of several variables which fits the class of holomorphic functions exactly. Almost any other theorem known for functions in k complex variables can be extended to certain classes of functions in $2k$ real variables considerably larger than the original class; on the other hand, certain facts from the classical theory of conformal mapping can be maintained only by imposing assumptions which would amount to taking a subclass of all holomorphic functions—and a badly circumscribed subclass at that. But Theorem 7 seems to fit the class of holomorphic functions precisely.

For the proof of this theorem one could of course imitate the one-dimensional procedure and set about making a "full" analysis of what happens if the Jacobian (32) has a zero "manifold" through the origin (which is now a $2(k-1)$-dimensional point set, topologically) and again obtain the conclusion, in particular, that (31) cannot then be one-to-one. But for $k \geqq 2$ this is easier said than done, and the task arises of reducing the full analysis to a minimum of information from which the desired conclusion would still follow.

It turns out that the theory of removable singularities may be used to good purpose; for $k = 1$ it applies in the following manner. If $\phi'(z^0) = 0$, $w^0 = \phi(z^0)$, then for $z \neq z^0$ we have, locally, $\phi'(z) \neq 0$, and since the map is one-to-one, it follows that $z = \psi(w)$ is holomorphic for $w \neq w^0$. However, $\psi(w)$ is a bounded function, and by Riemann's original theorem it must be holomorphic also at w^0.

For $k \geqq 2$ this scheme works as follows [8, Chap. VIII]. We take in the (z_j)-space the point set A^z on which the Jacobian (32) is zero, and its image A^w in the (w_j)-space under the transformation (31); the inverse functions $z_j = \psi_j(w)$ are then holomorphic for w not on A^w, and they are bounded as well. If now we wish to apply Theorem 6 toward proving that these functions are holomorphic throughout, then it suffices to know that we have $v(A_\epsilon^w) = o(\epsilon)$ as $\epsilon \to 0$, where A_ϵ^w is the ϵ-neighborhood of A^w and v is its k-dimensional volume. Also, it is fairly easy to see that this would follow from $v(A^z) = o(\epsilon)$, where A^z is the original zero variety of the Jacobian in the z-space. Topologically, A^z is $(2k-2)$-dimensional, and if it is "sufficiently regular" then we ought to have

$$v(A_\epsilon^z) = O(\epsilon^2), \tag{33}$$

which is even better than $o(\epsilon)$, of course. However, first impressions notwithstanding, it is not trivial to prove (33) directly as stated, and for the actual completion of the proof of Theorem 7 a certain induction on the dimension k of the space was resorted to, with (33) not actually being proved directly.

The difficulty in obtaining (33) directly is worth describing. It stems from the following circumstances. Take in E_r: $(t_1, \cdots, t_r)$ an (open) simplex S^t, say rectilinear; denote by $\bar{S}^t$ its point set closure, and by $\tilde{S}^t$ a neighborhood of $\bar{S}^t$. Take a one-to-one mapping

$$u_\sigma = \chi_\sigma(t_1, \cdots, t_r) \qquad \sigma = 1, \cdots, s \tag{34}$$

of $\tilde{S}^t$ into a point set $\tilde{S}^u$ in E_s: $(u_1, \cdots, u_s)$, with $s \geqq r + 1$; denote the images of S^t and $\bar{S}^t$ by S^u and $\bar{S}^u$ accordingly. Now if the functions (34) are in differentiability class C^1 on $\bar{S}^t$, or, what is even better, on $\tilde{S}^t$, then the s-dimensional volume $v(S_\epsilon^u)$ of the ϵ-neighborhood of $\bar{S}^u$ is $O(\epsilon^{s-r})$ and this is $O(\epsilon^2)$ if $s \geqq r + 2$. If, however, on $\bar{S}^t$ we know of the map only that it is continuous, then we cannot assert that we have $v(S_\epsilon^u) = o(\epsilon^{s-r-1})$, even if in the interior S^t of $\bar{S}^t$ the functions (34) are analytic.

Returning to our point set A^z, we note that it can be "triangulated" into a finite number of "curved" simplices S^z of topological dimension $\leqq 2k - 2$ each of which is a map of a certain rectilinear simplex S^t, the mapping being analytic in S^t. However, there is no precise statement in the literature on triangulation of holomorphic varieties from which to deduce enough "regularity" of this mapping on the *closures* $\bar{S}^t$ to serve as a basis for conclusion (33); consequently, we had to complete our proof without using such a triangulation; it would be of some interest to settle this point directly. In general, when employing the triangulation of holomorphic manifolds, the C^1-structure of the "triangles" must not be used, unless such use be justified from case to case.

5. Addition theorems for elliptic functions. The so-called Weierstrass preparation theorem, even when occurring in a strictly "classical" context, is a theorem in several variables. We have recently analyzed another such situation, perhaps even more pronounced, in which a statement presumably on one-variable functions is in reality a statement about several variables: it is the addition theorem for doubly periodic functions. The underlying general theorem is as follows [6]:

THEOREM 8. *Let A be a domain in the space of k complex variables $z = (z_1, \cdots, z_k)$ and let B be a domain in the space of l complex variables $w = (w_1, \cdots, w_l)$; let there be given a finite number of holomorphic functions $\phi^1(z), \cdots, \phi^r(z)$ in A, and a finite number of holomorphic functions $\psi^1(w), \cdots, \psi^s(w)$ in B; let a holomorphic function $f(z, w)$*

in $A \times B$ *have the property that for each* w *in* B *it is algebraic over the function field*

$$K[\phi^1(z), \cdots, \phi^r(z)] \tag{35}$$

with complex coefficients, and for each z *in* A *it is algebraic over*

$$K[\psi^1(w), \cdots, \psi^s(w)]. \tag{36}$$

Then in $A \times B$, $f(z, w)$ *is algebraic over*

$$K[\phi^1(z), \cdots, \phi^r(z); \psi^1(w), \cdots, \psi^s(w)]. \tag{37}$$

If a function $f(z, w)$ *is for each* w *in* B *contained in the field* (35) *and for each* z *in* A *contained in the field* (36), *then in* $A \times B$ *it is contained in the field* (37).

An application to one-variable functions arises, for instance, if we take a holomorphic function $F(z)$, say in a neighborhood of the origin, which has the property that, on putting $F_a(z) = F(a + z)$, the resulting family of functions $\{F_a(z)\}$ has a finite algebraic or rational basis over complex numbers there. If we denote a basis by $\phi^1(z), \cdots, \phi^r(z)$, then the function $F(z + w)$ is algebraic or rational over the field

$$K[\phi^1(z), \cdots, \phi^r(z); \phi^1(w), \cdots, \phi^r(w)],$$

and this is usually the meaning of the statement that $F(z)$ has an "addition theorem," no more and no less.

In the case of elliptic functions with given periods, there is algebraically only one independent element ($r = 1$), say the function $\wp(z)$, and rationally there are only two, say $\wp(z)$ and $\wp'(z)$. We thus obtain the "classical" statement that $\wp(z)$ satisfies an algebraic, nondegenerate, polynomial relation

$$P(\wp(z + w); \wp(z); \wp(w)) = 0,$$

and a fractional relation

$$\wp(z + w) = R(\wp(z), \wp'(z); \wp(w), \wp'(w));$$

but unless arithmetical considerations relative to the periods are being envisaged, there is not much profit from knowing this.

6. Automorphic forms. Other theorems on the existence of finite algebraic bases occur in the theory of automorphic functions. We shall state one of them, the one referring to (holomorphic and not meromorphic) automorphic forms, because we have all but trivialized the proof, and the "trivialization" is of some interest for $k = 1$ as well. The proof is a very brief and direct application of the Schwarz lemma, and nothing else, but in order to obtain the conclusion ready-made, the Schwarz lemma has to be applied to the local coordinates of the underlying compact complex space (closed Riemann "surface" for $k = 1$), and not to the coordinates of the uniformizing ordinary domain, even if such a domain exists. Actually, this very simple version of the traditional line of proof was used because of the wish to get away from the assumption usually made that a uniformizing domain exists; on a general compact space the reasoning could only simplify or fail (which it did not).

Let $V = V_{2k}$ be a compact complex coordinate space, let $\tilde{V}$ be its (noncompact) universal covering space, and let Γ be the fundamental group $\tilde{V}/V$. Since V is compact, there are no holomorphic functions on it (other than a constant), but on a noncompact $\tilde{V}$ there might be some; and we call a function f on $\tilde{V}$ automorphic if for every α in Γ we have

$$f(\alpha P) = \eta_\alpha(P)\cdot f(P) \tag{38}$$

for some suitable factor $\eta_\alpha(P)$, itself also holomorphic on $\tilde{V}$. An assemblage of functions

$$\{\eta_\alpha(P)\}, \qquad \alpha \in \Gamma, \tag{39}$$

will qualify for the role of such factors of automorphy if they satisfy the law of composition

$$\eta_\beta(P)\cdot\eta_\alpha(\beta P) = \eta_{\alpha\beta}(P) \tag{40}$$

for all pairs of elements α, $\beta \in \Gamma$ (and this is all they need satisfy). The theorem is as follows (see [5], [9]):

THEOREM 9. *If we are given V, $\tilde{V}$, Γ as just described and any fixed system of factors* (39) *satisfying* (40), *then any $k + 2$ holomorphic functions on V which are automorphic with regard to* (39) *satisfy an equation*

$$Q_n(f_1, \cdots, f_{k+2}) = 0,$$

where $Q_n(w_1, \cdots, w_{k+2})$ is a homogeneous polynomial, of some degree n, which is not $\equiv 0$. Also for given factors (39) *the degree of the polynomial can be chosen independently of the given function $f_1, \cdots, f_{k+2}$.*

The customary assumption (which is not necessary for our proof) is that V is a domain in Euclidean space E_{2k} which is covered by one coordinate system, and that either V is bounded, the elements of Γ are linear transformations

$$z_j^\alpha = f_j^\alpha(z, , \cdots, z_k), \qquad j = 1, \cdots, k, \tag{41}$$

and $\eta_\alpha(P)$ has the value

$$\left(\frac{\partial(z_1, \cdots, z_k)}{\partial(z_1^\alpha, \cdots, z_k^\alpha)}\right)^g \tag{42}$$

for some positive integer g, or that $\tilde{V}$ is the entire E_{2k}, Γ consists of all holomorphic translations so that V is a multitorus, and $\eta_\alpha(P)$ is of the form

$$e^{2\pi i P(z, \alpha)}, \tag{43}$$

where $P(z, \alpha)$ is linear in the space variables z and quadratic in the group parameters describing α.

For the latter case it has been shown by P. Appell (see [1], [10]) that even if we start with the most general automorphy factor $\eta_\alpha(P)$ of the kind we have described, then to within a certain "equivalence" it is nevertheless not different from the factor (43); but for bounded domains $\tilde{V}$ no such investigations have yet been undertaken, and even in the classical case of the unit circle

$$\tilde{V}: | z | < 1 \tag{44}$$

the factor

$$\left(\frac{\partial z}{\partial z^\alpha}\right)^g \tag{45}$$

is used exclusively. But actually there are known in the classical theory in (44) certain automorphy factors other than (45), namely,

$$\eta_\alpha(z) = \frac{\partial z}{\partial z^\alpha} \cdot \overset{0}{\eta}_\alpha,$$

where $\overset{0}{\eta}_\alpha$ is a number independent of z and $| \overset{0}{\eta}_\alpha | = 1$; the functions $f(z)$ which transform by these factors are the "Prym differentials." But we know of no investigation to determine under which assumptions a factor $\overset{0}{\eta}_\alpha(z)$ must be of the form $(\partial z/\partial z^\alpha)^g \cdot \overset{0}{\eta}_\alpha$, where $\overset{0}{\eta}_\alpha$ is bounded, or perhaps not, and g is a constant exponent, possibly a complex one. The problem is even more interesting if we set up the factor $\eta_\alpha(P)$ not as a single function but as a matrix function

$$\eta_\alpha^{mn}(P), \quad m, n = 1, \cdots, M, \tag{46}$$

and correspondingly set up $f(P)$ as a "vector" $f_m(P)$, so that the equation (38) now becomes

$$f_m(\alpha P) = \sum_{n=1}^{M} \eta_\alpha{}^{mn}(P) f_n(P), \tag{47}$$

and relations (40) are now to be read as matrix relations in the obvious manner.

In the classical theory, factors of the form (46) were introduced long ago [11], but have never been studied conclusively, although the field seems to be a promising one. As a token of what can be done in this direction, one rather general statement [4] may be made in concluding this paper: If we are given any pair of complex spaces V, $\tilde{V}$ as before in any number of variables, and if we are given any automorphy matrix factors (46), then the sets of solutions $\{f_m(P)\}$ of the relations (47) have always a finite additive basis for complex coefficients.

BIBLIOGRAPHY

1. Appell, P. *Sur les fonctions périodiques de deux variables*, J. Math. Pures Appl. (4) 7 (1891), 157–219.

2. Bochner, S. *Analytic and meromorphic continuation by means of Green's formula*, Ann. of Math. 44 (1943), 652–673.

3. —— *Linear partial differential equations with constant coefficients*, Ann. of Math. 47 (1946), 202–212.

4. —— *Tensor fields with finite bases*, Ann. of Math. 53 (1951), 400–411.

5. —— *Algebraic and linear dependence of automorphic functions in several variables*, J. Indian Math. Soc. 6 (1952), 1–6.

6. —— *On the addition theorem for multiply periodic functions*, Proc. Amer. Math. Soc. 3 (1952), 99–106.

7. —— *The theorem of Morera in several variables*, Ann. Mat. Pura Appl. (4) 34 (1953), 27–39.

8. —— and Martin, W. T. *Several complex variables*. Princeton, 1948.

9. —— —— *Complex spaces with singularities*, Ann. of Math. 57 (1953), 490–516.

10. Conforto, F. *Funzioni abeliane e matrici di Riemann*. Libreria dell'Università di Roma. Rome, 1942.

11. Ritter, E. *Über Riemannsche Formenscharen auf einem beliebigen algebraischen Gebilde*, Math. Ann. 47 (1896), 157–221.

Princeton University

FUNCTION-THEORETIC PROPERTIES OF CERTAIN ELLIPTIC SYSTEMS OF FIRST-ORDER LINEAR EQUATIONS*

AVRON DOUGLIS

1. Introduction. This paper is concerned with a topic in the function theory of elliptic systems of linear partial differential equations of the first order in two independent variables.[1]

A system of partial differential equations, written in matrix notation as

$$u_x + Bu_y = cu + d,$$

is said to be *elliptic* if no elementary divisor of the square coefficient matrix B is real. By linearly transforming the dependent variables and by recombining its constituent equations, an elliptic system can be put into a normal form that consists of a number of "blocks" of equations, one block corresponding to each elementary divisor of B. Each of these blocks is of the form:

$$L_p \equiv u_{p,x} + au_{p,y} - bv_{p,y} + u_{p-1,y} = \text{lower-order terms},$$

$$M_p \equiv v_{p,x} + av_{p,y} + bu_{p,y} + v_{p-1,y} = \text{lower-order terms},$$

$$\left(p = 0, 1, \cdots, r - 1; \qquad u_{p,x} = \frac{\partial u_p}{\partial x}, \text{etc.}\right)$$

where $u_{-1} = 0$, $v_{-1} = 0$, and where r is the multiplicity of the elementary divisor concerned.

In the case of an elliptic system of just two equations, the principal parts L_0, M_0 of the associated normal form are "Beltrami expressions," which, in general, can be reduced to Cauchy-Riemann expressions $u_x - v_y$, $u_y + v_x$, by suitably changing independent variables. The function theory of this case is in close correspondence with

* This paper represents results obtained at the California Institute of Technology in research done under the auspices of the Office of Naval Research.

[1] A fuller account of this theory is to be found in [2].

classical function theory, as has been shown by L. Bers in his comprehensive theory of pseudoanalytic functions.[2]

The function theory of more general elliptic systems of equations, by contrast, is as yet apparently totally undeveloped. We shall be concerned in this paper with a preliminary topic, the study of systems of equations of the form

$$L_p = 0, \qquad M_p = 0, \qquad p = 0, 1, \cdots, r-1.$$

These "generalized Beltrami equations" cannot be reduced ordinarily to the case of constant coefficients, but are governed, nevertheless, by a function theory that is closely analogous to classical function theory. First, each solution of such a system can be expressed as a hypercomplex-valued function belonging to a commutative, associative algebra such that the sum, the product, and the quotient (when it exists) of two solutions will again be a solution. Secondly, differentiation and line integration with respect to a hypercomplex analogue of z can be introduced in such a way that, when these operations are performed on a solution of the system, the result is again a solution. Finally, much of Cauchy's theory can be carried over to generalized Beltrami systems with ease.

This theory is perhaps of most immediate application to the theory of biharmonic functions. To any biharmonic function $p(x, y)$, in fact, there correspond supplementary functions $q(x, y)$, $u(x, y)$, $v(x, y)$ such that the following generalized Beltrami equations hold:

$$p_x - q_y + u_y = 0, \quad q_x + p_y + v_y = 0,$$
$$u_x - v_y = 0, \qquad v_x + u_y = 0.$$

Thus the possible singularities of $p(x, y)$, for instance, can be studied with the aid of the contour integral representations provided by our theory, which are analogous to those employed in the theory of harmonic functions. Like Beltrami's equations in the case of two dependent variables, the generalized equations of Beltrami are of some interest, moreover, in the study of arbitrary elliptic systems in a larger number of dependent variables. These possibilities, as yet, have been only superficially explored, but two examples can be cited here. The first is the fact that the theory of pseudoanalytic functions can be extended to a class of elliptic systems in more than two de-

[2] See [1] and the references cited there.

pendent variables by reasoning parallel to that of Bers; a complete extension of Bers's theory, however, is still to be achieved. The second example is a general proof of the fact that the solutions of elliptic systems of equations are uniquely determined by their Cauchy data, a well-known theorem originally proved by Carleman and by Lewy in the case of simple elementary divisors by the methods of classical function theory. (See [3].)

2. Hypercomplex representation of the solutions of generalized Beltrami equations. Let us introduce a commutative, associative algebra over the reals generated by two elements i, e subject to the multiplication rules

$$i^2 = -1, \qquad ie = ei, \qquad e^r = 0. \tag{2.1}$$

The elements of the algebra are the linear combinations with real coefficients of the $2r$ linearly independent elements

$$e^k, ie^i, k = 0, 1, \cdots, r-1,$$

where, by convention, $e^0 = 1$. An element

$$\textstyle\sum_{k=0}^{r-1} (a_k + ib_k)e^k, \qquad a_k, b_k \text{ real},$$

has an inverse if, and only if, $a_0 + ib_0 \neq 0$.

A generalized Beltrami system can be formulated in terms of hypercomplex quantities belonging to this algebra by means of the following identity:

$$\begin{aligned}\textstyle\sum_{k=0}^{r-1} (L_k + iM_k)e^k \\ = [D_x + (a + ib + e)D_y] \textstyle\sum_{k=0}^{r-1} (u_k + iv_k)e^k,\end{aligned} \tag{2.2}$$

as is easily checked from (2.1).[3] Using it in conjunction with the obvious formula

$$D(UV) = UDV + VDU, \qquad D = D_x + (a + ib + e)D_y, \tag{2.3}$$

holding for any continuously differentiable hypercomplex functions

$$U = \textstyle\sum_{k=0}^{r-1} (u_k' + iu_k'')e^k, \qquad V = \textstyle\sum_{k=0}^{r-1} (v_k' + iv_k'')e^k,$$

we are led at once to the significant facts that the product of two solutions of a generalized Beltrami system $DU = 0$ is again a solution

[3] The identity (2.2) was originally derived by a systematic method, which can also be applied to certain systems in more than two independent variables, as described in [2].

and, furthermore, that the inverse of a solution, if it exists, is a solution. Calling a solution $U = \sum_{k=0}^{r-1} (u_k' + iu_k'')e^k$ *degenerate* if $u_0' + iu_0'' = 0$, we thus have the following fundamental result: The solutions of a generalized Beltrami system of equations

$$[D_x + (a + ib + e)D_y] \sum_{k=0}^{r-1} (u_k' + iu_k'')e^k = 0$$

constitute an algebra, the nondegenerate solutions a subfield of the algebra.

3. Cauchy's theory for generalized Beltrami systems of equations. The generalized Beltrami systems are most conveniently studied in the form

$$DU \equiv [D_x + iD_y + e\{(a' + ia'')D_x + (b' + ib'')\, D_y\}] \cdot \sum_{k=0}^{r-1} (u_k' + iu_k'')e^k = 0,$$

to which they may be reduced, if the original coefficients are uniformly Hölder-continuous, by suitably changing independent variables. The solutions of a system of this reduced, "generalized Cauchy-Riemann" type are called *hyperanalytic functions;* a solution of the specific form

$$t(z) \equiv x + iy + \sum_{p=1}^{r-1} (t_p' + it_p'')e^p \equiv z + T(z) \qquad (T(z) \text{ nilpotent}),$$

is called a *generating solution.* A generating solution with Hölder-continuous first partial derivatives in a finite, sufficiently regular domain R is easily constructed if, for instance, the coefficients $a' + ia''$, $b' + ib''$ are continuous in the closure of R and uniformly Hölder-continuous in every closed subdomain of R. Any rational function of a generating solution $t(z)$ is a hyperanalytic function, and, more generally, if $S(z) \equiv \sum a_k z^k$ is a convergent power series for $|z| < c$, then the series $S[t(z)]$ converges for $|z| < c$ with respect to the norm defined by

$$\left| \sum_{p=0}^{r-1} (a_p + ib_p)e^p \right| = \sum_{p=0}^{r-1} | a_p + ib_p | ;$$

the convergence, moreover, is uniform and absolute for $|z| \leqq c_0 < c$, and the function represented by the series is hyperanalytic within the circle of convergence.

Cauchy's theory for hyperanalytic functions is based upon Green's identity, which states that, for any continuously differentiable hypercomplex functions U and W in a finite region R with sufficiently smooth boundary R^*, we have

$$\iint_R \frac{t_x}{i + e(b' + ib'')} (WDU + UDW)\, dx\, dy = -\int_{R^*} UW\, dt(z),$$

where $dt(z) = t_x\, dx + t_y\, dy$. Taking $W = 1$ in this formula, we obtain, first, a generalization of Cauchy's integral theorem: If $U(z)$ is a hyperanalytic function of class C' in a simply connected region G, and if C is a closed path contained in G, then $\int_C U(z)\, dt(z) = 0$. Taking $W = [t(z) - t(z')]^{-1}$ in Green's formula as applied to the part of R that lies outside a small disk $|z - z'| < \delta$, z' being a point of R, we similarly derive Cauchy's integral formula

$$U(z') = \frac{1}{2\pi i} \int_{R^*} U(z) \frac{dt(z)}{t(z) - t(z')} \qquad (z' \text{ in } R),$$

which expresses any hyperanalytic function U of class C' in R as a contour integral over R^*. Taylor's and Laurent's expansions for hyperanalytic functions are immediate consequences, exactly as in the classical case.

The condition that $U(z)$ be hyperanalytic and of class C' at a point z_0 is equivalent to the condition that the difference quotient $[U(z) - U(z_0)]/[t(z) - t(z_0)]$ have a limit dU/dt as $z \to z_0$ in any manner; the value of this "derivative with respect to t" of a hyperanalytic function of class C' in R admits of the integral representation

$$\frac{dU}{dt}(z_0) = -\frac{1}{2\pi i} \int_{R^*} \frac{U(z)\, dt(z)}{[t(z) - t(z_0)]^2};$$

thus dU/dt is also hyperanalytic. Again, as in the classical case, the indefinite integral $\int_{z_0}^{z} U(\zeta)\, dt(\zeta)$, known from Cauchy's integral theorem to be independent of the path in any simply connected domain in which U is hyperanalytic, defines a hyperanalytic function $F(z)$, and $dF/dt = U$. From this result Morera's theorem, the converse of Cauchy's theorem, at once follows in the usual way.

BIBLIOGRAPHY

1. BERS, L. *Local theory of pseudoanalytic functions.* (See the present volume, pp. 213–244.)

2. DOUGLIS, A. *A function-theoretic approach to elliptic systems of equations in two variables*, Comm. Pure Appl. Math. 6 (1953), 259–289.

3. —— *Uniqueness in Cauchy problems for elliptic systems of equations*, Comm. Pure Appl. Math. 6 (1953), 291–298.

NEW YORK UNIVERSITY

MODULAR FUNCTIONS DEFINED BY PERTURBATION MAPPINGS*

HARVEY COHN

1. Introduction. There seem to be at least two different methods of defining invariants $I(z)$ for Fuchsian groups, such as the *modular* group, given by the transformations

$$z \to z^T = (az + b)/(cz + d), \qquad ad - bc = 1, \tag{1}$$

where a, b, c, d are integers. The function $I(z)$ is to satisfy the condition

$$I(z^T) = I(z) \quad \text{for} \quad \operatorname{Im} z > 0. \tag{2}$$

The first method is to define the so-called Eisenstein series, formed with terms arising from the denominators of the transformations, such as

$$E_m(z) = \sum\nolimits_{p/q} (pz + q)^{-m} \tag{3}$$

summed (once) over each reduced fraction p/q (positive, negative, 0/1, and 1/0). It is easily seen that for even $m \geqq 4$ the series converges absolutely to a sum not identically zero and, from the convergence,

$$E_m(z^T) = (cz + d)^m E_m(z). \tag{4}$$

To form a genuine invariant (with property (2)), we take a combination [3] such as

$$J(z) = E_4^3(z)/[E_4^3(z) - E_6^2(z)], \tag{5}$$

giving $J(z)$, the well-known invariant. It turns out that all invariants are single-valued functions of $J(z)$.

The second method, due to Dedekind [1], is to start out with the fundamental domain, in the z-plane, and let $I(z)$ be an actual mapping function that identifies the portions of the boundary that correspond

* Research sponsored by the Office of Ordnance Research, U. S. Army.

under certain transformations (generating the group). In the case of the modular group the fundamental domain is $\mathfrak{D}_0$, in Figure 1 (extending to infinity), with sides AB and AB' matched by $z^T = -1/z$ and sides $D_0'B'$ and D_0B matched by $z^T = z + 1$. The function $J(z)$ can be found explicitly by means of the hypergeometric function [2].

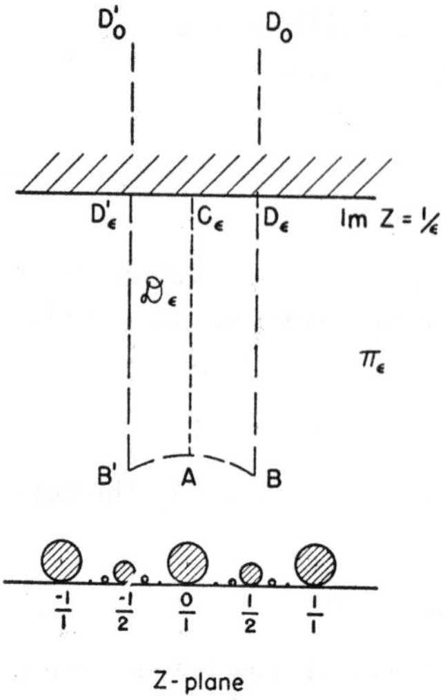

Fig. 1

Now these two methods have been generalized by Poincaré [4] and Fricke-Klein [2], respectively, to situations where finding the most general invariant is less simple. We here restrict ourselves to the modular group, hoping to make a general approach on a later occasion. Our purpose now is to indicate a basis for liaison between methods by showing that the Eisenstein series $E_4(z)$ can be defined through the conformal mapping of a region with a perturbation boundary (the individual term of the Eisenstein series being regarded as the contribution of a specific "perturbation circle"). Although the modular-function methods are quite classical, critical use is made of the more current idea of variation of the boundary.[1]

2. The perturbation map. We consider the perturbation caused to the fundamental domain $\mathfrak{D}_0$ by removing the portion above the line $\operatorname{Im} z = 1/\epsilon$ ($\epsilon < 1$). The remaining (finite) portion, $\mathfrak{D}_\epsilon$, is mapped by the modular group $z \to z^T$ (of equation (1)) onto a portion of the upper half z-plane, Π_ϵ, which is constructed by removing from the upper half z-plane the interior of a circle called $C_{p/q}(\epsilon)$, tangent to the real axis at p/q ($\neq 1/0$) and of diameter ϵ/q^2. (For consistency, "the interior of $C_{1/0}(\epsilon)$" denotes the region $\operatorname{Im} z > 1/\epsilon$). Thus Π_ϵ is a simply connected region of the z-plane, *invariant under the modular group*. (See Fig. 1.)

We now define $\zeta = \zeta_\epsilon(z)$ to be the mapping of Π_ϵ onto the upper

[1] Mr. D. C. Spencer informs me of work along such lines by M. Schiffer and himself.

half ζ-plane, with point and directions fixed at $z = \zeta = i$, $(d\zeta/dz > 0)$. We define the perturbation function

$$P(z) = -\frac{12}{\pi^2} \lim_{\epsilon \to 0} \frac{\zeta_\epsilon(z) - z}{\epsilon^2}. \tag{6}$$

The existence of such a limit is suggested by the next section, which indicates the connection with the Eisenstein series. The proof of its existence requires the major portion of this paper.

3. Approximation by superposition. The series expansion $P(z)$ is derived first from the assumption that each perturbing circle is approximately independent of the others. For instance, if just (the interior of) *one* circle $C_{p/q}(\epsilon)$ were deleted from the upper half z-plane, the corresponding mapping function $\zeta_\epsilon^{(p/q)}(z)$ (with fixed direction element at i) would easily be given by

$$\frac{\zeta_\epsilon^{(p/q)}(z) - i}{\zeta_\epsilon^{(p/q)}(z) + i} = \frac{qi - p}{-qi - p} \cdot \frac{\sinh \dfrac{\pi(z - i)}{2(qz - p)(qi - p)}}{\sinh \dfrac{\pi(z + i)}{2(qz - p)(-qi - p)}}. \tag{7}$$

Then, letting $\epsilon \to 0$, we should have the approximation

$$\zeta_\epsilon^{(p/q)}(z) = z - \frac{\pi^2 \epsilon^2}{12} \sum_{p/q} \frac{(z^2 + 1)(q + pz)}{(p - qz)(p^2 + q^2)^2}. \tag{8}$$

The terms in ϵ^2 are the "perturbation terms," which (see equation (7)) we should "superimpose" to obtain formally:

$$P(z) = \sum_{p/q} \frac{(z^2 + 1)(q + pz)}{(p - qz)(p^2 + q^2)^2} \tag{9}$$

or, reducing the general term, we should find

$$P(z) = z^3 - 5z/2 - \textstyle\sum_{q=1}^{\infty} \sum_{p/q} q^{-3}(p + qz)^{-1}. \tag{10}$$

Rather than justify the approximation directly (even on the assumption that the limit (6) exists), we shall give what we hope is a more revealing verification by deeper methods, more characteristic of the theory of modular functions. In the meantime we observe, term by term,

$$d^3P(z)/dz^3 = 6E_4(z), \tag{11}$$

which is the promised connection between the perturbation map and the indicated Eisenstein series.

If we were content with perturbation methods, we could obtain $E_6(z)$ in terms of a fifth derivative (where the perturbation circle has diameter ϵ/q^3, etc.). But since the perturbed upper half plane would not be invariant under the modular group, modular functions would be inapplicable.

4. Approximate fundamental domain. The preceding series expansions, in addition to requiring a majorant argument, are dependent on the special nature of the perturbation. The expansion (10) will therefore be proved by a more general method. Since the arguments are profuse and classical, it is hoped that a minimum of detail will prove satisfactory.

Returning to the perturbation map of § 2, we note that since the transformation $z \to z^T$ must map the upper half ζ-plane onto itself, this mapping must be via what we shall call $T(\epsilon)$, a linear fractional transformation. In other words, referring to the symbols in equation (1),

$$(12) \quad \zeta \to \zeta^{T(\epsilon)} = (a_\epsilon \zeta + b_\epsilon)/(c_\epsilon \zeta + d_\epsilon), \qquad a_\epsilon d_\epsilon - b_\epsilon c_\epsilon = 1,$$

where, as $\epsilon \to 0$, it can be seen that

$$(13) \quad \zeta \to z, \qquad a_\epsilon \to a, \qquad b_\epsilon \to b, \qquad c_\epsilon \to c, \qquad d_\epsilon \to d.$$

We shall differentiate equation (12) with respect to ϵ^2 (at $\epsilon = 0$) and obtain the transformations of $P(z)$, as defined in equation (6), under the modular group. (See § 7.)

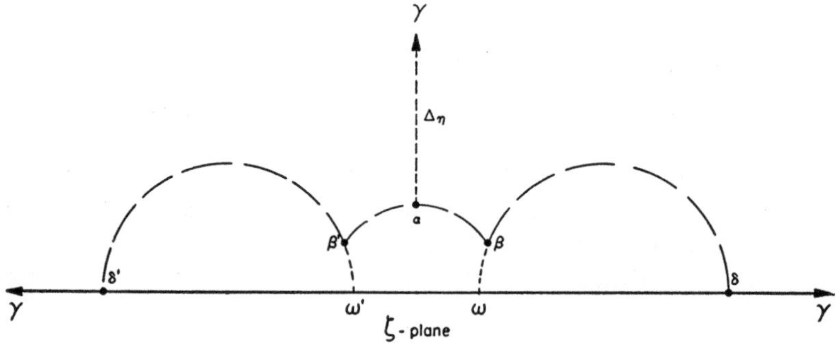

FIG. 2

Specifically, the transformation group generated by $T(\epsilon)$ has a fundamental domain which, in the case at hand, is clearly the region Δ_η shown in Figure 2, (where A, B, C_ϵ, D_ϵ become α, β, γ, δ, respectively). We can see this by noting that a mapping of $\mathfrak{D}_\epsilon$ into Δ_η (making the vertices correspond) can be reflected to provide a mapping of the "perturbed" upper half z-plane, Π_ϵ, onto the upper half ζ-plane, with fixed conditions at i.

Now the region Δ_η has one parameter η defined by

$$\beta = e^{i(\pi/3-\eta)}, \tag{14a}$$

so that $\eta \to 0$ as $\epsilon \to 0$. The condition that the angle at β is precisely $\pi/3$ determines the vertices

$$-\delta' = \delta = \frac{\sqrt{3}}{2}\cot\frac{\eta}{2} - \tfrac{1}{2} = \frac{\sqrt{3}}{\eta} - \tfrac{1}{2} - \frac{\sqrt{3}\eta}{12} + \cdots, \tag{14b}$$

$$-\omega' = \omega = \frac{\sqrt{3}}{2}\tan\frac{\eta}{2} + \tfrac{1}{2} = \tfrac{1}{2} + \frac{\sqrt{3}\eta}{4} + \cdots, \tag{14c}$$

and $-\beta' = \bar{\beta}$, the complex-conjugate of β.

To establish the relation between ϵ and η, we use the conformal equivalence of the "rectangles" $\mathfrak{D}_\epsilon$ and Δ_η.

5. Approximate mapping. We now consider a third plane, namely, the ψ-plane, in which lie the values of the function

$$\psi = \tfrac{1}{2}\sqrt{\frac{\sqrt{3}}{2\eta}}\log\frac{\sqrt{\delta\omega} + \zeta}{\sqrt{\delta\omega} - \zeta}. \tag{15}$$

It maps the region Δ_η onto the region (in Fig. 3) $\mathfrak{D}_\eta'$. If we choose

$$\eta = \sqrt{3}\epsilon^2/8, \tag{16}$$

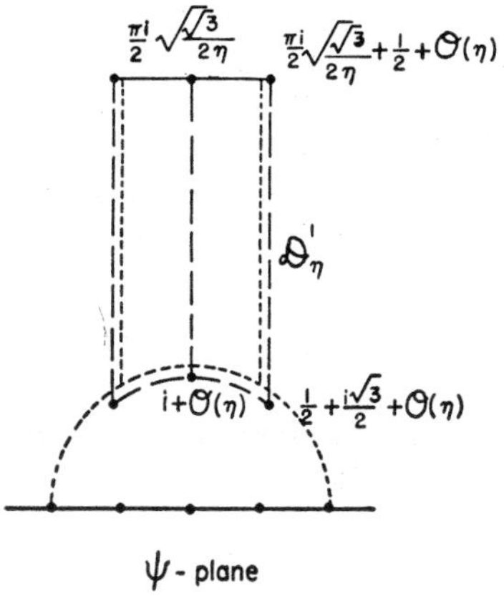

FIG. 3

then we find that $\mathfrak{D}_\eta'$ in the ψ-plane and $\mathfrak{D}_\epsilon$ in the z-plane have *boundaries* within $O(\eta)$ of one another and a point fixed to within $O(\eta)$ with a (perfectly) fixed direction.

The use of an "approximate mapping" is certainly not difficult to justify, since, for instance, the maximum-minimum principle can be applied to the Green's function to show that the proximity of the boundaries must provide an estimate for the proximity of the interior mapping. The fact that the (approximately) fixed point, i, lies on the boundary causes no trouble, since we should apply the approximations in any case not to $\mathfrak{D}_\epsilon$ and $\mathfrak{D}_\eta'$ but to, say, $\overline{\mathfrak{D}}_\epsilon$ and $\overline{\mathfrak{D}}_\eta'$, which are formed by reflecting each fundamental domain about its boundary arcs often enough to obtain larger domains in relation to which $\mathfrak{D}_\epsilon$ and $\mathfrak{D}_\eta'$ would be interior.

6. Order of magnitude. From the value of η in equation (16) it follows that for z in $\overline{\mathfrak{D}}_\epsilon$

$$\psi = z + O(\eta). \tag{17}$$

Using the power-series expansion of the logarithm, we find that ψ is approximated by $\zeta + O(\eta\zeta^3)$. Thus equation (17) leads to

$$\zeta + O(\eta\zeta^3) = z + O(\eta), \tag{18}$$

and from this,

$$(\zeta - z)/\epsilon^2 = O(\zeta^3), \tag{19}$$

which is $O(z^3)$ as $\epsilon \to 0$.

Now from (19) the limit (6), defining $P(z)$, must exist at least for a subsequence of ϵ. The *uniqueness* of the limit will follow, later, from the fact that we are dealing with a regular function, $P(z)$, completely characterized by certain transformation equations (21*) and (22*) (below), together with the estimate (from (19)),

$$P(z) = O(z^3) \tag{20}$$

as $z \to i\infty$ in $\mathfrak{D}_\epsilon$.

7. Transformation equations. From the definition of $\zeta_\epsilon(z)$ in § 2, it follows immediately that

$$\zeta_\epsilon(-1/z) = -1/\zeta_\epsilon(z). \tag{21}$$

To obtain the linear transformation representing $\zeta_\epsilon(z+1)$, we note that, in Figure 2, $z^T = z + 1$ must map the arc $\omega'\beta'$ onto $\omega\beta$. Thus we find

$$\frac{(\zeta_\epsilon(z+1) - \omega)(\beta - \bar{\beta})}{(\zeta_\epsilon(z+1) - \bar{\beta})(\beta - \omega)} = \frac{(\zeta_\epsilon(z) - \omega')(\beta' - \bar{\beta}')}{(\zeta_\epsilon(z) + \bar{\beta}')(\beta' - \omega')}. \tag{22}$$

Next, using the values given in § 5 together with equations (6) and (16), we obtain in a straightforward manner from the first-order terms in η:

$$P(-1/z) = P(z)/z^2, \tag{21*}$$

$$P(z+1) = P(z) + 3z^2 + 3z - \tfrac{3}{2}. \tag{22*}$$

More generally, by this technique we see that

$$P\left(\frac{az+b}{cz+d}\right) = \frac{P(z) + q(z)}{(cz+d)^2}, \tag{23}$$

where $q(z)$ is a quadratic polynomial. (Here $q(z)/(cz + d)^2$ is essentially $\partial z^{T(\epsilon)}/\partial\epsilon^2$ at $\epsilon = 0$.)

8. Final identification of the perturbation function. Here, armed with equations (20), (21*), and (22*), we can establish the expansion (10). Let the right-hand side of (10) be denoted by $S(z)$. It can be formally verified that $S(z)$ satisfies properties (20), (21*), and (22*). Thus, letting $U(z) = P(z) - S(z)$, we find

$$U(-1/z) = U(z)/z^2 \tag{24}$$

$$U(z+1) = U(z) \tag{25}$$

$$U(z) = O(z^3) \quad \text{as} \quad z \to i\infty, \tag{26}$$

and, in addition, $U(z)$ is regular when $\operatorname{Im} z > 0$.

Now we assert that such a $U(z)$ is identically zero. For since the function $\phi(z) = U(z)J'(z)$ is invariant under the modular group, by conditions (24) and (25), it is a single-valued function of $J(z)$. Furthermore, by condition (26), $\phi(z)$ is not ' large enough" to be anything but linear, i.e., $\phi(z) = \rho J(z) + \sigma$, for constants ρ and σ. Finally, the constants ρ, σ both vanish since $\phi(z) = 0$ at $z = i$ and $z = \frac{1}{2} + i\sqrt{3}/2$. This establishes the expansion (10) (which is, however, most naturally derived by the heuristic method of § 3).

BIBLIOGRAPHY

1. DEDEKIND, R. *Schreiben an Herrn Borchardt über die Theorie der elliptischen Modulfunktionen.* Ges. Math. Werke, I, 174–201. Braunschweig, 1930.

2. Fricke, R., and Klein, F. *Vorlesungen über die Theorie der elliptischen Modulfunktionen*, vol. I. Leipzig, 1890.

3. Fueter, R. *Vorlesungen über die singulären Moduln und die komplexe Multiplikation der elliptischen Funktionen*. Leipzig, 1924.

4. Poincaré, H. *Théorie des groupes fuchsiens*. Œuvres, II, 108–168. Paris, 1916.

Wayne University
Detroit, Michigan

HOLOMORPHIC CONTINUATION OF THE KERNEL FUNCTION AND THE BERGMAN METRIC IN SEVERAL COMPLEX VARIABLES*

H. J. BREMERMANN

Introduction

In the present paper methods of different parts of the theory of several complex variables are combined: the theories of domains of holomorphy, kernel functions, and pseudoconvex functions.[1]

The set of all square-integrable, single-valued, holomorphic functions in a domain G is a Hilbert space, and its reproducing kernel is the Bergman kernel function. The Bergman kernel function $K_G(z_1, z_2; \bar{t}_1, \bar{t}_2)$ of a domain G in the space of *two* complex variables is a holomorphic function of *four* complex variables in the product domain $G_z \times G_{\bar{t}}$ $(z = (z_1, z_2); \bar{t} = (\bar{t}_1, \bar{t}_2))$. If G is not a domain of holomorphy, then $K_G(z, \bar{t})$ can be continued into the envelope of holomorphy of $G_z \times G_{\bar{t}}$. We show that $H(G_z \times G_{\bar{t}}) = H(G_z) \times H(G_{\bar{t}})$; $H(G)$ denotes the envelope of holomorphy of a domain G. In particular, the real-valued function $K_G(z, \bar{z})$ (obtained by identifying $\bar{t}$ and $\bar{z}$) can be continued into $H(G)$, which yields a number of consequences. For example, for G to be a domain of holomorphy it is sufficient that $K_G(z, \bar{z})$ becomes infinite everywhere at the boundary of G (§ 2). If G is "smooth" the converse is true, but it is not true in general, as counterexamples show (§ 4).

The point sets $\{z \mid z \in G; K_G(z, \bar{z}) < M\}$ (M real) possess interesting properties, and we can show by using these properties that an arbitrary (schlicht) domain of holomorphy can be approximated by domains of holomorphy with real analytic boundaries (§ 3).

If the kernel function of a domain G can be continued holomorphically into a larger domain, $B_z \times B_{\bar{t}}$, $G \subset B$, then a representa-

* Prepared under contract N60ri-106 Task Order 5 (NR-043-992) for the Office of Naval Research.

[1] P. Lelong terms the pseudoconvex functions "plurisubharmonic functions" (see footnote 2).

tion of the kernel function by a complete set of orthonormal functions converges and represents the kernel function not only in $G_z \times G_{\bar{t}}$ but also in $B_z \times B_{\bar{t}}$ (§ 5). From this it follows that many properties of the Bergman kernel function (for instance, the reproducing property) are still valid in the larger domain B, in particular for $B = H(G)$. The preservation of properties is also true for the invariant Bergman metric which is generated by the kernel function. For example, the Bergman metric of a domain G is still defined, positive definite, and invariant in the envelope of holomorphy $H(G)$. It follows that, in order that the whole boundary of a domain be "infinite" with respect to the Bergman metric, the domain has to be a domain of holomorphy (§ 6). For the basic fact that the Bergman metric is positive definite we give a new and simple proof.

The real-valued function $K_G(z, \bar{t})$ is a *pseudoconvex* function. We compare it with general pseudoconvex functions and the Kähler metrics generated by them (§ 6).

J. Mehring and F. Sommer [17] worked independently in the same field and in some cases obtained results similar to mine. Later I received their preliminary manuscript (not yet published) and used some of their ideas in § 5.

I wish to express my gratitude to the Office of Naval Research for its sponsorship, to Dr. S. Bergman for valuable advice, and to Mr. J. M. Stark for his help in preparing the manuscript.

1. Notation and auxiliary theorems

1.1. In the present paper we shall consider functions, domains, and so on, in the space C of one complex variable and in the space C^n of n complex variables $(z_1, \cdots, z_n)$. (In most cases, however, n will be 2.) We write $w =_{\text{df}} (w_1, \cdots, w_n)$, $z =_{\text{df}} (z_1, \cdots, z_n)$, etc. (*Remark*. We use the symbol "$=_{\text{df}}$" if we have a defining equation by which a new symbol is defined.)

1.2. *A region* $B \subset C$ or $B \subset C^n$ is an *open point set* in C or C^n, respectively. A region need not be connected. Any maximal *connected* subset of a region B we call a *component* of B.

A domain $G \subset C$ or $G \subset C^n$ is an *open connected point set* in C or C^n, respectively. If $G^{(1)}$ is compact in $G^{(2)}$ we write $G^{(1)} \subset\subset G^{(2)}$.

Unless otherwise stated, we assume that the regions and domains are schlicht and bounded. In some sections we have to consider nonschlicht domains. But these nonschlicht domains will be concrete complex manifolds and will have no branch points as interior points.

1.3. Let C_z^n be the z-space, $C_{\bar{z}}^n$ the $\bar{z}$-space. If $\bar{z}$ is the conjugate of z we have a one-to-one transformation of the two spaces upon each other. Let G_z be a domain in C_z^n, then we denote by $G_{\bar{z}}$ the image domain of G_z in the space $C_{\bar{z}}^n$ with respect to the transformation "$\bar{z}$ the conjugate of z."

1.4. *Let $f(z)$ be a holomorphic function of z in G_z. Then*

$$\bar{f}(\bar{z}) =_{\mathrm{df}} \overline{f(z)}$$

is a holomorphic function of $\bar{z}$ in $G_{\bar{z}}$.

Proof. If $f(z)$ is holomorphic in G_z, we have:

$$\frac{\partial f}{\partial \bar{z}_j} = 0 \quad \text{for} \quad j = 1, \cdots, n.$$

According to the rules of operating with z and $\bar{z}$, we have:

$$\frac{\partial \overline{f(z)}}{\partial z_j} = \overline{\frac{\partial f(z)}{\partial \bar{z}_j}} \quad \text{for} \quad j = 1, \cdots, n.$$

Therefore $\displaystyle \frac{\partial \overline{f(z)}}{\partial z_j} = \overline{\frac{\partial f(z)}{\partial \bar{z}_j}} = 0 \quad \text{for} \quad j = 1, \cdots, n \quad \text{and} \quad \bar{z} \in G_{\bar{z}}.$

This means that $\bar{f}(\bar{z})$ is holomorphic in $G_{\bar{z}}$.

1.5. Let G be a schlicht and bounded domain in C^n. Then we denote by $L^2(G)$ the set of all functions $f(z)$ which are holomorphic and single-valued in G and for which the integral $\int_G |f(z)|^2 \, d\omega_z$ exists and is finite.

If we introduce as inner product $(f, g) =_{\mathrm{df}} \int_G f(z)\overline{g(z)} \, d\omega_z$, then $L^2(G)$ is a Hilbert space [1], [8, p. 40].

There exists always a "complete system of orthonormal functions" (briefly "complete orthonormal system") $\phi_\nu(z)$; that is, $(\phi_\mu, \phi_\nu) = \delta_{\mu\nu}$ ($\delta_{\mu\nu} =_{\mathrm{df}}$ Kronecker's symbol), and any function $f(z) \in L^2(G)$ can be represented by a series $f(z) = \sum_{\nu=1}^{\infty} a_\nu \phi_\nu(z)$ with $a_\nu = (f, \phi_\nu)$ and $\sum |a_\nu|^2 < \infty$. The series converges uniformly absolutely in every closed subdomain of G. Also, $\int_G |f(z)|^2 \, d\omega_z = \sum |a_\nu|^2$; see [8, pp. 1–14] and [6, pp. 18–30].

1.6. If a series or sequence converges uniformly in every closed subdomain of a domain G, we briefly say it converges uniformly "in the interior of G." The statement that a series "converges uniformly absolutely" means that the series of the absolute values of its terms converges uniformly.

1.7. The series $\sum_{\nu=1}^{\infty} \phi_\nu(z)\overline{\phi_\nu(t)}$ converges uniformly absolutely if z is in the interior of G and t in the interior of G. It represents the Bergman kernel function $K_G(z, \bar{t})$.

The kernel $K_G(z, \bar{t})$ has the "reproducing property": If $f(z) \in L^2(G)$, then $f(z) = \int_G f(t)K(z, \bar{t}) \, d\omega_t$.

Identifying the arguments: $\bar{t} = \bar{z}$, we obtain $K_G(z, \bar{z})$. For this function we have:

$$[K(z^{(0)}, \bar{z}^{(0)})]^{-1} = \min \int_G |f(t)|^2 \, d\omega_t,$$

the minimum being taken with respect to the set of all functions $f(z) \in L^2(G)$ that satisfy the condition $|f(z^{(0)})| \geqq 1$. If the domain G is not bounded, there may not exist a kernel function [8, pp. 21–24].

1.8. If $G^{(1)} \subset G^{(2)}$, then for the kernel functions of these domains the inequality $K_{G^{(1)}}(z, \bar{z}) \geqq K_{G^{(2)}}(z, \bar{z})$ holds for $z \in G^{(1)}$ (see [8, p. 36] and [7, p. 3]).

If $z_1^* = z_1^*(z_1, z_2)$, $z_2^* = z_2^*(z_1, z_2)$ is a holomorphic transformation of the domain G onto the domain G^*, the kernel function transforms according to the following law [6, p. 51]:

$$K_{G^*}(z_1^*, z_2^*; \bar{t}_1^*, \bar{t}_2^*) = K_G(z_1, z_2; \bar{t}_1, \bar{t}_2) \begin{vmatrix} \dfrac{\partial z_1}{\partial z_1^*} & \dfrac{\partial z_1}{\partial z_2^*} \\ \dfrac{\partial z_2}{\partial z_1^*} & \dfrac{\partial z_2}{\partial z_2^*} \end{vmatrix} \cdot \overline{\begin{vmatrix} \dfrac{\partial t_1}{\partial t_1^*} & \dfrac{\partial t_1}{\partial t_2^*} \\ \dfrac{\partial t_2}{\partial t_1^*} & \dfrac{\partial t_2}{\partial t_2^*} \end{vmatrix}}.$$

1.9. The kernel function of the unit circle is (see [8, p. 9]): $K_{\text{unit circle}}(z, \bar{t}) = \dfrac{1}{\pi(1 - z\cdot\bar{t})^2}$, and the kernel function of the bicylinder is:

$$K_{\text{bicylinder}}\,(z_1\,,\,z_2\,;\,\bar{t}_1\,,\,\bar{t}_2) = \frac{1}{\pi^2(1 - z_1\cdot\bar{t}_1)^2(1 - z_2\cdot\bar{t}_2)^2}.$$

1.10. Let $K_G(z, \bar{t})$ be the Bergman kernel function of the domain G. Then the Bergman metric

$$ds^2 = \sum \frac{\partial^2 \log K_G(z, \bar{z})}{\partial z_\mu\, \partial \bar{z}_\nu}\, dz_\mu\, d\bar{z}_\nu$$

is positive definite and invariant with respect to holomorphic transformations of G [6, pp. 51–53].

1.11. A domain H for which there exists a single-valued function that is holomorphic in the domain and singular in every boundary point is called a "domain of holomorphy" [4, Chap. VI]. A region is called a "*region of holomorphy*" if every component (see § 1.2) is a *domain* of holomorphy. Not every domain is a domain of holomorphy. The intersection of all domains of holomorphy that contain a given domain G is its "envelope of holomorphy." The envelope of holomorphy is itself a domain of holomorphy. The envelope of holomorphy of a schlicht domain can be a nonschlicht domain ([4, p. 79] and [10, p. 89]), which, however, possesses no branch points as interior points. Unless otherwise stated, we shall in the following analysis always assume that the domains we are considering are schlicht.

1.12. The intersection of all domains of holomorphy in which a given domain G is *compact* can be different from the envelope of holomorphy. This intersection is called *Nebenhülle.* If and only if a domain G can be approximated by domains of holomorphy in which G is compact, G does not possess a Nebenhülle [4, p. 81].

1.13. We say that a sequence of subsets G_ν of G converges toward a domain G if every point of G and a fixed neighborhood is contained in almost all G_ν (i.e., with the exception of at most finitely many G_ν). In this case we write: $\lim_{\nu\to\infty} G_\nu = G$. If every compact subset of G is contained in almost all G_ν, then obviously $\lim G_\nu = G$. (The limit of a family of regions is defined in analogous fashion.)

1.14. *Theorem of Behnke-Stein* [2]. Let H_ν be a sequence of (schlicht) domains of holomorphy, $H_\nu \subset H_{\nu+1} \subset H$, and $\lim_{\nu\to\infty} H_\nu = H$. Then H is a domain of holomorphy.

1.15. Let G be a (schlicht) domain and $f_\nu(z)$, $\nu = 1, \cdots, k$ be k functions holomorphic and single-valued in G. Let P be a component (in the sense of § 1.2) of the region $\bigcap_{\nu=1}^{k}\{z \mid z \in G; \mid f_\nu(z) \mid < 1\}$ and let $P \subset\subset G$. Then we call P an "analytic polyhedron." Any (schlicht) domain of holomorphy H can be approximated by a sequence of analytic polyhedrons P_ν in such a way that $P_\nu \subset\subset P_{\nu+1} \subset\subset H$ and $\lim_{\nu\to\infty} P_\nu = H$ (see [3]).

1.16. The intersection of a finite set of domains of holomorphy is a domain of holomorphy. If G is a domain of holomorphy in the z-space, H a domain of holomorphy in the w-space, then $G_z \times H_w$ is a domain of holomorphy in the (z, w)-space. (This follows immediately from the holomorph convexity of Cartan-Thullen.) If H is a domain such that there exists for every boundary point of H a function which is holomorphic in H but singular at the boundary point, then H is a domain of holomorphy [4, Chap. VI].

1.17. A real-valued function $V(z, \bar{z})$ is called "pseudoconvex in a domain G" [10, § 2.2] if it satisfies the following conditions:[2]

(a) $-\infty \leqq V(z, \bar{z}) < \infty$;
(b) $V(z, \bar{z})$ is upper semicontinuous, i.e.,

$$\lim_{z'\to z} V(z', \bar{z}') \leqq V(z, \bar{z});$$

(c) On every two-dimensional analytic plane $E =_{df} \{z \mid z = z^{(0)} + \lambda u\}$ the function $V(z, \bar{z})$ is a subharmonic function of the complex parameter λ in the intersection $E \cap G$ (u a complex vector).

1.18. A biharmonic function (real part of a holomorphic function) is a pseudoconvex function; also, if $f(z)$ is a holomorphic function, then $\mid f(z) \mid$, $\mid f(z) \mid^2$, and $\log \mid f(z) \mid$ are pseudoconvex functions [10, § 2], [15], [20, Chap. III].

If $V(z, \bar{z})$ possesses continuous partial derivatives of second order,

[2] The pseudoconvex functions were introduced independently and at about the same time by Oka [19] and Lelong [15, pp. 305–307]. The "Hartogs functions," introduced by Bochner and Martin [9, p. 143] are closely related to the pseudoconvex functions.

then a necessary and sufficient condition for $V(z, \bar{z})$ to be pseudo-convex is that the Hermitian form

$$\sum_{\mu,\nu=1}^{n} \frac{\partial^2 V(z, \bar{z})}{\partial z_\mu \partial \bar{z}_\nu} dz_\mu \, d\bar{z}_\nu$$

be positive semidefinite.

If $V(z, \bar{z})$ is pseudoconvex in G and G is transformed by a holomorphic transformation $z^* = z^*(z)$ upon the domain G^*, then $V^*(z^*, \bar{z}^*) =_{\text{df}} V[z(z^*), \bar{z}(\bar{z}^*)]$ is pseudoconvex in G^*.

2. Holomorphic continuation of the Bergman kernel function

2.1. *Let $K_G(z, \bar{t})$ be the Bergman kernel function of the domain G. Then $K_G(z, \bar{t})$ is a holomorphic function of the four complex variables $(z, \bar{t}) = (z_1, z_2; \bar{t}_1, \bar{t}_2)$ in the product domain $G_z \times G_{\bar{t}}$.* (For notation, see §§ 1.1 and 1.3.)

Proof. We represent $K_G(z, \bar{t})$ by means of a complete system of orthonormal functions $\phi_\nu(z)$ (see § 1.7):

$$K_G(z, \bar{t}) = \textstyle\sum_{\nu=1}^{\infty} \phi_\nu(z)\overline{\phi_\nu(t)}.$$

Here $\phi_\nu(z)$ is holomorphic in G_z; $\overline{\phi_\nu(t)}$ is, according to § 1.5, a holomorphic function of $\bar{t}$ in $G_{\bar{t}}$. Therefore the product $\phi_\nu(z)\overline{\phi_\nu(t)}$ is a holomorphic function of $(z, \bar{t})$ in the product domain $G_z \times G_{\bar{t}}$. The series $\sum_{\nu=1}^{\infty} \phi_\nu(z)\overline{\phi_\nu(t)}$ converges uniformly in the interior of $G_z \times G_{\bar{t}}$. Therefore $K_G(z, \bar{t})$ is holomorphic in the domain $G_z \times G_{\bar{t}}$.

2.2. A theorem of Hartogs [14, p. 15] can be stated in the following form: Let $f(z, w) = f(z_1, \cdots, z_k, w_1, \cdots, w_n)$, $(k, n \geqq 1)$ be a holomorphic function with respect to *all* variables in the polycylinder $\{(z, w) \mid |z_1| < a_1, \cdots, |z_k| < a_k; |w_1| < b_1, \cdots, |w_n| < b_n\}$ and let $f(z, w)$ be holomorphic with respect to $(z_1, \cdots, z_k)$ for $\{z \mid |z_1| < c_1, \cdots, |z_k| < c_k\}$ if $(w_1, \cdots, w_n)$ is *fixed* in $\{w \mid |w_1| < b_1, \cdots, |w_n| < b_n\}$. Then $f(z, w)$ is holomorphic with respect to all variables in the polycylinder

$$\{(z, w) \mid |z_1| < c_1, \cdots, |z_k| < c_k; |w_1| < b_1, \cdots, |w_n| < b_n\}$$

If we denote the polycylinder $\{z \mid |z_1| < a_1, \cdots, |z_k| < a_k\}$ by $P_z^{(1)}$, $\{z \mid |z_1| < c_1, \cdots, |z_k| < c_k\}$ by $P_z^{(2)}$, and

$$\{w \mid |w_1| < b_1, \cdots, |w_n| < b_n\}$$

by Q_w, we can state the theorem in the following way: Let $f(z, w)$ be holomorphic in $P_z^{(1)} \times Q_w$ and holomorphic with respect to z for $z \in P_z^{(2)}$ and w *fixed* in Q_w. Then $f(z, w)$ is holomorphic in $P_z^{(2)} \times Q_w$. (Of course we suppose that $P_z^{(1)} \subset P_z^{(2)}$; otherwise the theorem is trivial.)

2.3. We can extend this form of the theorem from polycylinders to arbitrary domains $G^{(1)}$, $G^{(2)}$, D. *Let* $f(z, w)$ *be holomorphic in* $G_z^{(1)} \times D_w$ *and holomorphic with respect to* z *for* $z \in G_z^{(2)}$ *for fixed* $w \in D_w$. *Then* $f(z, w)$ *is holomorphic in* $G_z^{(2)} \times D_w$. ($G_z^{(1)}$, $G_z^{(2)}$, D_w are not required to be schlicht domains, but may not contain branch points as interior points.)

Proof. We connect an arbitrary point $z^{(1)} \in G_z^{(2)}$ and some point $z^{(0)} \in G_z^{(1)}$ by a simple curve in $G_z^{(2)}$. This curve is a closed set in $G_z^{(2)}$ which we can cover—according to the theorem of Heine-Borel—by a finite number of neighborhoods. As neighborhoods we can choose in particular polycylinders $P_z^{(\nu)} \subset G_z^{(2)}$; $\nu = 1, \cdots, N$. We choose the $P_z^{(\nu)}$ in such a way that the center of the first one is $z^{(0)}$, the center of the last one is $z^{(1)}$, and the center of each of the polycylinders of the chain (except the first one) is an interior point of the preceding polycylinder. Around an arbitrary point $w^{(1)} \in D_w$ we take a polycylinder $Q_w \in H_w$.

By applying the Hartogs theorem of § 2.2, we first obtain that $f(z, w)$ is holomorphic in $P^{(1)} \times Q_w$; by applying it again, $f(z, w)$ is holomorphic in $P_z^{(2)} \times Q_w$, and so on. Finally we obtain that $f(z, w)$ is holomorphic in $P_z^{(N)} \times Q_w$, and this means that $f(z, w)$ is holomorphic in a neighborhood of $(z^{(1)}, w^{(1)})$. This point is an arbitrary point in $G_z^{(2)} \times D_w$. Therefore $f(z, w)$ is holomorphic in this domain. (Nothing has to be changed in the proof if $G_z^{(1)}$, $G_z^{(2)}$, D_w are no longer schlicht but do not contain branch points as interior points.)

2.4. LEMMA. *The envelope of holomorphy of a product domain* $G_z \times D_w$ *is equal to the product of the envelopes of holomorphy of the domains:*

$$H(G_z \times D_w) = H(G)_z \times H(D)_w .$$

Proof. This can be concluded from § 2.3. Any function holomorphic in $G_z \times D_w$ is, for w *fixed* in D_w, a holomorphic function of z

in G_z. Any function holomorphic in G_z is still holomorphic in $H(G)_z$. Therefore $f(z, w)$ is holomorphic in $G_z \times D_w$ and holomorphic *with respect to* z in $H(G)_z$ for w *fixed* in D_w. Therefore $f(z, w)$ is holomorphic in $H(G)_z \times D_w$ according to § 2.3. If we repeat this procedure we obtain: $f(z, w)$ is holomorphic in $H(G)_z \times H(D)_w$. Now $f(z, w)$ is an arbitrary function holomorphic in $G_z \times D_w$. Therefore

$$H(G_z \times D_w) \supseteq H(G)_z \times H(D)_w .$$

The product of two domains of holomorphy is a domain of holomorphy (§ 1.16). Therefore

$$H(G_z \times D_w) \subseteq H(G)_z \times H(D)_w .$$

This and the preceding inequality yield our theorem. (*Remark*. The envelope of holomorphy of a schlicht domain may be no longer schlicht; see § 1.11.)

2.5. THEOREM. *The kernel function* $K_G(z, \bar{t})$ *of a domain* G *is a holomorphic function of the four complex variables* $(z, \bar{t}) = (z_1, z_2; \bar{t}_1, \bar{t}_2)$ *in the domain* $H(G)_z \times H(G)_{\bar{t}}$.

The result follows immediately from the fact that $K_G(z, \bar{t})$ is holomorphic in $G_z \times G_{\bar{t}}$ (§ 2.1) and that $H(G)_z \times H(G)_{\bar{t}}$ is the envelope of holomorphy of this domain (§ 2.4).

2.6. COROLLARY. *The function* $K_G(z, \bar{z})$ *is defined and finite in the envelope of holomorphy* $H(G)$.

This is an immediate consequence of § 2.5.

2.7. THEOREM. *If the function* $K_G(z, \bar{z})$ *becomes infinite everywhere at the boundary of the domain* G, *then* G *is a domain of holomorphy.*

Remark. "$K_G(z, \bar{z})$ becomes infinite everywhere at the boundary of G" means: The point set $\{z \mid z \in G; K_G(z, \bar{z}) < M\}$ is compact in G for all (real) M.

If G were not a domain of holomorphy, then there would exist boundary points of G which are interior points of $H(G)$. In the neighborhood of such a point, $K_G(z, \bar{z})$ would be bounded according to § 2.6, and therefore $\{z \mid z \in G; K_G(z, \bar{z}) < M\}$ would not be compact in G for sufficiently large M.

2.8. *The function* $K_G(z, \bar{z})$ *is a (real-valued) pseudoconvex function in* G. (For the definition of pseudoconvex functions see § 1.17. Later, in § 6.5, we prove that $K_G(z, \bar{z})$ is pseudoconvex not only in G but also in $H(G)$.)

Proof. We represent $K_G(z, \bar{t})$ by a complete system of orthonormal functions (§ 1.5). Then

$$K_G(z, \bar{z}) = \sum_{\nu=1}^{\infty} | \phi_\nu(z) |^2.$$

The square of the absolute value of a holomorphic function is a pseudoconvex function. A uniformly convergent series of pseudoconvex functions is again a pseudoconvex function (§ 1.18). Therefore $K_G(z, \bar{z})$ is pseudoconvex.

3. Approximation of domains of holomorphy by sequences of domains of holomorphy with a real analytic boundary

3.1. THEOREM. *Let* G *be a domain,* $K_G(z, \bar{z})$ *its kernel function. If the point set*

$$G_M =_{\text{df}} \{z \mid z \in G;\ K_G(z, \bar{z}) < M\}$$

($M > 0$, *real) is compact in* G, *then* G_M *is a region of holomorphy.*

Proof. We consider the theorem to be true if G_M is empty. Otherwise, G_M is an open point set because the kernel function is continuous. In general, G_M will be a region: i.e., G_M is an open point set but not necessarily connected (see § 1.2). We have to show that every (connected) component of G_M is a domain of holomorphy (see § 1.11).

Let H_M be a component of G_M, $z^{(0)}$ an arbitrary boundary point of H_M. Then $K(z^{(0)}, \bar{z}^{(0)}) = M$. We represent $K_G(z, \bar{t})$ by a complete system of orthonormal functions. Then

$$K_G(z, \bar{z}^{(0)}) = \sum_{\nu=1}^{\infty} \phi_\nu(z)\overline{\phi_\nu(z^{(0)})}.$$

Applying Schwarz's inequality, we obtain

$$| K_G(z, z^{(0)}) |^2 \leqq \sum_{\nu=1}^{\infty} | \phi_\nu(z) |^2 \sum_{\nu=1}^{\infty} | \phi_\nu(z^{(0)}) |^2$$
$$= K_G(z, \bar{z}) \cdot K_G(z^{(0)}, \bar{z}^{(0)}) = K_G(z, \bar{z}) \cdot M;$$

on the other hand, for $z \in G_M$ we have by definition of G_M that $K_G(z, \bar{z}) < M$. Therefore, for $z \in G_M$ we have $| K_G(z, \bar{z}^{(0)}) |^2 < M^2$.

Now $K_G(z, \bar{z}^{(0)})$ is a holomorphic function in G, and therefore $K_G(z, \bar{z}^{(0)}) - M = 0$ is an analytic surface which goes through $z^{(0)}$ but does not intersect G_M because of the last inequality, and of course does not intersect H_M either.

Therefore for an arbitrary boundary point $z^{(0)}$ the function $[K_G(z, \bar{z}^{(0)}) - M]^{-1}$ is singular at $z^{(0)}$ but holomorphic throughout H_M. From this it follows that H_M is a domain of holomorphy (§ 1.16).

3.2. THEOREM. *If $K_G(z, \bar{z})$ becomes infinite everywhere at the boundary of G, then* (for the meaning of "$\lim_{M\to\infty} G_M = G$," see § 1.13):

(a) *G is a domain of holomorphy;*

(b) *If $M \to \infty$, then G_M is a family of regions of holomorphy with $G_{M_1} \subset\subset G_{M_2}$ for $M_1 < M_2$ and with* $\lim_{M\to\infty} G_M = G$;

(c) *One can select a sequence of (connected) components H_M of G_M (which are domains of holomorphy) for which $H_M \subset\subset H_{M+1} \subset\subset G$ and* $\lim_{M\to\infty} H_M = G$.

Proof of (b). In § 3.1 we have already proved that the G_M are regions of holomorphy; $G_{M_1} \subset\subset G_{M_2}$ for $M_1 < M_2$ follows from the fact that $K_G(z, \bar{z})$ is continuous and $G_M \subset\subset G$ is the assumption that $K_G(z, \bar{z})$ becomes infinite everywhere at the boundary. The condition $\lim_{M\to\infty} G_M = G$ means that every closed subset of G is contained in all G_M for $M > M_0$. On every closed subset of G the function $K_G(z, \bar{z})$ possesses a maximum. If we take M_0 greater than this maximum, the condition is obviously satisfied.

Proof of (c). For a fixed M_1 we select one of the components of G_{M_1} and denote it by H_{M_1}. From G_{M+1} we select that component which contains H_{M_1} and denote it by H_{M_1+1}, and so on. In this way we obtain a sequence H_M of domains of holomorphy. Obviously, $H_M \subset\subset H_{M+1} \subset\subset G$ holds. It remains to be shown that $\lim_{M\to\infty} H_M = G$.

Let S be a closed subset of G; then $K_G(z, \bar{z})$ has a finite maximum M_0 on S. Therefore S is contained in G_M for $M \geqq M_0 + 1$. The set S may be contained in a component of G_{M_0+1} which is different from H_{M_0+1}. But we can show that for sufficiently large M the components "flow" together. We connect an arbitrary point of H_{M_0+1} with a point of S by a curve in G. Then $K_G(z, \bar{z})$ assumes a finite maximum M_1 on this curve. Therefore, if we take $M > M_1$, then S and H_{M_0+1} are contained in the same connected component of G_M, and that means they are contained in H_M. This yields $\lim_{M\to\infty} H_M = G$.

Proof of (a). This result has already been obtained in § 2.7. However, it also follows from (c) by application of the theorem of Behnke-Stein (§ 1.14). The set G, being the limit of a sequence of domains of holomorphy, is a domain of holomorphy. This is a second proof of this result, and quite different from the one given in § 2.7.

3.3. THEOREM. *Let P be a bounded analytic polyhedron; then $K_P(z, \bar{z})$ becomes infinite everywhere at the boundary of P.* (Compare Mehring-Sommer [17].)

Proof. According to §1.15, P is a component of a point set

$$\bigcap_{\nu=1}^{k} \{z \mid z \in G; \mid f_\nu(z) \mid < 1\},$$

where the $f_\nu(z)$ are holomorphic in G and $P \subset\subset G$. It has to be shown that, for arbitrarily large (real) M,

$$\{z \mid z \in P; K_P(z, \bar{z}) < M\} \subset\subset P.$$

Let $\epsilon =_{\mathrm{df}} 1/M$. Let P_a be the point set

$$P_a =_{\mathrm{df}} \bigcap_{\nu=1}^{k} \{z \mid z \in P; \mid f_\nu(z) \mid < a\}.$$

Since P is bounded, we can determine an a, $0 < a < 1$, such that

$$\int_{P-P_a} d\omega < \frac{\epsilon}{4}.$$

This means that the area of $P - P_a$ is smaller than $\epsilon/4$. In P_a we have $\mid f_\nu(z) \mid < a < 1$ for $\nu = 1, \cdots, k$. Therefore we can make the maximum of $\mid f_\nu(z) \mid^n$ in $\bar{P}_a$ arbitrarily small if we chose n large enough. In particular, we can determine n so that

$$\int_{P_a} \mid f_\nu(z) \mid^{2n} d\omega < \frac{\epsilon}{4} \quad \text{for} \quad \nu = 1, \cdots, k.$$

Then for $\nu = 1, \cdots, k$,

$$\int_P \mid f_\nu(z) \mid^{2n} d\omega = \int_{P_a} \mid f_\nu(z) \mid^{2n} d\omega + \int_{P-P_a} \mid f_\nu(z) \mid^{2n} d\omega$$

$$< \int_{P_a} \mid f_\nu(z) \mid^{2n} d\omega + \int_{P-P_a} d\omega < \frac{\epsilon}{4} + \frac{\epsilon}{4} = \frac{\epsilon}{2}.$$

Let us now consider the point set

$$S =_{\text{df}} \bigcap_{\nu=1}^{k} \{z \mid z \in P; \mid f_\nu(z) \mid^{2n} < \tfrac{1}{2}\}.$$

Obviously, $S \subset\subset P$ holds. Let $z^{(0)}$ be an arbitrary point in $P - S$. Then, by definition of S, at least one of the functions $f_\nu(z)$ has the property that $\mid f_{\nu_0}(z^{(0)}) \mid^{2n} \geqq \frac{1}{2}$. Therefore, if $g(z) =_{\text{df}} [f_{\nu_0}(z)]^n\sqrt{2}$, then

$$\int_P \mid g(z) \mid^2 d\omega = 2 \int_P \mid f_{\nu_0}(z) \mid^{2n} d\omega < \epsilon.$$

On the other hand, $\mid g(z^{(0)}) \mid \geqq 1$. Therefore the minimum of the integral $\int_P \mid h(z) \mid^2 d\omega$ with respect to all functions that have an absolute value $\mid h(z^{(0)}) \mid \geqq 1$ is certainly smaller than ϵ; for even the function $g(z)$, which is not necessarily minimal, makes the integral smaller than ϵ. The minimum is equal to $[K_P(z^{(0)}, \bar{z}^{(0)})]^{-1}$ (see § 1.7). Therefore

$$[K_P(z^{(0)}, \bar{z}^{(0)})]^{-1} < \epsilon \quad \text{or} \quad K_P(z^{(0)}, \bar{z}^{(0)}) > M.$$

Now $z^{(0)}$ is an arbitrary point in $P - S$. Therefore in $P - S$, $K_P(z, \bar{z}) > M$ holds; this means: $\{z \mid z \in P; K_P(z, \bar{z}) < M\} \subset S$. On the other hand, S is compact in P. Therefore one obtains the desired result:

$$\{z \mid z \in P; K_P(z, \bar{z}) < M\} \subset\subset P.$$

3.4. THEOREM. *Any (schlicht) domain of holomorphy H can be approximated from the interior by a sequence of domains of holomorphy H_ν with a real analytic boundary. More precisely, the approximating H_ν can be chosen to have the following properties:*

(a) $H_\nu \subset\subset H_{\nu+1} \subset\subset H$ *and* $\lim_{\nu\to\infty} H_\nu = H$;

(b) *Each H_ν is a component of a point set $G_\nu =_{\text{df}} \{z \mid \Phi_\nu(z, \bar{z}) < 1\}$, where $\Phi_\nu(z, \bar{z})$ is a (real-valued) pseudoconvex function in a neighborhood of G_ν which can be continued analytically, while remaining single-valued, into a neighborhood of $G_{\nu z} \times G_{\nu\bar{z}}$.*

Proof. Any domain of holomorphy H_ν can be approximated by a sequence of bounded analytic polyhedrons in such a way that $P_{\nu-1} \subset\subset P_\nu \subset\subset H$ and $\lim_{\nu\to\infty} P_\nu = H$ (see § 1.15). Now $K_P(z, \bar{z})$ becomes infinite everywhere at the boundary of P_ν (§ 3.3).

Therefore, because $P_{\nu-1} \subset\subset P_\nu$, we can determine an M in such a way that $P_{\nu-1}$ is contained in $\{z \mid z \in P_\nu ; K_{P_\nu}(z, \bar{z}) < M\}$. On the other hand, $\{z \mid z \in P_\nu ; K_{P_\nu}(z, \bar{z}) < M\} \subset\subset P_\nu$. We denote by H_ν that component of $\{z \mid z \in P_\nu ; K_{P_\nu}(z, \bar{z}) < M\}$ which contains $P_{\nu-1}$. Obviously, $P_{\nu-1} \subset H_\nu \subset\subset P_\nu$. Therefore the properties of the approximation by polyhedrons $P_\nu \subset\subset P_{\nu+1} \subset\subset H$ and $\lim_{\nu\to\infty} P_\nu = H$, imply $H_\nu \subset\subset H_{\nu+1} \subset\subset H$ and $\lim_{\nu\to\infty} H_\nu = H$.

On the other hand, the function $K_{P_\nu}(z, \bar{z})$ is pseudoconvex in P_ν and $K_{P_\nu}(z, \bar{t})$ is holomorphic in $P_{\nu z} \times P_{\nu \bar{t}}$ (§§ 2.8, 2.5). If we introduce $\Phi_\nu(z, \bar{z}) =_{df} K_{P_\nu}(z, \bar{z})/M$, then $\Phi_\nu(z, \bar{z})$ has the same properties; P_ν is a neighborhood of

$$G_\nu = \{z \mid z \in P_\nu ; \Phi_\nu(z, \bar{z}) < 1\} = \{z \mid z \in P_\nu ; K_{P_\nu}(z, \bar{z}) < M\}.$$

H_ν is a component of G_ν and H_ν is a domain of holomorphy, according to § 3.1. Therefore we have determined a sequence H_ν and functions $\Phi_\nu(z, \bar{z})$ which possess all the properties required in our theorem.

3.5. We note that the theorem is true for one variable as well as for two variables. In the case of one variable every domain is a domain of holomorphy. Therefore the theorem yields that any schlicht domain in the z-plane can be approximated by domains with an analytic boundary.

4. The behavior of the kernel function at the boundary

In §§ 2 and 3 we obtained in particular these two results: If $K_G(z, \bar{z})$ becomes infinite everywhere at the boundary of the domain G, then G is a domain of holomorphy, and any domain of holomorphy can be approximated by domains in which the kernel function becomes infinite everywhere at the boundary. Therefore the question arises: If H is an arbitrary domain of holomorphy, does $K_H(z, \bar{z})$ become infinite everywhere at the boundary of H?[3] Examples show that there exist domains H for which this is not true.

[3] This question is also of interest for the following problem: The class $L^2(G)$, i.e., the set of all functions, which are holomorphic, single-valued, and square-integrable in a domain G, forms a Hilbert space. The inner product is $(f, g) = \int_G f(z)\overline{g(z)}\, d\omega$. Now it can happen that $L^2(G)$ is only a subset of the set of all functions that are holomorphic and single-valued in G. Different inner products will "cover" larger subsets. Such inner products can be obtained by introducing certain (real-valued) "weighting-functions" $w(z)$, which be-

4.1. Even in one variable we can give a counterexample. *Let H be the domain $\{z \mid 0 < |z| < 1\}$ (H is a domain of holomorphy). Then $K_H(z, \bar{t})$ is equal to the kernel function of the unit circle.* This means that $K_H(z, \bar{z})$ remains bounded in a neighborhood of the boundary point $z = 0$.

Proof. Any function $f(z)$ holomorphic and single-valued in H can be developed in a Laurent series around the origin: $f(z) = \sum_{-\infty}^{+\infty} a_n z^n$. Then

$$\int_H |f(z)|^2 \, d\omega > \int_{\delta<|z|<1-\delta} |f(z)|^2 \, d\omega = \sum_{-\infty}^{\infty} |a_n|^2 \int_{\delta<|z|<1-\delta} |z|^{2n} \, d\omega$$

$$\geqq |a_n|^2 \int_{\delta<|z|<1-\delta} |z|^{2n} \, d\omega.$$

(We can interchange the integration and summation because of the uniform convergence of the series in the interior of H. Also, the powers z^n are orthogonal with respect to H. Therefore we obtain the inequality above.) In order that $f(z) \in L^2(H)$, the integral $\int_H |f(z)|^2 \, d\omega$ has to be finite. In order that this integral be finite,

$$\lim_{\delta\to 0} \left(|a_n|^2 \cdot \int_{\delta<|z|<1-\delta} |z|^{2n} \, d\omega \right)$$

has to be finite.

This means that $a_n = 0$ for $n < 0$, so that we have no negative powers of z in the Laurent series. Any function $f(z) \in L^2(H)$ is holomorphic at the origin. This means $L^2(H) = L^2(\{z \mid |z| < 1\})$. Orthonormalization with respect to H is the same as that with respect to $\{z \mid |z| < 1\}$. Hence a complete set of orthonormal functions in H is also a complete orthonormal set in $\{z \mid |z| < 1\}$. Therefore the kernel function of H and the kernel function of the full unit circle coincide.

Remark. The same results holds, of course, for a punctured circular disk of arbitrary radius.

---

come zero at the boundary of G, and defining as inner product $(f, g) = \int_G f(z)\overline{g(z)}w(z) \, d\omega$. In particular, we can choose $K_G(z, \bar{z})^{-k}$ $(k > 0)$ as weight-function if $K_G(z, \bar{z})$ becomes infinite at the boundary of G. We will, however, not discuss this subject in the present paper. The idea is due to Bergman [5, p. 6]. Compare Nehari [18], "On Weighted Kernels."

4.2. *The kernel functions of the domains* $\{z_1 \mid 0 < |z_1| < 1\} \times \{z_2 \mid |z| < 1\}$ *and* $\{z_1 \mid 0 < |z_1| < 1\} \times \{z_2 \mid 0 < |z_2| < 1\}$ *coincide with the kernel function of the full bicylinder* $\{z_1 \mid |z_1| < 1\} \times \{z_2 \mid |z_2| < 1\}$; *in particular, they remain bounded in the neighborhood of boundary points* $|z_1| = 0$, $(|z_2| = 0)$.

This follows from § 4.1 and from the fact that the kernel function of a product domain is equal to the product of the kernel functions of the domains. (We give a proof of this lemma in § 4.9.)

4.3. The examples of §§ 4.1 and 4.2 have in common the feature that the considered domains of holomorphy H possess a Nebenhülle; that is, the intersection of all domains of holomorphy in which H is compact is different from H (§ 1.12). The Nebenhülle of $\{z \mid 0 < |z| < 1\}$ is the unit circle and the Nebenhülle of the domains in § 4.2 is the full bicylinder $\{z_1 \mid |z_1| < 1\} \times \{z_2 \mid |z_2| < 1\}$. Therefore in the examples of §§ 4.1 and 4.2 the kernel function coincides with the kernel function of the Nebenhülle. But this is not a general theorem, as the following example shows.

4.4. *The domain of holomorphy* $H = \{z \mid |z_2| < |z_1|\} \cap \{z \mid 0 < |z_1| < 1\}$ *possesses as its Nebenhülle the full bicylinder* $\{z_1 \mid |z_1| < 1\} \times \{z_2 \mid |z_2| < 1\}$, *but the kernel function* $K_H(z, \bar{z})$ *becomes infinite everywhere at the boundary of* H.

Proof. By the transformation $z_1^* = z_1$, $s = z_2/z_1$, we map H in a one-to-one fashion upon the domain

$$H^* = \{(z_1^*, s) \mid 0 < |z_1^*| < 1; |s| < 1\}.$$

According to § 4.2, the kernel function of H^* is equal to the kernel function of the bicylinder $\{(z_1^*, s) \mid |z_1^*| < 1; |s| < 1\}$ (see § 1.9). Therefore

$$K_{H^*}(z_1^*, s; \bar{z}_1^*, \bar{s}) = \frac{1}{\pi^2} \frac{1}{(1 - |z_1^*|^2)^2} \cdot \frac{1}{(1 - |s|^2)^2}.$$

The transformation law of the kernel function (see § 1.8) states that

$$K_H(z_1, z_2; \bar{z}_1, \bar{z}_2) = K_{H^*}(z_1^*, s; \bar{z}_1^*, \bar{s}) \begin{vmatrix} \dfrac{\partial z_1^*}{\partial z_1} & \dfrac{\partial z_1^*}{\partial z_2} \\ \dfrac{\partial s}{\partial z_1} & \dfrac{\partial s}{\partial z_2} \end{vmatrix}^2.$$

Therefore

$$K_H(z_1, z_2; \bar{z}_1, \bar{z}_2) = \frac{1}{\pi^2} \frac{1}{(1 - |z_1|^2)^2} \cdot \frac{1}{\left(1 - \frac{|z_2|^2}{|z_1|}\right)^2} |z_1|^{-2},$$

and one sees that K_H becomes infinite everywhere at the boundary.

4.5. Sufficient Criteria

(a) *$K_G(z, \bar{z})$ becomes uniformly infinite in the neighborhood of a boundary point $z^{(0)}$ of G if there exists a function $f(z) \in L^2(G)$ which becomes uniformly infinite in a neighborhood of $z^{(0)}$.*

(b) *$K_G(z, \bar{z})$ becomes infinite everywhere at the boundary if there exists a function $f(z)$ as described in* (a) *for every boundary point $z^{(0)}$ of G, and if G is bounded.*

Remark. "A function becomes uniformly infinite in a neighborhood of the boundary point $z^{(0)}$" means: For every (arbitrarily large) N there exists a neighborhood $U(z^{(0)})$ such that $|f(z)| > N$ in $G \cap U(z^{(0)})$.

Criterion (b) follows immediately from criterion (a) by the theorem of Heine-Borel.

Proof of (a). Let $f(z) \in L^2(G)$ and let $f(z)$ become uniformly infinite in a neighborhood of $z^{(0)}$. We have to show that for every M there exists a neighborhood $U(z^{(0)})$ such that $K_G(z, \bar{z}) > M$ in $U(z^{(0)}) \cap G$.

Since $\int_G |f(z)|^2 \, d\omega$ is finite, we can find N so that

$$\int_G \frac{|f(z)|^2}{N^2} \, d\omega < \frac{1}{M}.$$

Because $f(z)$ becomes uniformly infinite, we can determine a $U(z^{(0)})$ such that $|f(z)| > N$ in $U(z^{(0)}) \cap G$. Therefore

$$[K(z^{(1)}, \bar{z}^{(1)})]^{-1} = \min \int_G |h(z)|^2 \, d\omega < \frac{1}{M} \quad \text{for} \quad z^{(1)} \in U(z^{(0)}) \cap G$$

(the minimum being taken with respect to all functions in $L^2(G)$ whose absolute value at the point $z^{(1)}$ is greater than or equal to one), for even the function $f(z)/N$, which is not necessarily minimal, makes the integral smaller than $1/M$. Therefore the kernel function

$K_G(z, \bar{z})$ is larger than M for $z \in U(z^{(0)}) \cap G$. From this our theorem follows.

4.6. Let G be a bounded domain in the plane of one variable.

(a) *If $z^{(0)}$ is a boundary point such that there exists a neighborhood $U(z^{(0)})$ for which $U(z^{(0)}) \cap G$ is simply connected, then $K_G(z, \bar{z})$ becomes uniformly infinite at $z^{(0)}$.*

(b) *$K_G(z, \bar{z})$ remains bounded in the neighborhood of every isolated boundary point of G.*[4]

Proof of (a). In this case there exists another boundary point $z^{(1)}$ of G in $U(z^{(0)})$. The function $f(z) = \log(z - z^{(0)}) - \log(z - z^{(1)})$ is holomorphic, single-valued, and square-integrable in G and becomes uniformly infinite at $z^{(0)}$. Application of the first criterion of § 4.5 yields (a).

Proof of (b). If $z^{(0)}$ is an isolated boundary point, then there exists a punctured circular disk $D = \{z \mid 0 < |z - z^{(0)}| < \delta\}$ which is contained in G. According to § 1.8, we have $K_D(z, \bar{z}) \geqq K_G(z, \bar{z})$. According to § 4.1, $K_D(z, \bar{z})$ remains finite at $z^{(0)}$ and therefore $K_G(z, \bar{z})$ remains finite at $z^{(0)}$.

4.7. The result of § 4.6 does not hold for unbounded domains. If we transform the unit circle upon the upper half-plane by the transformation $w = i(1 - z)/(1 + z)$, we obtain by the transformation law of the kernel function:

$$K_{\text{half-plane}}(w, \bar{w}) = K_{\text{circle}}(z, \bar{z}) \left| \frac{dz}{dw} \right|^2 = \frac{1}{\pi} \cdot \frac{1}{(1 - |z|^2)^2} \cdot \frac{|z+1|^4}{4}.$$

If we approach -1 on the real axis in the z-plane we approach ∞ on the imaginary axis in the w-plane, and one sees that the limit of $K_{\text{half-plane}}$ for this approach is equal to 0; i.e., K does not become uniformly infinite in a neighborhood of the boundary point ∞.

The result of § 4.6 is a generalization of a theorem of Bergman ([8, pp. 37–39] and [7]). Bergman's theorem covers our result for those boundary points $z^{(0)}$ of a bounded domain G for which there exists an interior circular disk I and an exterior circular disk A with $z^{(0)}$ as a boundary point so that $I \subset G \subset A$. Then we have

[4] An "isolated boundary point" is a boundary point that possesses a full neighborhood containing no further boundary points of G.

$K_A(z, \bar{z}) \leqq K_G(z, \bar{z}) \leqq K_I(z, \bar{z})$ (see § 1.8) and, the kernel function of a circular disk being well known, we obtain an estimate for $K_G(z, \bar{z})$. This "method of domains of comparison" has the advantage that not only can we conclude that K_G *does* become infinite but we can also *estimate the order* of becoming infinite, as we know K_A and K_I and their orders. The knowledge of the order is of great interest as a quantitative statement, but the method has the disadvantage that G and its boundary have to be of such a type that there exist domains of comparison. We face the same situation in several complex variables.

4.8. We note without detailed proof:

Let H be a (schlicht) bounded domain of holomorphy which does not possess a Nebenhülle. Let the boundary of H possess continuous partial derivatives of second order and let H be totally pseudoconvex (i.e., the Levi differential expression is greater than 0 *everywhere on the boundary of H)* [4, p. 29]. *Then $K_H(z, \bar{z})$ becomes infinite everywhere at the boundary of H.*

The proof makes use of the fact that, because of the total pseudoconvexity of H, there exists at every boundary point $z^{(0)}$ of H an analytic surface $\{z \mid f(z) = 0\}$ which has except for $z^{(0)}$ no further points in common with the boundary of H and does not intersect H.

As H does not possess a Nebenhülle, H can be approximated by a sequence of domains of holomorphy from the exterior. In an approximating domain of holomorphy close enough to H, we can prescribe $f(z) = 0$ as pole surface of a Cousin I-distribution. In domains of holomorphy the first Cousin problem can be solved. Therefore we can find a function $F(z)$ which is holomorphic in H but possesses a pole at $z^{(0)}$, i.e., tends uniformly to infinity in a neighborhood of $z^{(0)}$.

We can also show that $F(z) \in L^2(H)$. Application of the criterion of § 4.5 yields our theorem.

A general domain of holomorphy can have a quite complicated structure. The boundary may be not differentiable, not even continuous. (Even product domains—which are special domains of holomorphy—may possess a complicated boundary.) The problem as to whether the kernel function of an arbitrary bounded domain of holomorphy which does not possess a Nebenhülle *does* become infinite everywhere at the boundary remains unsolved. I conjecture, however, that this is not true in general, not even in the case of one variable.

4.9. As an appendix to this section, we prove the following lemma, the usefulness of which is obvious.

LEMMA. *The kernel function of a product domain is equal to the product of the kernel functions of the domains:*

$$K_{G^{(1)}\times G^{(2)}}(z_1, z_2; \bar{t}_1, \bar{t}_2) = K_{G^{(1)}}(z_1, \bar{t}_1)\cdot K_{G^{(2)}}(z_2, \bar{t}_2).$$

Proof. Let $f(z_1, z_2)$ be an arbitrary single-valued holomorphic function, square-integrable in $G_{z_1}^{(1)} \times G_{z_2}^{(2)}$. If we fix one variable, for instance $z_2 = z_2^{(0)}$, then $f(z_1, z_2^{(0)})$ is a single-valued holomorphic function of z_1 for $z_1 \in G^{(1)}$. We show that $f(z_1, z_2^{(0)}) \in L^2(G^{(1)})$.

A well-known theorem for holomorphic functions states: *Let $g(z)$ be holomorphic in G, then:*

$$| g(z^{(0)}) |^2 \leqq \frac{1}{\pi r^2} \int_{|z-z^{(0)}|<r} | g(z) |^2 \, d\omega_z ,$$

if $z^{(0)} \in G$ and $\{z \mid | z - z^{(0)} | < r\} \subset G$. (See [8, p. 5]. This is also a theorem for general subharmonic functions [20, § 2.3].)

Applying this to $f(z_1, z_2)$, we obtain: if $z_1 \in G^{(1)}$, $z_2^{(0)} \in G^{(2)}$, and $\{z_2 \mid | z_2 - z_2^{(0)} | \leqq r \} \subset G^{(2)}$, then

$$| f(z_1, z_2^{(0)}) |^2 \leqq \frac{1}{\pi r^2} \int_{|z_2-z_2^{(0)}|<r} | f(z_1, z_2) |^2 \, d\omega_{z_2} .$$

Because $f(z) \in L^2(G_{z_1}^{(1)} \times G_{z_2}^{(2)})$ we can integrate and obtain:

$$\int_{G^{(1)}} | f(z_1, z_2^{(0)}) |^2 \, d\omega_{z_1} \leqq \frac{1}{\pi r^2} \int_{G^{(1)}} \left[\int_{|z_2-z_2^{(0)}|<r} | f(z_1, z_2) |^2 \, d\omega_{z_2} \right] d\omega_{z_1} .$$

$$< \frac{1}{\pi r^2} \int_{G^{(1)}\times G^{(2)}} | f(z_1, z_2) |^2 \, d\omega_{z_1 z_2} < \infty .$$

This means: $f(z_1, z_2^{(0)}) \in L^2(G^{(1)})$ for every fixed $z_2^{(0)} \in G^{(2)}$.

Let $\varphi_\nu(z_1)$ be a complete orthonormal system in $G^{(1)}$ and let $\psi_\mu(z_2)$ be a complete orthonormal system in $G^{(2)}$. As $f(z_1, z_2^{(0)}) \in L^2(G^{(1)})$, we can expand (see § 1.5):

$$f(z_1, z_2^{(0)}) = \sum_{\nu=0}^{\infty} a_\nu(z_2^{(0)}) \phi_\nu(z_1).$$

The coefficients are of course functions of z_2 if z_2 now varies. Because $f(z_1, z_2)$ is holomorphic in z_2 and because of the uniform convergence of the series, we have

$$\frac{\partial f(z_1, z_2)}{\partial \bar{z}_2} = 0 = \sum_{\nu=0}^{\infty} \frac{\partial}{\partial \bar{z}_2} a_\nu(z_2)\phi_\nu(z_1).$$

Since the expansion of any function $\in L^2(G_1)$ is unique, we obtain: $\partial a_\nu / \partial \bar{z}_2 = 0$ for all ν. This means that the $a_\nu(z_2)$ are holomorphic in $G^{(2)}$. And they are square-integrable because

$$\int_{G^{(1)}} |f(z_1, z_2)|^2 \, d\omega_{z_1} = \sum_{\nu=0}^{\infty} |a_\nu(z_2)|^2 \geqq |a_\nu(z_2)|^2.$$

It follows that

$$\infty > \int_{G^{(1)} \times G^{(2)}} |f(z_1, z_2)|^2 \, d\omega_{z_1 z_2} \geqq \int_{G^{(2)}} |a_\nu(z_2)|^2 \, d\omega_{z_2}$$

for every ν.

Therefore (since $a_\nu(z_2) \in L^2(G^{(2)})$), we can expand the $a_\nu(z_2)$ with respect to the system $\psi_\mu(z_2)$:

$$a_\nu(z_2) = \sum_{\mu=0}^{\infty} a_{\mu\nu} \psi_\mu(z_2).$$

Therefore

$$f(z_1, z_2) = \sum_{\nu=0}^{\infty} \left(\sum_{\mu=0}^{\infty} a_{\mu\nu} \psi_\mu(z_2)\right) \phi_\nu(z_1).$$

Applying Schwarz's inequality, we obtain:

$$\begin{aligned} \left|\sum_\nu \left(\sum_\mu a_{\mu\nu} \psi_\mu(z_2)\right) \phi_\nu(z_1)\right|^2 &\leqq \sum_\nu \left|\sum_\mu a_{\mu\nu} \psi_\mu(z_2)\right|^2 \cdot \sum_\nu |\phi_\nu(z_1)|^2 \\ &\leqq \sum_\nu \left(\sum_\mu |a_{\mu\nu}|^2 \sum_\mu |\psi_\mu(z_2)|^2\right) \cdot \sum_\nu |\phi_\nu(z_1)|^2 \\ &= K_{G^{(1)}}(z_1, \bar{z}_1) \cdot K_{G^{(2)}}(z_2, \bar{z}_2) \cdot \sum_{\mu,\nu} |a_{\mu\nu}|^2. \end{aligned}$$

One can also easily prove that $\sum_{\mu,\nu} |a_{\mu\nu}|^2 < \infty$. Hence the series

$$f(z_1, z_2) = \sum_{\mu,\nu} a_{\nu\mu} \phi_\nu(z_1) \psi_\mu(z_2)$$

converges uniformly absolutely in the interior of $G^{(1)} \times G^{(2)}$.

This means that every function $f(z_1, z_2) \in L^2(G^{(1)} \times G^{(2)})$ can be expanded with respect to the system $\phi_\nu(z_1) \cdot \psi_\mu(z_2)$. And, of course, this system is orthonormal in $G^{(1)} \times G^{(2)}$. Therefore it is a complete orthonormal system in $G^{(1)} \times G^{(2)}$.

Accordingly,

$$K_{G^{(1)}\times G^{(2)}}(z_1\,,\ z_2\,;\ \bar{t}_1\,,\ \bar{t}_2) \;=\; \textstyle\sum_{\mu,\nu=0}^{\infty} \phi_\nu(z_1)\psi_\mu(z_2)\overline{\phi_\nu(t_1)}\,\overline{\psi_\mu(t_2)}.$$

This series converges uniformly absolutely in the interior of $G^{(1)} \times G^{(2)}$. (One sees this immediately by applying Schwarz's inequality.) It is thus equal to

$$\left(\textstyle\sum_\nu \phi_\nu(z_1)\overline{\phi_\nu(t_1)}\right)\left(\textstyle\sum_\mu \psi_\mu(z_2)\overline{\psi_\mu(t_2)}\right) \;=\; K_{G^{(1)}}(z_1\,,\ \bar{t}_1)\cdot K_{G^{(2)}}(z_2\,,\ \bar{t}_2)\,.$$

Therefore

$$K_{G^{(1)}\times G^{(2)}}(z_1\,,\ z_2\,;\ \bar{t}_1\,,\ \bar{t}_2) \;=\; K_{G^{(1)}}(z_1\,,\ \bar{t}_1)\cdot K_{G^{(2)}}(z_2\,,\ \bar{t}_2)\,.$$

4.10. An immediate consequence of the lemma of § 4.9 for the invariant Bergman metric is the following result:

LEMMA. *Let ds_1^2 be the Bergman metric of the domain $G_{z_1}^{(1)}$, ds_2^2 the Bergman metric of the domain $G_{z_2}^{(2)}$, and ds^2 the Bergman metric of the product domain $G_{z_1}^{(1)} \times G_{z_2}^{(2)}$. Then*

$$ds^2 = ds_1^2 + ds_2^2.$$

Remark. We take as metric for one variable, $ds^2 =_{\mathrm{df}} (\partial^2 \log K(z, \bar{z})/\partial z \partial \bar{z})\, dz d\bar{z}$, and not, as usual, $ds^2 =_{\mathrm{df}} K(z, \bar{z}) \cdot dz d\bar{z}$. This latter definition is inconsistent with the general definition for several variables.

Proof:

$$\begin{aligned}
ds^2 &= \sum_{\mu,\nu} \frac{\partial^2 \log K_{G^{(1)}\times G^{(2)}}(z, \bar{z})}{\partial z_\mu\, \partial \bar{z}_\nu}\, dz_\mu\, d\bar{z}_\nu \\
&= \sum_{\mu,\nu} \frac{\partial^2[\log K_{G^{(1)}}(z_1, \bar{z}_1) + \log K_{G^{(2)}}(z_2\,, \bar{z}_2)]}{\partial z_\mu\, \partial \bar{z}_\nu}\, dz_\mu\, d\bar{z}_\nu \\
&= \frac{\partial^2 \log K_{G^{(1)}}(z_1\,, \bar{z}_1)}{\partial z_1\, \partial \bar{z}_1}\, dz_1\, d\bar{z}_1 + \frac{\partial^2 \log K_{G^{(2)}}(z_2\,, \bar{z}_2)}{\partial z_2\, \partial \bar{z}_2}\, dz_2\, d\bar{z}_2 \\
&= ds_1^2 + ds_2^2.
\end{aligned}$$

Obviously, this lemma (as well as that of § 4.9) is not limited to two variables and is valid for the products of domains of arbitrary complex dimensions (equal or unequal).

5. Continuation theorems

5.1. THEOREM. *Let G be a schlicht domain, B a schlicht or non-schlicht domain but without branch points as interior points. If*

$K_G(z, \bar{t})$ is holomorphic in $B_z \times B_{\bar{t}}$, $G \subset B$, then

(a) *If $\phi^{(\nu)}(z)$ is a complete set of orthonormal functions in G, then all $\phi^{(\nu)}(z)$ are still holomorphic in B;*

(b) *$\sum \phi^{(\nu)}(z)\overline{\phi^{(\nu)}(t)}$ converges uniformly in the interior of $B_z \times B_{\bar{t}}$ and represents $K_G(z, \bar{t})$ there.* (*Remark.* Result (b) is of special interest if B is the envelope of holomorphy of G.)

Proof. Let $(z^{(0)}, \bar{z}^{(0)})$ be an interior point of $G_z \times G_{\bar{t}}$ and let $D =_{\text{df}} \{z \mid |z_1 - z_1^{(0)}| < r, |z_2 - z_2^{(0)}| < r\}$ be compact in B. For the sake of simplicity, we assume now that $z^{(0)} = (0, 0)$. Since $K_G(z, \bar{t})$ is holomorphic in the closed polycylinder $D_z \times D_{\bar{t}}$, we can expand it in a power series:

$$K_G(z, \bar{t}) = \sum_{k,l,m,n} \frac{K_{kl\bar{m}\bar{n}}(00, 00)}{k!l!m!n!} z_1^k z_2^l \bar{t}_1^m \bar{t}_2^n .$$

(We write $K_{kl\bar{m}\bar{n}}(z, \bar{t}) =_{\text{df}} \partial^{k+l+m+n} K_G(z, \bar{t})/\partial z_1^k \partial z_2^l \partial \bar{t}_1^m \partial \bar{t}_2^n$.) On the other hand, we have in $G_z \times G_{\bar{t}}$ the expansion

$$K_G(z, \bar{t}) = \sum_\nu \phi^{(\nu)}(z)\overline{\phi^{(\nu)}(t)}.$$

Since (00, 00) belongs to $G_z \times G_{\bar{t}}$, the series converges uniformly in a neighborhood of this point. Therefore

$$K_{kl\bar{m}\bar{n}}(z, \bar{t}) = \sum \phi_{kl}^{(\nu)}(z)\overline{\phi_{mn}^{(\nu)}(t)}.$$

(We write $\phi_{kl}^{(\nu)}(z) =_{\text{df}} \partial^{k+l}\phi^{(\nu)}(z)/\partial z_1^k \partial z_2^l$ and we note that

$$\frac{\partial^{m+n}\overline{\phi^{(\nu)}(t)}}{\partial \bar{t}_1^m \partial \bar{t}_2^n} = \overline{\frac{\partial^{m+n}\phi^{(\nu)}(t)}{\partial t_1^m \partial t_2^n}} = \overline{\phi_{mn}^{(\nu)}(t)} .$$

Substituting in the power series, we obtain

$$K_G(z, \bar{t}) = \sum_{k,l,m,n} \frac{1}{k!l!m!n!} \Big(\sum_\nu \phi_{kl}^{(\nu)}(0, 0)\overline{\phi_{mn}^{(\nu)}(0, 0)}\Big) z_1^k z_2^l \bar{t}_1^m \bar{t}_2^n .$$

This series converges uniformly absolutely in the closed domain $\bar{D}_z \times \bar{D}_{\bar{t}}$—absolutely, however, in the sense that

$$\sum_{k,l,m,n} \frac{1}{k!l!m!n!} \Big| \sum_\nu \phi_{kl}^{(\nu)}(0, 0)\overline{\phi_{mn}^{(\nu)}(0, 0)} \Big| \, | z_1^k z_2^l \bar{t}_1^m \bar{t}_2^n |$$

converges. However, from the convergence of this series it follows that

$$\frac{1}{k!l!m!n!} \Big| \sum_\nu \phi_{kl}^{(\nu)} \overline{\phi_{mn}^{(\nu)}} \Big| r^{k+l+m+n} < M \text{ for all } k, l, m, n.$$

Therefore we obtain, if $m = k$, $n = l$,

$$\frac{r^{2(k+l)}}{(k!\,l!)^2} \sum_\nu |\phi_{kl}^{(\nu)}|^2 < M \quad \text{for all } k, l\,.$$

Accordingly,

$$\frac{r^{k+l+m+n}}{k!\,l!\,m!\,n!} \sum_\nu |\phi_{kl}^{(\nu)}|\,|\phi_{mn}^{(\nu)}|$$

$$\leqq \frac{r^{k+l+m+n}}{k!\,l!\,m!\,n!} \sqrt{\sum_\nu |\phi_{kl}^{(\nu)}|^2} \sqrt{\sum_\nu |\phi_{mn}^{(\nu)}|^2} < M,$$

and from this it follows in the usual way that

$$\sum_{k,l,m,n} \frac{z_1^k z_2^l \bar{t}_1^m \bar{t}_2^n}{k!\,l!\,m!\,n!} \cdot \sum_\nu |\phi_{kl}^{(\nu)}|\,|\overline{\phi_{mn}^{(\nu)}}|$$

converges uniformly in the *interior* of $D_z \times D_{\bar{t}}$.

Now we can rearrange the series and obtain:

$$K_G(z, \bar{t}) = \sum_\nu \left(\sum_{k,l} \frac{\phi_{kl}^{(\nu)}}{k!\,l!} z_1^k z_2^l\right)\left(\sum_{m,n} \frac{\overline{\phi_{mn}^{(\nu)}}}{m!\,n!} \bar{t}_1^m \bar{t}_2^n\right).$$

Also, because $\sum_\nu |\phi_{kl}^{(\nu)}/k!l!|^2 r^{2(k+l)} < M$, we have for every ν that $|\phi_{kl}^{(\nu)}/k!l!|^2 r^{2(k+l)} < M$ and $\sum_{k,l}(\phi_{kl}^{(\nu)}(0, 0))/(k!l!) z_1^k z_2^l$ converges in the interior of D. Since $\phi^\nu(z)$ is holomorphic at the origin, the power series represents the holomorphic continuation of $\phi^{(\nu)}$ into D.

Therefore we can write

$$K_G(z, \bar{t}) = \sum_\nu \phi^{(\nu)}(z)\overline{\phi^{(\nu)}(t)}$$

and this series converges in the interior of $D_z \times D_{\bar{t}}$.

In $G_z \times G_{\bar{t}}$ the series converges in any case. Therefore the series converges in $\{G_z \times G_{\bar{t}}\} \cup \{D_z \times D_{\bar{t}}\}$. But it converges also in $\{G_z \cup D_z\} \times \{G_{\bar{t}} \cup D_{\bar{t}}\}$ because of Schwarz's inequality:

$$\left|\sum \phi^{(\nu)}(z)\overline{\phi^{(\nu)}(t)}\right| \leqq \sqrt{\sum |\phi^{(\nu)}(z)|^2} \cdot \sqrt{\sum |\phi^{(\nu)}(t)|^2}.$$

If we now have an interior point $z^{(1)} \in G \cup D$ and a bicylinder $D^{(1)} = \{z \mid |z_1 - z_1^{(1)}| < r^{(1)}; |z_2 - z_2^{(1)}| < r^{(1)}\}$, $D^{(1)} \subset\subset B$, we can repeat the whole procedure for $G \cup D$, $z^{(1)}$, $D^{(1)}$ instead of G, $z^{(0)}$, D. According to the Heine-Borel theorem, we can cover any closed subdomain of B with finitely many bicylinders. That proves our theorem.

We note that nothing has to be changed if B is not schlicht but does not contain branch points as interior points. It is important that B is not required to be schlicht because we want to apply this theorem to the case where B is the envelope of holomorphy of G, and there exist schlicht domains the envelope of holomorphy of which is not schlicht.

5.2. Theorem. *Let G, B be as described in § 5.1 and let $K_G(z, \bar{t})$ be holomorphic in $B_z \times B_{\bar{t}}$. Then any function $f(z) \in L^2(G)$ is still holomorphic in B. If $f(z) = \sum a_\nu \phi_\nu(z)$ is the expansion of $f(z)$ with respect to the complete orthonormal system $\phi_\nu(z)$ of G, then the series converges uniformly absolutely in B and represents $f(z)$ there.*

Proof. If $f(z) \in L^2(G)$, then $f(z)$ can be expanded for $z \in G$: $f(z) = \sum a_\nu \phi_\nu(z)$ with $\sum | a_\nu |^2 < \infty$. Applying Schwarz's inequality, we obtain

$$(\sum | a_\nu | \, | \phi_\nu(z) |)^2 \leqq \sum | a_\nu |^2 \sum | \phi_\nu(z) |^2 .$$

According to § 5.1, $\sum | \phi_\nu(z) |^2$ converges uniformly in B. Therefore $\sum a_\nu \phi_\nu(z)$ converges uniformly absolutely in B and gives the holomorphic continuation.

5.3. Theorem. *Under the assumptions of § 5.1 the Bergman kernel function $K_G(z, \bar{t})$ possesses the reproducing property*

$$f(z) = \int_G f(t) \, K_G(z, \bar{t}) \, d\omega_t$$

not only for $z \in G$ but also for $z \in B$.

Proof. According to § 5.1, $K_G(z, \bar{t}) = \sum \phi_\nu(z)\overline{\phi_\nu(t)}$ converges uniformly in the interior of B for any fixed $z \in B$. Therefore

$$\int_G f(t) K_G(z, \bar{t}) \, d\omega_t = \int_G (\sum a_\nu \phi_\nu(t)) (\sum \phi_\mu(z)\overline{\phi_\mu(t)}) \, d\omega_t$$
$$= \sum a_\nu \phi_\nu(z) = f(z).$$

5.4. Theorem. *Under the assumptions of § 5.1, the formula*

$$[K_G(z^{(0)}, \bar{z}^{(0)})]^{-1} = \min \int_G | f(t) |^2 \, d\omega_t$$

holds not only for $z^{(0)} \in G$ but also for $z^{(0)} \in B$; the minimum is taken *with respect to the set of all functions* $f(z) \in L^2(G)$ *that satisfy the condition* $|f(z^{(0)})| \geqq 1$.

Proof. We note that it is consistent to require the condition $|f(z^{(0)})| \geqq 1$ for $z^{(0)} \in B$ because $f(z)$ can be continued into B.

According to § 5.2, we have in B:

$$|f(z)|^2 = |\sum a_\nu \phi_\nu(z)|^2 \leqq \sum |a_\nu|^2 \sum |\phi^{(\nu)}(z)|^2 .$$

The right-hand side is equal to $K_G(z, \bar{z}) \cdot \int_G |f(z)|^2 \, d\omega$. Therefore, if we consider only functions with $|f(z^{(0)})| \geqq 1$, then

$$[K_G(z^{(0)}, \bar{z}^{(0)})]^{-1} \leqq \int_G |f(z)|^2 \, d\omega.$$

On the other hand, there does exist a function in $L^2(G)$ for which the integral assumes its minimum: namely, $f(z) = K_G(z, \bar{z}^{(0)}) \cdot [K_G(z^{(0)}, \bar{z}^{(0)})]^{-1}$. That proves our theorem.

5.5. Lemma. *Let G and B be as described in* § 5.1 *and let* $K_G(z, \bar{t})$ *be holomorphic in* $B_z \times B_{\bar{t}}$. *Let* $G^* \supset G$. *Then* $K_{G^*}(z, \bar{z}) \leqq K_G(z, \bar{z})$ *holds in the intersection* $G^* \cap B$. (The essential point is that the inequality holds not only in G (that is well known) but also in $B \cap (G^* - G)$.)

Proof. Any function that is holomorphic, single-valued, and square-integrable in G^* has the same properties in G because $G \subset G^*$. Therefore $L^2(G) \supset L^2(G^*)$. According to § 5.2, all functions of $L^2(G)$ are still defined at any point $z^{(0)} \in B$. Hence

$$\min_{f \in L^2(G)} \int_G |f(z)|^2 \, d\omega \leqq \min_{g \in L^2(G^*)} \int_G |g(z)|^2 \, d\omega \leqq \min_{g \in L^2(G^*)} \int_{G^*} |g(z)|^2 \, d\omega,$$

the minima being taken under the same additional condition: $|f(z^{(0)})| \geqq 1$, $|g(z^{(0)})| \geqq 1$ for $z^{(0)} \in G^* \cap B$. The first integral represents $[K_G(z^{(0)}, \bar{z}^{(0)})]^{-1}$ in B (according to § 5.4), and the third integral represents $[K_{G^*}(z^{(0)}, \bar{z}^{(0)})]^{-1}$ in G^*.

5.6. *Let G be schlicht, let* $(z^{(0)}, \bar{z}^{(0)})$ *be an interior point of* $G_z \times G_{\bar{t}}$, *and let D be the bicylinder* $\{z \mid |z_1 - z_1^{(0)}| < r; |z_2 - z_2^{(0)}| < r\}$. *If* $K_G(z, \bar{t})$ *is holomorphic in* $\bar{D}_z \times \bar{D}_{\bar{t}}$, *then* $K_G(z, \bar{t})$ *is holomorphic in* $\{G_z \cup D_z\} \times \{G_{\bar{t}} \cup D_{\bar{t}}\}$.

Actually, this has already been shown in the proof of § 5.1! In the first step of the proof of the theorem of § 5.1 we used, among the assumptions of § 5.1, only those stated above, and we now obtain that $\sum \phi^{(\nu)}(z)\overline{\phi^{(\nu)}(t)}$ converges uniformly absolutely in the interior of $\{G_z \cup D_z\} \times \{G_{\bar{t}} \cup D_{\bar{t}}\}$.

5.7. THEOREM. *Let H be a bounded domain of holomorphy that does not possess a Nebenhülle. Then $K_H(z, \bar{z})$ cannot be continued real-analytically beyond H.*[5]

This can be formulated in a different way: *The manifold $\{(z, \bar{t}) \mid z \in \partial H; \bar{t} = \bar{z}\}$ belongs to the boundary of the domain of existence of $K_H(z, \bar{t})$.* (The symbol ∂H denotes the boundary of H.)

Proof. Suppose this not true. Then there would exist a boundary point $(z^{(1)}, \bar{z}^{(1)})$ of $H_z \times H_{\bar{t}}$ such that $K_H(z, \bar{t})$ is holomorphic in a neighborhood. Then we can find a point $z^{(0)}$ and a bicylinder $D = \{z \mid |z_1 - z_1^{(0)}| < r, |z_2 - z_2^{(0)}| < r\}$ such that $z^{(0)}$ is an interior point of H, that $K_H(z, \bar{t})$ is holomorphic in $\bar{D}_z \times \bar{D}_{\bar{t}}$, but that D intersects the boundary of H.

Applying the lemma of § 5.6, we obtain that $K_G(z, t)$ is holomorphic in $\{G_z \cup D_z\} \times \{G_{\bar{t}} \cup D_{\bar{t}}\}$, and therefore the lemma of § 5.5 can be applied in the following reasoning.

Since H does not possess a Nebenhülle and since H was assumed to be bounded, we can approximate H by bounded analytic polyhedrons P_ν, $H \subset\subset P_\nu$. In particular, we can choose P_ν so close to H that P_ν intersects D. According to the lemma of § 5.5, we have $K_{P_\nu}(z, \bar{z}) \leqq K_H(z, \bar{z})$ in $D \cap P_\nu$. If $z^{(2)}$ is a boundary point of P_ν in D, then of course $K_H(z, \bar{z})$ is bounded in a neighborhood, for $K_H(z, \bar{z})$ is finite in D. On the other hand, it should not be bounded because $K_{P_\nu}(z, \bar{z}) \leqq K_H(z, \bar{z})$ and $K_{P_\nu}(z, \bar{z})$, as the kernel function of an analytic polyhedron, becomes infinite everywhere at the boundary of P_ν (according to § 3.3). This yields a contradiction; our theorem is proved.

6. Metrization of domains of holomorphy by pseudoconvex functions; continuation of the invariant Bergman metric

The Bergman kernel function is a special pseudoconvex function (§ 1.17). In this section we shall compare properties of the invariant Bergman metric, which is generated by the kernel function,

[5] The idea of this theorem is due to Mehring-Sommer [17].

with properties of metrics which are generated by general pseudoconvex functions.

6.1. According to §§ 2.7 and 3.2, we have: If $K_G(z, \bar{z})$ becomes infinite everywhere at the boundary of a domain G, then G is a domain of holomorphy; and a region $\{z \mid z \in G;\ K_G(z, \bar{z}) < M\}$ is a region of holomorphy if it is compact in G. For general pseudoconvex functions, corresponding theorems hold. If $V(z, \bar{z})$ is pseudoconvex in G and becomes infinite everywhere at the boundary of G, then G is a domain of holomorphy. Also, if the region $\{z \mid z \in G;\ V(z, \bar{z}) < M\}$ is compact in a domain G where $V(z, \bar{z})$ is defined and pseudoconvex, then it is a region of holomorphy. The proof of these two general theorems,[6] however, is much more complicated than the proof of the corresponding theorems for the kernel function.

6.2. On the other hand, it was difficult to show that the kernel function becomes infinite everywhere at the boundary of a domain of holomorphy, and for quite general domains of holomorphy this is not true. However, if one requires only that there exists a pseudoconvex function that becomes infinite everywhere at the boundary, I have shown in an earlier paper (see [10, § 6]; cf. also [12] and [16]) the following: *Let $d_G(z, \bar{z})$ denote the Euclidean distance of the point z from the boundary of a domain G. Then* $\log\,[d_G(z, \bar{z})]^{-1}$ *is pseudoconvex in G.* Obviously, $\log\,[d_G(z, \bar{z})]^{-1}$ becomes infinite everywhere at the boundary of G (if G is bounded).

6.3. The kernel function as well as any (sufficiently differentiable) pseudoconvex function generates a Hermitian metric. Let G be a domain and $V(z, \bar{z})$ a pseudoconvex function in G. Let $V(z, \bar{z})$ possess continuous partial derivatives of second order. Then the Hermitian form

$$\sum_{\mu,\nu} \frac{\partial^2 V(z, \bar{z})}{\partial z_\mu \partial \bar{z}_\nu}\, dz_\mu d\bar{z}_\nu$$

is positive semidefinite (§ 1.18). Therefore we obtain a metric if we let ds^2 equal this form. (However, as the form is in general only semidefinite, the metric is not strictly positive.)

A metric of this type is always a Kähler metric, because the ex-

[6] See [11], [12], and [19].

ternal differential (in the sense of the calculus of the alternating differential forms) vanishes. (*Remark.* A pseudoconvex function is in general not differentiable or continuous. In such a case, however, the derivatives exist everywhere with the exception of a certain zero set [20, § 6.22].)

6.4. The property of a function to be pseudoconvex in a domain is invariant with respect to holomorphic transformations of the domain (§ 1.18). Therefore, a holomorphic transformation of the domain transforms a metric which is generated by a pseudoconvex function into a metric of the same type in the image domain.

6.5. *Among all functions which are pseudoconvex in a domain, the Bergman kernel function is distinguished in the following way:*

(a) $K_G(z, \bar{z})$ *is real-analytic in* G. *Moreover, if we replace* $\bar{z}$ *by the independent variable* $\bar{t}$, *then* $K_G(z, \bar{t})$ *is holomorphic in* $G_z \times G_{\bar{t}}$.

(b) *The Kähler metric generated by* $K_G(z, \bar{z})$ *(Bergman metric):*

$$(*) \qquad ds^2 = \sum_{\mu,\nu} \frac{\partial^2 \log K_G(z, \bar{z})}{\partial z_\mu \partial \bar{z}_\nu} dz_\mu d\bar{z}_\nu$$

is positive definite in G *(not merely semidefinite), and* ds^2 *is invariant with respect to holomorphic transformations of the domain* G. (See § 1.10.)

(c) $K_G(z, \bar{z})$ *possesses a pseudoconvex continuation in* $H(G)$. (By "pseudoconvex continuation" we denote a function that is pseudoconvex in a larger domain and coincides with the given function in the given domain. A pseudoconvex continuation is not unique.)

Proof. We represent $K_G(z, \bar{t})$ by a complete orthonormal system in G. $K_G(z, \bar{t}) = \sum \phi_\nu(z)\overline{\phi_\nu(t)}$. According to § 2.5, $K_G(z, \bar{t})$ is holomorphic in $H(G)_z \times H(G)_{\bar{t}}$. Therefore, because of § 5.1, the series converges uniformly absolutely in the interior of $H(G)_z \times H(G)_{\bar{t}}$. Hence $\sum | \phi_\nu(z) |^2$ converges uniformly absolutely in the interior of $H(G)$. A uniformly convergent series of squares of absolute values of holomorphic functions is a pseudoconvex function. (Compare the proof of § 2.8.)

6.6. *The pseudoconvex continuation of* $K_G(z, \bar{z})$ (which is obtained from the holomorphic continuation of $K_G(z, \bar{t})$) *preserves certain properties which* $K_G(z, \bar{z})$ *possesses in* G. We obtain these results immediately by combining the results of §§ 2.5 and 5. In particular, we obtain:

(a) *If* $K_G(z\,\bar{z},) = \sum_\nu |\phi_\nu(z)|^2$ *in* G, *this representation still holds in* $H(G)$.

(b) $[K_G(z^{(0)}, \bar{z}^{(0)})]^{-1} = \min \int_G |f(t)|\, d\omega_t$ *for* $z^{(0)} \in H(G)$, *the minimum being taken with respect to the set of all functions* $f(z)$ *in* $L^2(G)$ *that satisfy the condition* $|f(z^{(0)})| \geqq 1$.

6.7. *By the continuation of* $K_G(z, \bar{z})$ *the Bergman metric* (*) *is continued into* $H(G)$.

(a) *The coefficients* $\partial^2 \log K_G(z, \bar{z})/\partial z_\mu \partial \bar{z}_\nu$ *of the Hermitian form are continued real-analytically into* $H(G)$.

(b) *The associated alternating differential form is*

$$\sum_{\mu,\nu} \frac{\partial^2 \log K_G(z, \bar{t})}{\partial z_\mu\, \partial \bar{t}_\nu}\, dz_\mu\, d\bar{t}_\nu\,;$$

the coefficients $\partial^2 \log K_G(z, \bar{t})/\partial z_\mu \partial \bar{t}_\nu$ *are continued holomorphically into* $H(G)_z \times H(G)_{\bar{t}}$.

6.8. Theorem. *The Bergman metric is invariant with respect to holomorphic transformations not only of the domain* G *but also of* $H(G)$.

Let $z_1^* = z_1^*(z_1, z_2)$; $z_2^* = z_2^*(z_1, z_2)$

be a holomorphic transformation of the domain G upon G^* such that

$$\begin{vmatrix} \dfrac{\partial z_1^*}{\partial z_1} & \dfrac{\partial z_1^*}{\partial z_2} \\[2ex] \dfrac{\partial z_2^*}{\partial z_1} & \dfrac{\partial z_2^*}{\partial z_2} \end{vmatrix} \neq 0 \quad \text{in } G.$$

Then the kernel function transforms, for $(z, \bar{t}) \in G_z \times G_{\bar{t}}$, according to the law (see § 1.8):

$$K_{G^*}(z^*, \bar{t}^*) = K_G(z, \bar{t}) \begin{vmatrix} \dfrac{\partial z_1}{\partial z_1^*} & \dfrac{\partial z_1}{\partial z_2^*} \\[2ex] \dfrac{\partial z_2}{\partial z_1^*} & \dfrac{\partial z_2}{\partial z_2^*} \end{vmatrix} \cdot \begin{vmatrix} \dfrac{\partial \bar{t}_1}{\partial \bar{t}_1^*} & \dfrac{\partial \bar{t}_1}{\partial \bar{t}_2^*} \\[2ex] \dfrac{\partial \bar{t}_2}{\partial \bar{t}_1^*} & \dfrac{\partial \bar{t}_2}{\partial \bar{t}_2^*} \end{vmatrix}.$$

Each side is a holomorphic function in $G_z \times G_{\bar{t}}$ and therefore still holomorphic in $H(G_z \times G_{\bar{t}})$, which is equal to $H(G)_z \times H(G)_{\bar{t}}$ (according to § 2.4). Therefore the transformation law holds in $H(G)_z \times H(G)_{\bar{z}}$ and we have there:

$$\log K_{G^*}(z^*, \bar{z}^*) = \log K_G(z, \bar{z}) + \log \begin{vmatrix} \frac{\partial z_1}{\partial z_1^*} & \frac{\partial z_1}{\partial z_2^*} \\ \frac{\partial z_2}{\partial z_1^*} & \frac{\partial z_2}{\partial z_2^*} \end{vmatrix} + \log \begin{vmatrix} \frac{\partial \bar{z}_1}{\partial \bar{z}_1^*} & \frac{\partial \bar{z}_1}{\partial \bar{z}_2^*} \\ \frac{\partial \bar{z}_2}{\partial \bar{z}_1^*} & \frac{\partial \bar{z}_2}{\partial \bar{z}_2^*} \end{vmatrix}.$$

The determinants are holomorphic functions of z_1^*, z_2^* and $\bar{z}_1^*$, $\bar{z}_2^*$, respectively. Therefore differentiation with respect to $\bar{z}_\mu^*$ or z_ν^* yields zero and we obtain

$$\frac{\partial^2 \log K_{G^*}(z^*, \bar{z}^*)}{\partial z_\mu^* \partial \bar{z}_\nu^*} = \sum_{m,n} \frac{\partial^2 \log K_G(z, \bar{z})}{\partial z_m \partial \bar{z}_n} \frac{\partial z_m}{\partial z_\mu^*} \frac{\partial \bar{z}_n}{\partial \bar{z}_\nu^*}.$$

On the other hand,

$$\frac{\partial^2 \log K_G(z, \bar{z})}{\partial z_\mu \partial \bar{z}_\nu} = \overline{\frac{\partial^2 \log K_G(z, \bar{z})}{\partial \bar{z}_\mu \partial z_\nu}}.$$

We see that $\partial^2 \log K_G(z, \bar{z})/\partial z_\mu \partial \bar{z}_\nu$ transform as a covariant Hermitian tensor of second order. Therefore the Bergman metric is invariant with respect to holomorphic transformations.

Holomorphic transformations of G are holomorphic transformations of $H(G)$, because the functions $z_1^* = z_1^*(z_1, z_2)$ and $z_2^* = z_2^*(z_1, z_2)$ are still holomorphic in $H(G)$. If the determinant

$$\begin{vmatrix} \frac{\partial z_1^*}{\partial z_1} & \frac{\partial z_1^*}{\partial z_2} \\ \frac{\partial z_2^*}{\partial z_1} & \frac{\partial z_2^*}{\partial z_2} \end{vmatrix}$$

is different from zero in G, then it is different from zero in $H(G)$, since no function holomorphic in G assumes any values in $H(G)$ which it has not assumed in G.

Since the transformation law is still valid in $H(G)$, as we have seen above, the metric is still invariant in $H(G)$.

6.9. THEOREM. *The Hermitian form defining the Bergman metric is positive definite in $H(G)$.*

Remark. In proving our theorem by a new method we shall give at the same time a new and simpler proof of the basic fact that the form is positive definite in G. (Compare § 1.10.)

Proof. Let us consider an arbitrary fixed point $z^{(0)} \in H(G)$. Any Hermitian form can be transformed by a linear orthogonal coordinate transformation into such a form that the coefficients of the mixed terms vanish.

Let the transformation be $dz_j = \sum_k a_{jk}\, dz_k^*$. Then

$$ds^2 = \sum_{\mu,\nu} \frac{\partial^2 \log K_G(z, \bar{z})}{\partial z_\mu \partial \bar{z}_\nu} dz_\mu d\bar{z}_\nu$$

$$= \sum_{\mu,\nu} \frac{\partial^2 \log K_G(z, \bar{z})}{\partial z_\mu \partial \bar{z}_\nu} \Big(\sum_j a_{\mu j}\, dz_j^*\Big)\Big(\sum_k \bar{a}_{\nu k}\, d\bar{z}_k^*\Big)$$

$$= \sum_{j,k} \Big(\sum_{\mu,\nu} \frac{\partial^2 \log K_G(z, \bar{z})}{\partial z_\mu \partial \bar{z}_\nu} a_{\mu j}\, \bar{a}_{\nu k}\Big) dz_k^*\, d\bar{z}_k^* .$$

Let us denote the coefficients of the last form by b_{jk}^*. In particular, we have $b_{jk}^* = 0$ for $j \neq k$.

Now we transform G into G^* by the inverse of the holomorphic transformation $dz_j = \sum_k a_{jk}\, dz_k^*$. Since the Bergman metric is invariant throughout $H(G)$ (as proved in § 6.8), we obtain

$$ds^2 = \sum_{j,k} \frac{\partial^2 \log K_{G^*}(z^*, \bar{z}^*)}{\partial z_j^* \partial \bar{z}_k^*} dz_j^*\, d\bar{z}_k^* .$$

That means

$$b_{jk}^* = \frac{\partial^2 \log K_{G^*}(z^*, \bar{z}^*)}{\partial z_j^* \partial \bar{z}_k^*}\bigg|_{z^{*(0)}} = 0 \quad \text{for} \quad j \neq k .$$

Now

$$K_{G^*}(z^*, \bar{z}^*) = \sum_\nu | \phi_\nu^*(z^*) |^2.$$

Therefore

$$\frac{\partial^2 \log K_{G^*}(z^*, \bar{z}^*)}{\partial z_j^* \partial \bar{z}_j^*} = [\sum_\nu | \phi_\nu^*(z^*) |^2]^{-2}$$

$$\cdot \Big[\sum_\mu | \phi_\mu |^2 \cdot \sum_\nu \frac{\partial \phi_\nu^*}{\partial z_j^*} \cdot \overline{\frac{\partial \phi_\nu^*}{\partial z_j^*}} - \Big(\sum_\mu \frac{\partial \phi_\mu^*}{\partial z_j^*} \bar{\phi}_\mu^*\Big)\Big(\sum_\nu \phi_\nu^* \overline{\frac{\partial \phi_\nu^*}{\partial z_j^*}}\Big)\Big]$$

$$= \Big[\sum_\nu |\phi_\nu^*|^2\Big]^{-2} \cdot \Big[\sum_\mu | \phi_\mu^* |^2 \cdot \sum_\nu \Big|\frac{\partial \phi_\nu^*}{\partial z_j^*}\Big|^2 - \Big|\sum_\mu \frac{\partial \phi_\mu^*}{\partial z_j^*} \bar{\phi}_\nu^*\Big|^2\Big].$$

Because of Schwarz's inequality this is greater than or equal to zero.

Now Schwarz's inequality gives us zero if and only if

$$\lambda\ \phi_\nu{}^*(z^{*(0)}) = \left.\frac{\partial \phi_\nu{}^*(z^*)}{\partial z_j{}^*}\right|_{z^{*(0)}},$$

where λ is a complex constant.

This is impossible, for then we would have for any function $f \in L^2(G^*)$ at the point $z^{*(0)} \in H(G^*)$:

$$\left.\frac{\partial f(z^*)}{\partial z_j{}^*}\right|_{z^{*(0)}} = \frac{\partial}{\partial z_j{}^*} \sum_\nu a_\nu \phi_\nu{}^*(z^*) = \sum_\nu a_\nu \frac{\partial \phi_\nu{}^*(z^*)}{\partial z_j{}^*}$$
$$= \lambda \sum a_\nu\ \phi_\nu{}^*(z^{*(0)}) = \lambda\, f(z^{*(0)}).$$

The rational functions belong to $L^2(G^*)$, and $\partial f(z^*)/\partial z_j{}^* = \lambda f(z^*)$ certainly does not hold for the rational functions. Therefore

$$\left.\frac{\partial^2 \log K_{G^*}(z^*, \bar{z}^*)}{\partial z_j{}^* \partial \bar{z}_j{}^*}\right|_{z^{*(0)}} > 0 \quad \text{for} \quad j = 1, \cdots, n,$$

and $z^{*(0)} \in H(G^*)$. Therefore the Hermitian form

$$\sum_{j,k} \frac{\partial^2 \log K_{G^*}(z^*, \bar{z}^*)}{\partial z_j{}^* \partial \bar{z}_k{}^*}\, dz_j{}^*\, d\bar{z}_k{}^* = \sum_j \frac{\partial^2 \log K_{G^*}(z^*, \bar{z}^*)}{\partial z_j{}^* \partial \bar{z}_j{}^*}\, dz_j{}^*\, d\bar{z}_j{}^*$$

is positive definite at the arbitrary point $z^{*(0)} \in H(G^*)$. Since the property of being positive definite is invariant,

$$\sum_{\mu,\nu} \frac{\partial^2 \log K_G(z, \bar{z})}{\partial z_\mu\, \partial \bar{z}_\nu}\, dz_\mu\, d\bar{z}_\nu$$

is positive definite throughout $H(G)$, as asserted.

6.10. COROLLARY. *The function* $\log K_G(z, \bar{z})$ *is pseudoconvex in* $H(G)$.

This is an immediate consequence of §§ 6.9 and 1.18. In §§ 2.8 and 6.5(c) we have proved that $K_G(z, \bar{z})$ is pseudoconvex in $H(G)$. Our corollary yields the theorems of §§ 2.8 and 6.5(c) and is a stronger result, because a function $V(z, \bar{z})$ is pseudoconvex if $\log V(z, \bar{z})$ is pseudoconvex but not vice versa.

6.11. The variety of pseudoconvex functions that exist in a given domain is large. Therefore the variety of metrics is large.

An interesting question is: Given an arbitrary domain G, does there always exist a metric ds^2 generated by a pseudoconvex function such that the whole boundary of the domain is "infinite with respect to the metric ds^2"?[7]

THEOREM. *Let G be an arbitrary bounded domain. Then all those boundary points of G which are interior points of the envelope of holomorphy of G are finite with respect to the Bergman metric.*

This theorem is an immediate consequence of the fact that the Bergman metric is continued into $H(G)$ and therefore finite in $H(G)$ (§ 6.7).

COROLLARY. *If G is a domain the whole boundary of which is infinite with respect to the Bergman metric, then G is a domain of holomorphy.*

6.12. The example of § 4.2 shows that not every boundary point of an arbitrary domain of holomorphy is infinite with respect to the Bergman metric. Under certain assumptions about the domain, however, one could show that the whole boundary is infinite. These investigations would be quite similar to the investigations in § 4.

BIBLIOGRAPHY

1. ARONSZAJN, N. *Theory of reproducing kernels,* Trans. Amer. Math. Soc. 68 (1950), 337–404.

2. BEHNKE, H., AND STEIN, K. *Konvergente Folgen von Regularitätsgebieten und die Meromorphiekonvexität,* Math. Ann. 116 (1939), 204–216.

3. ——— *Die Konvexität in der Funktionentheorie mehrerer komplexer Veränderlichen,* Mitt. Math. Ges. Hamburg 8 (1940), 34–81.

4. —— AND THULLEN, P. *Theorie der Funktionen mehrer komplexer Veränderlichen.* Ergebnisse der Mathematik, Bd. 3, Heft 3. Berlin, 1934.

5. BERGMAN[N], S. *Über die Kernfunktion eines Bereichs und ihr Verhalten am Rande,* J. Reine Angew. Math. 169 (1933), 1–42, and 172 (1935), 89–128.

6. —— *Sur les fonctions orthogonales de plusieurs variables complexes ....* Mémorial des Sciences Mathématiques, No. 106. Paris, 1947.

7. —— *Sur la fonction-noyau d'un domaine ....* Mémorial des Sciences Mathématiques, No. 108. Paris, 1948.

---

[7] H. Grauert [13] will publish a paper in which he investigates this question and similar problems.

8. —— ***The kernel function and conformal mapping.*** Mathematical Surveys, No. 5. New York, 1950.

9. Bochner, S., and Martin, W. T. ***Several complex variables.*** Princeton, 1948.

10. Bremermann, H. J. *Die Charakterisierung von Regularitätsgebieten durch pseudokonvexe Funktionen.* Dissertation. Münster, 1951.

11. —— *Über die Äquivalenz der pseudokonvexen Gebiete und der Holomorphicgebiete im Raum von n komplexen Veränderlichen.* Math. Ann. 128 (1954), 63–91.

12. —— *Complex convexity.* Navy Report, Stanford, 1954. (An abstract was published in Bull. Amer. Math. Soc. 60 (1954), 392–393.)

13. Grauert, H. *Métrique kaehlerienne et domaines d'holomorphie.* C. R. Acad. Sci. Paris, 238 (1954), 2048–2050. (Also to appear in Math. Ann., in 1956.)

14. Hartogs, F. *Zur Theorie der analytischen Funktionen mehrerer unabhängiger Veränderlichen,* Math. Ann. 62 (1906), 1–88.

15. Lelong, P. *Les fonctions plurisousharmoniques,* Ann. École Norm. 62 (1945), 301–338.

16. —— *Domaines convexes par rapport aux fonctions plurisousharmoniques,* J. Analyse Math. 2 (1952), 178–208.

17. Mehring, J., and Sommer, F. *Kernfunktion und Hüllenbildung in der Funktionentheorie von mehreren Veränderlichen.* Unpublished manuscript.

18. Nehari, Z. *On weighted kernels,* J. Analyse Math. 2 (1952), 126–149.

19. Oka, K. *Sur les fonctions analytiques de plusieurs variables. VI. Domaines pseudoconvexes,* Tôhoku Math. J. 49 (1942), 15–52.

20. Radó, T. *Subharmonic functions.* Ergebnisse der Mathematik, Bd. 5, Heft 1. Berlin, 1937.

Stanford University

REGULARITY CRITERIA IN POTENTIAL THEORY

J. L. ULLMAN

The notion of irregular point was shown by Lebesgue [1] to be a key concept in the Dirichlet problem for arbitrary connected domains. We shall speak of domains in Euclidean three space, and discuss some recent developments in the theory. First, the Dirichlet problem will be formulated and some background material provided.

Let D be a connected domain and let $f(P)$ be a continuous function on the boundary B of D. The Dirichlet problem is the problem of showing whether a harmonic function exists in D, tending to the boundary value $f(P)$ as the boundary point P is approached from the interior of D.

Zaremba [4] pointed out that the problem was not always solvable. Lebesgue [1] showed that for a given domain D a solution existed for all continuous boundary functions if and only if each boundary point was regular, which meant that a certain local condition was satisfied at each point. This condition did not have a geometrical nature, and he posed the problem of finding geometrical criteria for regularity.

Wiener [3] presented the following criterion, whose geometric content will be examined. It is stated in full detail since an application will be made of it.

Let D be a connected domain, T the complement, Q a boundary point. Let λ be a number less than 1, let σ_n be a sphere of radius λ^n with center at Q, let e_n be the portion of T between σ_n and σ_{n+1}, and let γ_n be the Newtonian capacity of e_n. Then a necessary and sufficient condition that Q be a regular point is that

$$\sum \frac{\gamma_n}{\lambda^n} = \infty .$$

Now the capacity is not a geometric measure, but estimates can be obtained for the capacity of a set from its geometry. Hence this criterion does give a good idea of the geometric structure at Q which produces the irregular point.

In [2], Royden gave the following sufficient condition for regularity: If there are a sphere with center at Q, and straight lines from

Q to the sphere which intersect the surface in a set E of positive logarithmic capacity, and lie in T except for Q, then Q is a regular point.

Two comments concerning this result are of interest. First, by an unusual application of the regularity criterion, the following theorem will be proved:

THEOREM. *Let E be a set of points of positive logarithmic capacity and let I be a unit interval. Then the product set $E \times I$ has positive Newtonian capacity.*

Proof. Project the set E stereographically on a sphere Σ and connect the image points to the center. The interior of the sphere less the lines of connection is a domain, and Q is a regular point for this domain by Royden's criterion. Now apply Wiener's criterion—first note that the sets e_n and e_{n+1} are similar and in the ratio $1:\lambda$ and therefore $\lambda\gamma_n = \gamma_{n+1}$ or $\gamma_n/\lambda^n = \gamma_{n+1}/\lambda^{n+1}$. Thus $\sum\gamma_n/\lambda^{n+1} = \infty$ implies $\gamma_1 > 0$. Although γ_1 is the Newtonian capacity of a set which is not quite a product set, the theorem follows by using Fekete's definition of capacity by transfinite diameter. This definition enables us to show that e_1 can be mapped onto the product set of the theorem and retain its positive capacity.

The second remark concerns a natural extension of Wiener's criterion suggested by the nature of Royden's result, which we state here. In Wiener's theorem a dissection of a neighborhood of Q by spheres is made, but it has been shown that other nested surfaces can be used as well. Royden's theorem, however, suggests that the neighborhood be dissected into two-dimensional parts. More specifically, let $\gamma(r)$ be the logarithmic capacity of the part of T on σ_r, the sphere of radius r. Can a criterion analogous to Wiener's be formulated for the regularity at Q in terms of $\gamma(r)$?

BIBLIOGRAPHY

1. LEBESGUE, H. *Sur le cas d'impossibilité du problème de Dirichlet,* C. R. Soc. Math. France, 1913 (1913), 17.

2. ROYDEN, H. L. *On the regularity of boundary points in potential theory,* Proc. Amer. Math. Soc. 3 (1952), 82–85.

3. WIENER, N. *The Dirichlet problem,* J. Math. Phys. 3 (1924), 127–146.

4. ZAREMBA, S. *Sur le principe du minimum,* Bull. Int. Acad. Polon. 2 (1909), 197–264.

UNIVERSITY OF MICHIGAN

ANALYTIC FUNCTIONS OF CLASS H_p

WALTER RUDIN

1. Introduction. The classes H_p $(0 < p < \infty)$, consisting of those functions f which are analytic in the interior U of the unit circle and for which

$$\int_0^{2\pi} |f(re^{i\theta})|^p \, d\theta$$

is bounded as $r \to 1$, where introduced into analysis by G. H. Hardy [7]. The principal facts concerning the behavior of these functions at the boundary were established by F. Riesz [11]. Macintyre and Rogosinski [8] and H. S. Shapiro [12] have treated linear extremum problems (for $p \geqq 1$) in great detail. Walters [13] has discussed the structure of the linear spaces H_p for $0 < p < 1$.

These "classical" H_p classes will be denoted by $H_p(U)$ in the sequel. It is the purpose of this paper to define analogous classes of functions on arbitrary domains (in the extended complex plane) and to study their properties. Several open questions will be mentioned.

2. We base our definition on the observation that $|f|^p$ is subharmonic if f is analytic. The easiest proof of this well-known fact is probably the following: $\log |f|$ is subharmonic, $|f|^p = \exp(p \log |f|)$, and every convex increasing function of a subharmonic function is again subharmonic.

DEFINITION. For any domain D, and $0 < p < \infty$, we define $H_p(D)$ as the set of all functions f which are single-valued and analytic in D, and for which there exists a function u, harmonic in D, such that

$$|f(z)|^p \leqq u(z) \qquad (z \in D).$$

If $D = U$, it is easy to see that our definition coincides with the classical one; in fact, the following theorem shows that even in the general case we could define $H_p(D)$ by requiring certain integrals to be bounded:

THEOREM 1. *Fix a point $t \in D$, and let f be single-valued and analytic in D. Let Δ be any domain with smooth boundary Γ, such that $t \in \Delta$ and $\Delta \cup \Gamma \subset D$. Then $f \in H_p(D)$ if and only if there exists a constant M, independent of Δ, such that*

$$\frac{1}{2\pi} \int_{\Gamma} |f|^p \frac{\partial G}{\partial n} \, ds \leqq M.$$

Here G is Green's function of Δ, with pole at t, and the derivative is taken along the interior normal.

3. Analytic invariance of $H_p(D)$. The classes $H_p(D)$ are invariant under conformal one-to-one transformations of D. In fact, they enjoy a stronger property, which Ahlfors and Beurling [2] have called analytic invariance, and which is as follows:

THEOREM 2. *Let ψ be single-valued and meromorphic in a domain D_1 and suppose D is the range of ψ. For any $f \in H_p(D)$, define*

$$f_1(z) = f(\psi(z)) \qquad (z \in D_1).$$

Then $f_1 \in H_p(D_1)$.

This is clear if we note that for every harmonic majorant u of $|f|^p$ in D, the function u_1 defined in D_1 by $u_1(z) = u(\psi(z))$ is a harmonic majorant of $|f_1|^p$ in D_1.

4. It is interesting to consider, alongside $H_p(D)$, two other classes of single-valued functions analytic in D: the class $H_\infty(D)$, consisting of all bounded functions, and the class $\text{Log}^+(D)$, consisting of those functions f for which $\log^+ |f|$ has a harmonic majorant in D.

These two classes are also analytically invariant, and $\text{Log}^+(U)$ consists of the analytic functions of bounded characteristic in U. Theorem 2 holds for $\text{Log}^+(D)$, if $|f|^p$ is replaced by $\log^+ |f|$, since $\log^+ |f|$ is also subharmonic.

Let us note that

$$\text{Log}^+(D) \supset H_p(D) \supset H_q(D) \supset H_\infty(D) \qquad (p < q)$$

for any domain D. We call any of these classes trivial if it contains nothing but the constant functions.

It is a well-known unsolved problem, posed by Painlevé (see [1]), to find necessary and sufficient conditions on D under which $H_\infty(D)$ is nontrivial. If B is the (compact) boundary of D, it is necessary that the linear measure of B be positive [1, p. 2]; if B is a subset of an analytic arc, this is also sufficient [2, p. 122]; but little is known about the general case.

For $\mathrm{Log}^+(D)$, on the other hand, we can state a very simple criterion:

THEOREM 3. *The class* $\mathrm{Log}^+(D)$ *is nontrivial if and only if the boundary of D has positive logarithmic capacity.*

The following two questions now suggest themselves (and have not yet been answered):

(a) For what values of p (if any) is $H_p(D)$ nontrivial whenever B has positive capacity?

(b) For what values of p (if any) is $H_p(D)$ trivial whenever $H_\infty(D)$ is trivial?

5. Removable singularities. We have the following theorem:

THEOREM 4. *If D contains a compact subset N of capacity zero, and if $f \in H_p(D - N)$, then f can be defined on N so that $f \in H_p(D)$.*

For $H_\infty(D)$ a much stronger result holds, since singularities distributed over sets of linear measure zero are removable. On the other hand, our theorem is false for $\mathrm{Log}^+(D)$, where even isolated singularities may not be removable, as shown by the function $f(z) = 1/z$ in $0 < |z| < 1$.

To prove our theorem, we put $u(z) = p \log |f(z)|$ in $D - N$, so that u is subharmonic, and e^u has a harmonic majorant in $D - N$. Hence the theorem is a consequence of the following more general result which can be proved by standard potential-theoretic methods.

THEOREM 5. *Let u be subharmonic in $D - N$, where N is a compact set of capacity zero, and suppose e^u has a harmonic majorant in $D - N$. Then u can be defined on N so that u is subharmonic in D; the extended function e^u will have a harmonic majorant in D.*

6. The H_p-norm. Let t be a distinguished point of D. If f is single-valued and analytic in D, we define

$$\| f \|_p = [u(t)]^{1/p},$$

where u is the least harmonic majorant of $|f|^p$, provided $f \in H_p(D)$, and the right member is interpreted as $+\infty$ if $f \notin H_p(D)$ (it is well known that if a subharmonic function has a harmonic majorant in a domain, then there exists a *least* harmonic majorant). Thus $H_p(D)$ is characterized by the inequality $\| f \|_p < +\infty$. If $D = U$, we shall take $t = 0$.

If $p \geqq 1$, $\| f \|_p$ is a genuine norm, i.e., the triangle inequality holds:

$$\| f + g \|_p \leqq \| f \|_p + \| g \|_p \qquad (p \geqq 1).$$

This ceases to be true if $p < 1$; in that case we have, however,

$$\| f + g \|_p^p \leqq \| f \|_p^p + \| g \|_p^p \qquad (0 < p < 1).$$

In any event, the inequalities above, combined with the obvious homogeneity of the norm, show that $H_p(D)$ is a complex linear space.

The following lemma is useful:

LEMMA 1. *Let K be a compact subset of D. There exists a constant M, depending on D, K, t, p, but not on f, such that*

$$| f(z) | \leqq M \| f \|_p \qquad (f \in H_p(D),\ z \in K).$$

Hence, if $\| f_n - f \|_p \to 0$ as $n \to \infty$, then $f_n(z) \to f(z)$ uniformly on every compact subset of D.

7. The relation between $H_p(D)$ and $H_p(U)$. Since boundary components of capacity zero are removable, we may assume without loss of generality that D has at least three boundary points, of which one is the point at infinity. It follows then from the uniformization theorem that there exists a function ψ, regular in U, whose range is precisely D, and such that $\psi(0) = t$. This mapping function ψ is invariant under an infinite group G (the so-called automorphic group of D) of linear fractional transformations of U onto U, i.e., $\psi(g(z)) = \psi(z)$ for all $z \in U$ and all $g \in G$.

The analytic invariance of $H_p(D)$ now shows that for every $f \in H_p(D)$, the transformation

$$f_1(z) = f(\psi(z)) \qquad (z \in U) \tag{1}$$

defines a member f_1 of $H_p(U)$ which is invariant under the group G. Conversely, if $f_1 \in H_p(U)$, and f_1 is invariant under G, then the same is true of the least harmonic majorant of $| f_1 |^p$, so that (1) defines a member f of $H_p(D)$.

We may summarize this by saying that (1) *defines a natural norm-preserving isomorphism between $H_p(D)$ and the subspace of $H_p(U)$ which is invariant under G.*

This suggests that a study of the automorphic groups may shed some light on the questions stated after Theorem 3.

8. The strong topology of $H_p(D)$. We define a subset S of $H_p(D)$ to be open if for every $f_0 \in S$ there is an $r > 0$ such that $f \in S$ whenever $\| f - f_0 \|_p < r$.

If $p \geqq 1$, this gives the usual topology induced by the metric. If $0 < p < 1$, $H_p(D)$ is not a metric space, but the topology above nevertheless makes it into a linear Hausdorff space, i.e., a linear space which satisfies the Hausdorff separation axiom and in which addition and scalar multiplication are continuous operations. For $H_p(U)$ this was pointed out by Walters [13], and the general case follows from § 7.

If X is a linear topological space, a sequence $\{x_n\}$ of elements in X is said to be a Cauchy sequence if $(x_n - x_m) \to 0$ as $n, m \to \infty$. If every Cauchy sequence converges, X is said to be complete.

Denoting the boundary of U by C, we let $L_p(C)$ stand for the space of all measurable complex-valued functions on C, normed by

$$\| f \|_p = \left\{ (1/2\pi) \int_0^{2\pi} | f(e^{i\theta}) |^p \, d\theta \right\}^{1/p} .$$

Our preceding results yield the following theorem:

THEOREM 6. (a) *There is a natural norm-preserving isomorphism between $H_p(D)$ and a closed subspace of $H_p(U)$ which is invariant under G.*

(b) *There is a natural norm-preserving isomorphism between $H_p(U)$ and a closed subspace of $L_p(C)$.*

(c) *The space $H_p(D)$ is a complete separable linear Hausdorff space.*

(d) *If $p \geqq 1$, $H_p(D)$ is a Banach space; if $p > 1$, $H_p(D)$ is uniformly convex.*

(e) *Although the norm $\| f \|_p$ depends on the choice of the point $t \in D$, the induced topology does not.*

Part (b) follows directly from the work of F. Riesz [11]; the isomorphism is the correspondence between f and its boundary function. Parts (c) and (d) follow from (a) and (b), and (e) is a consequence of the fact that if a family of positive harmonic functions in D is bounded at any point, it is also bounded at any other point (which, incidentally, leads to a proof of Lemma 1).

9. Linear functionals. We define, as usual,

$$\| T \| = \sup (| Tf |/\| f \|_p) \qquad (f \in H_p(D)),$$

where T is any linear functional on $H_p(D)$; if $\| T \|$ is finite, T is said to be bounded. It is then an easy matter to verify that $H_p(D)^*$, the space of all bounded linear functionals on $H_p(D)$, is a Banach space, even if $p < 1$.

Although $L_p(C)$ has no nonzero bounded linear functionals if $p < 1$, $H_p(D)$ does admit such functionals; for instance, the functionals $T_{m,z}$ defined by

$$T_{m,z}f = f^{(m)}(z) \qquad (m = 0, 1, 2, \cdots; z \in D)$$

are bounded, no matter what p is; this follows from the Cauchy formula, and Lemma 1. These functionals even serve to separate elements of $H_p(D)$.

It would be interesting to find a representation of the elements of $H_p(D)^*$, for $0 < p < 1$, at least for the case $D = U$.[1]

10. Weak convergence. If $f_n \in H_p(D)$ and $f \in H_p(D)$, we say that $f_n \to f$ weakly provided that $Tf_n \to Tf$, as $n \to \infty$, for every $T \in H_p(D)$.

We shall now state various relations between strong, weak, and uniform convergence; K will denote a compact subset of D (or of U).

(a) *Strong convergence implies weak convergence.*

(b) *Weak convergence implies uniform convergence on every K. For $p \geqq 1$, weak convergence of $\{f_n\}$ also implies that $\{\| f_n \|_p\}$ is bounded.*

(c) *Uniform convergence on every K, plus boundedness of norms is not enough to assure strong convergence. Example: $f_n(z) = z^n$, $z \in U$.*

(d) *For $p > 1$, if $f_n(z) \to f(z)$ for every $z \in D$ and $\{\| f_n \|_p\}$ is bounded, then $f_n \to f$ weakly in $H_p(D)$.*

(e) *There exists a sequence $\{f_n\}$ in $H_1(D)$ such that $\{\| f_n \|_1\}$ is bounded and $f_n(z) \to 0$ uniformly on every K, although $\{f_n\}$ contains no weakly convergent subsequence, if D is of finite connectivity.*

---

[1] Added in proof: Such a representation has been found by Walters in [14].

We have not been able to settle the following question: Does weak convergence of $\{f_n\}$ in $H_p(D)$ $(0 < p < 1)$ imply boundedness of $\{\| f_n \|_p\}$?

11. Linear extremum problems. If $T \in H_p(D)^*$, let us consider the problem of maximizing $| Tf |$ under the restriction $\| f \|_p \leqq 1$.

If $p > 1$, the uniform convexity of $H_p(D)$ implies that there always exists [12] a unique $f_0 \in H_p(D)$ such that $Tf_0 = \| T \|$ and $\| f_0 \|_p = 1$ (for the uniqueness, the trivial case $T = 0$ must of course be disregarded).

If $p = 1$, there may not be an extremal function, and if there is one it need not be unique. Examples of this, for $H_1(U)$, may be found in [8], [12]. The present paper concludes with a study of a particular problem of this sort in $H_1(D)$, where D has finite connecitivity.

If $p > 1$, $H_p(D)$ is reflexive (Theorem 6(a), (b)). The example mentioned in (e) of § 10 shows that the unit sphere of $H_1(D)$ is not weakly compact, so that $H_1(D)$ is not reflexive, if the connectivity of D is finite. This leads to the question: Is $H_1(D)$ nonreflexive whenever it is nontrivial?

The case $p = 2$. By Theorem 6, $H_2(D)$ is (isometrically isomorphic to) a closed subspace of the Hilbert space $L_2(C)$, so that $H_2(D)$ is itself a Hilbert space, with an inner product (f, g). For fixed $x \in D$, $f(x)$ is a bounded linear functional on $H_2(D)$, so that there is a unique function $R_x \in H_2(D)$, which we call the H_2-kernel function of D [3, p. 40], with the reproducing property: $f(x) = (f, R_x)$.

If $\{\phi_n\}$ is a complete orthonormal set of functions in $H_2(D)$, we have

$$R_x(z) = \sum_{n=1}^{\infty} \overline{\phi_n(x)}\phi_n(z) \qquad (z \in D),$$

the series converging to R_x strongly, and hence uniformly on every compact subset of D. A more detailed study of this conformally invariant kernel function might well produce interesting results; at present, we merely note the identity

$$R_t(z) = \sum_{n=1}^{\infty} \overline{\phi_n(t)}\phi_n(z) = 1 \qquad (z \in D),$$

where t is the distinguished point used in the definition of the norm.

12. Domains with analytic boundary. Let D be a bounded domain, whose boundary B consists of k analytic simple closed curves.

Let $G(z) = G(z, t)$ be the Green's function of D, with pole at t. We let $A(D)$ denote the set of all functions which are single-valued and analytic on the closure of D. By $L_p(B)$ we mean the space of complex-valued measurable functions f^* on B, normed by

$$||f^*||_p = \left\{(1/2\pi) \int_B |f^*|^p (\partial G/\partial n)\, ds\right\}^{1/p}.$$

If $p \geqq 1$, we let $H_p(D)$ denote the (evidently closed) subspace of $L_p(B)$ consisting of those f^* for which

$$\int_B f^*(z)\phi(z)\, dz = 0$$

whenever $\phi \in A(D)$.

The following theorem describes the behavior of functions of class $H_p(D)$ near the boundary.

THEOREM 7. (a) *If $f \in H_p(D)$, there is a function f^*, defined on B, such that f has nontangential boundary values f^* almost everywhere on B.*

(b) *The mapping $\delta: f \to f^*$ is a norm-preserving isomorphism from $H_p(D)$ into $L_p(B)$.*

(c) *If $p \geqq 1$, the range of δ is $H_p(B)$, and the inverse of δ is given by*

$$f(z) = (1/2\pi i) \int_B f^*(w)/(w - z)\, dw \qquad (z \in D)$$

and also by

$$f(z) = (1/2\pi) \int_B f^*(\partial G/\partial n)\, ds,$$

where G is the Green's function of D, with pole at z.

The proof may be based on the fact that $A(D)$ is dense in $H_p(D)$.

13. Schwarz's lemma in $H_1(D)$. We again consider a bounded domain D whose boundary B consists of k analytic simple closed curves, and we let X_0 denote the set of all functions $f \in H_1(D)$ such that $||f||_1 \leqq 1$ and such that $f(t) = 0$, where t is the point of D with respect to which the norm $||f||_1$ is defined.

We are concerned with the problem of maximizing $|f'(t)|$ for $f \in X_0$. We put

$$\alpha = \alpha(t) = \sup_{f \epsilon X_0} |f'(t)|.$$

The corresponding problem in $H_\infty(D)$ has been the subject of investigations by Ahlfors [1], Garabedian [5], and Nehari [9]. The solution is as follows: if

$$\beta = \beta(t) = \sup |f'(t)| \qquad (f \in H_\infty(D), |f(z)| < 1 \text{ in } D),$$

there exists a unique function $F(z)$ such that $F'(t) = \beta$, $F \in H_\infty(D)$, and $|F(z)| < 1$ in D. This function F is analytic on the closure of D, $|F(z)| = 1$ for all $z \in B$, $F(t) = 0$, and F has precisely $k - 1$ other zeros at points $z_1, \cdots, z_{k-1}$ in D. These points are the zeros of the Szegö kernel function $K(z, t)$ of D; the relation $\beta = 2\pi K(t, t)$ makes explicit computation of β possible [3, Chap. VII].

It is evident that $\beta \leqq \alpha$.

In brief outline, our attack on the problem for $H_1(D)$ is as follows. The existence of at least one $f_0 \in X_0$ such that $f_0'(t) = \alpha$ is established by a normal family argument. Next, we consider the functional T defined on X by $Tf = f'(t)$, where X is the subspace of $H_1(D)$ consisting of those functions which vanish at t; since X may be regarded as a closed subspace of $L_1(B)$ (§ 12), T may be extended from X to $L_1(B)$, preserving its norm α (Hahn-Banach theorem). Thus T corresponds to a bounded function g on B. Consideration of f_0 shows that

$$f_0(z)g(z) \geqq 0, \qquad |g(z)| = \alpha \qquad \text{(p.p. on } B),$$

so that g is uniquely determined (i.e., there is only one norm-preserving extension of T from X to $L_1(B)$). It is also seen that g must be of the form

$$g(z) = \frac{1}{z - t} + \sum_{m=1}^{k-1} \frac{c_m}{z - t_m} + b(z). \tag{2}$$

Here $b \in H_\infty(D)$, $t_1, \cdots, t_{k-1}$ are the points in D at which the gradient of G (§ 12) is zero, the so-called critical points of G, and $c_1, \cdots, c_{k-1}$ are constants, some of which may conceivably be zero. If two or more of the critical points coincide, (2) must be modified so as to contain poles of the appropriate orders.

Two possibilities now present themselves:

Case I. The sets $(z_1, \cdots, z_{k-1})$ and $(t_1, \cdots, t_{k-1})$ are identical.

Case II. These sets are not identical.

With the aid of the Schwarz reflection principle (extended to

$H_1(D)$) and the argument principle, the following results are obtained:

THEOREM 8. (a) *The problem* 13 *always has at least one solution* $f_0 \in X_0$ *such that* $f_0'(t) = \alpha$. *Every such* f_0 *is analytic on the closure of* D.

(b) *There exists a unique function* g *of the form* (2), *analytic on* B, *such that* $|g(z)| = \alpha$ *on* B; *for every* f_0, $f_0(z)g(z) \geqq 0$ *on* B.

(c) *Depending on the choice of* t *and* D, *there exist integers* N, M, $1 \leqq M \leqq N \leqq k$, *such that* g *has* N *poles and* $N - M$ *zeros in* D, *and every* f_0 *has* M *zeros in* D. *Any zeros of* f_0 *on* B *are of even order and are to be counted with half their multiplicities in this enumeration.*

(d) *In Case* I, $M = N = k$, *and* $\alpha = \beta$. *In Case* II, $M < N$, *and* $\alpha > \beta$.

(e) *If two extremal functions* f_0 *have the same zeros, they are identical.*

It is perhaps worth noting that the maximum $\alpha(t)$ is a continuous function of t, despite the discontinuous manner in which the zeros of f_0 depend of the location of t (this discontinuity appears more explicitly in the next theorem).

The following questions have not yet been answered:

(a) Can Case I occur if $k > 2$?

(b) Is f_0 unique in Case II?

(c) Can more precise information be obtained about the possible values of M and N?

If $k = 2$, we can describe the situation much more completely:

Domains of connectivity two. Since every domain bounded by two curves can be mapped conformally onto an annulus $0 < r < |z| < 1$, we may restrict ourselves to that case. We also lose no generality by assuming that $r < t < 1$.

THEOREM 9. *If* $t \neq r^{\frac{1}{2}}$, *Case* II *occurs*; $N = 2$, $M = 1$, *and there is a unique extremal function* f_0.

If $t = r^{\frac{1}{2}}$, *Case* I *occurs, and* $N = M = 2$. *For every* $x \in [-1, -r]$ *there is an extremal function* f_0 *such that* $f_0(x) = 0$, *and every extremal function is obtained in this way. The ratio of any two of these is an elliptic function of* $\log z$.

In conclusion, we wish to point out that the results stated in Theorem 8 (with the exception of the assertions concerning analyticity on the boundary) are valid in any domain of connectivity k, without any smoothness assumptions on the boundary. This follows from the conformal equivalence of every such domain with one bounded by analytic curves.

BIBLIOGRAPHY

1. Ahlfors, L. V. *Bounded analytic functions*, Duke Math. J. 14 (1947), 1–11.

2. —— and Beurling, A. *Conformal invariants and function-theoretic null-sets*, Acta Math. 83 (1950), 101–129.

3. Bergman[n], S. *The kernel function and conformal mapping*, Mathematical Surveys, No. 5. New York, 1950.

4. Clarkson, J. A. *Uniformly convex spaces*, Trans. Amer. Math. Soc. 40 (1936), 396–414.

5. Garabedian, P. R. *Schwarz's lemma and the Szegö kernel function*, Trans. Amer. Math. Soc. 67 (1949), 1–35.

6. —— *The classes L_p and conformal mapping*, Trans. Amer. Math. Soc. 69 (1950), 392–415.

7. Hardy, G. H. *On the mean modulus of an analytic function*, Proc. London Math. Soc. (2) 14 (1915), 269–277.

8. Macintyre, A. J., and Rogosinski, W. W. *Extremum problems in the theory of analytic functions*, Acta Math. 82 (1950), 275–325.

9. Nehari, Z. *On bounded analytic functions*, Proc. Amer. Math. Soc. 1 (1950), 268–275.

10. Pettis, B. J. *A proof that every uniformly convex space is reflexive*, Duke Math. J. 5 (1939), 249–253.

11. Riesz, F. *Über die Randwerte einer analytischen Funktion*, Math. Zeit. 18 (1923), 87–95.

12. Rogosinski, W. W., and Shapiro, H. S. *On certain extremum problems for analytic functions*, Acta Math. 90 (1953), 287–318.

13. Walters, S. S. *The space H^p with $0 < p < 1$*, Proc. Amer. Math. Soc. 1 (1950), 800–805.

14. —— *Remarks on the space H^p*, Pacific J. Math. 1 (1951) 455–471.

University of Rochester

APPLICATIONS OF NORMED LINEAR SPACES TO FUNCTION–THEORETIC EXTREMAL PROBLEMS

HAROLD S. SHAPIRO

1. Introduction. Let $1 \leqq p < \infty$, and let L_p denote the set of measurable functions $F(\theta)$ on $0 \leqq \theta < 2\pi$ such that

$$\| F \|_p = \left(\frac{1}{2\pi} \int_0^{2\pi} | F(\theta) |^p \, d\theta \right)^{1/p} < \infty.$$

Further, define $\| F \|_\infty = \text{ess sup} \, | F(\theta) |$ and L_∞ as the set of measurable, essentially bounded functions.

Let H_p denote the set of $f(z)$ regular for $| z | < 1$ and such that $M_p(r) = \| f(re^{i\theta}) \|_p$ is bounded for $r < 1$. It is well known that if $f \in H_p$, then f has radial boundary values almost everywhere; furthermore, the boundary function $f(e^{i\theta})$ is in L_p and satisfies

$$\lim_{r \to 1} \| f(re^{i\theta}) - f(e^{i\theta}) \|_p = 0,$$

if $p < \infty$; if $p = \infty$, $f(re^{i\theta})$ converges boundedly to $f(e^{i\theta})$. The boundary functions are isometric, in the L_p metric, to H_p.

Let now $1 \leqq p \leqq \infty$ and $(1/p) + (1/p') = 1$. Let $K(e^{i\theta}) \in L_{p'}$. Define a linear functional T on H_p by

$$Tf = \frac{1}{2\pi i} \int_{|z|=1} f(z) K(z) \, dz. \tag{1}$$

We may then ask the following questions:

(i) Does $| Tf |$ attain a maximum on the unit sphere of H_p (i.e., the set of those f with $\| f \|_p = 1$)?

(ii) If so, what are the properties of the extremal functions? Have we uniqueness?

(iii) What is the value of $\| T \|$ (i.e., can we characterize it in some other way)?

In the case that $p = \infty$ and that $K(e^{i\theta})$ is the value of a rational function $K(z)$ on $| z | = 1$, these problems have been studied extensively—first, for special kernels, by numerous authors who find explicitly the extremal functions, and so on, and later, in a unified presentation, by Macintyre and Rogosinski [1], who study the general rational kernel. (For such a kernel, the integral in (1) may be evaluated by residues, and Tf is seen to be a linear combination of f and its derivatives evaluated at certain points.) In this case the following results are obtained:

(i) There exists an extremal function f^*; it is unique up to a constant factor $e^{i\alpha}$.

(ii) The function f^* is rational and $|f^*(e^{i\theta})| = 1$ everywhere.

(iii) A duality is established between the given extremal problem and the problem of finding the best L_1 approximation to the kernel by a boundary function of H_1.

The nature of this duality will be made precise later. For the present we merely remark that the relation between the original and the dual problems is the heart of the matter, and once it has been established, (i) and (ii) and a number of other interesting consequences may be deduced easily.

In this paper we assume merely that $K(e^{i\theta}) \in L_{p'}$, the weakest assumption under which the integral (1) has meaning. We show how the duality still persists, and hence, even in this generality, we can obtain rather precise information about the extremal function. Our proof uses the methods of normed linear spaces, and the underlying duality is seen to be a simple consequence of the Hahn-Banach theorem. Previous proofs, for rational kernels, were purely function-theoretic.

The main results, which are contained in § 2, were discovered independently (using the same method) by W. W. Rogosinski. They are being published (in a joint paper) in *Acta Mathematica* [2]; for that reason the proofs are merely sketched here.

2. The main theorem and the general duality principle

THEOREM 1. *Let $1 \leqq p \leqq \infty$, and $K(e^{i\theta}) \in L_{p'}$. If $p = 1$ we demand further that K be continuous on $|z| = 1$. Then the expression*

$$I(g) = \| K(e^{i\theta}) - g(e^{i\theta}) \|_{p'} \tag{2}$$

attains a minimum m as g ranges over all of $H_{p'}$, for a unique function $g^*(z)$. The expression

$$Tf = \frac{1}{2\pi i} \int_{|z|=1} f(z)K(z)\, dz \tag{3}$$

attains a maximum (in absolute value) M as f ranges over all functions in H_p of norm 1, *for some* $f^*(z)$. *Further,*

$$m = M, \tag{4}$$

and unless K is almost everywhere a boundary function of $H_{p'}$ (in which case $m = M = 0$), or $p = 1$, f^* is unique up to a constant factor $e^{i\alpha}$.

The theorem can be deduced from the following lemma, itself a simple corollary of the Hahn-Banach theorem:

LEMMA. *Let $\mathfrak{X}$ denote a normed linear space, and $\mathfrak{X}_0$ a linear subspace. Let T denote a bounded linear functional on $\mathfrak{X}$ and ρ its norm relative to $\mathfrak{X}_0$. Then ρ is equal to the distance, in the metric of the conjugate space $\mathfrak{X}^*$, from T to $\mathfrak{Y}^*$,* where *$\mathfrak{Y}^*$ is the annihilator of $\mathfrak{X}_0$, i.e., the set of functionals which vanish on all of $\mathfrak{X}_0$. Further, this distance is attained.*

Proof. Let σ denote the distance. We wish to prove $\rho = \sigma$. Let $x \in \mathfrak{X}_0$ and $Y \in \mathfrak{Y}^*$. Then

$$\| Tx \| = \| (T - Y)x \| \leqq \| T - Y \| \, \| x \|.$$

We take the sup over all x of norm 1; then $\rho = \| T \| \leqq \| T - Y \|$, $\rho \leqq \inf \| T - Y \|$, the inf being over all $Y \in \mathfrak{Y}^*$, and $\rho \leqq \sigma$. On the other hand, consider T only on $\mathfrak{X}_0$. By the Hahn-Banach theorem, there is an extension $\tilde{T}$ of T from $\mathfrak{X}_0$ to all of $\mathfrak{X}$ which also has norm ρ. Let $Y = T - \tilde{T}$. Then $Y \in \mathfrak{Y}^*$ and $\| T - Y \| = \| \tilde{T} \| = \rho$. But this shows that $\sigma \leqq \rho$ and also that the distance is attained by Y.

In practice, for the purpose of proving Theorem 1 in all details (notably the cases $p = 1$ and $p = \infty$), it is better to apply the reasoning of the proof above directly to the special spaces and functionals involved. However, for the sake of getting quickly at the main features of the theorem, we restrict ourselves to the case $1 < p < \infty$. (For the boundary cases some special devices are necessary, although the essential ideas are unchanged.) We identify $\mathfrak{X}$ with L_p and $\mathfrak{X}_0$ with boundary functions of H_p. Then the conjugate space $\mathfrak{X}^*$ is $L_{p'}$. T is identified with K, and the annihilator $\mathfrak{Y}^*$ of $\mathfrak{X}_0$ is then easily seen to be the set of boundary functions of $H_{p'}$, which we shall denote simply by $H_{p'}$. (Since H_p is isometric with its set of boundary functions, there is no ambiguity in this.) First, a routine compactness argument establishes the existence of an extremal function f^* with $|Tf^*| = M$. M is the norm of T relative to the subspace H_p of L_p, so by the duality theorem it equals the distance in the conjugate metric from T to the annihilator, i.e., $\min_g \| K - g \|_{p'}$; this proves (4), and the duality theorem tells us that the min is attained for some g^*. We have now only to prove the uniqueness assertions. Notice that we have, if f^* and g^* denote any extremals,

$$M = \left| \frac{1}{2\pi i} \int_{|z|=1} f^*(z)[K(z) - g^*(z)]\, dz \right| \leqq \|f^*\|_p \|K - g^*\|_{p'} = m;$$

thus equality holds throughout. Now since we have equality in Hölder's inequality, we can deduce (with f^* normalized so that $Tf^* = M$)

$$(5) \qquad e^{i\theta} f^*(e^{i\theta})[K(e^{i\theta}) - g^*(e^{i\theta})] \geqq 0 \quad \text{a.e.},$$

(6) $|f^*(e^{i\theta})|^p$ and $|K(e^{i\theta}) - g^*(e^{i\theta})|^{p'}$ are proportional a.e.

Suppose now we consider any fixed extremal f^*; then from result (i) we get, setting $h(z) = zf^*(z)g^*(z)$,

$$(7) \qquad \operatorname{Im} h(e^{i\theta}) = \operatorname{Im} e^{i\theta} f^*(e^{i\theta}) K(e^{i\theta}).$$

Since $h \in H_1$, it is completely determined once the boundary values of its imaginary part are known a.e. Hence g^* is completely fixed, i.e., g^* is unique. On the other hand, choose a fixed g^*; then from (6), $|f^*(e^{i\theta})|$ is determined a.e., while from (5), $\arg f^*(e^{i\theta})$ is determined a.e., so that f^* is also unique.

Examples can be given to show that in case $p = 1$ the restriction to a continuous kernel is necessary; otherwise, g^* can either fail to exist or it can fail to be unique; and in any case uniqueness of f^* may break down for $p = 1$. Of course, $M = m$ always holds in the form sup = inf.

3. Further properties of f^* and g^*. By using (5), (6), and the reflection principle, one may deduce results which give analytic continuations of f^* and g^* across arcs of the boundary on which $K(e^{i\theta})$ coincides with a regular function. We merely state the simplest of these results:

THEOREM 2. *Let $K(z)$ be regular for $t < |z| < 1/t$, where $0 < t < 1$. Then:*

(i) *For* $p = \infty$, f^* *is a rational function and* $|f(e^{i\theta})| \equiv 1$; g^* *is regular for* $|z| < 1/t$;

(ii) For $p = 1$, *every* f^* *is regular for* $|z| < 1/t$; g^* *is meromorphic in* $|z| < 1/t$;

(iii) *For* $1 < p < \infty$, f^* *has the form* $B(z)[h(z)]^{1/p}$, *where* $B(z)$ *is a rational function, regular for* $|z| \leqq 1$ *and having modulus* 1 *on* $|z| = 1$, *and* $h(z)$ *is regular for* $|z| < 1/t$ *and* $\neq 0$ *for* $|z| < 1$; g^* *is regular for* $|z| < 1/t$ *except possibly for isolated branch points in* $1 < |z| < 1/t$.

The statement (i) of this theorem shows that the type of extremal function which had previously been encountered with rational kernels persists in the case of kernels which are merely regular on $|z| = 1$.

These results hold, with the natural modifications, if we assume merely that $K(z)$ is regular in a neighborhood of some arc. The results on the continuability of f^* hold also if we restrict the f under consideration to satisfy a finite number of moment conditions of the type

$$\frac{1}{2\pi i}\int_{|z|=1} f(z)K_m(z)\,dz = c_m, \quad m = 1, 2, \cdots, N,$$

where the c_m are complex numbers, provided that the K_m belong to $L_{p'}$ and satisfy the same analytic conditions which are imposed on K. In particular, if the K_m are all regular on $|z| = 1$, f^* is rational. Of course, when these moment conditions are present, the dual extremal problem is not apparent and we have no good analogue of Theorem 1.

4. Remarks. Walter Rudin [3] using linear-space theory, has investigated extremal problems in general domains.

A theory of extremal problems for polynomials of fixed degree, analogous to the present one, is given by me in [4].

BIBLIOGRAPHY

1. Macintyre, A. J., and Rogosinski, W. W. *Extremum problems in the theory of analytic functions*, Acta Math. 82 (1950), 275–325.

2. Rogosinski, W. W., and Shapiro, H. S. *On certain extremum problems for analytic functions*, Acta Math. 90 (1953), 287–318.

A TOPOLOGICAL PROBLEM ORIGINATING IN THE THEORY OF RIEMANN SURFACES

WALTER BAUM

An analytic function defined on a Riemann surface F determines a Riemann surface $\bar{F}$ which lies over F, i.e., can be considered a covering surface of F. The covering mapping f of $\bar{F}$ onto F reflects properties of the given analytic function. Let F, $\bar{F}$ be represented as closed surfaces of genus q, p, respectively. If c is the number of sheets of $\bar{F}$ over F, and w the branching number of the covering, then the Hurwitz-Riemann relation (see [3]) restricts the possible covering surfaces $\bar{F}$ over F by the equality

$$p - 1 = \tfrac{1}{2}w + c(q - 1)$$

which must hold between p, q, c, w. One can also express this relation by using (instead of q, p) the Euler characteristics χ, $\bar{\chi}$ of F, $\bar{F}$, respectively, which are connected with the genus numbers by the known relationship. In terms of the Euler characteristics, L. Ahlfors [1] has generalized the Hurwitz-Riemann relation to Riemann surfaces with (relative) boundaries, employing both topological and metric properties of the surfaces which are imposed by the nature of the problem.

A purely topological extension of the Hurwitz-Riemann relation has been given by H. Kneser [4], [5]: Let F_p, F_q be two closed oriented two-dimensional manifolds ("surfaces") of genus p, q, respectively, and f a continuous single-valued mapping of F_p into F_q. Then the possible mappings f (characterized by their degree c) are restricted by Kneser's inequality

$$(1) \qquad p - 1 \geqq |c| \cdot (q - 1),$$

provided $p \geqq 1$, $q \geqq 1$. The last two conditions (where the condition $q \geqq 1$ could even be dropped) rule out only spheres for F_p, F_q; these cases can be treated separately without difficulty. Kneser's inequality has been proved again by H. Seifert [7] with the aid of the Euler characteristics of the surfaces F_p, F_q.

This inequality can be generalized to a class of complexes (of arbitrary dimension), and it can thus be shown that this relation between the three integers p, q, c which are determined by the mapping (namely, c) and the underlying spaces (p and q) does not depend on the manifold property of the spaces, but merely on their fundamental groups (i.e., a homotopy property):

If C_p, C_q are two connected complexes with fundamental groups G_p, G_q isomorphic to those of surfaces of genus p and q, respectively, then the possible continuous (simplicial) mappings of C_p into C_q are restricted by inequality (1), *where c is an integer depending on the mapping alone.*

(The number c plays the role of a generalized degree. Its dependence upon the mapping alone is to be understood, of course, as meaning only on the homotopy class of the mapping.)

The problem and the methods originated in the work of H. Hopf [2] on the connections between the fundamental group and the second homology group of a connected complex. With the fundamental group G of a connected complex C, Hopf has associated a group G_1^* which depends only upon G and not upon its representation by generators and relations. Furthermore, Hopf has proved that if G can be given by a finite number of generators with one essential relation, then G_1^* is either an infinite cyclic group or else consists of the unit element alone. (The alternative depends on whether the essential relation is a commutator word or not.) Using this theorem one can prove that a continuous single-valued mapping $f: C_p \to C_q$ induces a homomorphism of the associated group G_1^* of C_p into that of C_q which determines an integer c characterized by f (i.e., by the homotopy class of f). In this way one can not only establish a new algebraic proof of Kneser's inequality for surfaces, but can also extend it for complexes C_p, C_q of the type mentioned above and a simplicial mapping $f: C_p \to C_q$. The integers p, q, c are hereby defined algebraically in terms of the fundamental groups G and the associated Hopf groups G_1^* of C_p, C_q. In the case of two-dimensional closed oriented manifolds the algebraic definition (of p, q, c) yields the topological one. The proof of the extended Kneser inequality has been established by L. Robinson [6].

R. Bott has remarked (orally) that the extended Kneser inequality can also be obtained by considering the Eilenberg-MacLane spaces of C_p, C_q, provided Kneser's inequality for surfaces is assumed.

BIBLIOGRAPHY

1. AHLFORS, L. *Zur Theorie der Überlagerungsflächen*, Acta Math. 65 (1935), 157–194.

2. HOPF, H. *Fundamentalgruppe und zweite Bettische Gruppe*, Comment. Math. Helv. 14 (1942), 257–309.

3. HURWITZ, A. *Über Riemann'sche Flächen mit gegebenen Verzweigungspunkten*, Math. Ann. 39 (1891), 1–61.

4. KNESER, H. *Glättung von Flächenabbildungen*, Math. Ann. 100 (1928), 609–617.

5. —— *Die kleinste Bedeckungszahl innerhalb einer Klasse von Flächenabbildungen*, Math. Ann. 103 (1930), 347–358.

6. ROBINSON, L. *An extension of the Kneser inequality to complexes and a generalization of the concept of the degree of a mapping*. Thesis. Syracuse University, 1953.

7. SEIFERT, H. *Bemerkungen zur stetigen Abbildung von Flächen*, Abh. Math. Sem. Hansischen Univ. 12 (1937), 29–37.

SYRACUSE UNIVERSITY

EXPANSION THEOREMS FOR ANALYTIC FUNCTIONS. I*

R. C. BUCK

1. General remarks. Let $\mathcal{E}$ be a locally convex topological linear space, with $\mathcal{E}'$ as its dual space. A subset $P \subset \mathcal{E}$ is said to be total if the linear span of P is dense in $\mathcal{E}$; an equivalent condition is that no $F \in \mathcal{E}'$ can vanish on P without vanishing on $\mathcal{E}$. Let P henceforth be a total subset of $\mathcal{E}$ having a countable basis $p_n \in P$, $n = 0, 1, \cdots$. Every $p \in P$ has then a unique (finite) representation in the form $p = \sum c_n p_n$, where $c_n = 0$ for all large n. The sequence $\pi = \{p_n\}$ determines a subspace $E(\pi)$ of $\mathcal{E}$ consisting of all x which have convergent representations in the form $x = \sum c_n p_n$; $E(\pi)$, which is usually not a closed subspace, is called the expansion class for π. When $\mathcal{E}_0 \subset E(\pi)$, we say that π is effective for the set $\mathcal{E}_0$. The subspace $E(\pi)$ depends upon the sequence π and not merely upon the set $\{p_0, p_1, \cdots\}$. The sequence π is called a base for $\mathcal{E}$ if $E(\pi) = \mathcal{E}$ and if, in addition, the representation of an element $x \in \mathcal{E}$ is always unique—i.e., if $\sum c_n p_n = 0$ implies that $c_0 = c_1 = \cdots = 0$. A well-known equivalent condition due to Banach is that there shall be functionals $F_n \in \mathcal{E}'$ orthogonal to the p_n and such that, for all $x \in \mathcal{E}$, $x = \sum F_n(x) p_n$. When $E(\pi) = \mathcal{E}$ but we no longer have uniqueness, then π is termed a semibase, and the situation is much more complicated. Important here is the distinction between an *expansion formula* and simply an expansion. The former carries with it the particular method by which the coefficients c_n are to be obtained from the element x to be expanded. For example, since p_n is a basis for P, we may choose F_n defined on P only, so that $p = \sum F_n(p) p_n$. The extensions of these will yield one typical expansion formula. However, it may be possible to represent the members of P by quite different expansions if infinite rather than finite series are used. A frequently used example will be helpful here. Let $p_0 = 1$,

* Prepared under Contract DA-11-022-ORD-875 with the Office of Ordnance Research, U. S. Army.

$p_n(z) = z^n - nz^{n-1}$. Then, every entire function of exponential type less than 1 has the representation $f(z) = \sum c_n p_n(z)$, uniformly convergent on compact sets, where $c_n = (1/n!) \sum_n^\infty f^{(k)}(0)$. However, it is easily seen that *every* entire function has the representation $f(z) = \sum d_n p_n$, where $d_0 = 0$, and $d_n = (-1/n!) \sum_0^{n-1} f^{(k)}(0)$.

We have found the following restatement illuminating. Let $\mathfrak{S}$ be the space of complex sequences $c = \langle c_0, c_1, \cdots \rangle$ for which the series $\sum c_n p_n$ converges to a member of $\mathcal{E}$, and let U be the linear transformation of $\mathfrak{S}$ onto $E(\pi)$ sending c into $\sum c_n p_n$. Let S be any linear transformation whose domain is at least $P \subset E(\pi)$, whose range is in $\mathfrak{S}$, and which is a maximal right inverse for U. Let $E(\pi, S)$ be the set of all x in $E(\pi)$ for which $x = USx$. We then have $E(\pi) = \bigcup E(\pi, S)$. Moreover, any S has the form

$$\langle F_0, F_1, \cdots \rangle,$$

where the F_n are (algebraic) functionals on $E(\pi, S)$, and for each $x \in E(\pi, S)$ we have $x = \sum F_n(x) p_n$. By this analysis, we see that the independent expansion formulas arise from the maximal right inverses of U; the condition that $\{p_n\}$ is a base is equivalent to the assertion that U is one-to-one, so that U has only one right inverse, and hence only one expansion formula occurs.

Previous work on the expansion of analytic functions into series of polynomials has treated only the case where p_n is a base, or when this is not the situation, only one of the expansion formulas has been studied (Whittaker [22], Boas [1], Buck [8], Newns [15]).

A general method has often been used. If $\{q_n\}$ is a known base, and p_n is not too far away from q_n, then $\{p_n\}$ will also be a base. Explicit theorems of this type were proved by Paley and Wiener [16] for Hilbert space, and by Boas [1] for a Banach space. Both of these are instances of a simple observation. If $\mathcal{E}$ is a Banach space, and T is a linear transformation of the form $T = I + S$, where $\| S \| = \lambda < 1$, then $p_n = T(q_n)$ is a base (is total) whenever $\{q_n\}$ is a base (is total). For $T^{-1} = I - S + S^2 - \cdots$ exists, so that T is one-to-one, bicontinuous, and maps $\mathcal{E}$ onto itself, and hence carries a base (total set) into a base (total set). Since, in the case of a semibase, uniqueness is not required, less need be required of T. If T is continuous, and $\{q_n\}$ is a semibase for $\mathcal{E}$, then $p_n = T(q_n)$ is effective for $T(\mathcal{E})$. Thus one is led to the study of the algebra $\mathfrak{L}(\mathcal{E})$ of all continuous linear transformations of $\mathcal{E}$ into itself.

2. Polynomial spaces. Let P be the countable-dimension space of complex polynomials. One basis for P is the set of powers z^n, $n = 0, 1, \cdots$. A number of interesting topologies may be given to P. Let τ_r be the topology defined by the norm $\| p \|_r = \max | p(z) |$ for $| z | \leqq r$. If $r < r'$, then $\tau_r \subset \tau_{r'}$. Let $\tau_{R-} = \bigcup_{r<R} \tau_r$, and let $\tau_{R+} = \bigcap_{r>R} \tau_r$. In particular, set $\tau_\infty = \bigcup_{r<\infty} \tau_r$ and $\tau_0 = \bigcap_{r>0} \tau_r$. The completion of P in each of these is a familiar linear space of analytic functions:

τ_r : uniform convergence in $\| z \| \leqq r$;	$A_c(r)$, functions analytic in $\| z \| < r$, continuous in $\| z \| \leqq r$;
τ_{R-} : uniform convergence in all compact subsets of $\| z \| < R$;	$A(R)$, functions analytic in $\| z \| < R$;
τ_{R-} ;	$A^+(R)$, functions analytic in $\| z \| \leqq R$;
τ_∞ : uniform convergence on all compact sets;	$\mathcal{E}$, all entire functions;
τ_0;	$A(0)$, functions (power series) analytic at the origin.

The dual spaces of these may also be identified. For example, the dual space of $\langle A(R), \tau_{R-} \rangle$ is $\langle A^+(\rho), \tau_{\rho+} \rangle$ where $R\rho = 1$. Different choices of the family of topologies allows one to arrive at similar classes of functions, with circular domains replaced by arbitrary simply connected regions. (See also Newns [15].) For simplicity, and because this case permits of a more complete treatment, we shall restrict ourselves here to the choice τ_∞ and the space $\mathcal{E}$ of entire functions. (See Iyer [12].)

3. Linear transformations. We first seek useful representations of the algebra $\mathcal{L}(P)$.

THEOREM 1. *Let S be a locally nilpotent transformation in $\mathcal{L}(P)$ whose null space is the set of constants. Then, every $T \in \mathcal{L}(P)$ has a unique representation in the form $T = \sum a_n S^n$ with $a_n \in P$.*

We are here making use of the fact that P is also an algebra, so that P may be imbedded in $\mathcal{L}(P)$. Let $v_0 = 1$, and choose v_n so that $Sv_n = v_{n-1}$ for $n = 1, 2, \cdots$. The $\{v_n\}$ form a basis for P.

Given any $T \in \mathfrak{L}(P)$, let $a_0, a_1, \cdots$ be the unique solution in P of the system of equations:

$$Tv_0 = a_0,$$

$$Tv_1 = a_0v_1 + a_1,$$

$$Tv_2 = a_0v_2 + a_1v_1 + a_2, \cdots.$$

Define a transformation T_0 by: $T_0 = \sum a_nS^n$. Since S is locally nilpotent, the series $\sum a_nS^np$ terminates for each $p \in P$, so that no notion of convergence is needed here. It is evident that $T_0v_n = Tv_n$ for all n, so that $T = T_0$.

A particularly important choice of S is D, the differentiation operator d/dz. Here we may take $v_n = z^n/n!$.

COROLLARY. *Any $T \in \mathfrak{L}(P)$ has a unique representation in the form $T = \sum a_nD^n/n!$, where $a_n \in P$ and $D = d/dz$.*

In this case, the coefficients a_n may be given by:

$$a_n(z) = \sum_0^n \binom{n}{k} (-1)^{n-k}z^{n-k}q_k(z), \tag{1}$$

where $q_k = T(z^k)$. (See Sheffer [20], Curry [10].)

We next ask for conditions under which T is continuous on P in the topology τ_∞. Adopting the representation of T as an infinite-order differential operator, we let $\phi(z, \lambda) = \sum a_n(z)\lambda^n/n!$. For general T this may converge only when $\lambda = 0$; formally, T may be denoted by $\phi(z, D)$. We shall see that the behavior of T is closely linked to that of the function ϕ as an analytic function of both z and λ.

THEOREM 2. *T is τ_∞ continuous if and only if $\phi(z, \lambda)$ is an entire function of λ of uniformly bounded exponential type for all $|z| \leqq r$, and any r.*

Alternatively, set $\rho(r) = \limsup \| a_n \|_r^{1/n}$. Then T is τ_∞ continuous if and only if $\rho(r)$ is finite for each r. Sufficiency is easily seen. By the usual estimate from the Cauchy integral,

$$\| D^nf \|_r \leqq \frac{n!R}{(R-r)^{n+1}} \| f \|_R,$$

where $R > r$. Accordingly,

$$\| Tp \|_r = \left\| \sum \frac{a_n D^n p}{n!} \right\|_r \leqq \sum \| a_n \|_r (R-r)^{-n} \frac{R}{R-r} \| p \|_R.$$

If $R > \rho(r) + r$, then this series converges, and

$$\| Tp \|_r \leqq A(r) \| p \|_{R(r)} .$$

Conversely, suppose that T is τ_∞ continuous; T may then be extended (uniquely) to $\mathcal{E}$. Letting $T(z^n) = q_n(z)$, we have $T(e^{\lambda z}) = T(\sum \lambda^n z^n/n!) = \sum \lambda^n q_n(z)/n!$. Moreover,

$$\begin{aligned} e^{-\lambda z} T(e^{\lambda z}) &= \sum \frac{\lambda^m z^m (-1)^m}{m!} \sum \frac{\lambda^k q_k(z)}{k!} \\ &= \sum_{n=0}^{\infty} \sum_{0}^{n} \binom{n}{k} (-z)^{n-k} q_k(z) \lambda^n / n! \\ &= \sum a_n(z) \lambda^n / n! = \phi(z, \lambda), \end{aligned}$$

which is therefore an entire function of λ. Finally, for $| z | \leqq r$,

$$\begin{aligned} | \phi(z, \lambda) | &\leqq e^{|\lambda| r} \| T(e^{\lambda z}) \|_r \\ &\leqq e^{|\lambda| r} A(r) \| e^{\lambda z} \|_{R(r)} \\ &\leqq A(r) \exp [r + R(r)] | \lambda |, \end{aligned}$$

proving the stated property of $\phi(z, \lambda)$.

In passing, we remark that the argument above shows that if $\rho(r) + r < R_0$ for all $r < R_0$, then T is continuous in the topology $\tau_{R_0 -}$; however, this condition is not necessary. The relation $T = \phi(z, D)$, $\phi(z, \lambda) = e^{-\lambda z} T(e^{\lambda z})$ offers an alternative procedure for obtaining the differential representation of T.

This theorem characterizes those transformations which carry P into itself. The same methods yield at once the general result.

THEOREM 3. *The general linear transformation T in $\mathfrak{L}(\mathcal{E})$ has the form $T = \sum a_n D^n / n!$, where $a_n \in \mathcal{E}$ and where* $\limsup \| a_n \|_r^{1/n} < \infty$ *for each r.*

4. Subspaces of $\mathcal{E}$. Study of the "fine structure" of expansions requires that the members of $\mathcal{E}$ be further classified, e.g., by order and type. Let $\psi(t) = \sum C_n t^n$, where $C_n > 0$ and $C_{n+1}/C_n \downarrow 0$. Such a function will be called a comparison function; an important example is $\psi(t) = e^t$.

DEFINITION. An entire function $f \in \mathcal{E}$ is of ψ *type* A if

$$| f(re^{i\theta}) | = O(1) \psi(A' r)$$

for all $A' > A$, as $r \uparrow$.

The following result was first proved by Nachbin [14].

THEOREM 4. *If* $f(z) = \sum a_n z^n$, *then* f *is of* ψ *type* A *if and only if* $\limsup |a_n/C_n|^{1/n} \leqq A$.

Put $\gamma_n = \min \psi(x)/x^n$. An easy estimate of $\psi(\omega C_{n-1}/C_n)$ for $0 < \omega < 1$ yields the inequality $C_n \leqq \gamma_n \leqq (n+1)eC_n$. In particular, $(\gamma_n/C_n)^{1/n} \rightarrow 1$. If f is of ψ type A, then $|a_n| \leqq M(r)/r^n \leqq B\psi(A'r)/r^n$. Minimizing the right side for r variable, we have $|a_n| \leqq BA'^n\gamma_n$ and, dividing by C_n, $\limsup |a_n/C_n|^{1/n} \leqq A'$, where A' may now be replaced by A.

If $\psi(t)$ is specialized to $\sum_0^\infty t^n/(n!)^{1/p}$ or to $\sum t^n/\Gamma(1 + n/p)$, then "f is of ψ type A" is equivalent to "f is of order p and type A^p/p at most." The relation given in Theorem 4 then becomes the familiar one connecting the growth of f and that of its coefficients.

Let $K_\psi(A)$ be the set of all $f \in \mathcal{E}$ of ψ type at most A, and let $K_\psi = \bigcup_{A<\infty} K_\psi(A)$, the class of all entire functions of finite ψ type. For any $f \in K_\psi$ with $f(z) = \sum a_n z^n$, let $F(w) = \sum a_n/C_n w^{n+1}$. If f is of ψ type A, then by Theorem 4, F is analytic for $|w| > A$, and $F(\infty) = 0$. This correspondence sets up a linear transformation between K_ψ and the space of functions analytic at infinity which we call the generalized Borel transform. Let $D(f)$ be the set of singularities of F, including those points exterior to the domain of F. If Γ is any closed contour surrounding $D(f)$, then (see Buck [6]):

$$f(z) = \frac{1}{2\pi i} \int_\Gamma \psi(zw)F(w)\, dw. \tag{2}$$

This generalizes to entire functions of arbitrary growth the familiar Pólya representation for functions of exponential type which arises when ψ is chosen as e^t. It is to be expected that the set $D(f)$ will control not only the type of f, but also the rate of growth of f in specific directions. This requires the use of an inversion formula for (2).

Let us assume that the positive real numbers $\mu_n = 1/C_n$ obey the conditions allowing a solution of the Stieltjes moment problem. We then have

$$1/C_n = \int_0^\infty u^n\, d\alpha(u)$$

with α increasing and bounded.

THEOREM 5. *For any* $f \in K_\psi(A)$,

$$F(w) = \int_0^\infty f(u/w)w^{-1}\,d\alpha(u)$$

for all $|w| > A$.

We have $\int_0^\infty \psi(tu)\,d\alpha(u) = 1/(1-t)$ for all t, $0 < t < 1$ so that $\int_0^\infty f(u/w)\,d\alpha(u)$ exists for all w with $|w| > A$. Then

$$\int_0^\infty \sum a_n u^n/w^n\,d\alpha(u) = \sum a_n/C_n w^n = wF(w).$$

For $f \in K_\psi$, let $h(\theta)$ be the greatest lower bound of the real numbers A such that $|f(re^{i\theta})| = O(1)\psi(Ar)$; $h(\theta)$ is a measure of the rate of growth of f in the direction θ, and the maximum of $h(\theta)$ is the precise ψ type of f. Using this, we can sharpen somewhat the relation between f and F.

COROLLARY. *The generalized Borel transform F of f is regular at least for all points $w = \rho e^{i\phi}$ with $\rho > h(-\phi)$.*

When $\psi(t)$ is specialized, better results are possible. If, for example, we are concerned with functions of order p, we may choose $\psi(t) = \sum_0^\infty t^n/\Gamma(1 + n/p)$. The moment problem has the solution $\alpha(u) = 1 - \exp(-u^p)$, so that, for all functions of order p and finite type,

$$F(w) = \frac{p}{w}\int_0^\infty f\left(\frac{u}{w}\right) u^{p-1} e^{-u^p}\,du.$$

In this integral, the axis of integration may be replaced by a ray from the origin and additional information gained about the location of the singularities of F. With $p = 2$, take $f(z) = \exp z^2$, so that $F(w) = w/(w^2 - 1)$. It is easily seen that $h(\theta) = |\cos 2\theta|^{\frac{1}{2}}$, so that by the corollary above, $F(w)$ is regular outside the lemniscate $\rho^2 = \cos 2\phi$. The suggested modification of the axis of integration yields the more inclusive assertion that $F(w)$ is regular outside *all* the lemniscates $\rho^2 = \cos 2(\beta - \phi)/\cos 2\beta$ for $0 < \beta < \pi/4$. The union of these is the plane with the interval from -1 to 1 deleted, which accords with the known singularities of $F(w)$ at ± 1. (See also Macintyre [13] and Pólya [17].)

Any $T \in \mathfrak{L}(\mathcal{E})$ has a representation as a differential operator.

The generalized Borel transform and the Pólya representation formula lead to alternate representations of T. Let $G_\psi(z, \lambda)$ be the entire function obtained by applying T to $\psi(\lambda z)$, regarded as an entire function of z. Then a simple computation shows that for all $f \in K_\psi$

$$T(f)(z) = \frac{1}{2\pi i} \int_\Gamma G_\psi(z, w) F(w)\, dw,$$

where Γ may be taken as any contour surrounding $D(f)$. When $\psi(t)$ is again chosen as e^t, $G_\psi(z, \lambda) = e^{\lambda z}\phi(z, \lambda)$, where $T = \phi(z, D) = \sum a_n(z)\, D^n/n!$. A special case of considerable importance is that in which the coefficients a_n are constants, so that $T = \phi(D)$. In this case, the integral representation for T in the class of functions of exponential type becomes

$$T(f)(z) = \frac{1}{2\pi i} \int_\Gamma e^{zw} \phi(w) F(w)\, dw.$$

This permits a systematic development of the theory of differential equations of infinite order, with constant coefficients, of the form $T(f) = g$, when g is itself entire and of exponential type. (In this connection, see Gelfond [11] and L. Schwartz [18].) In the extension of this approach to operators T which do not have constant coefficients, it is important to find a class of T which have integral representations in a class K_ψ of a similar nature. The following theorem supplies an answer.

THEOREM 6. *Let* $S = b_1 D + z b_2 D^2/2! + z^2 b_3 D^3/3! + \cdots$, *where the* b_k *are real constants such that* $d_n = \sum_1^n \binom{n}{k} b_k \uparrow \infty$. *Let* $\psi(t) = 1 + \sum_1^\infty t^n/\, d_1 d_2 \cdots d_n$. *Then any* T *of the form* $\sum a_n S^n$ *where* $a_0, a_1, \cdots$ *are constants, has on* K_ψ *the representation:*

$$T(f)(z) = \frac{1}{2\pi i} \int_\Gamma \psi(zw) G(w) F(w)\, dw,$$

where Γ *encloses* $D(f)$ *and* $G(w) = \sum a_n w^n$.

It is easily verified that $S(z^n) = d_n z^{n-1}$, so that $S[\psi(\lambda z)] = \lambda\psi(\lambda z)$ and $T[\psi(\lambda z)] = G_\psi(z, \lambda) = G(\lambda)\psi(\lambda z)$. It should be remarked that in this case, Theorem 1 applies, so that if a_n is not required to be constant, every member of $\mathfrak{L}(P)$ has a representation in the form $\sum a_n S^n$.

5. Expansion theorems. Returning now to our original question, we let $\pi = \{p_n\}$ be a sequence of polynomials which is a basis for P. We seek information about the expansion class $E(\pi)$. Let T be the transformation defined on P by $T(z^n) = p_n$. Since z^n is a base for $\mathcal{E}$, π will be a semibase for $T(\mathcal{E})$ whenever T is continuous.

THEOREM 7. *T is τ_∞ continuous if and only if* $\limsup \| p_n \|_r^{1/n}$ *is finite for each r.*

The condition is clearly necessary. Its sufficiency follows at once from formula (1) and Theorem 3.

In order to study $T(\mathcal{E})$, let us introduce the special transformation S defined on P by $S(z^n) = C_n z^n$.

THEOREM 8. *Let T be τ_∞ continuous, and let $T^{-1}S$ be continuous from $\langle P, \tau_{R_0-}\rangle$ to $\langle P, \tau_\infty\rangle$. Then $E(\pi)$ contains all functions of ψ type less than* $1/R_0$.

The completion of $\langle P, \tau_{R_0-}\rangle$ is $A(R_0)$, so that the extension of $T^{-1}S$ maps $A(R_0)$ into $\mathcal{E}$. Thus $T(T^{-1}S)$ is a continuous map of $A(R_0)$ into $T(\mathcal{E})$. Since $TT^{-1}S = S$ on P, this must then be the (unique) extension of S from $\langle P, \tau_{R_0-}\rangle$ to $A(R_0)$. If $f(z) = \sum a_n z^n$ is in $A(R_0)$, then $\limsup | a_n |^{1/n} \leqq 1/R_0$, $S(f)(z) = \sum a_n C_n z^n$, and $\limsup | a_n C_n / C_n |^{1/n} \leqq 1/R_0$. By Theorem 4, $S(f) \in K(1/R_0)$. The converse also holds, so that S maps $A(R_0)$ onto $K(1/R_0)$. Hence $K_\psi(1/R_0) \subset T(\mathcal{E}) \subset E(\pi)$. We remark that this mapping S enables us to introduce a natural topology into the spaces $K_\psi(A)$ so that they become complete linear topological spaces.

This result, which can also be stated entirely in terms of the polynomial set $\{p_n\}$, is one which applies to a very general class of polynomial sets. Another very closely related result was obtained by Whittaker. With any set $\{p_n\}$ may be associated a pair of numbers called the "order" and the "type," and it then may be shown that every entire function of sufficiently slow growth (determined by these numbers) is in the expansion class (see [21], [22]). The polynomials given in § 1 are of order 1, type 1, and hence they are effective for all functions of order 1, type less than 1. We have seen, however, that in fact the polynomials are effective for all of $\mathcal{E}$. This is traceable to the particular form of the p_n. One may expect then to obtain greatly improved results if the polynomial set π has a certain type of inner structure. In a joint paper by R. P. Boas and myself, this will be discussed for the class of generalized Appell polynomials.

These are characterized by the fact that they arise from formal expansions

$$A(t)\psi(zw(t)) = \sum p_n(z)t^n. \tag{3}$$

The list of polynomial sets which may be defined by such generating relations is very inclusive. Under suitable conditions, which will not be specified here, (3) can be rewritten as

$$\psi(zw) = \sum p_n(z) \frac{[t(w)]^n}{B(w)} = \sum p_n(z)u_n(w),$$

uniformly convergent for w on a closed contour Γ. If this is substituted into the integral representation (2), we have at once

$$f(z) = \sum c_n p_n(z),$$

where

$$c_n = \frac{1}{2\pi i}\int_\Gamma u_n(w)F(w)\,dw,$$

for all $f \in K_\psi$ with $D(f)$ inside Γ.

This procedure for obtaining expansion formulas is not new. However, its scope and generality do not seem to have been observed. It has also the advantage of permitting the discussion of the summability of the expansion series. (For examples of this, see [8].) The general usefulness of expansions other than the Taylor series is now being recognized; every question asked of this special series may now be asked of these [5], [7], [9].

BIBLIOGRAPHY

1. Boas, R. P. *Expansions of analytic functions*, Trans. Amer. Math. Soc. 48 (1940), 467–487.
2. —— *Basic sets of polynomials, I*, Duke Math. J. 15 (1948), 717–724.
3. —— *Exponential transforms and Appell polynomials*, Proc. Nat. Acad. Sci. U. S. A. 34 (1948), 481–483.
4. —— *Polynomial expansions of analytic functions*, Indian Math. Soc. 14 (1950), 1–14.
5. Buck, R. C. *A class of entire functions*, Duke Math. J. 13 (1946), 541–559.
6. —— *Interpolation and uniqueness of entire functions*, Proc. Nat. Acad. Sci. U. S. A. 33 (1947), 288–292.

7. —— *Integral valued entire functions*, Duke Math. J. 15 (1948), 879–891.

8. —— *Interpolation series*, Trans. Amer. Math. Soc. 64 (1948), 283–298.

9. —— *On admissibility of sequences and a theorem of Pólya*, Comment. Math. Helv. 27 (1953), 75–80.

10. CURRY, H. B. *Abstract differential operators and interpolation formulas*, Portugaliae Math. 10 (1951), 135–162.

11. GELFOND, A. O. *Linear differential equations of infinite order with constant coefficients*, Trudy Mat. Inst. Steklov 38 (1951), 42–67. Amer. Math. Soc. Translation, No. 84.

12. IYER, V. GANAPATHY. *On the space of integral functions, I, II, III*, J. Indian Math. Soc. 12 (1948), 13–30; Quart. J. Math. Oxford Ser. 1 (1950), 86–96; Proc. Amer. Math. Soc. 3 (1952), 874–883.

13. MACINTYRE, A. J. *Laplace's transformation and integral functions*, Proc. London Math Soc. (2) 45 (1938–39), 1–20.

14. NACHBIN, L. *An extension of the notion of integral functions of the finite exponential type*, Anais Acad. Brasil. Ci. 16 (1944), 143–147.

15. NEWNS, W. F. *On the representation of analytic functions by infinite series*, Philos. Trans. Roy. Soc. London, Ser. A 245 (1953), 429–468.

16. PALEY, R. E. A. C., AND WIENER, N. *Fourier transforms in the complex domain*, Amer. Math. Soc. Colloquium Publications, No. 19. New York, 1934.

17. PÓLYA, G. *Untersuchungen über Lücken und Singularitäten von Potenzreihen*, Math. Zeit. 29 (1929), 549–640.

18. SCHWARTZ, L. *Théorie générale des fonctions moyenne-périodiques*, Ann. of Math. 48 (1942), 857–929.

19. SHEFFER, I. M. *Expansions in generalized Appell polynomials and a class of related linear functional equations*, Trans. Amer. Math. Soc. 31 (1928), 261–280.

20. —— *Some properties of polynomial sets of type zero*, Duke Math. J. 5 (1939), 590–622.

21. WHITTAKER, J. M. *Interpolatory function theory*, Cambridge Tracts, No. 33. Cambridge, 1935.

22. —— *Sur les séries de base de polynomes quelconques*. Paris, 1949.

UNIVERSITY OF WISCONSIN

ENTIRE FUNCTIONS AS LIMITS OF POLYNOMIALS*

JACOB KOREVAAR

1. Introduction. Let R be a set of points in the complex z-plane. An R-polynomial is a polynomial whose zeros lie in R. We are interested in the class $C(R)$ of all R-functions, that is, the entire functions $f(z) \not\equiv 0$ which may be obtained as the limit of a sequence $\{f_n(z)\}$ of R-polynomials, the convergence being uniform in every bounded domain (UBD convergence).

The study of $C(R)$ is interesting only if R is an unbounded set. Clearly, the limit of a UBD convergent sequence of R-functions belongs to $C(R)$. Thus $C(R) \equiv C(\bar{R})$, so that we may assume that R is closed. Let us consider the example where R is the half-line Re $z \geqq 0$, Im $z = 0$. In this case $\exp(-\lambda z) \in C(R)$ for every real $\lambda \geqq 0$, for $\exp(-\lambda z) = \lim (1 - \lambda z/n)^n$, where the convergence is uniform in every bounded domain. It is easy to show that in this case $C(R)$ is the class of the functions of the form

$$e^{a+bz} z^m \prod_p (1 - z/z_p),$$

where b is real and $\leqq 0$, m is a nonnegative integer, $z_p > 0$, and $\sum 1/z_p$ converges. This result is essentially due to Laguerre, who also considered the case where R consists of the entire real axis. Pólya investigated the case of an angle less than π, Pólya and Obrechkoff treated the case of a half-plane. Details of these investigations may be found in Obrechkoff's monograph on the subject [3].

In several previous papers [1], [2], I posed the problem of investigating $C(R)$ for arbitrary unbounded closed sets R, and obtained characterizations of $C(R)$ for practically all sets R. These characterizations involve certain relevant geometrical properties of R. An essential part is played by the asymptotic directions and the asymptotes of R, R^2, R^3, etc. (R^2 denotes the set of all points z^2 where $z \in R$, etc.). The case where R consists of an angle greater

* This is an abstract. The complete paper has appeared in the *Duke Mathematical Journal* 21 (1954), 533–548.

than π is interesting: in this case $C(R)$ consists of all entire functions not identically zero whose zeros lie in R. A set R with this property will be called *regular*. It was shown that a set R is certainly regular if the asymptotic directions of none of the sets R^j $(j = 1, 2, \cdots)$ lie in a (closed) half-plane.

2. Results. Various questions remained, however. Is it possible that $C(R)$ contains an entire function of infinite order if R is nonregular? The answer given in this paper is *no*. Again, is it possible that $C(R)$ contains entire functions of arbitrarily large finite order if R is nonregular? The answer to this question also turns out to be *no*. In other words, if R is not regular, then there is a finite least upper bound $\omega(R)$ to the orders ρ of the functions of $C(R)$.

The principal result of this paper is the following theorem: *Let $C(R)$ contain an entire function of order $\tau > 0$. Denote the greatest integer less than $\frac{1}{2}\tau$ by r. Then $C(R)$ contains all entire functions of order less than $r + 1$ whose zeros lie in R, and this bound $r + 1$ is best possible.* Hence if it is known that some function of order $\rho \geqq 0$ whose zeros lie in R does not belong to $C(R)$, then $\omega(R) \leqq 2[\rho]$.

Obviously, if $\exp\{g(z)\} \in C(R)$ and $\exp\{h(z)\} \in C(R)$, then $\exp\{g(z) + h(z)\} \in C(R)$. It follows by the methods used in this paper that $\exp\{g(z)\} \in C(R)$ implies that $\exp\{\lambda g(z)\} \in C(R)$ for every real number $\lambda \geqq 0$. It would be interesting if one could give a simple direct proof of this result, possibly by algebraico-topological methods.

3. Outline of the proof of the principal result. Let $C(R)$ contain the entire function $f(z)$ of order $\tau > 0$, where we may assume $f(0) = 1$. If $f(z)$ is written as the limit of a normalized UBD convergent sequence of R-polynomials

$$f_n(z) = \prod\nolimits_p (1 - z/z_{np}) \qquad (n = 1, 2, \cdots), \tag{3.1}$$

then the corresponding sequence of sums

$$\sum\nolimits_p | z_{np} |^{-t} \qquad (n = 1, 2, \cdots)$$

will be unbounded for every $t < \tau$.

If one has to show that $C(R)$ contains all entire functions of order less than $r + 1$ whose zeros lie in R, then by Hadamard's theorem it is sufficient to show that

$$\exp (b_1 z + \cdots + b_r z^r) \in C(R)$$

for every set of complex numbers $b_1, \cdots, b_r$.

Assume that

$$\exp (b_1 z + \cdots + b_{s-1} z^{s-1}) \in C(R) \tag{3.2}$$

for every set of complex numbers $b_1, \cdots, b_{s-1}$, where s is a positive integer $\leqq r$. In order to show that

$$\exp (b_s z^s) \in C(R) \tag{3.3}$$

for all b_s, we define directions of s-abundance of a sequence (3.1). We term α such a direction if there exists an increasing sequence of positive integers $\{n_k\}$, $k = 1, 2, \cdots$, with the property that for each $n = n_k$ one can determine a subset $(w_{n1}, w_{n2}, \cdots)$ of the set of zeros $(z_{n1}, z_{n2}, \cdots)$ of $f_n(z)$ in such a way that the resulting sequence of sets $(w_{n1}, w_{n2}, \cdots)$ satisfies the requirements

$$\left.\begin{matrix} \min_q | w_{nq} | \to \infty, & \sum_q | w_{nq} |^{-s} \to \infty \\ \min_q \arg w_{nq}^s \to \alpha, & \max_q \arg w_{nq}^s \to \alpha \end{matrix}\right\} \quad (n = n_k, \ k \to \infty).$$

If α is a direction of s-abundance of (3.1) and if (3.2) holds, then both $\exp (-\lambda e^{-i\alpha} z^s)$ and $f(z) \exp (\lambda e^{-i\alpha} z^s)$ belong to $C(R)$ for all real $\lambda \geqq 0$. It is shown that under certain circumstances a UBD convergent sequence of R-polynomials $\{f_n(z)\}$ may be modified so as to yield $f(z) \equiv 1$ as limit function. Hence under those conditions $\exp (\lambda e^{-i\alpha} z^s) \in C(R)$ for all real λ. A detailed study of the directions of s-abundance of sequences (3.1) shows that for $s < \frac{1}{2}r$ the sequence (3.1) has at least two directions of s-abundance α and β such that $| \alpha - \beta | < \pi$. Then

$$\exp \{(\lambda e^{-i\alpha} + \mu e^{-i\beta}) z^s\} \in C(R)$$

for all real λ, μ, which proves (3.3).

BIBLIOGRAPHY

1. Korevaar, J. *Approximation and interpolation applied to entire functions.* Thesis. University of Leiden, 1949.

2. —— *The zeros of approximating polynomials and the canonical representation of an entire function*, Duke Math. J. 18 (1951), 573–592.

3. Obrechkoff, N. *Quelques classes de fonctions entières limites de polynomes et de fonctions méromorphes limites de fractions rationnelles.* Actualités Scientifiques et Industrielles, No. 891. Paris, 1941.

University of Wisconsin

CURVE FAMILIES AND RIEMANN SURFACES*

WILFRED KAPLAN

1. Introduction. The purpose of this paper is to carry out a program which was described in 1948 [5, § 5.1] and whose goal is a simplification of the theory of regular curve families in the plane.

By a *regular curve family* is meant a family which is locally homeomorphic to a family of parallel lines [2, p. 155]. If F is a regular curve family filling the xy-plane, then every curve of F is open (homeomorphic to an open interval) and tends to infinity in both directions. The family F can be decomposed by a *normal subdivision* into a set of nonoverlapping subfamilies F_α, where α ranges over a finite or countably infinite indexing set A and each F_α is homeomorphic to a family of parallel lines. A function $f(x, y)$ can be constructed which has F as set of level curves, which is continuous in the xy-plane, and which has no local extrema. Proofs of these theorems are given in [2].

Each family F can be interpreted as a *chordal system*, i.e., as a system with three triadic relations: $C_1 \mid C_2 \mid C_3$, $\mid C_1, C_2, C_3 \mid^+$, $\mid C_1, C_2, C_3 \mid^-$ satisfying certain axioms [2, p. 165]. The relation $C_1 \mid C_2 \mid C_3$ signifies that the curve C_2 separates the curves C_1, C_3; the relation $\mid C_1, C_2, C_3 \mid^+$ signifies that C_1, C_2, C_3 are placed in a counterclockwise order in the xy-plane, as are the respective curves $y^2 = x - 1$, $y = x^2 + 1$, $y^2 = 1 - x$; $\mid C_1, C_2, C_3 \mid^-$ is the same as $\mid C_1, C_3, C_2 \mid^+$. The normal subdivision can be described completely in terms of these relations. In general, one defines a *normal chordal system* as an abstract system with triadic order relations satisfying the axioms referred to and having a normal subdivision [2, § 3.3].

With the aid of the theorems stated below, the following Main Theorem will be proved:

MAIN THEOREM. *For every abstract normal chordal system E there exists a function $u(x, y)$ harmonic for $x^2 + y^2 < 1$ or for $x^2 + y^2 <$*

* This paper was completed in the course of research supported by a grant to the University of Michigan from the National Science Foundation.

∞ *such that the family of level curves of u forms a chordal system isomorphic to E.*

In the case when the domain of definition of $u(x, y)$ is an open disk, the domain is regarded as a homeomorphic image of the plane. As pointed out in [5], one can always select u to have this domain (hyperbolic case).

In a previous paper [3] the following theorem was proved:

THEOREM 1. *If two curve families F_1, F_2 are isomorphic as normal chordal systems, then there exists an orientation-preserving homeomorphism of the xy-plane onto itself transforming F_1 onto F_2.*

The following theorems are corollaries of the Main Theorem and Theorem 1:

THEOREM 2. *Every normal chordal system is the chordal system of some family F.*

THEOREM 3. *Every family F is topologically equivalent to the family of solutions of differential equations $\dot{x} = f(x, y)$, $\dot{y} = g(x, y)$, where f and g are of class C^∞ and $f^2 + g^2 \neq 0$.*

THEOREM 4. *Every family F is topologically equivalent to the family of level curves of a harmonic function.*

Theorem 2 was proved in [3]. A proof of Theorem 3 was outlined in [4]. A proof of Theorem 4, depending on Theorem 3, was given in [5]; a new proof, not using Theorem 3, was recently published by Morse and Jenkins [6]. The Main Theorem itself is a consequence of Theorems 2 and 4. Therefore no new result is presented here. However, the new development forms a very considerable simplification of the previous proofs.

The principal tool in the proof of the Main Theorem is the construction of a *Riemann surface* R which is to be that of the inverse of the analytic function $u + iv$. From the given chordal system E the surface R is constructed of sheets corresponding to the normal subdivision of E. The elements of E are represented as lines $u = \text{const}$ on R.

2. Model for $\{c_\alpha\} \cup \theta(V_\alpha)$. In the following analysis the definitions and theorems of the papers [2] and [3] will be used extensively. We assume given a normal chordal system $E = E_0 \cup E_0^*$ (see [2,

§ 3.3]), so that $E_0 = \{c_1\} \cup \delta(c_1)$ and $E_0^* = \{c_1\} \cup \delta^*(c_1)$ are semi-normal. As in [2, § 4.1], we represent E_0 as

$$\bigcup_{\alpha \in A} \bigcup_{t \geqq 0} d_t^{\alpha},$$

where $d_0^{\alpha} = c_{\alpha}$. Then $V_{\alpha} = \{c_{\alpha}\} \cup \bigcup_k c_{\alpha,k}$, $\theta(V_{\alpha}) = \bigcup_{t>0} d_t^{\alpha}$, and $\lambda(V_{\alpha}) = V_{\alpha} \cup \theta(V_{\alpha})$. Below we shall use the notations: $E_{\alpha} = \bigcup_{t \geqq 0} d_t^{\alpha}$ and $\bar{E}_{\alpha} = \lambda(V_{\alpha})$. The bar is justified, since in the case of a curve family $\bar{E}_{\alpha}$ would be the closure of E_{α}.

We define (see [2, p. 183] and [3, p. 20]) ϵ_1 to be $+1$ and $\epsilon_{\alpha,k}$ to be $+1$ or -1 according as $c_{\alpha,k}$ is in $Y_{\alpha}^-(t) \cup Y_{\alpha}^+(t)$ or in $Z_{\alpha}^-(t) \cup Z_{\alpha}^+(t)$ and, if $\alpha = 1, k_2, k_3, \cdots, k_n$,

$$\eta_{\alpha} = \epsilon_1 \cdot \epsilon_{1,k_2} \cdots \epsilon_{\alpha},$$

$$u_1 = 0, \qquad u_{\alpha,k} = \eta_1 t_{1,k_2} + \eta_{1,k_2} t_{1,k_2,k_3} + \cdots + \eta_{\alpha} t_{\alpha,k}.$$

We also set $\zeta_{\alpha,k} = +1$ if $c_{\alpha,k} \in V^+$, $\zeta_{\alpha,k} = -1$ if $c_{\alpha,k} \in V_{\alpha}^-$.

We now reparametrize the elements of E_{α}, replacing the parameter t by u, where

$$u = u_{\alpha} + \eta_{\alpha} t, \qquad t \geqq 0,$$

so that u varies from u_{α} to $+\infty$ when $\eta_{\alpha} = +1$, and from $-\infty$ to u_{α} when $\eta_{\alpha} = -1$. We write

$$c_u^{\alpha} = d_t^{\alpha}, \quad \text{when} \quad u = u_{\alpha} + \eta_{\alpha} t.$$

Thus $c_{\alpha} = c_{u_{\alpha}}^{\alpha} = d_0$.

We now define a curve family F_{α} corresponding to the set E_{α}. Each element c_u^{α} of E_{α} will be represented by an open interval

$$\gamma_u^{\alpha}: \; p_{\alpha}(u) < v < q_{\alpha}(u)$$

on the corresponding line $u = \text{const}$ in the uv-plane. For each u except u_{α} we let $q_{\alpha}(u)$ be the smallest k, if there is one, such that $u_{\alpha,k} = u$; if no such k exists, we set $q_{\alpha}(u) = +\infty$; in both cases we set $p_{\alpha}(u) = -q_{\alpha}(u)$. The values $p_{\alpha}(u_{\alpha})$ and $q_{\alpha}(u_{\alpha})$ are defined below. We note that the functions $p_{\alpha}(u)$, $q_{\alpha}(u)$ are respectively upper and lower semicontinuous. Hence F_{α} fills the simply connected domain G_{α}: $p_{\alpha}(u) < v < q_{\alpha}(u)$, $\eta_{\alpha}(u - u_{\alpha}) > 0$, plus the interval

$$\gamma_{u_{\alpha}}^{\alpha} = \gamma_{\alpha}$$

on the boundary. The family F_α is regular at every interior point, and every point of γ_α lies on the boundary of an r-neighborhood ([2, § 1.4]) in G_α.

We now proceed to define $p_\alpha(u_\alpha)$ and $q_\alpha(u_\alpha)$ or, what is the same, the intervals γ_α. We define γ_1 to be the interval $(-1, 1)$ on $u = 0$. Each $c_{\alpha,k}$ falls into one of eight classes, depending on the values of η_α, $\eta_{\alpha,k}$, and $\zeta_{\alpha,k}$. Each such class of $c_{\alpha,k}$ is simply ordered by Theorem 3 in [3], and the corresponding intervals $\gamma_{\alpha,k}$ are chosen as a set of nonoverlapping open intervals lying on $u = u_{\alpha,k}$ and having the *same* or *opposite* order, with respect to increasing v. The $\gamma_{\alpha,k}$ of each class are to lie in the *upper* interval: $v > q_\alpha(u_{\alpha,k})$, or in the *lower* interval: $v < p_\alpha(u_{\alpha,k})$. The choice of same or reversed order and the interval are determined in accordance with Table 1.

TABLE 1

$\eta_\alpha, \eta_{\alpha,k}, \zeta_{\alpha,k}$	1, 1, 1	1, 1, −1	1, −1, 1	1, −1, −1
order	same	opposite	opposite	same
interval	lower	upper	lower	upper

$\eta_\alpha, \eta_{\alpha,k}, \zeta_{\alpha,k}$	−1, 1, 1	−1, 1, −1	−1, −1, 1	−1, −1, −1
order	same	opposite	opposite	same
interval	upper	lower	upper	lower

A similar procedure is carried out for E_0^* to give families F_α^*. We proceed exactly as above, except that we define ϵ_1^* to be -1. Thus, in particular, G_1 and G_1^* do not intersect but have the boundary interval $\gamma_1 = \gamma_1^*$ in common.

3. The Riemann surface R. The surface will be built of two pieces R_0 and R_0^*, corresponding to E_0. To each point $w = u + iv$ lying on an interval γ_u^α of F_α is assigned a point $(w; \alpha)$ of R_0; to each point w of an interval $\gamma_u^{\alpha *}$ in F_α^* is assigned a point $(w; \alpha; *)$ of R_0^*. These are regarded as distinct points except that we identify $(iv; 1)$ with $(iv; 1; *)$ for $-1 < v < 1$. We now define: $\pi(w; \alpha) = w$ and $\pi(w; \alpha; *) = w$. Thus π is a projection of R onto the w-plane.

Let $(w_0; \alpha)$ be such that $\pi(w_0; \alpha) \in G_\alpha$ and let $\epsilon_0 > 0$ be chosen so that the open disk $|w - w_0| < \epsilon_0$ lies in G_α. Then for $\epsilon < \epsilon_0$

the neighborhood $U_\epsilon(w_0 ; \alpha)$ is defined as the set of all $(w; \alpha)$ for which $|w - w_0| < \epsilon$. A similar procedure is followed for points $(w_0 ; \alpha; *)$.

If $\pi(w_0 ; \alpha, k)$ lies on $\gamma_{\alpha,k}$, we can choose ϵ_0 so small that every point of the open disk $|w - w_0| < \epsilon_0$ lies in $G_{\alpha,k} \cup \gamma_{\alpha,k}$, or lies in G_α but not in $G_{\alpha,k} \cup \gamma_{\alpha,k}$. For $\epsilon < \epsilon_0$, we define $U_\epsilon(w_0 ; \alpha, k)$ to be the set of all $(w; \alpha, k)$ such that $|w - w_0| < \epsilon$, plus the set of all $(w; \alpha)$ for which $|w - w_0| < \epsilon$ but $w \notin G_{\alpha,k} \cup \gamma_{\alpha,k}$; the two sets correspond to an open semicircle plus its open diameter and an open semicircle. A similar procedure is followed for points $(w_0 ; \alpha, k; *)$ when w_0 is on $\gamma_{\alpha,k}^*$.

If w_0 lies on γ_1, ϵ_0 is chosen to be $1 - |w_0|$ and, for $\epsilon < \epsilon_0$, $U_\epsilon(w_0 ; 1) = U_\epsilon(w_0 ; 1; *)$ is defined as the set of all $(w; 1)$ and $(w; 1; *)$ for which $|w - w_0| < \epsilon$.

From these definitions it follows that R is a connected Hausdorff space and is, moreover, an open surface. The circular neighborhoods $U_\epsilon(w; \alpha)$ and $U_\epsilon(w; \alpha; *)$ with the mapping π define local conformal coordinates w on R, so that we can regard R as a Riemann surface. We let R_α be the set of $(w; \alpha)$ for which $w \in G_\alpha \cup \gamma_\alpha$ and let R_α^* be the set of $(w; \alpha; *)$ for which $w \in G_\alpha \cup \gamma_\alpha$; we let $R_0 = \bigcup_{\alpha \in A} R_\alpha$ and let $R_0^* = \bigcup_{\alpha \in A^*} R_\alpha^*$, so that $R = R_0 \cup R_0^*$. We write

$$\Gamma_u^\alpha = \pi^{-1}(\gamma_u^\alpha) \cap R_\alpha, \quad \Gamma_u^{\alpha *} = \pi^{-1}(\gamma_u^{\alpha *}) \cap R_\alpha^*,$$

$$\Gamma_\alpha = \Gamma_{u_\alpha}^\alpha, \quad \Gamma_\alpha^* = \Gamma_{u_\alpha^*}^{\alpha *}.$$

R is simply connected. To prove this, we first remark that by construction each R_α is homeomorphic to $G_\alpha \cup \gamma_\alpha$ and is hence simply connected. Each $R_{\alpha,k}$ has a common boundary with R_α, consisting of $\Gamma_{\alpha,k}$, which is homeomorphic to an open interval; $\bar{R}_{\alpha,k}$ and $\bar{R}_{\alpha,l}$ do not intersect for $k \neq l$. We now prove that R_0 is simply connected. Let C be a closed path on R_0. Since every point of R_0 has a neighborhood meeting at most two sets R_α, it follows from the Heine-Borel theorem that C meets at most a finite number of sets R_α. Hence we need only show that a connected union $\bigcup_{i=1}^n R_{\alpha_i}$ is simply connected. We prove this by induction. It is true for $n = 1$ by construction. We suppose it true for $n = m$ and prove it for $n = m + 1$. Given $S_{m+1} = \bigcup_{i=1}^{m+1} R_{\alpha_i}$, we can choose an α_i whose sequence has maximal length—e.g., α_{m+1}. The set $R_{\alpha_{m+1}}$ has then a common boundary with at most one R_{α_i} in $S_m = \bigcup_{i=1}^m R_{\alpha_i}$. This common boundary must be the curve $\Gamma_{\alpha_{m+1}}$. Since $R_{\alpha_{m+1}}$ and S_m are simply connected, it follows that $S_{m+1} = R_{\alpha_{m+1}} \cup S_m$ is simply connected (cf. Eilenberg [1, p. 72]). Accordingly, R_0 is simply connected and, similarly, R_0^* is simply connected. Since R_0 and R_0^* have $\Gamma_1 = \Gamma_1^*$ as common boundary, $R = R_0 \cup R_0^*$ is simply connected.

R is therefore an open simply connected Riemann surface. Accordingly, R can be mapped conformally onto D_∞, the xy-plane, or D_1, the disk $x^2 + y^2 < 1$. We let $(w; \alpha) = \psi(z)$ be this mapping. Then $w = \pi[\psi(z)]$ is an analytic function $f(z)$.

4. The family ϕ isomorphic to E. The curves Γ_u^α and $\Gamma_u^{\alpha*}$ form a curve family Φ filling R. Under the mapping ψ, Φ is transformed onto a family ϕ of curves C_u^α, $C_u^{\alpha*}$ filling D_∞ or D_1. Since $u =$ const on each curve of Φ, the curves of ϕ are the level curves: $u = \operatorname{Re}[f(z)] =$ const in the xy-plane. We note that u has no critical points, so that ϕ is necessarily regular; we can also verify directly that Φ is regular.

It remains to verify that ϕ is isomorphic to E. From the construction we conclude that the families $\phi_\alpha = \bigcup_u C_u^\alpha$, $\phi_\alpha^* = \bigcup_u C_u^{\alpha*}$ determine a normal subdivision of ϕ. By virtue of Theorem 4 in [3] we need only verify that $CS[\bar{\phi}_\alpha]$ is isomorphic to $\bar{E}$ and that $CS[\bar{\phi}_\alpha^*]$ is isomorphic to $\bar{E}_\alpha^*$. By Theorem 1 in [3] (see a correction in § 5 below), we need only verify this for triples of form (α): c_α, $c_{\alpha,k}$, d_t^α, and for those of form (β): c_α, $c_{\alpha,k}$, $c_{\alpha,l}$, where $c_{\alpha,k}$ and $c_{\alpha,l}$ are both in the same one of the four sets $Y_\alpha^+(t)$, $Y_\alpha^-(t)$, $Z_\alpha^+(t)$, $Z_\alpha^-(t)$.

To verify the relations in the two cases, we recall [2, pp. 167–168] that, for a curve family, $C_1 \mid C_2 \mid C_3$ is defined to mean that C_2 separates C_1 from C_3 and that $\mid C_1, C_2, C_3 \mid^+$ is defined to mean that there exists a simple closed curve $P_1P_2P_3P_1$, where P_i is a point on C_i, meeting $C_1 \cup C_2 \cup C_3$ only at these three points and positively oriented by the direction P_1 to P_2 to P_3. Both of these properties can at once be transferred to the family Φ filling R.

In the case (α), one has eight cases to consider, corresponding to the table in § 2 above. We consider a typical case, the reasoning in the others being similar: let $\eta_\alpha = +1$, $\eta_{\alpha,k} = -1$, $\zeta_{\alpha,k} = -1$. Then $\epsilon_{\alpha,k} = -1$, so that $c_{\alpha,k} \in Z_\alpha^-(t) \cup Z_\alpha^+(t)$, and $\zeta_{\alpha,k} = -1$, so that $c_{\alpha,k} \in V_\alpha^-$. Accordingly, $\mid c_\alpha, c_{\alpha,k}, d_t^\alpha \mid^-$ for $t > t_{\alpha,k}$,

$$c_\alpha \mid d_t^\alpha \mid c_{\alpha,k} \quad \text{for} \quad t \leqq t_{\alpha,k}.$$

Since $\eta_\alpha = +1$, this can be restated as follows: $| c_\alpha, c_{\alpha,k}, c_u^\alpha |^-$ for $u > u_{\alpha,k}$, $c_\alpha | c_u^\alpha | c_{\alpha,k}$ for $u \leqq u_{\alpha,k}$. According to the table, $c_{\alpha,k}$ is represented by an interval $\gamma_{\alpha,k}$ on the interval $q_\alpha(u_{\alpha,k}) < v < \infty$, $u = u_{\alpha,k}$; $G_{\alpha,k}$ lies in the set $u < u_{\alpha,k}$ and G_α lies in the set $u > u_\alpha$. If $u > u_{\alpha,k}$, then we can choose P_1 on $C_1 = \Gamma_\alpha$, P_2 on $C_2 = \Gamma_u^\alpha$, P_3 on $C_3 = \Gamma_{\alpha,k}$, as above, so that $| \Gamma_\alpha, \Gamma_u^\alpha, \Gamma_{\alpha,k} |^+$ or $| \Gamma_\alpha, \Gamma_{\alpha,k}, \Gamma_u^\alpha |^-$. Now in the case at hand the definition of neighborhoods above makes it impossible to join Γ_α to $\Gamma_{\alpha,k}$ on R without crossing every Γ_u^α for $u \leqq u_{\alpha,k}$; hence $\Gamma_\alpha | \Gamma_u^\alpha | \Gamma_{\alpha,k}$ for $u \leqq u_{\alpha,k}$. We conclude that $[c_1, c_2, c_3] \sim [C_1, C_2, C_3]$ for triples of type (α).

In the case (β) one has again eight cases to consider, depending on which class $c_{\alpha,k}$ and $c_{\alpha,l}$ lie in. We again consider a typical case: $\eta_\alpha = +1$, $\eta_{\alpha,k} = \eta_{\alpha,l} = +1$, $\zeta_{\alpha,k} = \zeta_{\alpha,l} = +1$. Then again G_α lies in the set $u > u_\alpha$, but $G_{\alpha,k}$ and $G_{\alpha,l}$ lie in the set $u > u_{\alpha,k} = u_{\alpha,l}$; $\gamma_{\alpha,k}$ and $\gamma_{\alpha,l}$ are intervals on the interval $-\infty < v < p_\alpha(u_{\alpha,k})$, $u = u_{\alpha,k}$, and $\gamma_{\alpha,k}, \gamma_{\alpha,l}$ lie in the *same* order as $c_{\alpha,k}, c_{\alpha,l}$. We can suppose $c_{\alpha,k} < c_{\alpha,l}$, so that $| c_\alpha, c_{\alpha,k}, c_{\alpha,l} |^+$, and $\gamma_{\alpha,l}$ lies "above" $\gamma_{\alpha,k}$. From the definition of neighborhoods above, we can choose P_1 on Γ_α, P_2 on $\Gamma_{\alpha,k}$, P_3 on $\Gamma_{\alpha,l}$, as above, so that $| \Gamma_\alpha, \Gamma_{\alpha,k}, \Gamma_{\alpha,l} |^+$ and again $[c_1, c_2, c_3] \sim [C_1, C_2, C_3]$.

Accordingly, $\bar{\phi}_\alpha$ is isomorphic to $\bar{E}_\alpha = \lambda(V_\alpha)$ and similarly $\bar{\phi}_\alpha^*$ is isomorphic to $\bar{E}_\alpha^*$, so that $CS[\phi]$ is isomorphic to E. The Main Theorem is now proved.

5. Two corrections to earlier papers. I take this opportunity to correct two errors, one in [2] and one in [3].

The proof of Theorem 35 in [2, p. 176] is incorrect and should be replaced by the following: "We proceed exactly as in the proof of Theorem 33, replacing $\mathfrak{D}(C_0)$ throughout by H. We thus obtain C_0, C_{n_2} in H, and C_Q such that $C_0 | C_{n_2} | C_Q$. By Corollary 1 to Theorem 29, we conclude that $C_Q \subset H$ and by Corollary 2 we conclude that there exists C' in H such that $C' | C_Q | C_0$ and $d(C') > d(C_Q) = r$. This is a contradiction and the theorem follows."

In [3, p. 17] the definition of the class (β) in the lemma is incorrect. The class (β) should consist of all relations for triples c_α, $c_{\alpha,k}$, $c_{\alpha,l}$ such that k and l have the same sign and such that

$$B(c_{\alpha,k}) = B(c_{\alpha,l}).$$

The proof of the lemma should be modified as follows. After the first paragraph of the proof the following sentence should be inserted:

"From (β) it follows that the order of each set of elements $c_{\alpha,k}$ for fixed sign of k and fixed value of $B(c_{\alpha,k})$ is known and hence, by Theorem 3, that all relations among triples $c_{\alpha,k}$, $c_{\alpha,l}$, $c_{\alpha,m}$ of such a set are known."

BIBLIOGRAPHY

1. Eilenberg, S. *Transformations continues en circonférence et la topologie du plan*, Fund. Math. 26 (1936), 63–112.
2. Kaplan, W. *Regular curve-families filling the plane, I*, Duke Math. J. 7 (1940), 154–185.
3. —— *Regular curve-families filling the plane, II*, Duke Math. J. 8 (1941), 11–46.
4. —— *Differentiability of regular curve families on the sphere.* Lectures in Topology, pp. 299–301. Ann Arbor, 1941.
5. —— *Topology of level curves of harmonic functions*, Trans. Amer. Math. Soc. 63 (1948), 514–522.
6. Morse, M., and Jenkins, J. A. *The existence of pseudoconjugates on Riemann surfaces*, Fund. Math. 39 (1952), 269–287.

University of Michigan

THE IMAGE OF THE BOUNDARY UNDER A LOCAL HOMEOMORPHISM

C. J. TITUS

1. General problem. Let D denote an open disk of the z-plane with closure $\bar{D}$. Let δ be the positively oriented boundary of D and let f be a continuous mapping of δ onto an oriented curve ζ in the w-plane. The general problem is the determination of conditions on f such that there exists a continuous extension, $w = w(z)$, of f to $\bar{D}$ which is holomorphic on D. The topological part of the general problem is as follows: Let ζ be an oriented curve in the w-plane. Under what topological conditions on ζ does there exist a mapping $w = w(z)$, interior on D and continuous on $\bar{D}$, which maps δ onto ζ?

This problem has, roughly speaking, two topological aspects—the local and the global—of which only the global will concern us here. For since a curve can have an extension of holomorphic type and yet fill a region, it seems reasonable, in an initial study of the global conditions on ζ, to restrict the local behavior. The problem in such a restricted form was mentioned to the author in 1948 by C. Loewner, together with the suggestion that the condition of non-negative circulation might play an important role, as indeed it does, in the sufficiency direction.

2. Preliminary definition and assumptions. Let $\xi = \xi(t), \eta = \eta(t)$ be a pair of continuous real functions of period 2π. Assume that $\zeta(t) = \xi(t) + i\eta(t)$, $0 \leqq t < 2\pi$, has the following properties:

(1a) The curve ζ intersects itself a finite number of times; i.e., there exists a finite set T of numbers t such that $\zeta(t') = \zeta(t'')$, $t' \neq t''$, implies that $t' \in T$ and $t'' \in T$.

(1b) If ζ intersects itself, then it actually crosses itself. More precisely, if $\zeta(t') = \zeta(t'')$, $t' \neq t''$, then there is an $h > 0$ such that the curves

$$\alpha = \{\zeta(t) \mid t' - h < t < t' + h\},$$

$$\beta = \{\zeta(t) \mid t'' - h < t < t'' + h\}$$

are arcs which have only the point $\zeta(t') = \zeta(t'')$ in common and which cross each other at this point.

(1c) Every intersection point is a double point; i.e., there are at most two values of t at which ζ has a given value.

These conditions are convenient if the problem is to have a simple geometrical sense. Since all curves are limits of curves satisfying conditions (1abc) it seems inappropriate to be any more sophisticated.

Let us assume also that the following condition holds:

(2) The curve ζ is oriented by increasing t, and the curve which is the boundary of the unbounded component of the complement of ζ is thereby positively oriented. This condition is easily seen to be necessary.

Finally, let $t = 0$ correspond to a simple point of ζ which lies on the boundary of the unbounded component of the complement of ζ. Let t increase from 0 to 2π. Each double point has exactly two pre-images in $(0, 2\pi)$, say t' and t'', where $t' < t''$. Let t_k', t_k'', $k = 1, 2, \cdots, n$, be the set of pairs of values of t which correspond to double points, where $t_1' < t_2' < \cdots < t_n'$. Let $\zeta(t_k')$ be called the k-th double point P_k; it is simply the k-th double point encountered by $\zeta(t)$ as t increases from 0. The double point will be called positive (negative) if, for h sufficiently small, the oriented arc

$$\alpha_k = \{\zeta(t) \mid t_k'' - h < t < t_k'' + h\}$$

crosses the oriented arc $\alpha_k' = \{\zeta(t) \mid t_k' - h < t < t_k' + h\}$ from the left of α_k' to the right (from the right to the left). For example, the curve in Figure 1 has three double points numbered according to the choice of $\zeta(0)$. Here, the first double point is positive and the second and third are negative.

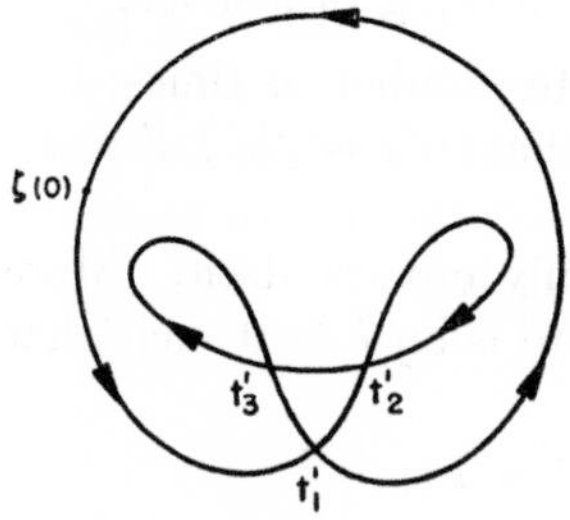

FIG. 1

The ordering $P_k \ll P_i$ will mean that the interval $T_k = (t_k', t_k'')$ is contained in the interval $T_i = (t_i', t_i'')$ and thus has the properties of a partial ordering (including reflexivity). The curve ζ will be called properly nested if, given any distinct pair of double points P_j and P_k, either $T_j \subset T_k$, or $T_k \subset T_j$, or the set $T_j \cap T_k$ is empty. Thus, saying that P_j and P_k are incomparable will mean that $T_j \cap T_k$ is empty.

Finally, it is assumed:

(3) The curve ζ is properly nested. This condition is an essential restriction on the phenomena one would like to study. There is some empirical evidence, however, that this class will play the role of a kind of canonical form. A curve which satisfies conditions (1abc), (2), and (3) will be said to belong to the class $\mathcal{P}$.

3. Statement of the theorem. Define the following integral-valued functions on the set of double points $\{P_k\}$, $(k = 1, 2, \cdots, n)$:

$$\mu(k) = \begin{cases} 1 \text{ if } P_k \text{ is a positive double point,} \\ -1 \text{ if } P_k \text{ is a negative double point;} \end{cases}$$

$$\lambda(k) = \textstyle\sum_{P_j << P_k} \mu(j).$$

A double point P_k is called maximal if, for all P_j comparable with P_k, $P_j \ll P_k$. If an oriented curve ζ is the image of the positively oriented boundary of the disk D under a mapping which is a sense-preserving local homeomorphism on D and continuous on $\bar{D}$, then ζ will be called an *h-boundary.*

THEOREM. *A necessary and sufficient condition that a curve ζ in $\mathcal{P}$ be an h-boundary is that*

(i) *if P_k is maximal, then* $\lambda(k) = 0$, *and*
(ii) *for all P_k*, $\lambda(k) \leqq 0$.

The proof of this theorem will be given elsewhere. For the curve in Figure 1, $P_2 \ll P_1$ and $P_3 \ll P_1$, $\lambda(1) = \lambda(2) = \lambda(3) = -1$, and thus (i) is violated. Therefore the curve is not an h-boundary.

There are several problems which can be stated in this context. For example, what are the conditions on the λ-function so that a curve in $\mathcal{P}$ be the image of the boundary of the disk under an interior mapping? This is analogous to the general case of a holomorphic function, whereas the local homeomorphism is analogous to the case in which the complex derivative does not vanish on the disk. Is there a way to define a λ-type function over the double points if the assumption of proper nestedness is not made?

UNIVERSITY OF MICHIGAN